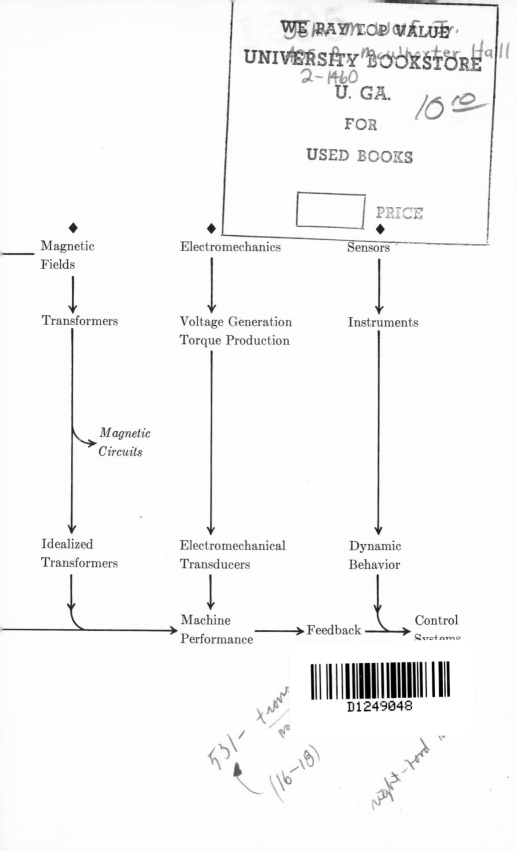

CIRCUITS,
DEVICES,
AND SYSTEMS

Also By RALPH J. SMITH:

Engineering As A Career
SECOND EDITION

CIRCUITS, DEVICES, AND SYSTEMS

A first course in electrical engineering

RALPH J. SMITH

Professor of Electrical Engineering, Stanford University

John Wiley & Sons Inc., New York · London · Sydney

SECOND CORRECTED PRINTING, SEPTEMBER, 1968

Library of Congress Catalog Card Number: 66-17612
Printed in the United States of America

To Kent, a scholar
and Dan, an engineer

Preface

TEACHING THE INTRODUCTORY COURSE in electrical engineering is an exciting and challenging assignment. It is exciting because new developments in the form of versatile circuits, ingenious devices, and sophisticated systems provide an inexhaustible supply of interesting topics for discussion, and because refined techniques and powerful methods are available to predict the behavior of the new devices and systems. It is challenging because the relatively few topics which can be treated in the available time must be carefully selected, and because the approaches employed must provide motivation for students with a wide variety of interests.

The rapid introduction of new devices and the corresponding obsolescence of old devices make it clear that only fundamental principles and universal methods are important. On the other hand, learning occurs best when the student sees a use for the material presented. Perhaps the ideal textbook for the introductory course should employ modern approaches and interesting applications in developing mastery of basic principles and general methods.

Objectives. This book has been designed to provide an understanding of the fundamental principles of electrical engineering, a familiarity with the viewpoint and terminology of electrical engineers, and an introduction to some modern techniques for the solution of difficult problems in all branches of engineering. It should prepare electrical engineering students for more effective study of advanced courses, and it should prepare other students to work with and communicate with electrical engineers.

It is assumed that students using this book have completed basic physics courses in mechanics, electricity, and magnetism; however, the essential physical concepts are reviewed as they are introduced. It is also assumed that students have a working knowledge of differential and integral calculus. Prior knowledge of differential equations is not required. The analytical technique employed here provides a good introduction to the formulation and solution of first- and second-order linear differential equations in engineering situations.

Topics and approaches have been selected to provide the basis for further work in circuits, electronics, electromechanics, or control systems. For electrical engineers who will later study all these in detail, a primary objective of this book is to provide a clear picture of the relationships among these subject areas. A major in another department should gain a good grasp of the fundamentals in these areas which will help him select courses for subsequent study as well as provide a solid background for such study.

Contents. The content is primarily "engineering science" in that the emphasis is on principles rather than practice. However, the topics selected are those of "practical" importance in modern electrical engineering. The subject is rich in interesting applications, and the illustrative examples are designed to appeal to students with various interests (including those with "no interest in EE"). While a wide range of topics is included, this is more than just a survey. By limiting the discussions to the more basic aspects of each major topic, there is time to treat these aspects with sufficient rigor so that the material is meaningful, quantitative, and useful.

Certain topics deserve special mention. Although the discussion of electronics starts with simple vacuum tubes, the emphasis is on semiconductor devices. The material on wave-shaping and logic circuits is of great interest at the present time because of applications to computers and instrumentation in general. The chapter on instrumentation is designed to be useful to all engineers engaged in experimental work.

Electromechanical devices such as loudspeakers, relays, and instrumentation transducers are included along with the important electrical machines. In treating rotating machines, the emphasis is on steady-state behavior, but dynamic behavior is discussed in connection with control systems. Feedback in amplifiers and control systems is treated in detail. The analog computer is included because it is important in engineering design and simulation, and it provides good illustrations of topics treated earlier in the book.

Approaches. The *Concept Flow Chart* shown in the front end-paper indicates how unity and coherence have been achieved in treating diverse topics. Electrical phenomena are introduced and their applications to real circuits and devices are described. The devices are then represented by linear models and the models are treated by means of linear systems analysis. In addition, the nonlinear aspects of real devices are studied and special methods are developed for predicting their behavior. Repeatedly the student examines a new physical concept, sees its application in an engineering device, and then learns to predict the behavior of systems incorporating the basic concept.

The central themes are modeling and linear systems analysis. Unusual emphasis is placed on deriving linear models of circuit components, electronic devices, and electromechanical devices. The same modeling process is employed for tubes, transistors, transformers, commutator machines, induction motors, synchronous machines, and instruments. As a result of repeated experience, students should become skilled in making simplifying assumptions and deriving models of the desired precision.

With linear models available, the prediction of device or system behavior is based on linear analysis techniques. The powerful pole-zero concept is introduced early and used repeatedly. This approach is just one step beyond the usual solution of the characteristic equation in determining natural response and it can be employed in solving a variety of problems. Another basic tool used frequently is the impedance function, or, for two-port devices, the transfer function.

The pole-zero interpretation of the transfer function contains the essence of the Laplace transform method. After careful consideration, however, I decided to avoid the formalism of Laplace transformation. In an introductory course there is insufficient time for a thorough introduction to the method, and the use of transforms by rote is unsound pedagogically. On the basis of our experience here, I believe that it is much better for the beginning student to retain a feel for the physical behavior as he proceeds with the analysis.

Three types of assignments are provided at the end of a typical chapter. The *Review Questions* are primarily for the student's own use in testing his qualitative understanding of the concepts and terminology introduced in that chapter. The *Exercises* vary in difficulty but, in general, they are straightforward applications of new principles to specific situations. The *Problems* are more involved and may require extending a concept to the general case, or making simplifying assumptions, or putting ideas together in a simple design.

Courses for which this book might be suitable include: A year course (90 class hours) on circuits, devices, and systems; a semester course (45 hours) emphasizing circuits and electronics; a semester course (45 hours) emphasizing circuits and electromechanics; a course (45–60 hours) including circuits, electronics, and instrumentation; and a course (45–60 hours) on circuits, electromechanics, and systems. Possible arrangements of the subject matter to suit these various purposes are included in the instructor's manual, available on request.

One point should be emphasized. Many of the concepts presented here are abstract and some of the techniques are quite sophisticated; it would be easy to overwhelm the reader. Therefore, at each stage of the development I have tried to keep in mind just what the student has learned and how big a step he is prepared to take. Each forward step is based on a firm foundation and illuminated by an illustrative example. My purpose in writing this book is *not* to provide an intellectual obstacle course, but rather to help the student master principles and methods which I believe are useful for all engineers.

RALPH J. SMITH

Stanford, California
February 1966

Acknowledgments

IN THE PREPARATION of this book I was greatly influenced by the teaching and writing of my Stanford colleagues Hugh Skilling, Willis Harman, and David Tuttle, Jr. It is a pleasure to acknowledge their contributions to my thinking.

The entire manuscript was read by W. T. Zink (Clemson), and by Col. E. C. Cutler, Jr., Lt. Col. W. T. Lincoln, and members of their staff (U.S.M.A., West Point). The finished result is much the better for their efforts. Portions of the manuscript were reviewed critically by M. E. Van Valkenburg (Illinois), Paul Gray (M.I.T.), G. R. Slemon (Toronto), R. Panholzer (U.S.N.P-G.S., Monterey), and J. L. Costanza (California, Berkeley). Because of the pressure of time and space I was unable to accommodate all their suggestions. However, the book is greatly improved as a result of their careful scrutiny and I am deeply indebted to them.

Among the many others who assisted in the preparation, I should like to thank J. Bumgardner, J. Thurlow, K. Thomassen, S. Amer, C. Burrus, K. Belser, P. Gary, J. Allen, J. Harris, M. Sites, H. Sonnenberg, C. McIntyre, T. Bartley, L. Griffiths, A. Baer, R. Townsend, A. Young, G. Esmer, and K. Senne. For her skillful handling of a difficult typing job, I thank Charlotte Austin. For her generous assistance at critical points in the preparation of the manuscript, I am grateful to Gerda Schumaker. For her sympathetic interest, efficient cooperation, and continued support throughout the entire project, I am especially indebted to my wife, Louise.

R. J. S.

Contents

PART I   CIRCUITS

◆
◆
◆

CHAPTER 1

Introduction

Electrical engineering is a broad and diverse field, impossible to define in a few words. We can say, however, that the electrical engineer is primarily concerned with phenomena involving electric charges, particularly forces between charges and energy interchanges between charges. In some situations energy is the important quantity, and in others energy is merely a means of conveying information. In conversion of the power of falling water to electrical form in an hydroelectric plant, transmission at high voltage to urban load centers, and utilization in lights, motors, and industrial processes, energy is the significant quantity. In contrast, when information or intelligence is transmitted by a series of dots and dashes the periods between the signals, periods of no energy transmission, are just as important as the signals themselves. In general, the electrical engineer is responsible for optimizing the generation, storage, transmission, control, and conversion of energy or information.

But all engineers make use of electrical products and processes, and effective use of electrical energy and information depends on mastery of the fundamentals of electrical engineering. Observations over the past 200 years, some random and some the result of careful experiment, have been organized and interpreted and made available to us in the form of a relatively few basic principles. Along with the principles, powerful techniques and ingenious methods have been developed for applying them to the analysis of existing devices and in the creation of new and improved designs. This combination of fundamental principles and effective procedures constitutes the subject matter of this book.

Forces and Fields

Electric charges are defined by the forces they exert on one another; experimentally, the forces are found to depend on the magnitudes of the charges, their relative positions, and their velocities. Forces due to the position of charges are called *electric* forces, and those due to the velocity of charges are called *magnetic* forces. All electric and magnetic phe-. nomena of interest in electrical engineering can be explained in terms of the forces between charges.

Electric and magnetic phenomena are characterized by "action at a distance" similar to the gravitational forces between two bodies such as the earth and the moon, or between the earth and bodies near its surface. As an alternative to calculating the forces between two masses m_1 and m_2 (by Newton's law), we may define the *field of influence*, or just the gravitational *field* of mass m_1, and calculate the force on the mass m_2 in the field of mass m_1. If mass m_1 is the earth, then the earth's gravitational field strength is

$$g = \frac{F}{m_2} \tag{1-1}$$

The strength of the gravitational field or the field *intensity* is defined as the force per unit mass; similarly, *electric field intensity* is defined as the force per unit charge (Eq. 2-4) and *magnetic field intensity* is defined in terms of the force per unit of charge momentum (charge times velocity) (Eq. 2-6). In each case, the field is a convenient concept and its determination is usually an intermediate step in the process of calculating some other quantity rather than being an end in itself.

As Newton observed, g varies as the square of the distance from the center of the earth. Since the earth is not a perfect sphere, the strength of its gravitational field varies from point to point on its surface as well as with distance from the surface. It is characteristic of fields that they are distributed throughout a region and must be defined in terms of two or three dimensions.

Circuits

In contrast to fields, the behavior of a *circuit* can be completely described in terms of a single dimension, the position along the path constituting the circuit. An hydraulic circuit can be described in terms of the pressure and velocity distribution along the pipe; a freeway has the characteristics of a circuit when traffic speed and density are known as functions of position along the highway. However, velocity distribution across a pipe section and traffic density in a downtown area are field phenomena.

As you recall from physics, in an electric circuit the variables of interest are the voltage and current at various points along the circuit. In circuits in which voltages and currents are constant (not changing with time), the currents are limited by resistances. In the case of a battery being charged by a generator, 100 ft of copper wire may provide a certain resistance to limit the current flow. The same effect could be obtained by 1 ft of resistance wire, or by 1 in. of resistance carbon. When the dimensions of a component are unimportant and the total effect can be considered to be concentrated at a point or "lumped," it can be represented by a *lumped parameter*. In contrast, the behavior of 100 ft of copper wire as an antenna is dependent on its dimensions and the way in which voltage and current are distributed along it; an antenna must be represented by *distributed parameters*. In this book, we are concerned with lumped parameter circuits only.

Circuits, Devices, and Systems

Circuits are important in guiding energy within *devices* and also to and from devices which are combined into *systems*. Electrical devices perform such functions as generation, amplification, modulation, and detection of signals. For example, at a radio broadcasting station a modulator changes the amplitude of the transmitted wave in accordance with a musical note to produce amplitude modulation. A *transducer* is a device which converts energy or information from one form to another; a microphone is a transducer which converts the acoustical energy in an input sound wave into the electrical energy of an output current.

Systems incorporate circuits and devices to accomplish desired results. A communication system includes a microphone transducer, an oscillator to provide a high-frequency carrier for efficient radiation, a modulator to superimpose the sound signal on the carrier, an antenna to radiate the electromagnetic wave into space, a receiving antenna, a detector for separating the desired signal from the carrier, various amplifiers and power supplies, and a loudspeaker to transduce electrical current into a replica of the original acoustic signal. A space-vehicle guidance system includes a transducer to convert a desired heading into an electrical signal, an error detector to compare the actual heading with the desired heading, an amplifier to magnify the difference, an actuator to energize the vernier control jets, a sensor to determine the actual heading, and a feedback loop to permit the necessary comparison.

Models

Circuits are important for another reason: frequently it is advantageous to represent a device or an entire system by a *circuit model*. Assume that the 100 ft of copper wire mentioned previously is wound into the form of a multiturn coil, and that a voltage of variable frequency is applied. If the ratio of applied voltage V to resulting current I is measured as a function of frequency, the observations will be as shown in Fig. 1.1. Over region A, the coil can be represented by a single lumped parameter (resistance R); in other words, the results obtained from the circuit of Fig. 1.1a are approximately the same as the results obtained from the actual coil of wire. Similarly, the behavior of the coil in region B can be represented by the circuit in Fig. 1.1b which contains another lumped parameter (inductance L). To represent the coil over a wide range of frequencies, an additional parameter (capacitance C) is necessary, and the circuit model of Fig. 1.1c is used. (These terms are defined in Chapter 2.)

The technique of representing, approximately, a complicated physical device by a relatively simple model is an important part of electrical engineering. In this book we use circuit models to represent such devices as the synchronous motor and the solid-state transistor (Fig. 1.2). One advantage of such a model is that it is amenable to analysis, using well-known mathematical methods.

The circuit representation for the transistor is called a *functional* model because its external behavior is similar to that of the transistor which it represents. As another example, the "ideal gas" defined by the mathematical equation $PV = NKT$ is a functional model of many actual gases. In contrast, the kinetic theory of gases provides a *physical* model which relates the external behavior of gases to internal physical action. A

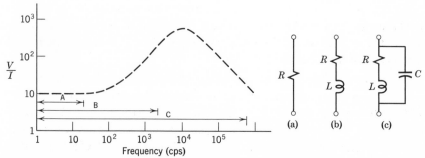

Fig. 1.1   Coil characteristics and circuit models.

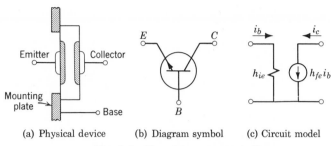

(a) Physical device   (b) Diagram symbol   (c) Circuit model

Fig. 1.2 Transistor representation.

physical model of the transistor is available,† but it is more complicated and is used only when simpler models are inadequate.

The Modeling Process

The model of the atom proposed in 1913 by the Danish physicist Niels Bohr is useful in explaining many electrical phenomena. Bohr suggested that negative electrons in orbit around positive nuclei possess energies corresponding to certain definite levels related to orbit radii. When an electron jumps from a higher energy orbit to a lower, a quantum of electromagnetic energy is emitted in the form of a photon. Starting with the simplest atom, hydrogen, all elements can be considered to consist of massive nuclei, containing protons and neutrons, surrounded by light electrons arranged in orbits or shells in a systematic way. The conductivity of a metal like copper is explained by saying that the single electron in the outer shell of the atomic model is relatively free and available for electrical conduction. The electrons in an insulating element such as sulfur completely fill the outer shell and are unavailable. As we shall see later, the Bohr model is inadequate for explaining some of the important processes of conduction in a semiconductor.

The modeling process is an essential part of scientific advancement and engineering development. The scientist first observes natural phenomena and conducts carefully planned experiments. On the basis of the information obtained, he proposes a tentative model of the physical unit under study. Using the model, he predicts behavior under various conditions and proceeds to test the hypothetical model in the laboratory. An adequately tested hypothesis is called a *theory*. A theory which is repeatedly confirmed under all circumstances with never a contradiction

† See J. G. Linvill, *Models of Transistors and Diodes*, McGraw-Hill Book Co., 1963.

is called a *law*.   This process of reasoning from specific observations to a general law is called *induction* and is important in all scientific discovery.

Engineers use inductive reasoning to establish new truths.   They also use the process of *deduction*, application of the general law to a specific case.   Representing a transistor by a circuit model permits the use of well-known circuit laws in predicting the behavior of the actual transistor.   As another example, the cause of unstable behavior in a chemical process-control system may be identified as positive feedback.   Representing the process by a suitable model, perhaps on an analog computer, may indicate the changes in system parameters necessary to remove the instability.

Preview of This Text

The organization of this book reflects the emphasis on circuits, devices, and systems.   The first part, Circuits, is devoted to developing the set of basic principles and powerful techniques needed to predict the behavior of a wide variety of circuits.   Emphasis is placed on the fact that these principles and techniques are equally valuable in dealing with "circuits" consisting of mechanical, or thermal, or hydraulic elements.

The next two parts, Electronics and Electromagnetics, deal with devices.   In each case, the operation of the device is explained in terms of physical laws and then a suitable model is derived.   The behavior of the model—whether of a sensitive transistor or of a powerful motor—is then predicted using the circuit laws and techniques previously mastered.

In the final part, Systems, emphasis is on combinations of circuits and devices working together for an overall purpose.   Here the interrelations between devices are more important than the details of device operation and special techniques are developed.   Using established circuit laws, known device characteristics, and these special techniques, the behavior of complicated systems can be predicted and, if necessary, modified.

While this book is primarily concerned with electrical phenomena, many of the principles, techniques, and approaches discussed are of basic importance and they find application throughout engineering.

- ♦ **ELECTRICAL QUANTITIES**
- ♦ **CIRCUIT ELEMENTS**
- ♦ **CIRCUIT LAWS**

CHAPTER **2**

Definitions and Laws

In beginning the study of circuits, we must first define the important circuit quantities and adopt a standard set of units, symbols, and abbreviations. Much of this material is a review of basic physics, but it deserves careful attention because it constitutes the "language" in which ideas are presented, concepts formed, and conclusions stated.

Next we take a new look at three laws based on early experiments conducted on resistors, inductors, and capacitors. Using these experimental results and modelling techniques, we invent idealized circuit components with highly desirable characteristics, and then see how they behave in circuits and how they transform energy.

Once the behavior of these individual components is established we can investigate, with the help of two more well-known experimental laws, the behavior of circuits made up of several components. Our objective is to learn how to formulate and solve circuit equations.

ELECTRICAL QUANTITIES

MKS Units

In engineering, we must be able to describe physical phenomena quantitatively in terms which will mean the same thing to everyone. We need a standard set of units which are consistent among themselves and reproducible any place in the world. In electrical engineering, we use the MKS system† in which the *meter* is the unit of length, the *kilogram* the unit of mass, and the *second* the unit of time. Another basic quantity is temperature, which in the MKS system is measured in *degrees Kelvin*. To define electrical quantities, an additional unit is needed; taking the *ampere* as the unit of electric current satisfies this requirement. All quantities encountered in this book can be defined in terms of the five units displayed in Table 2-1. When data are specified in

TABLE 2-1   Basic Quantities

Quantity	Symbol	Unit	Abbreviation
Length	l	meter	m
Mass	m	kilogram	kg
Time	t	second	sec
Temperature	τ	degree Kelvin	°K
Current	i	ampere	A

other units, they are first converted to MKS units and then substituted in the applicable equations. Two conversions frequently needed are: 1 meter = 39.37 inches and 1 kilogram = 2.205 pounds.

Definitions

For quantitative work in circuits, we need to define the quantities displayed in Table 2-2. These are probably familiar from your previous study, but a brief review here may be helpful.

Force. A force of 1 newton is required to cause a mass of 1 kilogram to change its velocity at a rate of 1 meter per second per second. In this text we are concerned primarily with electric and magnetic forces.

Energy. An object requiring a force of 1 newton to hold it against the force of gravity (i.e., an object weighing 1 newton) receives 1 joule of potential energy when it is raised 1 meter. A mass of 1 kilogram moving with a velocity of 1 meter per second possesses $\frac{1}{2}$ joule of kinetic energy.

Power. Power measures the rate at which energy is transformed. The transformation of 1 joule of energy in 1 second represents an aver-

---

† In working with electric and magnetic fields, the basic equations are simplified if certain constants are absorbed in the definitions of material properties. Engineers are eager to take advantage of such simplifications and the resulting *rationalized* MKS system is used almost universally.

TABLE 2-2 Important Derived Quantities

Quantity	Symbol	Definition	Unit	Abbrev.	(Alternate)
Force	f	push or pull	newton	N	(kg-m/sec^2)
Energy	w	ability to do work	joule	J	(N-m)
Power	p	energy per unit of time	watt	W	(J/sec)
Charge	q	integral of current	coulomb	C	(A-sec)
Current	i	rate of flow of charge	ampere	A	(C/sec)
Voltage	v	energy per unit charge	volt	V	(W/A)
Electric field strength	ε	force per unit charge	volt/meter	V/m	(N/C)
Magnetic flux density	B	force per unit charge momentum	tesla	T	(Wb/m^2)
Magnetic flux	ϕ	integral of magnetic flux density	weber	Wb	(T-m^2)

age power of 1 watt. In general, instantaneous power is defined by

$$p = \frac{dw}{dt} \tag{2-1}$$

Charge. The integral of current with respect to time is electric charge, a concept useful in explaining physical phenomena. Charge is said to be "conservative" in that it can be neither created or destroyed. It is said to be "quantized" because the charge on 1 electron (1.602 $\times$ 10^{-19} C) is the smallest amount of charge that can exist. The coulomb can be defined as the charge on 6.24 $\times$ 10^{18} electrons, or as the charge experiencing a force of 1 newton in an electric field of 1 volt per meter, or as the charge transferred in 1 second by a current of 1 ampere.

Current. Electric field effects are due to the presence of charges; magnetic field effects are due to the motion of charges. The current through an area A is defined by the electric charge passing through per unit of time. In general, the charges may be positive and negative, moving through the area in both directions. The current is the *net* rate of flow of positive charges, a scalar quantity. In the specific case of positive charges moving to the right and negative charges to the left, the effect of both actions is positive charge moving to the right; the current to the right is

$$i = + \frac{dq^+}{dt} + \frac{dq^-}{dt} \tag{2-2}$$

In a neon light, for example, positive ions moving to the right and negative electrons moving to the left contribute to the current flowing to the right.   In a current of 1 ampere, charge is being transferred at the rate of 1 coulomb per second.

Voltage.   The energy-transfer capability of a flow of electric charge is determined by the potential difference or voltage through which the charge moves.   A charge of 1 coulomb receives or delivers an energy of 1 joule in moving through a voltage of 1 volt or, in general,

$$v = \frac{dw}{dq} \tag{2-3}$$

The function of an energy source such as an automobile battery is to add energy to the current; a 12-V battery adds twice as much energy per unit charge as a 6-V battery.

Electric Field Strength.   The "field" is a convenient concept in calculating electric and magnetic forces.   Around a charge we visualize a region of influence called an "electric field."   The electric field strength, a vector, is defined by the magnitude and direction of the force on a unit positive charge in the field.   In vector notation the defining equation is

$$\mathbf{f} = q\mathbf{\varepsilon} \tag{2-4}$$

where ε could be measured in newtons per coulomb.   However, bearing in mind the definitions of energy and voltage, we note that

$$\frac{\text{force}}{\text{charge}} = \frac{\text{force} \times \text{distance}}{\text{charge} \times \text{distance}} = \frac{\text{energy}}{\text{charge} \times \text{distance}} = \frac{\text{voltage}}{\text{distance}}$$

and electric field strength in newtons per coulomb is just equal and opposite to the *voltage gradient*† or

$$\varepsilon = - \frac{dv}{dl} \quad \text{in V/m} \tag{2-5}$$

---

† In the vicinity of a radio transmitter, the radiated field may have a strength of a millivolt per meter; in other words, one meter of antenna may develop a millivolt of signal voltage which can be fed into a receiver for amplification.

Magnetic Flux Density.   Around a moving charge or current we visualize a region of influence called a "magnetic field." In a bar magnet the current consists of spinning electrons in the atoms of iron; the effect of this current on the spinning electrons of an unmagnetized piece of iron results in the familiar force of attraction. The intensity of the magnetic effect is determined by the magnetic flux density, a vector defined by the magnitude and direction of the force exerted on a moving charge in the field. In vector notation the defining equation is

$$\mathbf{f} = q\mathbf{u} \times \mathbf{B} \tag{2-6}$$

A force of 1 newton is experienced by a charge of 1 coulomb moving with a velocity (u) of 1 meter per second normal to a magnetic flux density of 1 tesla.

Magnetic Flux.   Historically, magnetic fields were first described in terms of *lines of force* or *flux.* The flux lines (so called because of their similarity to flow lines in a moving fluid) are convenient abstractions which can be visualized in the familiar iron-filing patterns. Magnetic flux in webers is a total quantity obtained by integrating magnetic flux density over an area. The defining equation is

$$\phi = \int \mathbf{B} \cdot d\mathbf{A} \tag{2-7}$$

Because of this background, magnetic flux density is frequently considered as the derived unit and expressed in webers per square meter. In this text, however, we consider B in teslas as the primary unit.

Electrical Power and Energy

A common problem in electric circuits is to predict the power and energy transformations in terms of the expected currents and voltages. Since, by definition, $v = dw/dq$ and $i = dq/dt$, instantaneous power is

$$p = \frac{dw}{dt} = \frac{dw}{dq}\frac{dq}{dt} = vi \tag{2-8}$$

Therefore, total energy is

$$w = \int p\, dt = \int vi\, dt \tag{2-9}$$

EXAMPLE 1

The starter motor of a modern automobile draws an initial current of 200 A. Calculate the power input to the starter.

SOLUTION.   Assuming a 12-V system and applying Eq. 2-8,

$$p = vi = 12 \times 200 = 2400 \text{ W}$$

EXAMPLE 2

If the current of Example 1 decreases uniformly to zero in 2 sec, calculate the energy supplied to the starter.

SOLUTION.   The current as a function of time can be expressed as

$$i = 200 - 100t \text{ A} \qquad \text{for } 0 < t \leq 2 \text{ sec}$$

Assuming a 12-V system and applying Eq. 2-9,

$$w = \int vi \, dt = \int_0^2 12(200 - 100t) \, dt = 2400t - 1200t^2/2 \Big]_0^2$$
$$= 4800 - 2400 = 2400 \text{ J}$$

Experimental Laws

In contrast to the foregoing arbitrary definitions, there are five laws which were originally formulated (about 200 years ago) from experimentally observed facts.   Our present understanding of electrical phenomena is much more sophisticated and these laws are readily derived from basic theory.   At this stage in our treatment of circuits, however, it is preferable to consider these relationships as they would be revealed in experiments on real devices in any laboratory.   From observations on the behavior of real devices we can derive idealized models of circuit elements and the rules which govern the behavior of such elements when combined in simple or complicated circuits.

Resistance

Consider an experiment (Fig. 2.1a) in which a generator is used to supply a current i (measured by an ammeter not shown) to a copper rod. The resulting voltage v (measured by a voltmeter not shown) is plotted as a function of current i in Fig. 2.1b.   If all other factors (such as tem-

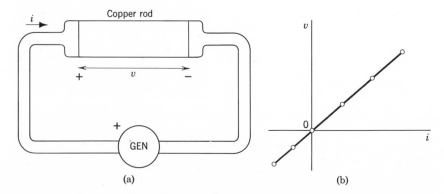

(a)   (b)

Fig. 2.1 Experimental determination of resistor characteristics.

perature) are held constant, the voltage is observed to be approximately proportional to the current. The experimental relation for this *resistor* can be expressed by the equation

$$v \cong Ri \qquad (2\text{-}10a)$$

where R is a constant of proportionally. Equation 2-10a defines the *resistance R* in *ohms* (abbreviated Ω) and is called Ohm's law in honor of Georg Ohm, the German physicist, whose original experiments led to this simple relation. The same relation can be expressed by the equation

$$i \cong Gv \qquad (2\text{-}10b)$$

which defines the *conductance G* in mhos ($\mho$).

We now know that a metallic conductor contains many relatively free electrons. The application of a voltage creates an electric field which tends to accelerate these *conduction* electrons, and the resulting motion is superimposed on the random thermal motion of the electrons at, say, room temperature. Electrons are accelerated by the field, collide with copper atoms, and give up their energy. They are again accelerated, gaining energy from the electric field, collide again, and give up their energy. Superimposed on the random motion due to thermal energy, there is an average net directed motion or *drift* due to the applied electric field. The speed of drift is found to be directly proportional to the applied electric field. In a given conducting element, therefore, the rate of flow of electric charge or the current is directly proportional to the electric field which, in turn, is directly proportional to the applied voltage. In this way, Ohm's law can be derived directly from a consideration of the conduction mechanism (see Chapter 9).

Capacitance

Now consider an experiment (Fig. 2.2a) in which the copper rod is cut and reshaped into two flat plates separated by air as an insulator. Available, but not shown, are a voltmeter, an ammeter, and an electroscope to measure voltage, current, and charge. When a voltage is applied as shown, it is observed that positive charge appears on the left-hand plate and negative on the right. If the generator is disconnected, the charge persists. Such a device which stores charge is called a *capacitor*.

As long as the voltage is constant, the charge is maintained and no current flows. If the voltage is changed and the current is measured, the result is as indicated in Fig. 2.2b. The current is observed to be approximately proportional to the *rate of change* of voltage. The experi-

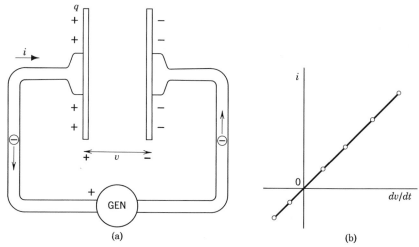

Fig. 2.2   Experimental determination of capacitor characteristics.

mental relation can be expressed by the equation

$$i \cong C \frac{dv}{dt} \tag{2-11}$$

where C is a constant of proportionality called *capacitance* and measured in *farads* (abbreviated F) in honor of the ingenious English experimenter, Michael Faraday.

Equation 2-11 can be obtained in two other ways. If the charge on the capacitor is measured accurately, it is observed to be approximately proportional to the voltage applied or

$$q \cong Cv \tag{2-12}$$

where C has the same value as determined previously. Equation 2-11 can be derived from this relation since $i = dq/dt$ by definition.

Another approach is to use our knowledge of electric fields. For large conducting plates separated a short distance l and carrying a voltage v, the voltage gradient or electric field strength ε is uniform over the insulating space with a value

$$\varepsilon = -\frac{v}{l} \quad \text{volts/meter or newtons/coulomb}$$

We expect the extent of the charge separation, and therefore the amount of charge which is stored in a given capacitor, to be proportional to the force per unit charge. We conclude that the charge stored is directly proportional to the electric field strength and therefore proportional to the voltage, confirming Eq. 2-12.

Inductance

If, instead, the copper rod is drawn out and formed into the configuration of Fig. 2.3a, an entirely different result is obtained. Now the generator is used to supply current to a multiturn coil. It is observed that only a small voltage is required to maintain an appreciable steady current, but to produce a rapidly changing current a relatively large voltage is required. As indicated in Fig. 2.3b, the voltage is observed to be approximately proportional to the *rate of change* of current. The experimental relation can be expressed by the equation

$$v \cong L \frac{di}{dt} \tag{2-13}$$

where L is a constant of proportionality called *inductance*† and measured in *henrys* (abbreviated H) in honor of the American inventor and experimenter, Joseph Henry.

This important relation can be derived by using our knowledge of magnetic fields. We know that charge in motion produces a magnetic field and the multiturn coil is an efficient configuration for concentrating the effect of all the moving charges in the conductor. In the region in and around the coil, the magnetic flux density is high for a given current. But we also know (and this was Henry's great discovery) that a changing

---

† More properly "self inductance"; mutual inductance is discussed in Chapter 8.

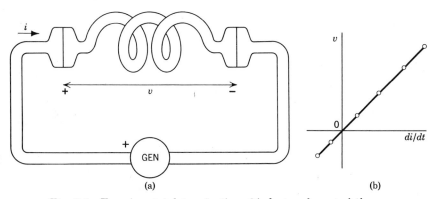

Fig. 2.3 Experimental determination of inductor characteristics.

magnetic field *induces* a voltage in any coil which it links and the induced voltage is directly proportional to the rate of change of the magnetic field. If the magnetic field is due to the current in the coil itself, the induced voltage always tends to oppose the change in current which produces it. The voltage required of the generator is determined primarily by this voltage of *self-induction* and is approximately proportional to the time rate of change of magnetic flux density. For the coil of Fig. 2.3, magnetic flux density is proportional to current and Eq. 2-13 is confirmed.

EXAMPLE 3

A current varies as a function of time as shown by the solid line in Fig. 2.4.

(a) Determine and plot the voltage produced by this current in a 3000-Ω resistor.

SOLUTION. Assuming that this is a linear resistor whose behavior is defined by $v = Ri$, the voltage is directly proportional to the current. For $i = 0.02$ A, $v = 3000 \times 0.02 = 60$ V and the voltage as a function of time is shown by the dotted line.

(b) Determine and plot the voltage produced by this current in a coil of 50 Ω resistance and 4 H inductance.

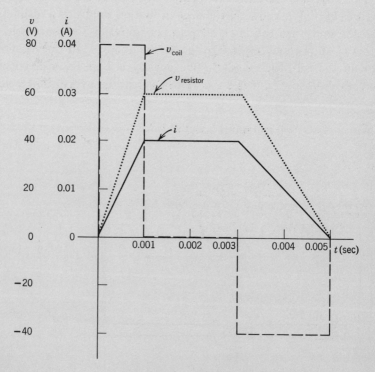

Fig. 2.4   Example 3.

SOLUTION. For the maximum current of 0.02 A, the voltage due to the coil resistance is

$$v_R = Ri = 50 \times 0.02 = 1 \text{ V}$$

The voltage due to the coil inductance is:

$$0 < t < 0.001 \qquad v_L = L\frac{di}{dt} = 4\,\frac{0.02}{0.001} = 80 \text{ V}$$

$$0.001 < t < 0.003 \qquad v_L = L\frac{di}{dt} = 4\,\frac{0}{0.001} = 0$$

$$0.003 < t < 0.005 \qquad v_L = L\frac{di}{dt} = 4\,\frac{-0.02}{0.002} = -40 \text{ V}$$

Later in this chapter we shall learn how to combine these two effects. For many purposes, however, satisfactory results can be obtained by neglecting v_R where v_L is large and considering v_R where v_L is small. On this basis the voltage across the coil is shown by the dashed line.

Decimal Notation

To specify the *value* of a measurable quantity, we must state the *unit* and also a *number*. We shall use the rationalized MKS units, but the range of numbers encountered in electrical engineering practice is so great that a special notation has been adopted for convenience. For example, the power of a public utility system may be millions of watts, whereas the power received from a satellite transmitter may be millionths of a watt. The engineer describes the former in *mega*watts and the latter in *micro*watts.

The notation is based on the decimal system which uses powers of 10. The standard prefixes in Table 2-3 are widely used to designate multiples

TABLE 2-3   Standard Decimal Prefixes

Multiplier	Prefix	Abbreviation	Pronounciation
10^{12}	tera	T	tĕr′ ȧ
10^{9}	giga	G	jĭ′ gȧ
10^{6}	mega	M	mĕg′ ȧ
10^{3}	kilo	k	kĭl′ ŏ
10^{2}	hecto	h	hĕk′ tŏ
10^{1}	deka	da	dĕk′ ȧ
10^{-1}	deci	d	dĕs′ ĭ
10^{-2}	centi	c	sĕn′ tĭ
10^{-3}	milli	m	mĭl′ ĭ
10^{-6}	micro	μ	mī′ krŏ
10^{-9}	nano	n	năn′ ŏ
10^{-12}	pico	p	pē′ cŏ
10^{-15}	femto	f	fĕm′ tŏ
10^{-18}	atto	a	ăt′ tŏ

and submultiples of the fundamental units. Thus 20 MW is read "20 megawatts" and is equal to 20×10^6, or 20 million watts; and 20 μW is read "20 microwatts" and is equal to 20×10^{-6}, or 20 millionths of a watt. Sometimes combinations of prefixes are used, such as kilomegacycles for $10^3 \times 10^6$ cycles, but the term gigacycles is preferred. Similarly, the term picofarads is preferred over the older designation of micromicrofarads.

EXAMPLE 4

The current in a 0.5-H inductor is changing at the rate of 30 mA per μsec. Calculate the induced voltage.

SOLUTION. $v = L\dfrac{di}{dt} = 5 \times 10^{-1} \times \dfrac{30 \times 10^{-3}}{10^{-6}} = 150 \times 10^2$

$$= 15 \times 10^3 = 15 \text{ kV}$$

Note that all numerical quantities are first converted to MKS units before substituting in the applicable equations.

Dimensional Checking

In most engineering problems the ultimate test is a *practical application,* but other methods of solution are quicker or less expensive. An *experimental* solution may be obtained in a laboratory. *Simulation* on a computer may be less expensive than actual experiment. *Estimating* is a valuable engineering approach, especially when used to predict results of more precise methods. In college courses the emphasis is usually on *analytical* solutions based on a knowledge of fundamental principles derived from previous practice and experiment.

Someone has said: "To err is human; to check is engineering." There are so many opportunities for mistakes in solving engineering problems that effective methods for checking the results of analysis and calculation must be used. Blunders can be corrected by careful repetition of individual steps, but a good check should be based on an independent approach such as *dimensional analysis.*

A useful aspect of any physical quantity is how its units are related to the fundamental quantities of length, mass, time, and charge. We say that the *dimensions* of area are "length squared" or, using the conventional representation, $[L^2]$. Similarly the dimensions of velocity are $[LT^{-1}]$, force $[MLT^{-2}]$, and electric field strength $[MLT^{-2}Q^{-1}]$. The dimensions may be obtained from any equation involving the variable, neglecting dimensionless quantities such as pure numbers and derivative and integral signs. The dimensions of velocity are the same whether we work from $u = \sqrt{2gh}$ or $u = dx/dt$ or $u = \int a\, dt + U_0$. What are the dimensions of energy? Of voltage?

Dimensional checking is based on the fact that an analytical equation must be dimensionally homogeneous; every term must have the same dimensions. If an equation has been derived for velocity, every term must have the dimensions $[LT^{-1}]$; if not, a mistake has been made.

EXAMPLE 5

For a mechanical system (which will be studied in Chapter 4) the following equation is derived:

$$\tfrac{1}{2}M\frac{du}{dt} + Du + K\int u\, dt = f$$

where u is velocity in m/sec and K is the spring compliance in m/N.

(a) What must be the units of D?

(b) Check the equation dimensionally.

SOLUTION. (a) Since the right-hand side of the equation is force with the dimensions $[MLT^{-2}]$, every term on the left must have the same dimensions. Therefore,

$$[D][LT^{-1}] = [MLT^{-2}]$$

or

$$[D] = \frac{[MLT^{-2}]}{[LT^{-1}]} = [MT^{-1}]$$

and the MKS units of D are kilograms per second.

(b) The dimensions of the first term are $[M][LT^{-1}]/[T] = [MLT^{-2}]$ which is correct for force. Note that there is no confirmation of the validity of the factor $\tfrac{1}{2}$; it looks suspicious and should be checked by some other method. The units of K are m/N; therefore, the dimensions of the last term are

$$[L/MLT^{-2}][LT^{-1}][T] = [M^{-1}LT^2] \neq [MLT^{-2}]$$

The dimensions are not those of force and, therefore, the last term is not right. What simple change would correct it?

CIRCUIT ELEMENTS

Circuits and Circuit Components

An electric circuit consists of an interconnection of components. Components which carry the same current are said to be connected in *series*. A simple series circuit might include a battery, a switch, a lamp, and the connecting wires. The terms *circuit* and *network* are sometimes used

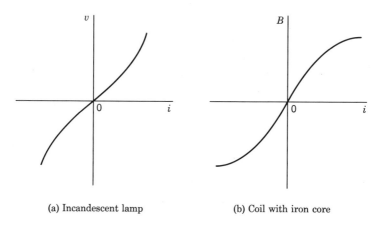

(a) Incandescent lamp   (b) Coil with iron core

Fig. 2.5   Characteristics of real circuit components.

interchangeably, but usually network implies a more complicated interconnection such as the communication network provided by the telephone
company.   There is also an implication of generality when we refer to
network analysis or network theorems.

From our standpoint, the distinguishing feature of a circuit component
is that its behavior is described in terms of a voltage-current relation at
the terminals of the component.   This relation, called the "*v-i* characteristic," may be obtained analytically by using field theory in which the
geometry of the associated electric or magnetic field is important, or it
may be obtained experimentally by using measurements at the terminals.
Once the *v-i* characteristic is known, the behavior of the component in
combination with other components can be determined by the powerful
methods of *circuit theory*, the central topic of this part of the book.

Using hypothetical experiments and applying elementary field concepts, we obtained *v-i* characteristics for a resistor, a capacitor, and an
inductor.   In writing mathematical expressions for the *v-i* characteristics
(Eqs. 2-10, 2-11, and 2-13) we neglected the distributed nature of the fields
involved and we assumed linearity.   But we know that no real physical
device is exactly linear.   For example, the resistance of the incandescent
lamp of Fig. 2.5a increases rapidly with current, and the inductance of
the coil of Fig. 2.5b is greatly affected by the value of average current.†
Therefore we shall invent three ideal circuit components, or models,
which are linear.

---

† Since *v* is proportional to dB/dt and, in general, B is a nonlinear function of i.

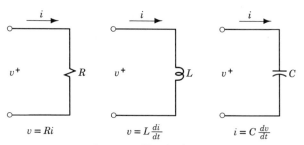

Fig. 2.6　Circuit elements.

There are good reasons for doing this. In the first place, real components can, within limits, be represented by such lumped linear models in many problems. In other cases, a real component can be represented accurately by a combination of two or more ideal components. Also, by using the mathematical methods applicable to linear models we can derive general results of great value in predicting the behavior of complicated devices and systems of devices.

Circuit Elements

The three linear models are shown symbolically in Fig. 2.6 along with their defining equations.† As you may recall, a real coil or inductor exhibits the property of inductance; but every real inductor also exhibits the property of resistance. The corresponding linear model is called an "ideal inductor" or, since it exhibits only a single property, it is called an "inductance element," or simply an "inductance." The three linear models—resistance, inductance, and capacitance—are referred to as *circuit elements;* with these elements as building blocks, an infinite number of circuits can be devised.

Energy Storage in Linear Elements

Valuable insights into the behavior of real circuit components can be obtained by considering the energy transformations which occur in the corresponding linear models. Recalling that energy $w = \int vi \, dt,$ we see that, once the v-i characteristic is defined, the energy storage or dissipation property is determined.

---

† The plus sign above the "v" indicates that the upper terminal is the positive reference direction of potential. The arrow under the "i" indicates that flow to the right is the positive reference direction of current. These conventions are discussed in detail in the section on circuit laws.

Inductance.   Where $v = L\,di/dt$ and $i = 0$ at $t = 0$,

$$w_L = \int_0^t L\frac{di}{dt}\,i\,dt = \int_0^i Li\,di = \tfrac{1}{2}Li^2 \tag{2-14}$$

The total energy input to an inductance is directly proportional to the square of the final current.   The constant of proportionality is $L/2$; in fact, this expression for energy could have been used to define inductance. *Inductance is a measure of the ability of a device to store energy in the form of moving charge* or, we could say, *in the form of a magnetic field.*   The equation reveals that the energy is stored rather than dissipated.   If the current is increased from zero to some finite value and then decreased to zero, the upper limit of the integration is zero and the net energy input is zero; the energy input was stored in the field and then returned to the circuit.

Capacitance.   Where $i = C\,dv/dt$ and $v = 0$ at $t = 0$,

$$w_C = \int_0^t vC\frac{dv}{dt}\,dt = \int_0^v Cv\,dv = \tfrac{1}{2}Cv^2 \tag{2-15}$$

Is the line of reasoning clear?   Can *you* interpret this equation?   In words, the total energy input to a capacitance is directly proportional to the square of the final voltage.   The constant of proportionality is $C/2$. *Capacitance is a measure of the ability of a device to store energy in the form of separated charge or in the form of an electric field.*   If the final voltage is zero, the energy stored in the field is returned to the circuit.

These expressions for stored energy remind us of the expressions for kinetic energy of a moving mass and potential energy of a stretched spring.   In such mechanical systems, displacement $dx = u\,dt$ and $w = \int f\,dx$.

Mass.   Where $f = M\,du/dt$ and $u = 0$ at $t = 0$,

$$w_M = \int_0^t M\frac{du}{dt}\,u\,dt = \int_0^u Mu\,du = \tfrac{1}{2}Mu^2 \tag{2-16}$$

As expected, this equation indicates that the mass M of a body is a measure of its ability to store kinetic energy.

Spring.   Where $f = K'x$ and $x = 0$ at $t = 0$,

$$w_{K'} = \int_0^x K'x\,dx = \tfrac{1}{2}K'x^2 \tag{2-17}$$

In a similar way, the spring stiffness K' (the reciprocal of the compliance K) is a measure of the spring's ability to store potential energy.

Energy Dissipation in Linear Elements

Each of these four elements (and there are others in thermal and chemical systems) has the ability to store energy and then return it to the circuit or system. When a similar analysis is made of an electrical resistance, the results are quite different.

Resistance. Where $v = Ri$ and $i = 0$ at $t = 0$,

$$w_R = \int_0^t Ri\, i\, dt = \int_0^t Ri^2\, dt \tag{2-18}$$

To evaluate the total energy supplied, we must know current i as a function of time t. For the special case where the current is constant or $i = I$,

$$w_R = \int_0^t RI^2\, dt = RI^2t \tag{2-19}$$

In general, for finite values of i (either positive or negative) and finite values of t, the energy supplied to the resistor is finite and positive. There is no possibility of controlling the current in such a way as to return any energy to the circuit; the energy has been *dissipated*. In a real resistor, the dissipated energy appears in the form of heat; in describing the behavior of the linear model we say that the energy has been dissipated in an *irreversible transformation*, irreversible because there is no way of heating an ordinary† resistor and obtaining electrical energy.

The *rate* of dissipation of energy or power is a useful characteristic of resistive elements. By definition, $p = dw/dt$; therefore,

$$p_R = \frac{dw_R}{dt} = Ri^2 \tag{2-20}$$

The power dissipation in a resistance is directly proportional to the square of the current. The constant of proportionality is R and this expression for power is frequently used to define resistance. *Resistance is a measure of the ability of a device to dissipate power irreversibly.*

Friction. At this point an alert student would wonder if there is in mechanical systems a corresponding dissipative element. There is and it is called *frictional resistance*. The shock absorber is a friction device designed to dissipate the energy received by an automobile when it goes over a bump in the road. The shock absorber, or "dash pot," contains a viscous fluid in a piston-cylinder arrangement. Relative motion of the

---

† In Chapter 14 we investigate some extraordinary "resistors."

body and chassis forces the fluid through a small hole and the kinetic energy is converted to heat in an irreversible process.

Over limited ranges, the friction force developed is approximately proportional to velocity or

$$f = Du \tag{2-21}$$

where D is the frictional resistance in units of newtons/(meters per sec) or newton-seconds/meter. In the linear model of a dash pot where $f = Du$ and $u = 0$ at $t = 0$,

$$w_D = \int_0^x f\, dx = \int_0^t Du\, u\, dt = \int_0^t Du^2\, dt \tag{2-22}$$

and

$$p_D = \frac{dw}{dt} = Du^2 \tag{2-23}$$

Continuity of Stored Energy

It is common knowledge that a massive body tends to oppose rapid changes in velocity; we say that such a body has *inertia*. In solving problems in dynamics we take advantage of the fact that the velocity of a mass cannot be changed instantaneously; for example, the velocity just after a force is applied must be the same as that just before the force is applied. Similar conclusions can be drawn about electric circuit quantities by applying the fundamental principle that in any physical system the energy must be a continuous function of time.

Since power is the time rate of change of energy $(p = dw/dt)$, an instantaneous change in energy would require an infinite power. But the existence of an infinite power is contrary to our concept of a physical system, and we require that the energy stored in any element of a system, real or ideal, be a continuous function of time. Recalling that the energy of a moving mass is $\frac{1}{2}Mu^2$, we conclude that the velocity u cannot change instantaneously.

Following the same line of reasoning, we note that the energy stored in an inductance is $\frac{1}{2}Li^2$ and, therefore, *the current in an inductance cannot change instantaneously*. Since the energy stored in a capacitance is $\frac{1}{2}Cv^2$, *the voltage across a capacitance cannot change instantaneously.* Note that there is no such limitation on the rapidity with which inductance voltage, or capacitance current can change. Also since resistance does not store energy, there is no limitation on the rapidity with which resistance voltage and current changes can occur. These concepts are particularly useful in predicting the behavior of a circuit just after an abrupt change, such as closing a switch.

EXAMPLE 6

The ignition coil of an automobile can be represented by a series combination of inductance L and resistance R (Fig. 2.7). A source of voltage V, the battery, is applied through contacts or "points" represented by a switch S.

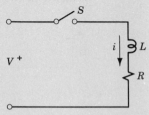

(a) With the switch open, the current i is zero. What is the current just after the switch is closed?

SOLUTION. Since the current in the inductance cannot change instantaneously, the current just after closing the switch must be zero (but increasing rapidly for proper operation of the ignition system).

(b) After a finite time the current has reached a value of 1 A and the switch is suddenly opened. What is the current just after the switch is opened?

Fig. 2.7 Example 6.

SOLUTION. The current just after the switch is opened is still 1 A.

(c) But how can a current flow through an open switch?

SOLUTION. The energy stored in the inductance ($\frac{1}{2}Li^2$) must be dissipated. Some of the energy goes to ionize the air between the switch contacts and an arc is formed; the points are "burned." The role of the "condenser" (a capacitor) in minimizing arcing by absorbing energy from the coil will become more clear in Chapter 4.

Energy Sources and Reversible Transformations

Energy can be stored in inductance or capacitance and dissipated in resistance. These are called *passive* circuit elements in contrast to *active* elements which can serve as sources of electrical energy. The many different forms of electrical "generators" include the rotating dynamo, the chemical storage battery, the solar cell, the fuel cell, and the thermocouple. In each of these real devices the electrical energy is "generated" by the conversion of some other form of energy. The conversion represents a *reversible transformation* in that the conversion process can go either way, in contrast to the situation in a resistor. To illustrate: in a dynamo operating as a "generator," mechanical energy is converted into electrical energy; but electrical input to a typical dynamo will cause it to operate as a "motor" producing mechanical energy.

The energy-conversion processes involved are discussed in Chapter 14; right now we are interested in the circuit characteristics of these generators. Although every generator supplies both voltage and current ($w = \int vi\, dt$), it is desirable to distinguish between two general classes of devices. If the voltage output is relatively independent of the cir-

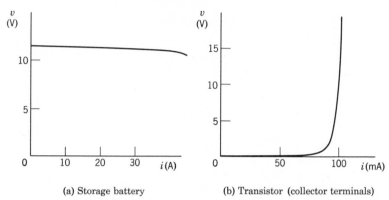

(a) Storage battery   (b) Transistor (collector terminals)

Fig. 2.8   Characteristics of real voltage and current generators.

cuit to which it is connected (as in the battery of Fig. 2.8a), the device is called a "voltage generator." If over wide ranges the output current tends to be independent of the connected circuit (as in the transistor of Fig. 2.8b), it is treated as a "current generator."

An ideal voltage generator in which the output voltage is completely independent of the current is called a "pure voltage source," or simply a "voltage source." The output voltage is specified, usually as a function of time, and is unaffected by changes in the circuit to which it is connected. At low currents, an automobile battery supplies a nearly constant voltage and may be represented by a 12-V voltage source. At high currents, however, the output voltage is appreciably less than 12 V.† The difference is due to the fact that the energy-conversion process is not perfect; part of the chemical energy is converted to heat in an irreversible process. This suggests the possibility of representing a real electrical generator by a linear model consisting of a pure voltage source and a resistance, the resistance accounting for the irreversible energy transformation.

The circuit symbol and defining equation for a voltage source are shown in Fig. 2.9a. The corresponding ideal current generator or "current source" is shown in Fig. 2.9b. Note that here the output current is specified, usually as a function of time, and is independent of the voltage across the source. As we shall see, a combination of a current source and a resistance also may be used to represent a real generator in predicting the behavior of real circuits. There is a finite limit to the power supplied by such a combination, whereas a pure voltage or current source can supply, or absorb, an unlimited amount of power.

---

† How is this fact evidenced when an automobile is started with the headlights on?

Two additional circuit elements need to be defined before we begin circuit analysis. The *open circuit* shown symbolically in Fig. 2.9c is characterized by finite voltage and zero current; the *short circuit* is characterized by finite current and zero voltage. (To what real components do open and short circuits correspond?) While other circuit elements are conceivable (and, in fact, will be desirable later on), the passive elements R, L, and C, the active sources $v(t)$ and $i(t)$, and the open and short circuits constitute a set which will be sufficient to describe a large number of useful circuits whose behavior we can predict with the aid of two fundamental circuit laws.

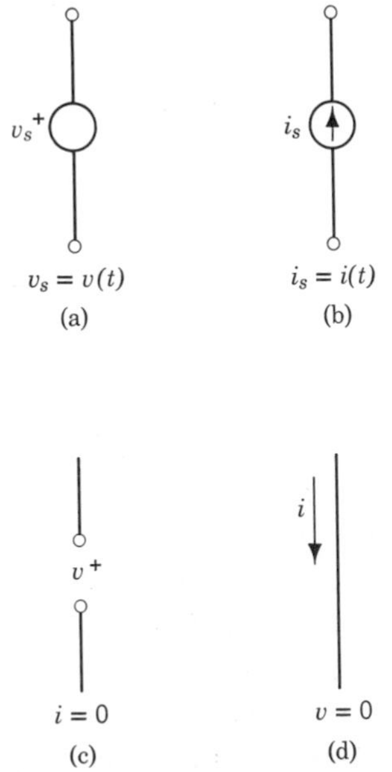

v_s +

$v_s = v(t)$
(a)

i_s

$i_s = i(t)$
(b)

CIRCUIT LAWS

The emphasis so far has been on the voltage-current characteristics of real components and the related ideal circuit elements. Now we are ready to consider combinations of elements into circuits. In the following discussion, a *branch* is part of a circuit with two terminals to which connections can be made, a *node* is the point where two or more branches come together, and a *loop* is a closed path formed by connecting branches.

v +

$i = 0$
(c)

i

$v = 0$
(d)

Fig. 2.9 (a) Voltage source. (b) Current source. (c) Open circuit. (d) Short circuit.

Kirchhoff's Current Law

The foundations of network theory were laid over 200 years ago by Gustav Kirchhoff, a German university professor, whose careful experiments resulted in the laws which bear his name. To repeat his experiments in the laboratory, we could arrange to measure the currents in a number of conductors or "leads" soldered together (Fig. 2.10a). In every case, we would find that the sum of the currents flowing into the common point at any instant is just equal to the sum of the currents flowing out.

In Fig. 2.10b, a circuit model is used to represent an actual connection. The arrows define the *reference* direction for positive current. The quan-

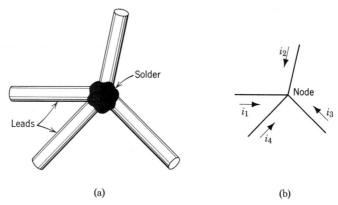

(a)   (b)

Fig. 2.10   (a) A soldered connection.   (b) The circuit model.

tity "i_1" specifies the *magnitude* of the current and its algebraic *sign* with
respect to the reference direction.   If i_1 has a value of "$+5$ A", the effect
is as if positive charge is moving toward the node at the rate of 5 C/sec.
If $i_1 = +5$ A flows in a metallic conductor in which charge is transported
in the form of negative electrons, the electrons are actually moving away
from the node but the effect is the same.   If i_2 has a value of "-3 A,"
positive charge is in effect moving away from the node.   In a practical
situation the direction of current flow is easy to determine; if an ammeter
reads "upscale," the current is flowing from the meter terminal marked $+$
through the meter to the terminal marked $-$.

By Kirchhoff's current law, *the algebraic sum of the currents into a node
at any instant is zero.*   It is sometimes convenient to abbreviate this statement and write "$\Sigma i = 0$."   As applied to Fig. 2.10b,

$$\Sigma i = 0 = i_1 + i_2 + i_3 + i_4 \qquad (2\text{-}24)$$

Obviously some of the currents must be negative.

EXAMPLE 7

In Fig. 2.10, if $i_1 = +5$ A, $i_2 = -3$ A, and $i_4 = +2$ A, what is the value of i_3?
SOLUTION.   Substituting in Eq. 2.24,

$$\Sigma i = 0 = +5 - 3 + i_3 + 2$$

or

$$i_3 = -5 + 3 - 2 = -4 \text{ A}$$

Note that we could just as well say that the algebraic sum of the currents *leaving*
a node is zero.

Kirchhoff's Voltage Law

The current law was originally formulated on the basis of experimental data. The same result can be obtained from the principle of conservation of charge and the definition of current. Kirchhoff's voltage law also was based on experiment, but the same result can be obtained from the principle of conservation of energy and the definition of voltage.

To repeat Kirchhoff's observations about voltages, we could set up an electrical circuit and arrange to measure the voltages across a number of components that form a closed path. Only a portion of the circuit is shown in Fig. 2.11a, but the combination of a battery, a resistor, an inductor, and associated leads forms the desired closed path. In every case, we would find that the voltages around the loop, when properly combined, add up to zero.

The circuit model of Fig. 2.11b is more convenient to work with. Here the voltages are labelled and the + signs define the *reference* direction for positive voltage or potential difference. The quantity "v_s" specifies the *magnitude* of the voltage and its algebraic *sign* with respect to the reference. If v_s has a value of "+12 V," the voltage of node b with respect to node a is positive. Since, by definition, voltage is energy per unit charge, a positive charge of 1 C moving from node a to b gains 12 J of energy from the voltage source. If v_L has a value of "+5 V," a positive charge of 1 C moving from b to c loses 5 J of energy; this energy is removed from the circuit and stored in the magnetic field of inductance L. If v_R

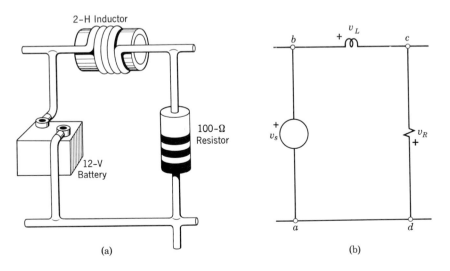

Fig. 2.11 (a) A closed path. (b) A circuit model.

has a value of "-7 V," node c is at a higher voltage than d and a positive charge of 1 C moving from d to c *gains* 7 J of energy. Another interpretation is that a positive charge of 1 C moving from c to d *loses* 7 J of energy.

By Kirchhoff's voltage law, *the algebraic sum of the voltages around a loop at any instant is zero.* As an abbreviation, we may write "$\Sigma v = 0$." As applied to Fig. 2.11b,

$$\Sigma v = 0 = v_{ba} + v_{cb} + v_{dc} + v_{ad} \qquad (2\text{-}25)$$

where v_{ba} means "the voltage of b with respect to a"; if v_{ba} is positive, terminal b is at a higher potential than terminal a. In applying the law, the loop should be traversed in one continuous direction, starting at one point and returning to the same point. Starting from node a in this case,

$$\Sigma v = 0 = +v_S - v_L + v_R + 0 \qquad (2\text{-}26)$$

A minus sign is affixed to the v_L term because the plus sign on the diagram indicates that node b is nominally at a higher potential than c or $v_{cb} = -v_L$.

EXAMPLE 8

In Fig. 2.11b, if $v_S = +12$ V and $v_L = +5$ V, what is the value of v_R?
SOLUTION. Substituting in Eq. 2.26,

$$\Sigma v = 0 = +12 - 5 + v_R + 0$$

or

$$v_R = -12 + 5 = -7 \text{ V}$$

The loop can be traversed in either direction, starting at any point. Going counterclockwise, starting at node c,

$$\Sigma v = 0 = +v_L - v_S + 0 - v_R$$

which agrees with Eq. 2-26.

Application of Kirchhoff's Laws

To illustrate the application of Kirchhoff's laws in solving electric circuits, consider the circuit shown in Fig. 2.12. In this case, the source voltages and the resistances are given and the element currents and voltages are to be determined.

The first step is to label the unknown currents arbitrarily; as drawn, the arrow to the right indicates the *positive direction* of i_1. If the value of i_1 is calculated and found to be positive, current i_1 actually flows to the right and an ammeter inserted between node a and the 2-Ω resistor with the $+$ terminal at a would read *upscale* or positive. If the value of i_1 is

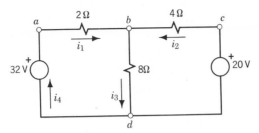

Fig. 2.12 Application of Kirchhoff's laws.

found to be negative, current i_1 actually flows to the left (the ammeter inserted as previously would read *downscale* or negative).

Applying Kirchhoff's current law to node a,

$$\Sigma i_a = 0 = +i_4 - i_1$$

or

$$i_4 = i_1$$

From this we conclude that the current is the same at every point in a series circuit. Since $i_4 \equiv i_1$, it is not another unknown and will be considered no further. Note that i_2 is the current in the 20-V source as well as in the 4-Ω resistance.

The next step is to define the unknown element voltages in terms of the arbitrarily assumed currents. In flowing from a to b, the positive charges constituting current i_1 lose energy in the 2-Ω resistance; this loss in energy indicates that the potential of a is higher than that of b, or $v_{ab} = Ri = +2i_1$. The left-hand terminal of the 2-Ω resistance can be marked with a neat $+$ to indicate the polarity of the element voltage *in terms of the assumed current direction.* Following the same analysis, the upper end of the 8-Ω resistance and the right-hand end of the 4-Ω resistance could be marked $+$ in accordance with the following *element equations:*

$$v_{ab} = +2i_1 \quad \text{or} \quad v_{ba} = -2i_1$$

$$v_{bd} = +8i_3 \quad \text{or} \quad v_{db} = -8i_3 \tag{2-27}$$

$$v_{cb} = +4i_2 \quad \text{or} \quad v_{bc} = -4i_2$$

Additional relations are obtained in the form of *connection equations.* Applying Kirchhoff's current law to node b,

$$\Sigma i_b = 0 = +i_1 + i_2 - i_3 \tag{2-28}$$

Since we are summing the currents *into* node b, i_3 is shown with a minus sign. Applying the current law to node d,

$$\Sigma i_d = 0 = -i_1 - i_2 + i_3$$

Note that this equation is *not independent;* it contributes no new information.

Applying the voltage law to the left-hand loop *abda*, and considering each element in turn,

$$\Sigma v = 0 = v_{ba} + v_{db} + v_{ad} \tag{2-29}$$

For the right-hand loop *bcdb*,

$$\Sigma v = 0 = v_{cb} + v_{dc} + v_{bd} \tag{2-30}$$

Kirchhoff's voltage law applies to any closed path; for the outside loop *abcda*,

$$\Sigma v = 0 = v_{ba} + v_{cb} + v_{dc} + v_{ad}$$

But this equation is just the sum of Eqs. 2-29 and 2-30 and no new information is obtained.   While this equation is not independent, it can be valuable in checking.

It is always possible to write as many independent equations as there are unknowns.   For a circuit with six unknowns (three voltages and three currents), we have written six equations (three element and three connection equations).   Other equations could be written but they would contribute no new information.   If the currents are of primary interest, the unknown voltages may be eliminated by substituting Eqs. 2.27 into Eqs. 2-29 and 2-30 which become

$$\Sigma v_{abd} = 0 = -2i_1 - 8i_3 + 32$$
$$\Sigma v_{bcd} = 0 = +4i_2 - 20 + 8i_3$$

When these are rewritten along with Eq. 2.28 we have

$$i_1 + i_2 - i_3 = 0 \tag{2-31}$$

$$+2i_1 \qquad + 8i_3 = 32 \tag{2-32}$$

$$+ 4i_2 + 8i_3 = 20 \tag{2-33}$$

To evaluate the unknowns, these three equations are to be solved simultaneously.   Some commonly employed methods are illustrated in the solution of this problem.

Solution by Determinants

The method of determinants is valuable because it is systematic and general; it can be used to solve complicated problems or to prove general theorems. The first step is to write the equations in the *standard form* of Eqs. 2-31, 2-32, and 2-33 with the constant terms on the right and the corresponding current terms aligned on the left.

A determinant is an array of numbers or symbols; the array of the coefficients of the current terms is a *third-order* determinant

$$D = \begin{vmatrix} 1 & 1 & -1 \\ 2 & 0 & 8 \\ 0 & 4 & 8 \end{vmatrix} \tag{2-34}$$

The value of a determinant of second order is

$$\begin{vmatrix} a_1 & a_2 \\ b_1 & b_2 \end{vmatrix} = a_1 b_2 - a_2 b_1 \tag{2-35}$$

The value of a determinant of third order is

$$\begin{vmatrix} a_1 & a_2 & a_3 \\ b_1 & b_2 & b_3 \\ c_1 & c_2 & c_3 \end{vmatrix} = \begin{aligned} &+ a_1 b_2 c_3 + a_2 b_3 c_1 + a_3 b_1 c_2 \\ &- a_1 b_3 c_2 - a_2 b_1 c_3 - a_3 b_2 c_1 \end{aligned} \tag{2-36}$$

A simple rule for second- and third-order determinants is to take the products "from upper left to lower right" and subtract the products "from upper right to lower left." Determinants of higher order must be evaluated by the process called "expansion by minors."[†]

Using the rule stated in Eq. 2.36,

$$D = \begin{vmatrix} 1 & 1 & -1 \\ 2 & 0 & 8 \\ 0 & 4 & 8 \end{vmatrix} = \begin{aligned} &+ (1)(0)(8) + (1)(8)(0) + (-1)(2)(4) \\ &- (1)(8)(4) - (1)(2)(8) - (-1)(0)(0) \end{aligned}$$

$$= 0 + 0 - 8 - 32 - 16 - 0 = -56$$

Replacing the coefficients of i_3 with the constant terms on the right-hand side of the equations in the standard form yields a new determinant:

$$D_3 = \begin{vmatrix} 1 & 1 & 0 \\ 2 & 0 & 32 \\ 0 & 4 & 20 \end{vmatrix} = 0 + 0 + 0 - 128 - 40 - 0 = -168 \tag{2-37}$$

By Cramer's rule for the solution of equations by determinants,

$$i_3 = \frac{D_3}{D} = \frac{-168}{-56} = 3 \text{ A}$$

Currents i_1 and i_2 could be obtained in a similar manner.

[†] See Britton and Snively: *College Algebra*, Rinehart and Co., New York, 1953, or any other college algebra text.

Substitution Method

When the number of unknowns is not large, the method of *substitution* is sometimes more convenient than using determinants. In this method, one of the equations is solved for one of the unknowns and the result is substituted in the other equations, thus eliminating one unknown. Solving Eq. 2-31 for i_3 yields

$$i_3 = i_1 + i_2$$

Substituting in Eqs. 2.32 and 2.33 yields

$$2i_1 + 8(i_1 + i_2) = 32$$

$$4i_2 + 8(i_1 + i_2) = 20$$

which can be rewritten as

$$(2 + 8)i_1 + \qquad\quad 8i_2 = 32 \qquad\qquad (2\text{-}38)$$

$$8i_1 + (8 + 4)i_2 = 20 \qquad\qquad (2\text{-}39)$$

Solving Eq. 2-38 for i_1 yields

$$i_1 = \frac{32 - 8i_2}{10}$$

Substituting in Eq. 2-39 yields

$$8\frac{32 - 8i_2}{10} + 12i_2 = 20$$

or

$$i_2 = \frac{-56}{56} = -1 \text{ A}$$

and

$$v_{cb} = 4i_2 = 4(-1) = -4 \text{ V}$$

The interpretation of the minus sign is that in reality node b is at a higher potential than c, and positive current flows to the right in the 4-Ω resistance.

Loop Current Method

The reduction in the number of unknowns and in the number of simultaneous equations achieved by substitution can be obtained automatically by an ingenious approach to circuit analysis. A *loop current* I_1 is assumed to circulate around loop *abda* in Fig. 2.13, and another loop

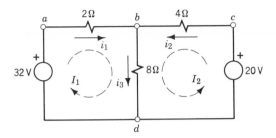

Fig. 2.13   Loop currents.

current I_2 is assumed to circulate around loop *cbdc*.   By inspection, the branch current i_1 is the same as loop current I_1, and i_2 is the same as I_2; but branch current i_3 is the sum of loop currents I_1 and I_2.

By applying Kirchhoff's voltage law to the two loops we obtain

$$\Sigma v_{abd} = 0 = -2I_1 - 8(I_1 + I_2) + 32$$
$$\Sigma v_{cbd} = 0 = -4I_2 - 8(I_1 + I_2) + 20$$

which can be rewritten as

$$(2 + 8)I_1 \qquad + 8I_2 = 32 \tag{2-40}$$

$$8I_1 + (8 + 4)I_2 = 20 \tag{2-41}$$

These are identical with Eqs. 2-38 and 2-39, but the physical interpretation is different.   Equation 2-40 says: "The source voltage in loop 1 is equal to the sum of two voltage drops.   The first, $(2 + 8)I_1$, is the product of loop current I_1 and the sum of all the resistances in loop 1. The second, $8I_2$, is the product of loop current I_2 and the sum of all resistances which are common to loops 1 and 2."   The *self-resistance* of loop 1 is $2 + 8 = 10$ Ω; the *mutual resistance* between the two loops is 8 Ω.   A similar statement could be made by using Eq. 2-41.   To obtain I_1, multiply Eq. 2-40 by 3 and Eq. 2-41 by (-2) and add the resulting equations.   Then

$$
\begin{array}{r}
30I_1 + 24I_2 = 96 \\
-16I_1 - 24I_2 = -40 \\
\hline
14I_1 = 56 \quad \text{or} \quad I_1 = 4 \text{ A} = i_1
\end{array}
$$

Checking

In solving complicated circuits there are many opportunities for mistakes and a reliable check is essential.   This is particularly true when the solution is obtained in a mechanical way, using determinants.   A new equation such as that obtained by writing Kirchhoff's voltage law around the outside loop of Fig. 2.13 provides a good check. With a little experience you will be able to write (by inspection, without first writing the element equations)

$$\Sigma v = 0 = -2i_1 + 4i_2 - 20 + 32$$

Substituting $i_1 = 4$ A and $i_2 = -1$ A,

$$\Sigma v = 0 = -2(4) + 4(-1) - 20 + 32 = 0$$

and the solution is checked.

Node-Voltage Method

The wise selection of loop currents can significantly reduce the number of simultaneous equations to be solved in a given problem. In the preceding example, the number of equations was reduced from three to two by using loop currents. Would it be possible to get all the important information in a single equation with a single unknown? In this particular case, the answer is "yes" if we choose as the unknown the voltage of node b with respect to a properly chosen reference. In some practical devices many components are connected to a metal "chassis" which, in turn, is "grounded" to the earth. Such a ground, often shown as a common lead at the bottom of a circuit diagram, is a convenient reference. In this problem the greatest simplification will result if we choose node d; now the potential of any node is understood to be with respect to node d. (See Fig. 2.14.)

Next, apply Kirchhoff's current law to each independent node. Here there is only one independent node, so

$$\Sigma i_b = 0 = i_1 + i_2 - i_3 \qquad (2\text{-}42)$$

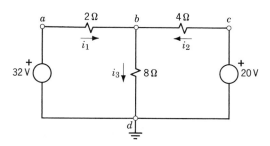

Fig. 2.14 Nodal analysis.

The current i_1 to node b from node a is equal to the difference in potential between nodes a and b divided by the resistance between a and b, or

$$i_1 = \frac{v_a - v_b}{R_{ab}} \tag{2-43}$$

Similarly,

$$i_2 = \frac{v_c - v_b}{R_{cb}} \quad \text{and} \quad i_3 = \frac{v_b - 0}{R_{bd}} \tag{2-44}$$

where all voltages are in reference to node d. In this particular problem, v_a is given as $+32$ V, and v_c is given as $+20$ V.

Finally, bearing in mind Eq. 2-42 and the concepts represented by Eqs. 2-43 and 2-44, we write one equation with a single unknown,

$$\Sigma i_b = 0 = \frac{32 - v_b}{2} + \frac{20 - v_b}{4} - \frac{v_b - 0}{8} \tag{2-45}$$

Multiplying through by 8,

$$128 - 4v_b + 40 - 2v_b - v_b = 0$$

or

$$v_b = \tfrac{168}{7} = 24 \text{ V}$$

By inspection of Fig. 2.14 we can write

$$i_3 = \frac{24}{8} = 3 \text{ A}, \quad i_1 = \frac{32 - 24}{2} = 4 \text{ A} \quad \text{and} \quad i_2 = \frac{20 - 24}{4} = -1 \text{ A}$$

which agree with the results previously obtained.

Formulation of Equations

There are many books devoted to electrical and mechanical network analysis at intermediate and advanced levels; these books give a thorough treatment of a variety of methods for solving networks of great complexity and generality. While many significant problems can be solved by using the four approaches outlined in this chapter, the discussion here is intended to be introductory and illustrative rather than comprehensive.

At this point you should be familiar with electrical quantities (their definitions, units, and symbols), you should understand the distinction between real circuit components and idealized circuit elements, you should know the voltage-current characteristics of active and passive circuit elements, and you should be able to apply Kirchhoff's laws to obtain circuit equations. In engineering, the solution of equations is

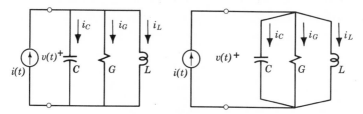

Fig. 2.15   Parallel CGL circuit.

usually less demanding than the formulation, and it is proper to place primary emphasis on the formulation of equations.

If voltages and currents are unchanging with time, as in the preceding example, the behavior of a circuit is determined by resistance alone. A more general problem is illustrated in Fig. 2.15 which resembles the tuning circuit found in every transistor radio. Following the procedure used previously, we write element equations and then connection equations. Assuming a voltage $v(t)$ with the reference polarity indicated by the $+$ sign, the corresponding current directions are as shown. Assuming no initial current in the inductance ($i_L = 0$ at $t = 0$), the element equations are:

$$i_C = C\frac{dv}{dt}, \qquad i_G = Gv, \qquad i_L = \frac{1}{L}\int_0^t v\, dt \qquad (2\text{-}46)$$

Applying Kirchhoff's current law to the upper node to obtain the connection equation,

$$\Sigma i = 0 = i(t) - i_C - i_G - i_L$$

Substituting and rearranging,

$$C\frac{dv}{dt} + Gv + \frac{1}{L}\int_0^t v\, dt = i(t) \qquad (2\text{-}47)$$

If the element values and $i(t)$ are known, the solution of this *integro-differential* equation consists in finding $v(t)$. In the general case, this can be quite difficult (see Chapter 6).

As another illustration, consider the dynamics problem of Fig. 2.16a. A mass restrained by a spring slides on a friction surface under the action of an applied force. The similarity between an electric circuit and this

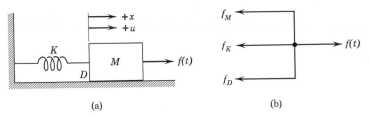

Fig. 2.16 (a) Dynamics problem. (b) Freebody diagram.

mechanical circuit is made clear by the application of d'Alembert's principle. This principle, which changes the dynamics problem into a statics problem, states that the resultant of the external forces acting on a body and the inertia force equals zero. In other words, if the inertia force (a reaction) is considered in the same manner as external forces, the sum of the forces acting equals zero, or $\Sigma f = 0$.

Again we write "element" equations and "connection" equations. For positive displacement to the right, the force f_K of a linear spring is to the left and proportional to the displacement. The friction force f_D may be assumed to be proportional to velocity and in such a direction as to oppose motion. The inertia force f_M is proportional to the mass and in such a direction as to oppose acceleration. Assuming no initial displacement and no initial velocity, the element equations are:

$$f_K = \frac{1}{K} x = \frac{1}{K} \int_0^t u \, dt, \qquad f_D = Du, \qquad f_M = Ma = M \frac{du}{dt} \quad (2\text{-}48)$$

as shown in Fig. 2.16b. The connection equation, obtained by applying d'Alembert's principle, is:

$$\Sigma f = 0 = f(t) - M \frac{du}{dt} - Du - \frac{1}{K} \int_0^t u \, dt \quad (2\text{-}49)$$

If the element values and $f(t)$ are known, the solution of this integro-differential equation consists in finding $u(t)$.

There are two conclusions to be drawn from these examples. First, there is a basic procedure in formulating equations which is applicable to a variety of electrical circuits and to problems in other fields as well. The equations are formulated by considering the characteristics of the elements and the way in which they are connected. Second, for even simple circuits the equations are formidable if the variables are functions of time. If practical problems are to be solved, it appears that special mathematical tools and techniques are necessary. Fortunately, such tools and techniques are available and they are treated in the next five chapters.

TABLE 2-4

Element	Unit	Symbol	Characteristic
Resistance	ohm		$v = Ri$
(Conductance)	(mho)	(G)	$(i = Gv)$
Inductance	henry		$v = L\dfrac{di}{dt}$ $i = \dfrac{1}{L}\displaystyle\int_0^t v\,dt\ + I_0$
Capacitance	farad		$i = C\dfrac{dv}{dt}$ $v = \dfrac{1}{C}\displaystyle\int_0^t i\,dt + V_0$
Short circuit			$v = 0$
Open circuit			$i = 0$
Voltage source	volt		$v = v_s$
Current source	ampere		$i = i_s$

SUMMARY

◆ The important electrical quantities, their definitions, and their MKS units are summarized in Tables 2-1 and 2-2.

◆ In electrical terms, power and energy are expressed by:

$$p = \frac{dw}{dt} = vi \quad \text{and} \quad w = \int p\,dt = \int vi\,dt$$

◆ Derived expressions can be checked dimensionally since an analytical equation must be dimensionally homogeneous.

◆ The approximate behavior of real circuit components is used to define the five passive and two active circuit elements displayed in Table 2-4.

◆ Voltage and current sources represent reversible energy transformations.

◆ Resistance is a measure of the ability of a device to dissipate energy irreversibly ($p_R = Ri^2$).

◆ Inductance is a measure of the ability of a device to store energy in a magnetic field ($w_L = \frac{1}{2}Li^2$).

◆ Capacitance is a measure of the ability of a device to store energy in an electric field ($w_C = \frac{1}{2}Cv^2$).

◆ Energy stored in an element must be a continuous function of time. The current in an inductance cannot change instantaneously. The voltage on a capacitance cannot change instantaneously.

◆ The algebraic sum of the currents into a node at any instant is zero ($\Sigma i = 0$).

◆ The algebraic sum of the voltages around a loop at any instant is zero ($\Sigma v = 0$).

◆ The general procedure for formulating equations for circuits is:

    1. Arbitrarily assume a consistent set of current directions and voltage polarities.

    2. Write the element equations by applying the element definitions and write the connection equations by applying Kirchhoff's laws.

    3. Combine the element and connection equations to obtain the governing circuit equation in terms of the unknowns.

◆ D'Alembert's principle permits the application of this procedure to problems in dynamics.

◆ Two methods for solving the resulting simultaneous equations are: Successive substitution to eliminate all but one unknown, convenient when the number of unknowns is small. Use of determinants and Cramer's rule, valuable in solving complicated problems or in proving general theorems.

◆ Use of loop currents or node voltages may greatly reduce the number of unknowns and simplify the solution.

◆ Checking is essential because of the many opportunities for mistakes in sign and value.

REVIEW QUESTIONS

(These questions are primarily for use by the student in checking his familiarity with the ideas in the text.)

1. Without referring to the text, list with their symbols and units the five quantities basic to the MKS system.

2. Without referring to the text, define force, energy, and power, and give their symbols and units.

—3. Without referring to the text, define current, voltage, electric field strength, and magnetic flux density, and give their symbols and units.

4. Some automobile manufacturers are considering going to an 18-V battery. What specific advantages would this have?

5. Explain the minus sign in Eq. 2-5.

6. Given two points a and b in a field of known strength $\mathcal{E}$, how could voltage v_{ab} be calculated?

7. Explain the difference between an "electric signal" which moves along a wire at nearly the speed of light and a "electric charge" which drifts along at only a fraction of 1 m/sec.

8. Would it be physically possible to have a passive circuit component for which the voltage was proportional to the second derivative of current? If a current $i = I_m \sin t$ flowed in such a component, what power would be absorbed?

—9. Define resistance, inductance, and capacitance in terms of voltage-current characteristics and also in terms of energy transformation characteristics.

10. Draw a curve representing current as a function of time and sketch on the same graph curves of the corresponding voltage across inductance and capacitance.

11. Draw a curve representing voltage as a function of time and sketch on the same graph curves of the corresponding current in an inductance and a capacitance.

12. How can a current flow "through" a capacitor containing an insulator?

13. Explain the basis for dimensional checking.

14. Once the effect of an electric field has been represented by a circuit element, is the geometry of the field significant?

15. The circuit characteristic of a component is defined by $v = 100i + i^2$. What is the component, in technical terminology?

16. List three physical elements not mentioned in the text which have the ability to store energy.

17. The concept of continuity of stored energy places what restrictions on the circuit behavior of inductances and capacitances?

18. Give three examples of reversible transformations involving electrical energy.

19. Explain in terms of source characteristics, the dimming of the house lights when the refrigerator motor starts.

—20. What real circuit component corresponds to a short circuit on a circuit diagram? To an open circuit?

21. Distinguish between an "inductor" and an "inductance"; give an example of each.

22. Write out in words a physical interpretation of Eq. 2-41.

23. Outline a three-step procedure for applying the node-voltage method.
24. Outline a three-step procedure for applying the loop-current method.

EXERCISES

(These exercises are intended to be straight-forward applications of the concepts of this chapter.)

1. Calculate the number of electrons that would flow through a 120-V, 60-W light bulb in 1 hour. What total charge does this represent?
2. A metal sphere 0.1 m in diameter is suspended by a fine wire in an insulating medium. The charge on the sphere as a function of time is known to be $200e^{-20t}$ μC.
   (a) Calculate the current in the wire as a function of time.
   (b) In what direction are the charged particles moving?
3. A voltage is applied across a long glass tube containing an ionized gas. The density of the positive ions is 10^{12} ions/m^3, and the density of the free electrons can be assumed to be the same. The cross-sectional area of the tube is 10^{-3} m^2. At a particular cross section, the positive ions are moving with an average axial velocity of 10^4 m/sec, and the velocity of the electrons is twice as great. Calculate the electric current.
4. A cubic meter of copper at room temperature contains about 8.5×10^{28} free electrons moving at random thermal velocities of the order of 10^5 m/sec.
   (a) A typical design figure for copper is a million A/m^2. Under these conditions, estimate the average drift velocity of the electrons.
   (b) What current would result if all the electrons in a copper conductor 1 mm square moved in the same direction at the thermal velocity?
5. The beam of electrons in a TV picture tube is accelerated by a voltage of 20 kV. The beam current is 50 μA.
   (a) Find the energy gained by each electron in moving through this potential difference.
   (b) If all the energy is released upon collision with the fluorescent screen, find the average power delivered to the screen.
6. Two plates are supported 10 cm apart in an evacuated space. The potential distribution (as a function of distance between the plates) is given as $v = 100l^2$ V where l is in meters. Calculate:
   (a) The total voltage across the plates.
   (b) The electric field as a function of position.
   (c) The force on an electron midway between the plates.
   (d) The voltage gradient at a point midway between the plates.
7. A potential difference of 1200 V is applied across two plates at the ends of an evacuated glass tube 50 cm long. Calculate:
   (a) The average electric field and the force on an electron introduced into the space.
   (b) The potential energy of an electron adjacent to the negative terminal.
8. For a 125-V, 100-W incandescent lamp, calculate the operating resistance and current, and the number of electrons per hour passing a point on the filament.

9. The generator in the circuit of Fig. 2.17 provides a voltage output which varies with time as shown. For time $t = 2$ sec, calculate:
   (a) The power dissipated in the 100-Ω resistor.
   (b) The power supplied to the 100-μF capacitor.
   (c) The power delivered by the generator.
   (d) The total energy dissipated in the resistor.

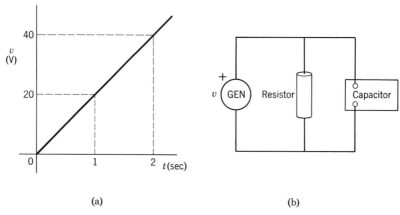

(a)   (b)

Fig. 2.17

10. A generator provides a current output which varies with time as shown in Fig. 2.18. It is connected in the given circuit. For time $t = 5$ sec, calculate:
   (a) The power dissipated in the 10-Ω resistor.
   (b) The power supplied to the 15-H inductor.
   (c) The power delivered by the generator.
   (d) The total energy dissipated in the resistor.

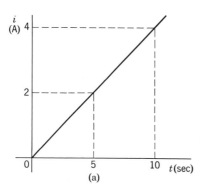
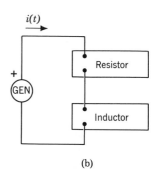

(a)   (b)

Fig. 2.18

11. Predict the behavior of the electric light in Fig. 2.19 when the switch is closed, and later, opened.

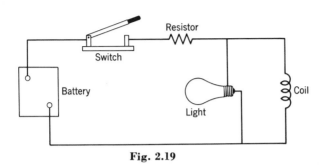

Fig. 2.19

12. (a) Let Fig. 2.20 represent the current flowing in a 2-H inductor. Plot to scale a graph of $v_L(t)$.
(b) Repeat for Fig. 2.21.

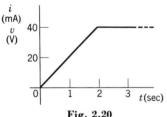

Fig. 2.20

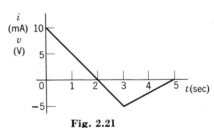

Fig. 2.21

13. (a) Let Fig. 2.20 represent the voltage across a 5-μF capacitor. Plot to scale a graph of $i_C(t)$.
(b) Repeat for Fig. 2.21.

14. (a) Let Fig. 2.20 represent the current flowing in an initially uncharged capacitor of 5 μF. Plot to scale a graph of $v_C(t)$.
(b) Repeat for Fig. 2.21.

15. (a) Let Fig. 2.20 represent the voltage across a 2-H inductor (no initial current). Plot to scale a graph of $i_L(t)$.
(b) Repeat for Fig. 2.21. What general statement can you make about the current in an inductance at an instant when the voltage is zero?

16. A current i is described as follows: starts from zero and increases uniformly with time, reaching a value of 2 mA in 20 msec; constant at 2 mA until time $t = 30$ msec; decreases uniformly with time reaching zero at $t = 40$ msec; remains zero until $t = 50$ msec.
(a) Draw a graph of current i versus t.

(b) If the current i flows through a 50-mH inductor, calculate values and draw a graph of v_L versus t.

(c) If the current i flows into a 5-μF capacitor (assume no initial charge), calculate and draw a graph of v_C versus t.

17. The current of Exercise 16 flows in a circuit which can be represented by a series combination of $R = 1$ kΩ and $L = 30$ H.   Calculate:

(a) The power delivered to the circuit at $t = 10$ msec.

(b) The power delivered to the circuit at $t = 35$ msec.

(c) The total energy stored at $t = 35$ msec.

18. In terms of the dimensions of the basic units, derive the units of (a) inductance and (b) magnetic flux density.

19. In terms of the dimensions of the basic units, derive the dimensions of (a) capacitance and (b) electric field strength.

20. In terms of the dimensions of the basic units, derive the dimensions of (a) resistance and (b) the gravitational constant g.

21. Check the following equations dimensionally, indicate any errors, and suggest possible corrections:

$$\text{(a)} \ i = \frac{V}{R_1 + R_2}(1 - e^{-Rt/C}), \qquad \text{(b)} \ \frac{1}{t} = -\frac{R}{2L} + \left[\frac{R}{4L^2} - LC\right]^{\frac{1}{2}}$$

Note that you need not understand the phenomena to find errors in the results.

22. A 20-mH inductance carries a current of 10 A.   The current is increased to 12 A in 50 μsec.

(a) How much energy is supplied?

(b) Where does this energy go?

(c) What average voltage is required?

23. A 50-μF capacitance carries a voltage of $+100$ V.   The voltage is reduced to zero and increased to -60 V in 0.2 msec.

(a) How much energy is required from the circuit?

(b) What average current flows?

24. A pendulum is set in motion by raising the bob of mass m a height h and releasing it.   Derive an expression for the velocity of the bob at the bottom of its arc.

25. An electrical oscillation is produced by charging a capacitance C to a voltage V_n and shorting it across an inductance.   Reasoning by analogy with Exercise 24, derive an expression for the maximum current in the inductance.

26. Measurements on a coil provide the following data: at a steady current of 2 A, power input is 64 W; when the current is changed from -0.1 A to $+0.1$ A in 20 msec, the average voltage is 40 V.   Devise a linear circuit model to represent the coil.

27. A computer grade capacitor is rated at 1000 μF at 50 V.   Laboratory tests at rated voltage indicate a capacitance of 1010 μF and a "leakage current" of 20 μA after 50,000 hours.   Devise a linear circuit model to represent the capacitor.

28. Tests on a direct-current generator yield the results shown in Fig. 2.22.

(a) Devise a linear model to represent the generator for currents up to 50 A.

(b) The generator is to be connected to a load resistor of 5 Ω.   Using the model, predict the current which will flow.   Check your result on the graph.

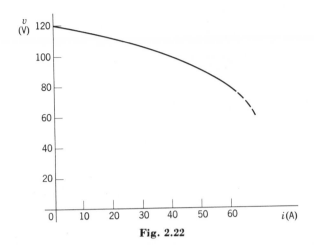

Fig. 2.22

29. Represent the direct-current generator, whose output characteristics are shown in Fig. 2.22, by a linear model incorporating a *current* source. Specify numerical values valid for currents up to 40 A.

30. In Fig. 2.23, $v_C = 20t$ V, $i_1 = 10$ A, and $i_2 = 5 \cos t$ A. Find: (a) v_L, (b) v_{ab} and v_{cd}, and (c) the energy stored in L and C.

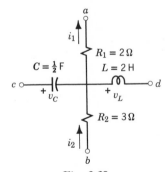

Fig. 2.23

31. Solve Exercise 30 for $v_C = 10e^{-t}$ V, $i_1 = -10$ A, and $i_2 = 2e^{-t}$ A.

32. In Fig. 2.23, $i_1 = 10$ A, $i_2 = 8$ A, and i_L (into d) $= 2t$ A; at $t = 0$, $v_C = +10$ V. Determine v_C as a function of time.

33. A portion of a complex network is shown in Fig. 2.24. The switch S is closed at $t = 0$. There is an initial charge V_0 on the capacitor. By definition v_{ba} is the potential of b with respect to a and i_{ba} is the current from b to a.

(a) Using the *given* currents and circuit elements, evaluate the following: $v_{ba}, v_{cb}, i_{cd}, v_{cd}, i_{ad}, v_{ad}$.

(b) Write Kirchhoff's voltage equation for loop $abcda$.

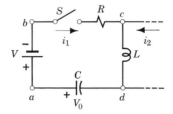

Fig. 2.24

34. Given the circuit of Fig. 2.25, calculate the current in the 10-Ω resistance using: (a) element currents, (b) loop currents, (c) node voltages. Include an adequate check.

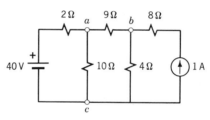

Fig. 2.25

35. Given the circuit of Fig. 2.25, calculate the voltage across the 9-Ω resistance using: (a) element currents, (b) loop currents, (c) node voltages. Include an adequate check.

36. Given the circuit of Fig. 2.26, calculate the current in the 10-Ω resistance using: (a) element currents, (b) loop currents, (c) node voltages.

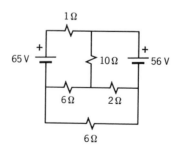

Fig. 2.26

37. Given the circuit of Fig. 2.26, calculate the voltage across the 2-Ω resistance using: (a) element currents, (b) loop currents, (c) node voltages.

38. In Fig. 2.27, V_0 is an initial voltage on C. Using only the *specified* variables, formulate the voltage equation for loop *abcda* with the switch closed.

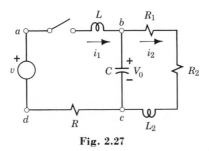

Fig. 2.27

39. A solid disk of radius r (Fig. 2.28) has a polar moment of inertia J. It is supported by an elastic shaft ($\tau_K = K'\theta$) and damped by a friction brake ($F_D = D\omega$). (*Note:* θ = angular displacement in radians, ω = angular velocity in rad/sec.) Apply d'Alembert's principle and formulate the equation of motion under an applied torque τ.

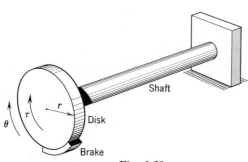

Fig. 2.28

PROBLEMS

(*Note:* The results of Problems 1 to 5 are quite useful in circuit analysis and should be written in your notebook.)

~**1.** Derive an expression for the single resistance R_s which is equivalent to resistances R_1 and R_2 connected in series. Extend your result to the case of n resistances connected in series.

~**2.** Derive an expression for the single resistance R_p which is equivalent to resistances R_1 and R_2 connected in parallel. Extend your result to the case of 3 resistances connected in parallel. Check your results dimensionally.

~**3.** The voltage divider of Fig. 2.29 is a useful circuit. Derive an expression for the output voltage v_2 in terms of the input voltage v and the resistances R_1 and R_2.

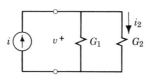

Fig. 2.29 Voltage divider.

~**4.** The current divider of Fig. 2.30 is a useful circuit. Derive an expression for the output current i_2 in terms of the input current i and the conductances G_1 and G_2.

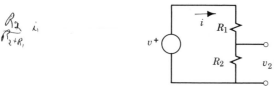

Fig. 2.30 Current divider.

—**5.** Repeat Problem 4, expressing the current division in terms of resistances R_1 and R_2.

_**6.** In the circuit of Fig. 2.31, switch S has been closed a long time. What does this imply regarding i, v_{C_1}, and v_{C_2}? What can be said about i_{C_1} and i_{C_2}? Derive an expression for the charge on C_1 in terms of the given quantities.

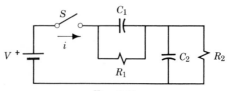

Fig. 2.31

— **7.** A capacitance C is charged to a voltage V_m. At $t = 0$, an inductance L is connected to the terminals of the capacitance (Fig. 2.32). It is observed (on an oscilloscope) that the voltage is a cosine wave or $v = V_m \cos \omega t$ and that the current is a sine wave or $i = I_m \sin \omega t$.

(a) What is the energy stored in C when $v = 0$?

(b) When $v = 0$, what is the current in terms of V_m, L, and C?

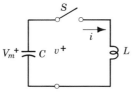

Fig. 2.32

(c) What is the rate of change of current at $t = 0$?

(d) From the result of (c) and knowing that i is sinusoidal, derive an expression for ω the "frequency of the oscillation" in rad/sec.

(e) Check your result for (d) dimensionally.

— **8.** As applied to the dynamic network of Fig. 2.16a, the law of conservation of energy says that the rate of change of energy stored (in kinetic and potential energy) plus the rate of energy dissipation must be just equal to the rate of energy input. Express this relation mathematically in terms of the given quantities and derive Eq. 2-49.

Exponentials, Sinusoids, and Phasors

The definitions and laws of Chapter 2 provide the basis for formulating the equations governing the behavior of any circuit consisting of lumped linear elements. Well-established mathematical methods are available for solving the circuit equations, but these general methods are often quite laborious. Engineers are always interested in techniques which turn difficult problems into simple ones and, at the same time, give valuable insight into physical behavior. This chapter is concerned with some special techniques useful in circuit analysis.

In analyzing circuits, the general procedure is to write element equations and connection equations and solve them simultaneously. The voltages and currents used in transmitting all intelligence and most power are functions of time. Since the element equations include time derivatives and integrals, our first question might be: What time functions are important in engineering? Since the connection equations hold at every instant, our second question might be: How can continuously varying voltages and currents be added conveniently? In answering these questions, we shall first look at a variety of time functions or *signals*, study the exponential and the sinusoidal functions in detail, and then develop an efficient technique for handling sinusoids in practical problems.

Signal Waveforms

Certain patterns of time variation or *waveforms* are of special significance in electrical engineering because they are encountered so frequently. Some of these are shown in Fig. 3.1.

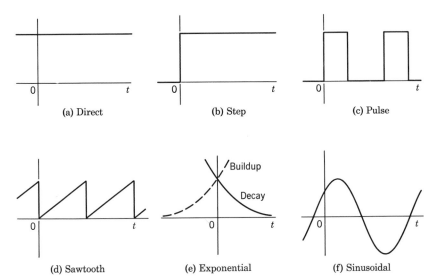

Fig. 3.1 Common signal waveforms.

A *direct* or *continuous* wave of voltage is supplied by a storage battery or a direct-current (d-c) generator.   A *step* of current flows when a switch is thrown, suddenly applying a direct voltage to a resistance; the current in an automobile headlight is an example.   A *pulse* of current flows if the switch is turned ON and then OFF; the output of a radar consists of short pulses of high-intensity radiation.   A *sawtooth* wave increases linearly with time and then resets; this type of voltage variation causes the electron beam to move across the screen of a television picture tube.   A decaying *exponential* current flows if energy is stored in the electric field of a capacitor and allowed to leak off through a resistor; in an unstable system, a voltage may build up exponentially.   A *sinusoidal* voltage is generated when a coil is rotated at a constant speed in a uniform magnetic field; also, oscillating circuits are frequently characterized by sinusoidal voltages and currents.

EXPONENTIALS

Exponential and sinusoidal wave-forms are easy to generate and easy to analyze because of their simple derivatives and integrals; we shall pay

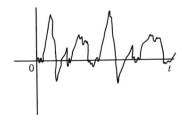

Fig. 3.2 Speech waveform.

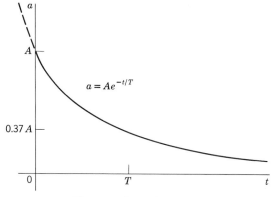

Fig. 3.3 Decaying exponential.

them special attention because they are encountered frequently and also because they are useful in the analysis of more complicated waves, such as the speech waveform of Fig. 3.2.

The General Exponential

In general, an exponentially decaying quantity (Fig. 3.3) can be expressed as

$$a = Ae^{-t/T} \tag{3-1}$$

where a = instantaneous value,

A = amplitude or maximum value,

e = base of natural logarithms = 2.718 . . . ,

T = time constant in sec, and

t = time in sec.

The temperature of a hot body in cool surroundings, the angular velocity of a freely spinning bicycle wheel, and the current of a discharging capacitor can all be approximated by decaying exponential functions of time.

Time Constant

Since the exponential factor in Eq. 3-1 only approaches zero as t increases without limit, such functions theoretically last forever. In the same sense, all radioactive disintegrations last forever. To distinguish between different rates of disintegration physicists use the term "half-life," where the half-life of radium, say, is the time required for any amount of radium to be reduced to one-half of its initial amount. In the case of an exponentially decaying current it is more convenient to use the value of time which makes the exponent -1. When $t = T =$ the *time constant,* the value of the exponential factor is

$$e^{-t/T} = e^{-1} = \frac{1}{e} = \frac{1}{2.718} = 0.368 \tag{3-2}$$

In other words, when the time in seconds is equal to the time constant, the exponential factor is reduced to approximately 37% of its initial value.

EXAMPLE 1

The capacitor of Fig. 3.4a is charged to a voltage of 6 V and then, at time $t = 0$, it is switched across the resistor and observations are made of current as a function of time. The experimental data are plotted in Fig. 3.4b. Determine the time constant for this circuit and derive an equation for the current.

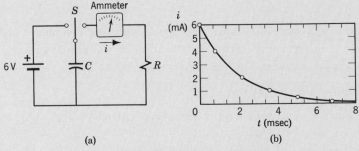

(a)   (b)

Fig. 3.4   Example 1.

SOLUTION. A smooth curve is drawn through the experimental points. The amplitude of the exponential is determined by noting that at $t = 0$, $i = I_0 = 6$ mA. The time constant is determined by noting that when $i = I_0 e^{-1} = 6(0.368) \cong 2.2$ mA, $t = T \cong 2$ msec. Then $1/T = 1/0.002 = 500$ and the current equation is

$$i = I_0 e^{-t/T} = 6e^{-500t} \text{ mA} \tag{3-3}$$

In terms of the initial value, what is the current when $t = 2T = 4$ msec?

Normalized Exponentials

All exponential equations can be reduced to a common form by expressing the variables in terms of dimensionless ratios or *normalizing* the variables. When this is done, Eq. 3-1 becomes

$$\frac{a}{A} = e^{-t/T} \tag{3-4}$$

This equation leads to the *universal* exponential curve of Fig. 3.5. After 2 time constants, $t = 2T$ and the function is down to $1/e^2$ times its initial value, or $a/A = (0.368)^2 = 0.135$. After 5 time constants, $t = 5T$ and the normalized function is down to $1/e^5 = 0.0067$. This is less than the

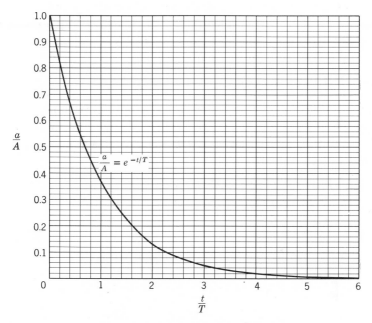

Fig. 3.5 Universal exponential curve.

error expected in many electronic measurements, and it may be assumed that after 5 time constants an exponential current is practically negligible.

Taking the logarithm of each side of Eq. 3-4,

$$\ln \frac{a}{A} = -\frac{1}{T} t \qquad (3\text{-}5)$$

This is the equation of a straight line with a negative slope equal to the reciprocal of the time constant (Fig. 3.6). The same result is obtained

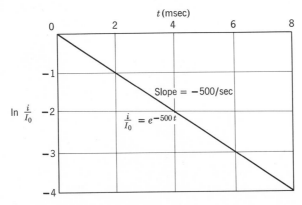

Fig. 3.6 Logarithmic plot of the normalized current.

if Eq. 3-4 is plotted on semilog graph paper.   As another interpretation
of the time constant (see Problem 1), it can be demonstrated that if the
exponential decay continued at its *initial rate*, the duration of the function would be just equal to the time constant.

Exponential Voltages and Currents

Exponentials are important because many natural phenomena follow
an exponential time variation.   Also, the simplicity of the mathematical
relations between exponentials and their derivatives and integrals makes
them particularly valuable in circuit analysis.

EXAMPLE 2

In Fig. 3.7a the current $i = 5e^{-2t}$ A.
(a) Determine the voltage $v(t)$.
SOLUTION.

$$v_R = Ri = 4 \times 5e^{-2t} = 20e^{-2t} \text{ V}$$

$$v_L = L\frac{di}{dt} = 1(-2)5e^{-2t} = -10e^{-2t} \text{ V}$$

$$v = v_R + v_L = 20e^{-2t} - 10e^{-2t} = +10e^{-2t} \text{ V}$$

(b) If the current $i = 5e^{-2t}$ A flows in an initially uncharged 0.25-F capacitance
($v_C = 0$ at $t = 0$), determine the voltage $v_C'(t)$.
SOLUTION.

$$v_C(t) = \frac{1}{C}\int_0^t i\, dt + V_0 = \frac{1}{0.25}\int_0^t 5e^{-2t}\, dt + 0 = \frac{5}{0.25(-2)} e^{-2t}\Big]_0^t$$
$$= 10 - 10e^{-2t} \text{ V}$$

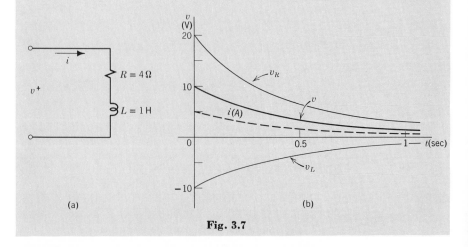

Fig. 3.7

SINUSOIDS

There are three principal reasons for emphasis on sinusoidal functions of time. First, many natural phenomena are sinusoidal in character; the vibration of a guitar string, the projection of a satellite on the rotating earth, and the simple harmonic motion generated in uniform rotation are examples. Second, sinusoids are important in the generation and transmission of electric power and in the communication of intelligence; since the derivatives and integrals of sinusoids are themselves sinusoidal, a sinusoidal source always produces sinusoidal responses in any linear circuit. Third, other periodic waves can be represented by a series of sinusoidal components by means of Fourier analysis;† this means that techniques for handling sinusoids are useful in predicting the behavior of circuits involving pulses and sawtooth waves as well. Clearly, an efficient technique for analyzing circuits involving sinusoidal voltages and currents is essential. Since the application of Kirchhoff's laws involves summations of currents and voltages, we need a convenient method for adding quantities which are continually varying functions of time.

The General Sinusoid

In general, a sinusoidally varying quantity can be expressed as

$$a = A \cos (\omega t + \alpha) \tag{3-6}$$

where a = instantaneous value,
A = amplitude or maximum value
ω = frequency in radians per second (omega),
t = time in seconds,
α = phase angle in radians (alpha).
Since an angle of 2π rad corresponds to one complete cycle,

$$f = \frac{\omega}{2\pi} = \text{frequency in cycles per second (cps)} \tag{3-7}$$

The time for one complete cycle is

$$T = \frac{1}{f} = \text{period in sec} \tag{3-8}$$

---

† See Skilling, H. H.: *Electrical Engineering Circuits*, Second edition, John Wiley and Sons, New York, 1965, Chapter 14.

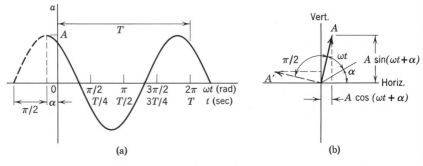

Fig. 3.8   The general sinusoid.

The same sinusoid can be expressed by the sinewave function

$$a = A \sin\left(\omega t + \alpha + \frac{\pi}{2}\right) \tag{3-9}$$

since $\sin(x + \pi/2) = \cos x$ for all values of x. In either case, the instantaneous value varies from positive maximum to zero to negative maximum to zero repeatedly; a current which varies sinusoidally is called an *alternating current*.

Sometimes it is convenient to associate the sinusoidal variation with the projection of a radial line of length A rotating with frequency ω from an initial or phase angle α. For radial line A of Fig. 3.8b, the horizontal projection is $a = A \cos(\omega t + \alpha)$. The vertical projection of radial line A' is $a' = A' \sin(\omega t + \alpha + \pi/2)$, which is just equal to a; clearly, either a horizontal projection or a vertical projection can be used.

EXAMPLE 3

A sinusoidal current with a frequency of 60 cps reaches a positive maximum of 20 A at $t = 2$ msec. Write the equation of current as a function of time.

SOLUTION. In the form of Eq. 3-6, $A = 20$ A and $\omega = 2\pi f = 2\pi(60) = 377$ rad/sec. The positive maximum is reached when $(\omega t + \alpha) = 0$ or any multiple of 2π. Letting $(\omega t + \alpha) = 0$,

$$\alpha = -377 \times 2 \times 10^{-3} = -0.754 \text{ rad} = -0.754 \times \frac{360°}{2\pi} = -43.2°$$

Therefore, the current equation is

$$i = 20 \cos(377t - 0.754) \text{ A}$$

Letting $(\omega t + \alpha) = 2\pi$,

$$\alpha' = 2\pi - 0.754 = +5.53 \text{ rad} = 5.53 \times \frac{360°}{2\pi} = +316.8°$$

The current equation can also be written

$$i = 20 \cos (377t + 5.53) \text{ A}$$

Customarily, the smallest value of α is used, and since it is easier for most of us to visualize angles in degrees, the usual form is

$$i = 20 \cos (377t - 43.2°) \text{ A}$$

Note that the angle in parentheses is a convenient hybrid; to avoid confusion, the degree symbol is essential.

In a linear circuit consisting of resistances, inductances, and capacitances, if any voltage or current is a sinusoid, all voltages and currents will be sinusoids of the same frequency. To perform the addition and subtraction of voltages and currents required in the application of Kirchhoff's laws, three procedures are possible. In *graphical* addition (see Fig. 3.9), sinusoids are plotted and the curves added point by point; this is time-consuming and lacks the generality needed to arrive at comprehensive solutions. The use of *trigonometric identities* permits the addition or subtraction of functions of time in general form, but this is laborious at best (see Exercise 19). The convenient and general method which we shall use is based on complex algebra and an ingenious transformation of functions of time into constant quantities.

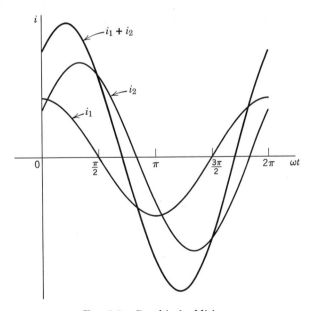

Fig. 3.9 Graphical addition.

Fig. 3.10   The system of real numbers.

Imaginary Numbers

A brief review may be worthwhile.   In our numbering system, *positive* numbers correspond to distances measured along a line, starting from an origin.   *Negative* numbers enable us to solve equations like $x + 2 = 0$, and are represented in Fig. 3.10 by distances to the left of the origin. *Zero* is a relatively recent concept with some peculiar characteristics; for example, division by zero must be handled carefully.   Numbers corresponding to distances along the line of Fig. 3.10 are called *real* numbers. To solve equations like $x^2 + 4 = 0$, so-called *imaginary* numbers were invented; these add a new dimension to our numbering system.

Imaginary numbers are plotted along the *imaginary axis* of Fig. 3.11 so that $j2$† lies at a distance of 2 units along an axis at right angles to the *real axis*.   The imaginary number $-j2$ lies along the imaginary axis but in the opposite direction from the origin.   Note that all numbers are

---

† Engineers use j instead of i for imaginary numbers to avoid confusion with the symbol for current.   Charles P. Steinmetz, who first used combinations of real and imaginary numbers in circuit analysis, called them "general numbers."   See *IEEE Spectrum*, April, 1965.

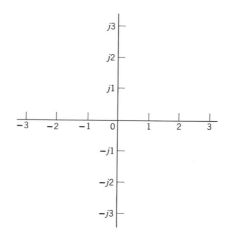

Fig. 3.11   The complex plane.

abstractions, and calling one number "real" and another "imaginary" just differentiates between their mathematical properties.

It may be helpful to think of j as an *operator*. An operator like "$\sqrt{\ }$" or "sin" means a particular mathematical operation; $\sqrt{\ }$ operating on 4 yields 2 and sin operating on 30° yields 0.5. In the same way, the minus sign $(-)$ is an operator such that $(-)$ operating on a directed line segment yields a reversal or a 180° rotation. Similarly, we define the operator j to mean a 90° counterclockwise rotation. The operator j taken twice, or $(j)(j)$, indicates a 180° rotation or a reversal, and $(j)(j)$ is equivalent to $(-)$ in effect. This concept is important because it provides an algebraic interpretation for a geometrical operation.

Just as $\sin^2 \theta$ (theta) is defined to mean $(\sin \theta)^2$ and not $\sin(\sin \theta)$, so the properties of jb must be defined. It is understood that

$$j(jb) = j^2 b = -b \qquad \text{or we say } j^2 = -1$$

$$j(j^2 b) = j^3 b = -jb \qquad \text{or we say } j^3 = -j \qquad (3\text{-}10)$$

$$j(j^3 b) = j^4 b = +b \qquad \text{or we say } j^4 = +1$$

The equation $j^2 = -1$ is a statement that the two *operations* are equivalent and does *not* imply that j is a number. However, and this is the beauty of the concept, in all algebraic computations imaginary numbers can be handled as if j had a numerical value of $\sqrt{-1}$.

Complex Numbers

The real and imaginary axes define the *complex plane*. The combination of a real number and an imaginary number defines a point in the complex plane and also defines a *complex number*. The complex number may be considered to be the point or the directed line segment to the point; both interpretations are useful.

Given the complex number **W** of magnitude M and direction θ, in *rectangular* form,

$$\mathbf{W} = a + jb$$

or

$$\mathbf{W} = M(\cos \theta + j \sin \theta)$$

by inspection of Fig. 3.12. By Euler's theorem,†

$$\cos \theta + j \sin \theta = e^{j\theta} \qquad (3\text{-}11)$$

Therefore,

$$\mathbf{W} = M e^{j\theta} \qquad (3\text{-}12)$$

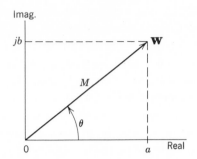

Fig. 3.12 A complex number.

This is called the *exponential* or *polar* form and can be written symbolically as

$$\mathbf{W} = M \,\underline{/\theta} \tag{3-13}$$

which is read "magnitude M at angle θ." (In this book complex numbers are always in boldface type.)

To convert complex numbers to *polar* form from rectangular,

$$M = \sqrt{a^2 + b^2} \qquad \theta = \arctan \frac{b}{a} \tag{3-14}$$

To convert complex numbers to *rectangular* form from polar,

$$a = M \cos \theta \qquad b = M \sin \theta \tag{3-15}$$

PHASORS

The complex constant $\mathbf{W} = Me^{j\theta}$ is represented by a fixed radial line. If the line rotates at an angular velocity ω, as shown in Fig. 3.13, $\mathbf{W}$ is a

---

† The validity of Euler's theorem is evident when series expansions are written as follows:

$$e^{\theta} = 1 + \theta + \frac{\theta^2}{2!} + \frac{\theta^3}{3!} + \frac{\theta^4}{4!} + \frac{\theta^5}{5!} + \cdots$$

$$\cos \theta = 1 - \frac{\theta^2}{2!} + \frac{\theta^4}{4!} - \cdots$$

$$\sin \theta = \theta - \frac{\theta^3}{3!} + \frac{\theta^5}{5!} - \frac{\theta^7}{7!} + \cdots$$

Then

$$\cos \theta + j \sin \theta = 1 + j\theta - \frac{\theta^2}{2!} - j\frac{\theta^3}{3!} + \frac{\theta^4}{4!} + j\frac{\theta^5}{5!} - \cdots = e^{j\theta}$$

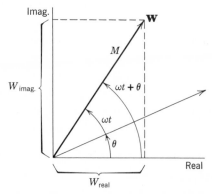

Fig. 3.13 A complex function of time.

complex function of time and

$$\mathbf{W}(t) = Me^{j(\omega t + \theta)} \tag{3-16}$$

The projection of this line on the real axis is

$$W_{\text{real}} = f(t) = M \cos (\omega t + \theta)$$

and the projection on the imaginary axis is

$$W_{\text{imag}} = f(t) = M \sin (\omega t + \theta)$$

Either component could be used to represent a sinusoidal quantity; in this book we shall always work with the real components.

Phasor Representation

If an instantaneous voltage is described by a sinusoidal function of time such as

$$v(t) = V \cos (\omega t + \theta) \tag{3-17}$$

then $v(t)$ can be interpreted as the "real part of" a complex function or

$$v(t) = \text{Re} \left\{ Ve^{j(\omega t + \theta)} \right\} = \text{Re} \left\{ (Ve^{j\theta})(e^{j\omega t}) \right\} \tag{3-18}$$

In the second form of Eq. 3-18, the complex function in braces is separated into two parts; the first is a complex constant, the second is a function of time which implies rotation in the complex plane. The first part we define as the *phasor* **V** where

$$\mathbf{V} = Ve^{j\theta} = V \underline{/\theta} \tag{3-19}$$

Note that the phasor $Ve^{j\theta}$ contains the important information: amplitude and phase angle. The term $e^{j\omega t}$ indicates rotation at angular velocity ω, but this is the same for all voltages and currents associated with a given source and therefore may be put to one side until needed.

The phasor **V** is called a *transform* of the voltage $v(t)$; it is obtained by transforming a function of time into a complex constant which retains the essential information. A similar transformation with which you are already familiar is used in multiplication by logarithms or exponents. As a simple illustration, consider the product of 8 times 16, using exponents.

$$\text{Algebraic equation:} \qquad 8 \times 16 = x$$

$$\text{Exponential representation:} \quad 2^3 \times 2^4 = x$$

$$\text{Transform equation:} \qquad 3 + 4 = X$$

In this illustration the transform of 8 is 3 and the transform of x is X. By making this transformation, a multiplication is replaced by an addition. The calculation is performed by using the transforms, and the result, $X = 7$, is the transform of the desired answer. The final step is to perform the inverse transformation whence $x = 2^7 = 128$. The same sequence of steps is followed in applying phasor methods to circuit problems.

EXAMPLE 4

(a) Write the equation of the current shown in Fig. 3.14a as a function of time and represent the current by a phasor.

SOLUTION. The current reaches a positive maximum of 10 A at $\pi/6$ rad or 30° before $\omega t = 0$; therefore the phase angle θ is $+ \pi/6$ rad and the equation is

$$i = 10 \cos \left(\omega t + \frac{\pi}{6} \right) \text{A}$$

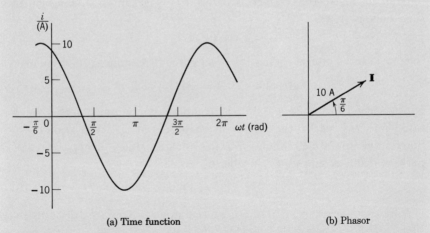

(a) Time function   (b) Phasor

Fig. 3.14   Example 4.   Phasor representation.

This could also be expressed as

$$i(t) = \text{Re}\,\{10e^{j(\omega t + \pi/6)}\} = \text{Re}\,\{10e^{(j\pi/6)}e^{j\omega t}\}\ \text{A}$$

By comparison with the defining Eq. 3.19, the current phasor is

$$\mathbf{I} = 10e^{(j\pi/6)}\ \text{A}$$

as shown in Fig. 3.14b.

(b) Represent the current $i = 20 \sin(\omega t + \pi/6)$ A by a phasor.

SOLUTION. Our definition of phasor is based on the cosine function as the real part of the complex function of time. Since $\cos(x - \pi/2) = \sin x$, we first write

$$i = 20 \cos\left(\omega t + \frac{\pi}{6} - \frac{\pi}{2}\right) = 20 \cos\left(\omega t - \frac{\pi}{3}\right)\ \text{A}$$

Then

$$\mathbf{I} = 20e^{-j(\pi/3)}\ \text{A}$$

Complex Algebra

The advantage of representing sinusoids by phasors is due to the fact that algebraic processes are simplified by using complex constants in place of trigonometric functions of time. Operations such as addition and subtraction, multiplication and division, raising to powers, and extracting roots are performed easily if the complex numbers are in the most convenient form. The following examples indicate the rules of complex algebra as applied to the two complex numbers

$$\mathbf{A} = a + jb = Ae^{j\alpha} = A\,\underline{/\alpha}\qquad \text{(read: ``A at angle alpha'')}$$

and

$$\mathbf{C} = c + jd = Ce^{j\gamma} = C\,\underline{/\gamma}\qquad \text{(read: ``C at angle gamma'')}$$

Equality. Two complex numbers are equal if and only if the real parts are equal and the imaginary parts are equal.

If

$$\mathbf{A} = \mathbf{C}, \qquad\qquad \text{then } a = c \text{ and } b = d \qquad\qquad (3\text{-}20)$$

EXAMPLE 5

The voltage phasors across two branches in parallel (Fig. 3.15) are $\mathbf{V}_1 = 2 + jy$ and $\mathbf{V}_2 = V\,\underline{/60°}$. Find y and V.

SOLUTION. For branches in parallel, the voltages are equal and therefore the voltage phasors must be equal; hence,

$$2 + jy = V\,\underline{/60°}$$

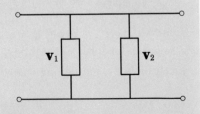

Fig. 3.15 Example 5.

This appears to be a single equation with two unknowns, but applying the rule for equality,

$$2 = V \cos 60° \qquad \text{and} \qquad y = V \sin 60°$$

Therefore,

$$V = \frac{2}{\cos 60°} = 4 \qquad \text{and} \qquad y = 4 \sin 60° = 2\sqrt{3}$$

Addition. Two complex numbers in rectangular form are added by adding the real parts and the imaginary parts separately.

$$\mathbf{A} + \mathbf{C} = (a + c) + j(b + d) \tag{3-21}$$

Subtraction can be considered as addition of the negative.

$$\mathbf{A} - \mathbf{C} = (a - c) + j(b - d) \tag{3-22}$$

Addition and subtraction are not convenient in the polar form.

EXAMPLE 6

In Fig. 3.16, $\mathbf{I}_1 = 3 - j4$ and $i_2(t) = 2 \cos(\omega t - 90°)$. Find $i_3(t)$.

SOLUTION. By inspection we write $\mathbf{I}_2 = 2\,\underline{/-90°}$, but the polar form is not convenient so we convert to rectangular form as $\mathbf{I}_2 = 0 - j2$. Then

$$\mathbf{I}_3 = \mathbf{I}_1 - \mathbf{I}_2 = (3 - j4) - (0 - j2)$$
$$= 3 - j4 + j2 = 3 - j2$$

In polar form, by Eq. 3.14,

$$\mathbf{I}_3 = \sqrt{3^2 + 2^2}\,\underline{/\arctan \frac{-2}{+3}} = 3.6\,\underline{/-33.7°}$$

Therefore,

Fig. 3.16   Example 6.

$$i_3(t) = 3.6 \cos(\omega t - 33.7°)$$

Multiplication. Multiplication and division of complex numbers in polar form are based on the laws of exponents. In multiplication the magnitude of the product is the product of the individual magnitudes, and the angle of the product is the sum of the individual angles.

$$(\mathbf{A})(\mathbf{C}) = (Ae^{j\alpha})(Ce^{j\gamma}) = ACe^{j(\alpha+\gamma)} = AC\,\underline{/\alpha + \gamma} \tag{3-23}$$

If the numbers are given in rectangular form and the product is desired in rectangular form, it may be more convenient to perform the multiplication directly, employing the concept that $j = \sqrt{-1}$ and $j^2 = -1$.

$$(\mathbf{A})(\mathbf{C}) = (a + jb)(c + jd) = ac + j^2bd + jbc + ajd$$
$$= (ac - bd) + j(bc + ad) \tag{3-24}$$

EXAMPLE 7

In a certain alternating-current circuit $\mathbf{V} = \mathbf{ZI}$, where $\mathbf{Z} = 7.07\ \underline{/-45°} = 5 - j5$ and $\mathbf{I} = 10\ \underline{/+90°} = 0 + j10$. Find $\mathbf{V}$.

SOLUTION. In polar form,

$$\mathbf{V} = (7.07\ \underline{/-45°})(10\ \underline{/+90°}) = 7.07 \times 10\ \underline{/-45° + 90°} = 70.7\ \underline{/+45°}$$

In rectangular form,

$$\mathbf{V} = (5 - j5)(0 + j10) = (5 \times 0 + 5 \times 10) + j(-5 \times 0 + 5 \times 10) = 50 + j50$$

Division. Applying the laws of exponents to division,

$$\frac{\mathbf{A}}{\mathbf{C}} = \frac{Ae^{j\alpha}}{Ce^{j\gamma}} = \frac{A\ \underline{/\alpha}}{C\ \underline{/\gamma}} = \frac{A}{C}\ \underline{/\alpha - \gamma} \tag{3-25}$$

The result consists of the quotient of the magnitudes and the difference of the angles.

Division in rectangular form is inconvenient but possible by using the *complex conjugate* of the denominator. Given a complex number $\mathbf{C} = c + jd$, the complex conjugate of $\mathbf{C}$ is defined as $\mathbf{C}^* = c - jd$; that is, the sign of the imaginary part is reversed. (Here the asterisk means "the complex conjugate of . . . .") Multiplying the denominator by its complex conjugate *rationalizes* the denominator (converts it to a real number) and simplifies division. To preserve the value of the quotient, the numerator is multiplied by the same factor.

EXAMPLE 8

In the alternating-current circuit of Example 7,

$$\mathbf{V} = 130\ \underline{/-67.4°} = 50 - j120 \qquad \text{and} \qquad \mathbf{Z} = 5\ \underline{/126.9°} = -3 + j4$$

Find $\mathbf{I}$.

SOLUTION. In polar form,

$$\mathbf{I} = \frac{\mathbf{V}}{\mathbf{Z}} = \frac{130\ \underline{/-67.4°}}{5\ \underline{/126.9°}} = 26\ \underline{/-194.3°} = 26\ \underline{/+165.7°}$$

In rectangular form,

$$\mathbf{I} = \frac{\mathbf{V}}{\mathbf{Z}} = \frac{50 - j120}{-3 + j4} \cdot \frac{-3 - j4}{-3 - j4} = \frac{(-150 - 480) + j(360 - 200)}{9 + 16}$$

$$= \frac{-630}{25} + j\frac{160}{25} = -25.2 + j6.4 = 26\ \underline{/+165.7°}$$

Powers and Roots. Applying the laws of exponents to a complex number in polar form,

$$\mathbf{A}^n = (Ae^{j\alpha})^n = A^n e^{jn\alpha} = A^n\ \underline{/n\alpha} \tag{3-26}$$

The same result is obtained from the rule for multiplication by recognizing that raising to the nth power is equal to multiplying a number by itself n times.

Extracting the nth root of a number is equivalent to raising the number to the $1/n$th power and the same rule is applicable:

$$\mathbf{A}^{1/n} = (Ae^{j\alpha})^{1/n} = A^{1/n}e^{j\alpha/n} = A^{1/n}\underline{/\alpha/n} \tag{3-27}$$

EXAMPLE 9

Perform the indicated operations.
(a) $(8.66 - j5)^3 = (10\underline{/-30°})^3 = 1000\underline{/-90°} = 0 - j1000$
(b) $(-5.66 + j5.66)^{1/3} = (8\underline{/+225°})^{1/3} = 2\underline{/+75°}$

Recalling that the number of distinct roots is equal to the order of the root (if n is an integer), locate the other roots in (b)

SOLUTION.   Since $8\underline{/225°} = 8\underline{/225° + N360°}$ where N is any integer, three distinct roots are obtained by assigning values of $N = 0, 1, 2$.

For $N = 1$, $(8\underline{/225° + 360°})^{1/3} = 2\underline{/75° + 120°} = 2\underline{/195°}$
For $N = 2$, $(8\underline{/225 + 720°})^{1/3} = 2\underline{/75° + 240°} = 2\underline{/315°}$

The three cube roots are found to be complex numbers of the same magnitude but differing in angle by $360°/3 = 120°$ (see Fig. 3.17).

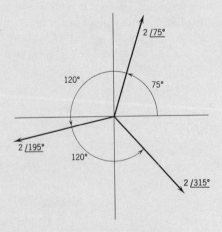

Fig. 3.17   Cube roots of a complex number.

Phasor Diagrams

Electrical engineering deals with practical problems involving measurable currents and voltages which could exist in and across real circuit components connected to the electric power line supplying the building in which you are now. In solving circuit problems, however, we choose to deal with abstractions rather than physical currents and voltages. Learning to read and write and interpret such abstractions is an essential part of your engineering education. Working with the abstract concept that we call a phasor will provide some good experience in this important activity.

The phasor has much in common with the plane vector which is so valuable in solving problems in mechanics. As you recall, vector representation of forces permits the use of graphical methods for the composition and resolution of forces. Also, and this may be more important, the use of vector representation, in free-body diagrams for example, provides a picture of the physical relationships which is not provided by the algebraic equations alone. In the same way, *phasor diagrams* can be used for graphical solution, as a quick check on an algebraic solution, and to gain new insight into voltage and current relations.

EXAMPLE 10

Given: $v_1 = 150 \cos (377t - \pi/6)$ V and $\mathbf{V}_2 = 200\ \underline{/+60°}$ V.

Find: $v = v_1 + v_2$.

SOLUTION. The expression for v_1 is a mathematical abstraction carrying a great deal of information: a voltage varies sinusoidally with time, completing $377/2\pi = 60$ cps and reaching a positive maximum value of 150 V when $t = (\pi/6)/377 = 0.00139$ sec. By now such an interpretation should be easy for you.

The expression for $\mathbf{V}_2$ is "an abstraction of an abstraction"; part of the information is specified and part is only implied. The maximum value is clearly 200 V and the phase angle is 60°; the sinusoidal character is implied by the bold-face phasor notation. Since v_1 and v_2 are associated, we assume that they have the same angular frequency or $\omega_2 = 377$. Reading "between the lines," we conclude that $v_2 = 200 \cos (377t + \pi/3)$ V.

To work with sinusoids v_1 and v_2, we first transform the time functions to phasors. If $v_1(t) = 150 \cos (377t - \pi/6)$ V, then $\mathbf{V}_1 = 150\ \underline{/-30°}$ V. If $v_2(t) = 200 \cos (377t + \pi/3)$ V, then $\mathbf{V}_2 = 200\ \underline{/+60°}$ V.

The phasor diagram of Fig. 3.18 shows the complex quantities $\mathbf{V}_1$ and $\mathbf{V}_2$ plotted to scale. Like vectors, the phasors have magnitude and direction, and they can be resolved into components. The parallelogram law for adding vectors is based on the fact that the horizontal (or vertical) component of the resultant is just equal to the sum of horizontal (or vertical) components of the individual forces. This is consistent with the rule for adding complex quantities by adding real and imaginary components separately so the parallelogram law should work in graphical addition of phasors. The construction is shown in Fig. 3.18; scaling off the resultant, it appears that $\mathbf{V}$ has a magnitude of about 250 V at an angle of approximately 23°.

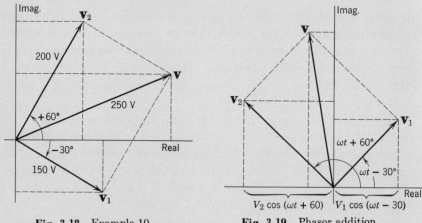

Fig. 3.18   Example 10.   Fig. 3.19   Phasor addition.

To perform the addition algebraically, the rectangular form is more convenient and we write, using Eq. 3.15,

$$\mathbf{V}_1 = 150 \cos (-30°) + j150 \sin (-30°) = 130 - j75 \text{ V}$$

$$\mathbf{V}_2 = 200 \cos 60° + j200 \sin 60° = 100 + j173 \text{ V}$$

By the rules for equality and addition,

$$\mathbf{V} = \mathbf{V}_1 + \mathbf{V}_2 = 230 + j98 = 250 \underline{/23.1°} \text{ V}$$

Performing the inverse transformation on $\mathbf{V}$, we obtain

$$v = v_1 + v_2 = 250 \cos (377t + 23.1°) \text{ V}$$

Looking again at Fig. 3.18, we see that in Example 10 the algebraic addition involves the same components as the graphical addition, and we can conclude that phasor diagrams can be used for graphical calculations with the phasors treated just like vectors. A second virtue of the phasor diagram is that a quick sketch only approximately to scale provides a good check on algebraic calculations. Mistakes in sign, decimal point, or angle are easily spotted.

How is it possible that the sum of two constants can completely describe the sum of two continuously varying functions? In other words, will the real part of $\mathbf{V}e^{j\omega t}$ always be just equal to the sum of the real parts of $\mathbf{V}_1 e^{j\omega t}$ and $\mathbf{V}_2 e^{j\omega t}$? The phasor diagram can provide insight into this relationship. In Fig. 3.19, the phasors have been converted to complex functions of time by multiplying by $e^{j\omega t}$ and the rotating radial lines corresponding to the complex functions are drawn for a general instant of time. By Eq. 3-18, a voltage $v(t)$ is represented by the projection of $\mathbf{V}e^{j\omega t}$ on the real axis. Fig. 3.19 shows that for any instant of time, that is, for any value of ωt, the real part of $\mathbf{V}e^{j\omega t}$ is equal to the sum of the real parts of $\mathbf{V}_1 e^{j\omega t}$ and $\mathbf{V}_2 e^{j\omega t}$. We conclude that v, the inverse transform of $\mathbf{V}$, is just equal to the sum of v_1 and v_2 and the phasor approach is valid.

SUMMARY

◆ Signal waveforms encountered frequently include: direct, step, pulse, sawtooth, exponential, and sinusoidal waves.

◆ The simplicity of the mathematical relations between exponentials and their derivatives and integrals makes them valuable in circuit analysis.

◆ The general decaying exponential is $a = Ae^{-t/T}$.

◆ The time constant T is a measure of the rate of decay.
When $t = T$, $a/A = 1/e = 0.368$.
When $t = 5T$, $a/A = 1/e^5 = 0.0067$, and the exponential quantity is practically negligible.

◆ Sinusoids are important because they occur naturally, they are common in power and communication, they are easy to handle mathematically, and they can be used to represent other periodic waves.

◆ The general sinusoid is $a = A \cos (\omega t + \alpha)$.
Frequency $\omega = 2\pi f$ rad/sec.
Frequency $f = 1/T$ cps, where period T is in seconds.

◆ In the imaginary number jb, j is an operator indicating a 90° counterclockwise rotation; in algebraic manipulation, $j^2 1 = -1$ or $j = \sqrt{-1}$.

◆ The combination of a real number a and an imaginary number jb defines a complex number $\mathbf{W} = a + jb = Me^{j\theta} = M \,\underline{/\theta}$.
For conversion,

$$a = M \cos \theta \qquad M = \sqrt{a^2 + b^2}$$

$$b = M \sin \theta \qquad \theta = \arctan b/a$$

◆ A sinusoidal function of time $a = A \cos (\omega t + \alpha)$ can be interpreted as the real part of the complex function $Ae^{j(\omega t + \alpha)} = Ae^{j\alpha} \cdot e^{j\omega t}$.

◆ The complex constant $Ae^{j\alpha}$ is defined as phasor $\mathbf{A}$.
Phasor $\mathbf{A}$ is called the transform of the time function $a(t)$.

◆ Phasor calculations follow the rules of complex algebra.
Where $\mathbf{A} = a + jb = A \,\underline{/\alpha}$ and $\mathbf{C} = c + jd = C \,\underline{/\gamma}$,
Equality: $\quad \mathbf{A} = \mathbf{C}$, if $a = c$ and $b = d$
Addition: $\quad \mathbf{A} + \mathbf{C} = (a + c) + j(b + d)$

Multiplication: $(\mathbf{A})(\mathbf{C}) = AC\ \underline{/\alpha + \gamma}$, or

$$(\mathbf{A})(\mathbf{C}) = (ac - bd) + j(bc + ad)$$

Division: $\dfrac{\mathbf{A}}{\mathbf{C}} = \dfrac{A}{C}\ \underline{/\alpha - \gamma}$

Conjugate: $\mathbf{C}^* = c - jd$

Powers: $(\mathbf{A})^n = A^n\ \underline{/n\alpha}$

◆ Phasor diagrams follow the rules for vector diagrams and can provide an approximate answer, a quick check, or a clear visualization.

◆ The general procedure when using phasor representation is:
1. Transform functions of time into constant phasors.
2. Perform indicated operations on phasors, using complex algebra and phasor diagrams.
3. Transform the resulting phasors into functions of time.

REVIEW QUESTIONS

1. Show by means of a sketch how a pulse can be obtained from two steps.
2. Write the general equation of an exponentially *increasing* function.
3. Justify the statement: "In a linear circuit consisting of resistances, inductances, and capacitances, if any voltage or current is an exponential all voltages and currents will be exponentials with the same time constant."
4. Write a statement for sinusoids similar to the foregoing statement for exponentials and justify it.
5. Write out in words a definition of a phasor.
6. How can a phasor, a constant quantity, represent a variable function of time?
7. Given $i_1 = 10 \cos (1000t + \pi/2)$ and $i_2 = 5 \cos 2000t$. Is the phasor method applicable to finding $i_1 + i_2$? Explain.
8. Indicate the process of division by using logarithms. Write the "transform equation." What is the "inverse transform" called here?
9. Write a statement of the condition for equality of two complex quantities in polar form. (Careful!)
10. How are a quantity and its conjugate related on the complex plane?
11. Describe the quantity designated by the code symbols $\mathbf{I} = 20\ \underline{/\pi/4}$, $\omega = 60$.
12. Sketch three phasors on the complex plane and show the graphical construction to obtain $\mathbf{V}_1 + \mathbf{V}_2 - \mathbf{V}_3$.
13. Write a mathematical equation for $i(t)$ in terms of $\mathbf{I}$.
14. How can we neglect the imaginary part of the exponential function used in phasor representation?
15. Make up a table of trigonometric functions of 0, 30°, 45°, 60°, and 90° and for a 3-4-5 triangle; keep it handy for reference.
16. Study your sliderule manual and outline the procedure for converting complex numbers in rectangular form to polar form and vice versa. Practice until you can perform these operations for all quadrants rapidly without mistake.

EXERCISES

1. A sawtooth voltage wave has a maximum value of 20 V and resets 10 times each sec. Sketch the wave and write a mathematical expression for $v(t)$.

2. An exponential current has an initial value of 20 mA and at $t = 6$ msec a value of 1 mA. Write the equation for $i(t)$.

3. An exponential current has a value of 4.35 A at $t = 2$ sec and a value of 1.6 A at $t = 5$ sec. Write the equation for $i(t)$.

4. An exponential voltage has a value of 68 V at $t = 5$ msec and a value of 25 V at $t = 10$ msec. Write the equation for $v(t)$.

5. Given a current $i = Ie^{-at}$, write an equation for $i(t)$, using the base 10. What advantage is there in using the base e?

6. Throwing a switch in an experimental circuit introduces a transient voltage $v = 120e^{-10t}$ V. If measurements in the circuit are accurate to 0.5%, approximately how long does the switching transient "last"?

7. A voltage $v = 20e^{-100t}$ V appears across a parallel combination of $R = 2\ \Omega$ and $L = 40$ mH. Determine the current in each element and the total current.

8. A current $i = 2e^{-50t}$ A flows in a series combination of R and C (C is initially uncharged). (a) If $R = 50$ kΩ and $C = 1\ \mu$F, what total voltage exists across the combination? (b) If R is reduced to 20 kΩ, repeat part (a). (A physical interpretation of this result is given in Chapter 4.)

9. Sketch approximately to scale, the following functions:
    (a) $i = 2 \cos (377t + \pi/4)$ A.
    (b) $v = 50 \cos (628t - \pi/3)$ V.
    (c) $v = 100 \sin (628t + 60°)$ V.

10. Write an equation, first in general and then in specific terms, for each of the following sinusoidal waves:
    (a) A voltage with a period of 6 msec and passing through a positive maximum of 120 V at $t = 1$ msec.
    (b) A current with a period of 2 msec and passing through a positive maximum of 6 A at $t = 0.25$ msec.
    (c) A current with a frequency of 125 cps and passing through a *negative* maximum of -6 A at $t = 3$ msec.
    (d) A voltage which reaches a positive maximum of 20 V at $t = 6\ \mu$sec and the next negative maximum at $t = 16\ \mu$sec.

11. Where h is defined as an operator producing a 120° counterclockwise rotation, express the following in polar and rectangular form (in terms of j): (a) $h1$, (b) h^21, (c) $(h2)^3$, (d) $\sqrt{h1}$, (e) $(-h)1$, (f) $\sqrt{(-h)4}$.

12. Given: $\mathbf{A} = 3 + j4$, $\mathbf{B} = 10e^{j60°}$, and $\mathbf{C} = 5\ \underline{/-30°}$. Sketch the three quantities on the complex plane and find: (a) $\mathbf{A} + \mathbf{B}$, (b) $\mathbf{AB}$, (c) $\mathbf{B} - \mathbf{C}$, (d) $\mathbf{A}/\mathbf{B}$, (e) $\mathbf{B}/\mathbf{C}$, (f) $(\mathbf{A} - \mathbf{C})/\mathbf{B}$, (g) $\mathbf{A^*C}$.

13. Repeat Exercise 12 given: $\mathbf{A} = 5e^{j\pi/4}$, $\mathbf{B} = 4 - j3$, and $\mathbf{C} = 10\ \underline{/-120°}$.

14. Find: (a) the cube roots of $(-2 + j\sqrt{3})$, (b) the fourth roots of $-4\ \underline{/135°}$.

15. Represent the time functions of Exercise 9 by phasors in polar and rectangular form.

16. Represent the following time functions by phasors in polar and rectangular form: (a) $i = 2 \cos (\omega t - 30°)$, (b) $i = 5 \cos (\omega t + 5\pi/4)$, (c) $i =$
10 sin $(\omega t + 60°)$.

17. Write the time functions corresponding to: (a) the phasors given in Exercise
12, (b) the phasors given in Exercise 13.

18. Write the first six terms of the series expansion for e^x. Evaluate each term
for $x = j1$. On the complex plane, plot each term to scale, adding onto the
preceding term. Measure the sum of the six terms and express it in polar
form. Is the result what you expected?

19. Find the sum of the two voltages in Exercise 9 by: (a) point-by-point addition, (b) trigonometric expansion, (c) phasor addition. Draw a conclusion
regarding the relative ease of the three methods.

20. Given: $i_1 = 2 \cos 1000t$ and $i_2 = 3 \sin (1000t - 30°)$. Find $i_1 + i_2$ by:
(a) point-by-point addition, (b) trigonometric expansion, (c) phasor addition.
Draw a conclusion regarding the relative ease of the three methods.

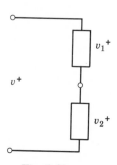

Fig. 3.20

21. Given $v_1 = 20 \cos (\omega t + 30°)$ and $v_2 = 50 \cos (\omega t - 45°)$ in Fig. 3.20,
determine $\mathbf{V} = \mathbf{V_1} + \mathbf{V_2}$ graphically from a phasor diagram drawn to scale.
Check by an analytical solution and determine $v(t) = v_1 + v_2$.

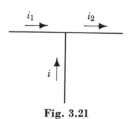

Fig. 3.21

22. Given $i_1 = 2 \cos (\omega t + 30°)$ and $i_2 = 6 \cos (\omega t + 150°)$ in Fig. 3.21,
determine $\mathbf{I}$ graphically from a phasor diagram drawn to scale. Check by an
analytical method and determine $i(t)$.

PROBLEMS

1. Demonstrate analytically that if an exponential continued to decay at its initial rate, the duration of the function would be just equal to the time constant.

2. A voltage $v(t) = V \cos \omega_1 t$ exists across a series combination of R and L and a current $i(t)$ flows.

   (a) Draw and label the circuit and write the governing differential equation, using element and connection equations.

   (b) Assume a solution $i = I \cos (\omega t - \theta)$, substitute into the equation of part (a) and simplify (eliminate sine terms).

   (c) Determine the values of ω, θ, and I which hold for all values of time t.

   (d) Transform the simplified equation of part (b) by writing the phasor of each term. Express voltages across R and L in terms of the phasor of the assumed current.

   (e) Solve the equation of part (d) for the current phasor in polar form, transform the result into a time function, and compare the answer to that from part (c). (This is the basis for a general approach to a-c circuit problems.)

3. Derive Euler's theorem starting with $\mathbf{W} = \cos \theta + j \sin \theta$. First express $d\mathbf{W}/d\theta$ in terms of $\mathbf{W}$. Then solve for $d\mathbf{W}/\mathbf{W}$ and integrate to obtain $\ln \mathbf{W}$. Evaluate the constant of integration by letting $\theta = 0$ in the original equation. Finally convert $\ln \mathbf{W}$ to an exponential.

4. Given $\mathbf{A} = A \underline{/\alpha}$ and $\mathbf{C} = C \underline{/\gamma}$, prove that $\mathbf{AC} = AC \underline{/\alpha + \gamma}$ without using exponentials.

5. Using the concept of a complex number as an exponential, determine: (a) $\ln (1 \underline{/\pi/2})$, (b) $\ln (-j2)$, (c) $\ln (-10)$, (d) $\ln (3 + j4)$.

6. Prove analytically, without reference to lines and angles, that $e^{j3\pi/2} = 1/j$.

CHAPTER **4**

Natural Response

In predicting the behavior of electrical circuits or mechanical systems, we must take into account two different sources of energy. The behavior determined by an *external* energy source we call a *forced* response; the behavior due to *internal* energy storage we call a *natural* response. For example, a stretched string may be forced to vibrate at any frequency by an externally applied alternating force; if the string is plucked and released, however, it will vibrate at its characteristic frequency, its natural frequency, due to the internal energy stored in the plucking. As another example, an automobile may go fast or slow, forward or backward, as energy from the engine is controlled by the operator; but if the moving automobile is taken out of gear, it will coast to rest in a predictable manner as the internal energy is dissipated.

In an electrical circuit, the external energy source or *forcing function* may be continuous or sinusoidal, or may have any of the other waveforms shown in Fig. 3.1. Energy may be stored internally in the electric field of a capacitor or the magnetic field of an inductor. In a chemical system, energy may be stored internally in the temperature of a liquid, in the potential energy of a compressed gas, or in the kinetic energy of a moving fluid. In the general problem, both external and internal energy sources are present and both forced and natural responses must be considered.

Forced responses can be maintained indefinitely by the continual input of energy. In contrast, because of unavoidable dissipation in electrical resistance or mechanical friction, natural responses tend to die out. After the natural behavior has become negligibly small, conditions are said to have reached the *steady state*. The period beginning with the initiation of a natural response and ending when the natural response becomes negligible is called the *transient* period.

While the natural behavior of a system is not itself a response to any external function, a study of natural behavior will reveal characteristics of a system which will be useful in predicting the forced response as well. Our approach is first to investigate the natural behavior, then to study the forced behavior, and finally to consider the general case of forced and natural behavior. In this chapter the emphasis is on the natural behavior of electrical circuits with some applications to mechanical and thermal systems. We start with relatively simple systems, derive the basic concepts, and then formulate a general procedure. The methods developed are powerful and they are applicable to problems in many branches of engineering.

EQUATIONS OF FIRST-ORDER SYSTEMS

In general, the behavior of an electrical circuit or any other physical system can be described by an integrodifferential equation. In electrical circuits, the governing equation is obtained by applying the experimental laws for circuit elements and combinations of elements, taking into account external and internal energy sources.

In the circuit of Fig. 4.1, for example, a coil of inductance L and resistance R carrying a current I_0 is suddenly shorted by closing switch S at time $t = 0$. The equation governing current i as a function of time t after the switch is closed can be obtained by applying Kirchhoff's voltage law to the shorted series circuit. For all time $t > 0$, the sum of the voltages around the closed path must be zero or

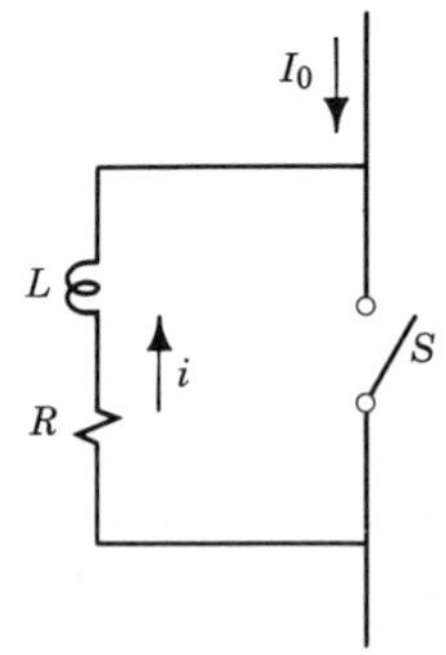

Fig. 4.1 *L-R* example.

$$\Sigma v = 0 = -Ri - L\frac{di}{dt}$$

or

$$L\frac{di}{dt} + Ri = 0 \qquad (4\text{-}1)$$

Note that there is no voltage across the short circuit even if current I_0 continues to flow.

As another example, in Fig. 4.2 capacitance C with initial voltage V_0 (or initial charge $Q_0 = CV_0$) is suddenly shorted across a resistance R at time $t = 0$. For all time $t > 0$,

$$\Sigma v = 0 = V_0 - \frac{1}{C} \int_0^t i \, dt - Ri$$

Differentiating to eliminate the integral and rearranging the terms,

$$R \frac{di}{dt} + \frac{1}{C} i = 0 \qquad (4\text{-}2)$$

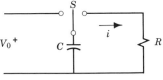

Fig. 4.2 *R-C* example.

In Fig. 4.3, the mass M is sliding on a surface for which the coefficient of friction is D. The driving force is removed at $t = 0$ when the velocity is U_0 (or M is given an initial momentum MU_0). If the mass is allowed to coast, the only forces acting on M are those due to inertia and friction. Applying d'Alembert's principle, for all time $t > 0$,

$$\Sigma f = 0 = -M \frac{du}{dt} - Du$$

or

$$M \frac{du}{dt} + Du = 0 \qquad (4\text{-}3)$$

These examples result in analogous, first-order, linear, homogeneous, ordinary differential equations—*analogous* because they are of the same mathematical form, *first-order* because that is the order of the highest derivative present, *linear* because the variable and its derivatives appear only to the first power, *homogeneous* because there are no constant terms or forcing functions, and *ordinary* because there is a single independent variable t.

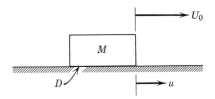

Fig. 4.3 *D-M* example.

The homogeneous equation contains only terms relating to the circuit itself; the solution of this equation is independent of any forcing function and therefore it is the natural response of the circuit. This type of equation occurs so frequently that we must learn a convenient method for solving it.

Solving the Equation

The solution of a differential equation consists in finding a function which satisfies the equation. Consider the equation for the circuit of Fig. 4.2,

$$R\frac{di}{dt} + \frac{1}{C}i = 0 \tag{4-2}$$

This equation says that the combination of a function $i(t)$ and its derivative di/dt must equal zero; the function and its derivation must cancel somehow. This implies that the form of the function and that of its derivative must be the same and suggests an exponential function. If we let

$$i = Ae^{st}, \qquad \text{then} \qquad \frac{di}{dt} = sAe^{st} \tag{4-4}$$

where A is an amplitude and s is a frequency.† Substituting these expressions into the homogeneous equation,

$$RsAe^{st} + \frac{1}{C}Ae^{st} = 0$$

or

$$\left(Rs + \frac{1}{C}\right)Ae^{st} = 0 \qquad \text{for all values of } t \tag{4-5}$$

In looking for solutions to this equation, $A = 0$ is one possibility, but this is the trivial case. The other possibility is to let $(Rs + 1/C) = 0$. This yields

$$s = -1/RC$$

and

$$i = Ae^{(-1/RC)t} \tag{4-6}$$

To evaluate the amplitude A, we return to the original equation

$$V_0 - \frac{1}{C}\int_0^t i\,dt - Ri = 0 \tag{4-7}$$

---

† Note that the units of s are "per sec." The reason for calling s a "frequency" is explained on p. 96.

and consider a time $t = 0^+$, the first instant of time after $t = 0$. The integral of current over time represents the flow of charge and it takes a finite time for charge to be transferred. At $t = 0^+$, no time has elapsed and $\int_0^{0^+} i \, dt = 0$. Therefore the initial conditions are that

$$V_0 - 0 - Ri_0 = 0 \qquad \text{or} \qquad i_0 = \frac{V_0}{R} \qquad (4\text{-}8)$$

By Eq. 4-6, at $t = 0^+$,

$$i_0 = A e^{s(0)} = A e^0 = A$$

Therefore,

$$A = i_0 = \frac{V_0}{R}$$

and for all values of time after the switch is closed

$$i = \frac{V_0}{R} e^{-t/RC} \qquad (4\text{-}9)$$

The physical explanation of this mathematical expression is based on the fact that resistor current is proportional to voltage, whereas capacitor current is proportional to rate of change of voltage. Upon closing the switch, the full voltage of the capacitor is applied across the resistor and initial current is high ($i_0 = V_0/R$). But this current flow removes charge and reduces the voltage ($dv_C/dt = i/C$) across the capacitor and resistor and therefore the current is reduced. As the voltage decreases, the current is reduced, the voltage changes more slowly, and the current becomes ever smaller.

As another approach to evaluating i_0, we recall that the energy stored in a capacitance is $\frac{1}{2}Cv^2$ and this energy cannot be changed instantaneously since that would involve an infinite power. Therefore, the voltage on a capacitance cannot be changed instantaneously and we conclude that the voltage just after switching (at $t = 0^+$) must equal the voltage just before switching, V_0. When the switch is closed, this voltage appears across the resistance and

$$v_C = V_0 = v_R = i_0 R$$

hence

$$i_0 = \frac{V_0}{R}$$

as before.

General Procedure

An analysis of the steps followed in this example indicates a general procedure for determining the natural behavior of an electrical circuit:

1. Write the governing equation, using Kirchhoff's laws.
2. Reduce this to a homogeneous differential equation.
3. Assume an exponential solution with undetermined constants.
4. Determine the exponents from the homogeneous equation.
5. Evaluate the coefficients from the given conditions.

In a dynamic mechanical system, the first step usually involves the application of d'Alembert's principle and the equation for forces in equilibrium. Chemical engineering systems involving mass and energy transport may be analyzed in a similar way. Any such lumped linear system can be described by an ordinary differential equation which can be reduced to the homogeneous equation by eliminating constant terms and forcing functions. The solution of such an equation is always expressible in terms of exponential functions. The evaluation of the coefficients, which may be the most difficult step, is usually based on consideration of the energies stored in the system.

EXAMPLE 1

A coil of 2 H inductance and 10 Ω resistance is short-circuited at time $t = 0$. If the initial current in the coil is 10 A, predict the current after 1 sec has elapsed. How long will it take for the natural behavior current to become zero?

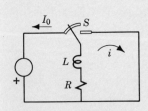

Fig. 4.4 Example 1.

SOLUTION. As shown in Fig. 4.4, the switch S is arranged to disconnect the source and simultaneously short-circuit the coil. The direction of the resulting current i is arbitrarily assumed and drawn as shown.

1. By Kirchhoff's voltage law, the sum of the voltages around the closed path must be zero or, traversing in a clockwise direction,

$$\Sigma v = 0 = -Ri - L\frac{di}{dt}$$

Going in the direction of the assumed current i, energy is extracted from the circuit (for positive i and positive di/dt) and, therefore, the voltage terms are negative.

2. Rearranging terms yields the homogeneous equation

$$L\frac{di}{dt} + Ri = 0$$

3. Assuming an exponential solution, we write

$$i = Ae^{st}$$

where s and A are to be determined.

4. Substituting the assumed solution into the homogeneous equation

$$LsAe^{st} + RAe^{st} = 0$$

or

$$(sL + R)Ae^{st} = 0$$

Setting

$$sL + R = 0, \qquad s = -\frac{R}{L},$$

and

$$i = Ae^{-(R/L)t}$$

5. The energy stored in an inductance is $\frac{1}{2}Li^2$ and this energy cannot be changed instantaneously. Therefore, the current in the coil cannot be changed instantaneously and the current just after the switch is thrown must equal the current just before the switch is thrown. At $t = 0^+$,

$$i = I_0 = Ae^0 = A \qquad \text{or} \qquad A = I_0$$

hence the general solution is

$$i = I_0 e^{-(R/L)t} \tag{4-10}$$

In this specific example,

$$i = 10e^{-(10/2)t} = 10e^{-5t} \text{ A}$$

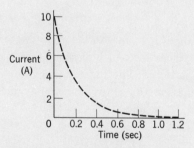

Fig. 4.5 Current decay in *R-L* circuit.

As shown in Fig. 4.5, after 1 sec,

$$i = 10e^{-5 \times 1} = 10 \times 0.0067 = 0.067 \text{ A}$$

In answer to the second question, note that the current decreases with an increase in time but never becomes zero.

If current is the rate of transfer of charge and if the current flows "forever," will an infinite charge be transferred? To answer this question, express the total charge as the integral of current over an infinite

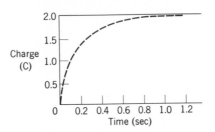

Fig. 4.6 Charge transfer in R-L circuit.

time, or

$$q = \int_0^t i \, dt = \int_0^\infty 10e^{-5t} \, dt$$

$$= -\left. \frac{10}{5} e^{-5t} \right]_0^\infty = -\frac{10}{5}(0-1) = 2 \text{ C}$$

While the current flows "forever," the rate of flow is decreasing in such a way that the total charge transferred approaches a finite limit (Fig. 4.6). The same is true of the energy dissipated in the resistance R (see Exercise 6).

Time Constant

The term "first-order system" refers to a system involving only a single energy-storage element for which the governing equation is a first-order differential equation. The natural behavior obtained by solving the homogeneous equation will always be similar in form to the decay of current in an RC circuit, where

$$i = I_0 e^{-t/RC} \tag{4-11}$$

In the circuit of Fig. 4.7a if $V_0 = 6$ V, $R = 1000$ Ω, and $C = 2$ μF, the specific equation becomes

$$i = \frac{V_0}{R} e^{-t/RC} = \frac{6}{10^3} e^{-t/10^3 \times 2 \times 10^{-6}} = 6e^{-500t} \text{ mA}$$

This result is plotted in Fig. 4.7b. By definition (Eq. 3.3), the *time constant* is the time at which the exponential factor is $e^{-1} = 0.368$. Here the time constant $T = RC = 0.002$ sec.

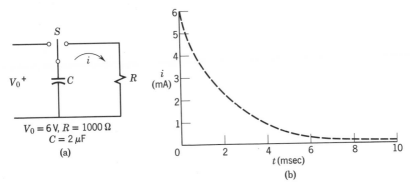

Fig. 4.7 Natural behavior of an *RC* circuit.

NATURAL RESPONSE OF SECOND-ORDER SYSTEMS

If there is more than one energy-storage element, the behavior of the system is more complicated but the analysis follows the same procedure as for the simpler systems. In an *RLC* circuit, energy may be stored in the inductance or in the capacitance. In the series circuit of Fig. 4.8, assume that an initial voltage V_0 exists on the capacitance C. With the switch S open there is no current in the inductance L and therefore no energy storage in its magnetic field. The resistance R is incapable of energy storage.

Following the general procedure for determining natural behavior, we first write the governing equation, using Kirchhoff's voltage

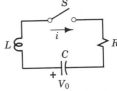

Fig. 4.8 *RLC* circuit.

law. Traversing the loop (after the switch is closed) in a clockwise direction, we have

$$\Sigma v = 0 = -L\frac{di}{dt} - Ri + V_0 - \frac{1}{C}\int_0^t i\,dt$$

By differentiating and rearranging terms, the homogeneous equation is

$$L\frac{d^2i}{dt^2} + R\frac{di}{dt} + \frac{1}{C}i = 0 \qquad (4\text{-}12)$$

The presence of the second energy-storage element has increased the order of the highest derivative appearing in the homogeneous equation. This equation is typical of a *second-order* system.

Assuming an exponential solution, let $i = Ae^{st}$. Substituting in the homogeneous equation yields

$$s^2 LAe^{st} + sRAe^{st} + \frac{1}{C} Ae^{st} = 0$$

which is satisfied when

$$Ls^2 + Rs + \frac{1}{C} = 0 \tag{4-13}$$

This equation is noteworthy. For this series circuit it is the sum of three terms, each relating to a circuit element. It contains no voltages or currents, only terms characteristic of the circuit. Also, from this equation we expect to obtain information about the character of the natural behavior; it is called the *characteristic equation* and is very useful in circuit analysis.

The roots of the characteristic equation (Eq. 4-13) are

$$s_1 = -\frac{R}{2L} + \sqrt{\frac{R^2}{4L^2} - \frac{1}{LC}} \quad \text{and} \quad s_2 = -\frac{R}{2L} - \sqrt{\frac{R^2}{4L^2} - \frac{1}{LC}} \tag{4-14}$$

If either $i_1 = A_1 e^{s_1 t}$ or $i_2 = A_2 e^{s_2 t}$ satisfies a linear homogeneous equation, i.e., make it zero, then the sum of the two terms also satisfies the equation. The most general solution then is

$$i = A_1 e^{s_1 t} + A_2 e^{s_2 t} \tag{4-15}$$

where A_1 and A_2 are determined by the initial conditions and s_1 and s_2 are determined by the circuit constants.

The values of R, L, and C are all real and positive, but the values of s_1 and s_2 may be real, complex, or purely imaginary. The clue to the character of the natural response of a second-order system is found in the quantity under the radical sign—the *discriminant*. If the discriminant is positive, the roots of the characteristic equation will be real, negative, and distinct. If the discriminant is zero, the two roots will be real, negative, and identical. If the discriminant is negative, the roots will be complex numbers or, in the special case where $R = 0$, purely imaginary.

Roots Real and Distinct

If the discriminant in Eq. 4-14 is positive, s_1 and s_2 are real, negative, and distinct, and the natural behavior is the sum of two decaying exponential responses.

EXAMPLE 2

Given the circuit values shown in Fig. 4.9a, determine and plot the current response as a function of time after the switch is closed.

SOLUTION. Since

$$\frac{R}{2L} = \frac{4}{2 \times 1} = 2 \quad \text{and} \quad \frac{R^2}{4L^2} - \frac{1}{LC} = \frac{16}{4} - \frac{1}{1 \times \frac{1}{3}} = 4 - 3 = 1$$

$$s_1 = -2 + 1 = -1 \quad \text{and} \quad s_2 = -2 - 1 = -3$$

and from Eq. 4-15,

$$i = A_1 e^{-t} + A_2 e^{-3t} \tag{4-16}$$

To evaluate the constants, consider the initial conditions. At the instant the switch was closed, the voltage across the capacitance $v_c = V_0$ and the current in the inductance $i_L = 0$. Because energy cannot be changed instantaneously, these values must hold just after closing the switch, at $t = 0^+$, say. At $t = 0^+$, the current in each element in this series circuit must be zero or (Eq. 4-16):

$$i = i_0 = 0 = A_1 e^0 + A_2 e^0 = A_1 + A_2, \quad \text{therefore } A_2 = -A_1$$

Also, the voltage iR across the resistance is zero and

$$v_L = v_c \quad \text{or} \quad L\frac{di}{dt} = V_0 \quad \text{and} \quad \frac{di}{dt} = \frac{V_0}{L}$$

From Eq. 4-16 at $t = 0^+$

$$\frac{di}{dt} = \frac{V_0}{L} = -A_1 e^0 - 3A_2 e^0 = -A_1 - 3A_2 = -A_1 + 3A_1 = +2A_1$$

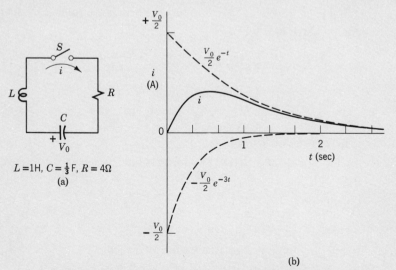

$$L = 1\text{H}, C = \tfrac{1}{3}\text{F}, R = 4\Omega$$
(a)

(b)

Fig. 4.9 Response of an overdamped second-order system.

Solving,

$$A_1 = + \frac{V_0}{2L} = + \frac{V_0}{2} \quad \text{and} \quad A_2 = -A_1 = - \frac{V_0}{2}$$

The specific equation for the current response, plotted in Fig. 4.9b, becomes

$$i = \frac{V_0}{2} e^{-t} - \frac{V_0}{2} e^{-3t}$$

Roots Complex

If the discriminant in Eq. 4-14 is negative, s_1 and s_2 are complex conjugates and the natural behavior is an exponentially damped sinusoid.

EXAMPLE 3

In the circuit of Example 2, let $R = 2 \ \Omega$, $L = 1$ H, and $C = \frac{1}{17}$ F. Derive an expression for the natural response.

SOLUTION. From Eq. 4-14, now

$$\frac{R}{2L} = \frac{2}{2 \times 1} = 1 \quad \text{and} \quad \frac{R^2}{4L^2} - \frac{1}{LC} = \frac{4}{4} - \frac{1}{\frac{1}{17}} = 1 - 17 = -16$$

Therefore,

$$s_1 = -1 + \sqrt{-16} = -1 + j4 \quad \text{and} \quad s_2 = -1 - \sqrt{-16} = -1 - j4$$

and the natural response is

$$i = A_1 e^{(-1+j4)t} + A_2 e^{(-1-j4)t} \tag{4-17}$$

The physical interpretation of Eq. 4-17 is not immediately clear. To gain insight into this type of response, let us consider the case of complex roots in a general way. The mathematics will be simplified by arbitrarily defining three new terms:

$$\alpha = \frac{R}{2L} \quad \omega_n{}^2 = \frac{1}{LC} \quad \omega^2 = \frac{1}{LC} - \frac{R^2}{4L^2} = \omega_n{}^2 - \alpha^2 \tag{4-18}$$

Now,

$$s_1 = -\alpha + j\omega \quad \text{and} \quad s_2 = -\alpha - j\omega$$

and the general form of Eq. 4-17 is:

$$i = A_1 e^{(-\alpha+j\omega)t} + A_2 e^{(-\alpha-j\omega)t} \tag{4-19}$$

By Euler's equation (Eq. 3-11),

$$e^{j\omega t} = \cos \omega t + j \sin \omega t \quad \text{and} \quad e^{-j\omega t} = \cos \omega t - j \sin \omega t$$

Factoring out the $e^{-\alpha t}$ and substituting for $e^{j\omega t}$ yields

$$i = e^{-\alpha t}[(A_1 + A_2) \cos \omega t + j(A_1 - A_2) \sin \omega t]$$

where A_1 and A_2 are constants which may be complex numbers. In fact, since these are physical currents, the coefficients of the cos ωt and sin ωt terms, $(A_1 + A_2)$ and $j(A_1 - A_2)$, must be real numbers which could be called B_1 and B_2 so that

$$i = e^{-\alpha t}[B_1 \cos \omega t + B_2 \sin \omega t] \qquad (4\text{-}20)$$

But the sum of a cosine function and a sine function must be another sine function (properly displaced in phase), so Eq. 4-20 can be rewritten to give a natural response of

$$i = Ae^{-\alpha t} \sin (\omega t + \theta) \qquad (4\text{-}21.)$$

This is evidently a sinusoidal function of time with an exponentially decaying amplitude, a so-called "damped sinusoid," where A and θ are constants† to be determined from initial conditions.

EXAMPLE 4

Rewrite Eq. 4-17 in Example 3 as a damped sinusoid and determine the natural response after closing the switch.

SOLUTION. For $\alpha = \dfrac{R}{2L} = 1$ and $\omega = \sqrt{\dfrac{1}{LC} - \dfrac{R^2}{4L^2}} = 4$

Eq. 4-21 becomes

$$i = Ae^{-t} \sin (4t + \theta)$$

and

$$\frac{di}{dt} = Ae^{-t}4 \cos (4t + \theta) - Ae^{-t} \sin (4t + \theta)$$

To evaluate the constants, recall that just after the switch is closed the current must be zero (since $i_L = 0$) and the rate of change of current must be $V_0/L = V_0$ (since $v_C = V_c = v_L = L\, di/dt$). At $t = 0^+$,

$$i = 0 = Ae^0 \sin (0 + \theta) = A \sin \theta$$

A is finite; therefore $\theta = 0$ and

$$\frac{di}{dt} = V_0 = Ae^0 4 \cos (0) - Ae^0 \sin (0) = 4A; \qquad \text{therefore } A = \frac{V_0}{4}$$

Hence,

$$i = \frac{V_0}{4} e^{-t} \sin 4t \qquad (4\text{-}22)$$

The exponentially damped sinusoidal current shown in Fig. 4.10b passes through zero with a frequency ω rad/sec or $f = \omega/2\pi$ cps. (In Example 4,

---

† To obtain Eq. 4-21 from Eq. 4-20, let $B_1 = A \sin \theta$ and $B_2 = A \cos \theta$.

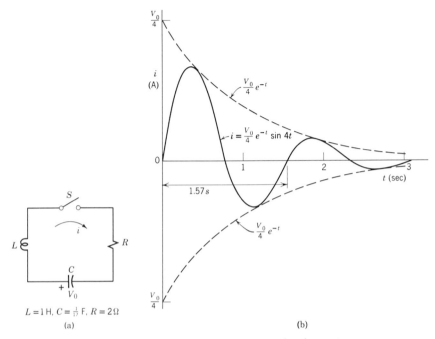

Fig. 4.10   Response of an oscillatory second-order system.

the period of the oscillation is $1/f = 2\pi/\omega = 2\pi/4 = 1.57$ sec.) The envelope of the response is defined by $Ae^{-\alpha t}$ where α is a "damping coefficient" per second. If α is large, the response dies out rapidly. (In Example 4, $\alpha = 1$ sec^{-1} and the time constant of the envelope is 1 sec.)

Roots Real and Equal

A system described by an equation with complex roots† is said to be "oscillatory" or "underdamped"; in contrast, when the roots are real the system is said to be "overdamped." The limiting condition for oscillation, called the "critically damped" case, occurs when the roots are real and equal. For this case, the discriminant is equal to zero. Physically this is not an important case since it merely represents the borderline between the two regimes. Mathematically it is an interesting case, requiring a special form of solution.

---

† Since for this case ω^2 is a negative number, the imaginary terms of the roots will be equal and opposite or the roots are always *complex conjugates;* in other words, complex roots always appear in conjugate pairs.

EXAMPLE 5

Given the RLC series circuit with $L = 1$ H and $C = \frac{1}{3}$ F, calculate the value of R for critical damping.

SOLUTION. For equal roots, the discriminant must be zero or

$$\frac{R^2}{4L^2} - \frac{1}{LC} = 0, \qquad R^2 = \frac{4L^2}{LC} = \frac{4}{\frac{1}{3}} = 12 \qquad \text{or} \qquad R = \sqrt{12} = 3.46 \ \Omega$$

If the roots are equal, $s_2 = s_1 = s$. Following the general procedure,

$$i = A_1 e^{st} + A_2 e^{st} = (A_1 + A_2)e^{st} = A e^{st}$$

but this is not sufficiently general for a second-order differential equation. For this case a second term must be included† and the general solution is

$$i = A_1 e^{st} + A_2 t e^{st} \qquad (4\text{-}23)$$

Plotting this response for values in Example 5 is left to the student (see Exercise 28).

Roots in the Complex Plane

We have observed that the character of the natural response of a second-order system is determined by the roots of the characteristic equation. Where the roots are real, negative, and distinct, the response is the sum of two decaying exponentials and the response is said to be overdamped. Where the roots are complex conjugates, the natural response is an exponentially decaying sinusoid and the response is said to be underdamped or oscillatory.

For a general view of this behavior which will give added insight into the response of higher-order systems, consider the effect on the location of the roots of a change in one system parameter. In general, roots are located in the complex plane, the location being defined by coordinates measured along the real or σ (sigma)‡ axis and the imaginary or $j\omega$ axis. This is referred to as the s plane or, since s has the units of frequency,

---

† See H. B. Phillips, *Differential Equations*, 3rd ed., John Wiley and Sons, New York, 1951, or any other differential equations text.
‡ The damping coefficient α was defined as $R/2L$, a positive number, so that the decaying nature of $e^{-\alpha t}$ would be evident; positive values of α correspond to negative values of σ and lie in the left half of the complex plane.

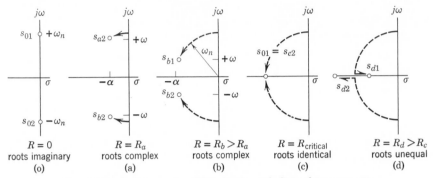

Fig. 4.11 Root locus for RLC circuit with R as the parameter.

as the *complex frequency plane*. Specifically, let us consider the locus of the roots for a series RLC circuit as R varies from zero to infinity.

For this circuit the characteristic equation (Eq. 4-13) is

$$Ls^2 + Rs + \frac{1}{C} = 0$$

and the roots are

$$s = -\frac{R}{2L} \pm j \sqrt{\frac{1}{LC} - \frac{R^2}{4L^2}} = -\alpha \pm j\omega$$

For $R = 0$, $s = \pm j \sqrt{1/LC} = \pm j\omega_n$, defining values of the *undamped natural frequency* ω_n. In other words, for $R = 0$, $\alpha = 0$ and the response is oscillatory with no damping. The roots corresponding to the undamped case are located on the imaginary axis of Fig. 4.11o. For $R = R_a$, small but finite, a real part of s appears and the values of s are complex conjugates. As R increases to R_b, the roots move along a path to points s_b. The radial distance from the origin to either root is given by

$$\sqrt{\alpha^2 + \omega^2} = \sqrt{\left(-\frac{R}{2L}\right)^2 + \left(\frac{1}{LC} - \frac{R^2}{4L^2}\right)} = \sqrt{\frac{1}{LC}} = \omega_n \quad (4\text{-}24)$$

a constant. Therefore, the locus is a circular arc of radius ω_n.

The critical value of resistance is defined by $\omega = 0$ or, in other words, where the discriminant equals zero. For this condition $\sigma = -R/2L = -\sqrt{1/LC}$. At this value of $R = R_c$, the roots coincide on the real axis. As R increases to R_d, s_{d1} moves toward the origin and s_{d2} moves out along the negative real axis. As R increases without limit, s_1 approaches the origin and s_2 increases without limit.

With a different circuit parameter the locus takes on a different shape (see Exercise 24). In any such plot, called a *root locus*, the location of the roots determines the character of the natural response, and the effect of changes in a parameter is clearly visible to the initiated. The first step in developing this powerful tool is mastery of a new concept—*impedance*.

IMPEDANCE TO EXPONENTIALS

If we limit the discussion to exponential waveforms, some interesting and valuable relations between voltage and current can be established. Actually this is not a severe restriction; already we have used exponentials to represent sinusoids, and exponentials with $s = 0$ can be used to represent direct currents. The range of exponential functions for positive and negative, large and small real values of s is indicated in Fig. 4.12.

The key property of an exponential function is that its time derivative is also an exponential. For example, if

$$i = I_0 e^{st}, \qquad \frac{di}{dt} = sI_0 e^{st} = si \qquad (4\text{-}25)$$

or if

$$v = V_0 e^{st}, \qquad \frac{dv}{dt} = sV_0 e^{st} = sv \qquad (4\text{-}26)$$

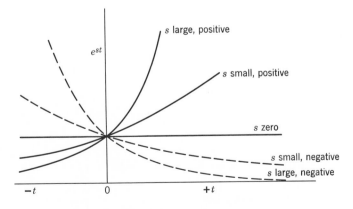

Fig. 4.12 Range of exponential functions.

This property greatly facilitates calculating the response of circuits containing resistance, inductance, and capacitance because of the simple voltage-current relations which result.

The ratio of voltage to current for exponential waveforms is defined as the *impedance Z*. For a resistance, $v = Ri$ and

$$Z_R = \frac{v}{i} = \frac{Ri}{i} = R \text{ in ohms} \tag{4-27}$$

For an inductance, $v = L(di/dt) = sLi$ and

$$Z_L = \frac{v}{i} = \frac{\varepsilon Li}{i} = sL \text{ in ohms} \tag{4-28}$$

For a capacitance, $i = C(dv/dt) = sCv$ and

$$Z_C = \frac{v}{i} = \frac{v}{sCv} = \frac{1}{sC} \text{ in ohms} \tag{4-29}$$

The impedances Z_R, Z_L, and Z_C are constants of proportionality between exponential voltages and currents. It can be demonstrated that in each case the dimensions of impedance are the same as those of resistance. (Can you do it?) The general relation

$$v = Zi \tag{4-30}$$

corresponds to Ohm's law for purely resistive circuits, but it must be emphasized that impedance is defined *only for exponentials* and for waveforms which can be represented by exponentials.† With this restriction, impedances can be combined in series and parallel just as resistances are.

EXAMPLE 6

Given the circuit shown in Fig. 4.13 where $i = 3e^{2t}A$, $R = 0.6 \, \Omega$, and $L = 0.7$ H. Find the voltage v across the combination.

SOLUTION.

$$v = v_R + v_L = Ri + Z_L i = (R + Z_L)i = (R + sL)i$$
$$Z = R + sL = 0.6 + 2 \times 0.7 = 0.6 + 1.4 = 2.0 \, \Omega$$
$$v = Zi = 2.0 \times 3e^{2t} = 6e^{2t} \text{ V}$$

----

† Assume another waveform such as $i = I_0 t$; then $v_L = L(di/dt) = LI_0$ and the ratio $v_L/i = LI_0/I_0 t = L/t$ a function of time and *not* a constant as it is for exponentials.

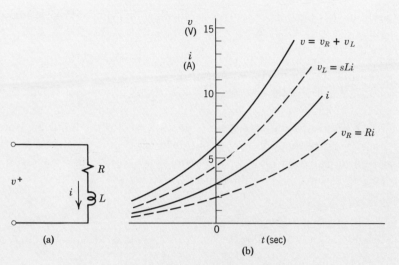

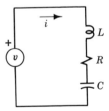

Fig. 4.13   Example of the impedance concept.

Checking by basic relations,

$$v = Ri + L\frac{di}{dt} = 0.6 \times 3e^{2t} + 0.7 \times 2 \times 3e^{2t} = 6e^{2t} \text{ V}$$

THE IMPEDANCE FUNCTION

For the circuit of Fig. 4.14, the governing equation is

$$L\frac{di}{dt} + Ri + \frac{1}{C}\int i\,dt = v \qquad (4\text{-}31)$$

For an exponential current $i = I_0 e^{st}$ this becomes

$$Lsi + Ri + \frac{1}{sC}i = v$$

Fig. 4.14   Series *RLC* circuit.

and

$$Z = \frac{v}{i} = sL + R + \frac{1}{sC} \qquad (4\text{-}32)$$

Note that when the characteristic equation (Eq. 4-13) is divided through by s), Eq. 4-32 results; but Eq. 4-32 was obtained by expressing the impedance as a ratio of an exponential voltage to an exponential current. The same relation could also have been obtained by considering that the resultant of impedances in series is the algebraic sum of the impedances or

$$Z = Z_L + Z_R + Z_C = Z(s)$$

where $Z(s)$ signifies the impedance to exponentials of the form Ae^{st}.

Because the impedance function $Z(s)$ contains the same information as the characteristic equation, it is a useful concept in predicting the natural behavior of a system and it can be extended to include the prediction of steady-state response. As indicated in the following example, the impedance function can be obtained easily in a circuit for which the governing equation may be quite complicated (i.e., may consist of a set of simultaneous integro-differential equations).

EXAMPLE 7

Given the circuit of Fig. 4.15a with $i = I_0 e^{st}$.

(a) Find $Z(s)$ in general form.

SOLUTION. A great advantage of the impedance concept is the ease with which impedances may be combined. Here

$$Z(s) = Z_1 + \frac{Z_R Z_C}{Z_R + Z_C} = R_1 + \frac{R(1/sC)}{R + 1/sC} = R_1 + \frac{R}{RsC + 1} = \frac{sR_1 RC + R_1 + R}{sRC + 1}$$

(b) If $i = 6e^{2t}$, find v.

SOLUTION. For $s = 2$,

$$Z(s) = Z(2) = \frac{(2)(2)(4)(\frac{1}{4}) + 2 + 4}{(2)(4)(\frac{1}{4}) + 1} = \frac{10}{3} = 3\tfrac{1}{3} \ \Omega$$

$$v = Zi = (\tfrac{10}{3})6e^{2t} = 20e^{2t} \ \text{V}$$

(c) Determine and plot $Z(s)$ for real values of s.

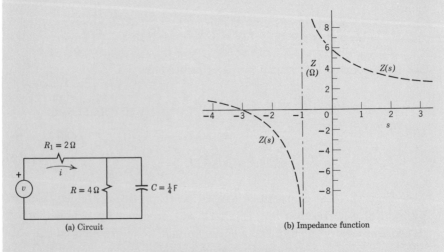

(a) Circuit   (b) Impedance function

Fig. 4.15   Example 7.

SOLUTION. For the given element values,

$$Z(s) = \frac{2s + 6}{s + 1} = 2\frac{s + 3}{s + 1}$$

From the graph of Fig. 4.15b and from the expression for $Z(s)$ it is seen that $Z(s) = 0$ at $s = -3$, and that $Z(s)$ increases without limit as s approaches -1.

POLES AND ZEROS

In Example 7, $Z(s)$ is plotted for real values of s. Since each value of s corresponds to a particular exponential function, the impedance $Z(s_1)$ is the ratio of voltage to current for the particular exponential function of time $i = I_0 e^{s_1 t}$. For instance, to determine the opposition to direct current flow, the impedance is calculated for $s = 0$ since $i = I_0 e^{(0)t} = I_0$, a direct current. In Example 7, $Z(0) = 6 \ \Omega$, the equivalent of the two resistances in series. This is physically correct because under steady conditions with no change in the voltage across the capacitor, no current flows in C and the circuit, in effect, consists only of the two resistors.

Every point in the complex frequency plane defines an exponential function and the complete plane represents all such functions. The magnitude of the impedance, $|Z(s)|$, can be plotted as a vertical distance above the s plane and, in general, the result will be a complicated surface.

EXAMPLE 8

Plot the magnitude of the impedance function of the circuit of Fig. 4.15a for real values of s and for imaginary values of s, and then sketch the impedance surface.

SOLUTION. The magnitude of $Z(s)$ for real values of s corresponds to the graph of Fig. 4.15b with negative quantities plotted above the axis. For imaginary values of s ($\pm j1$, $\pm j2$, etc.) the magnitude of $Z(s)$ is calculated and plotted in a similar way. For $s = -j$,

$$Z(s) = 2\frac{3 - j}{1 - j} \quad \text{and} \quad |Z| = \frac{2\sqrt{10}}{\sqrt{2}} \cong 4.5 \ \Omega$$

For $s = -1 - j2$,

$$Z(s) = 2\frac{2 - j2}{0 - j2} \quad \text{and} \quad |Z| = \frac{2\sqrt{8}}{\sqrt{4}} \cong 2.5 \ \Omega$$

Using the profiles of Figs. 4.16a and b and additional points in the complex plane, the impedance surface is plotted in Fig. 4.16c.

Typically, the impedance function in three dimensions has the appearance of a tent pitched on the s plane. The height of the tent (magnitude of Z) becomes very great (approaches infinity) for particular values of s

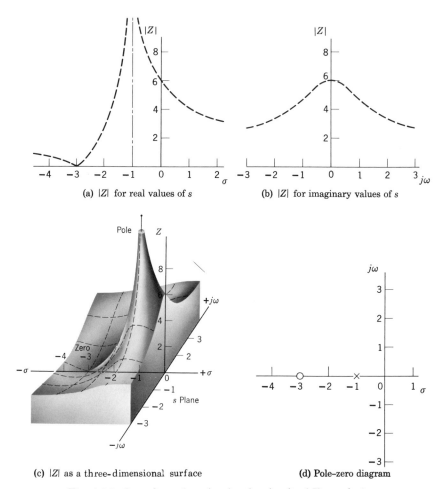

(a) |Z| for real values of s   (b) |Z| for imaginary values of s

(c) |Z| as a three-dimensional surface   (d) Pole–zero diagram

Fig. 4.16 Impedance function for the circuit of Example 8.

appropriately called *poles*. The tent touches the ground at particular
values of *s* called *zeros*. The equation of the surface is usually quite
complicated, but the practical use of the impedance function in network
analysis or synthesis is relatively simple for two reasons. In the first
place, we are usually interested in only a single profile of the surface; for
example, the profile along the *jω* axis indicates the response to sinusoidal
functions of various frequencies. Second, just as two points define a
straight line and three points define a circle, the poles and zeros uniquely
define the impedance function, except for a constant scale factor. As a
result, the *pole-zero diagram* of Fig. 4.16d contains the essential infor-

mation of the impedance function sketched in Fig. 4.16c. The locations of the poles (X) and zeros (0), which are relatively easy to find, tell us a great deal about the natural response.

Physical Interpretation of Poles and Zeros

In the general relation between exponential voltage and current

$$v = Zi$$

what is the meaning of "zero impedance"? If the impedance is small, a given current can exist with a small voltage applied. Carrying this idea to the limit, under conditions of zero impedance† a current can exist with *no applied voltage;* but a current with no applied voltage is, by definition, a natural current response. We conclude, therefore, that each zero, $s = s_1$, of the impedance function for any circuit designates a possible component, $I_1 e^{s_1 t}$, of the natural response current of that circuit. This conclusion is supported by the fact that for the circuit of Fig. 4.14, the zeros of the impedance function (Eq. 4-32) are identical with the roots of the characteristic equation (Eq. 4-13). Knowing the locations of the impedance zeros, we can immediately identify the exponential components of the natural current.

EXAMPLE 9

Given the circuit shown in Fig. 4.17, determine the poles and zeros of impedance. If energy is stored in the circuit in the form of an initial voltage V_0 on the capacitor, predict the current i which will flow when the switch S is closed.

SOLUTION. As previously determined, the impedance function looking into the circuit at terminals ab is

$$Z(s) = 2\frac{s+3}{s+1}$$

Where $s = -1$, the denominator is zero and $Z(s) = \infty$; therefore,
$s = -1$ is a pole.
Where $s = -3$, the numerator is zero and $Z(s) = 0$; therefore,
$s = -3$ is a zero.

---

† To get the "feel" of zero impedance in a physical system, perform the following mental experiment. Grasp the bob of an imaginary pendulum between your thumb and forefinger. Applying a force, cause the bob to move along its arc with various motions. For motions against gravity or against inertia, appreciable force is required; the mechanical impedance is appreciable. To maintain a purely sinusoidal motion at the natural frequency of the pendulum only a little force (just that needed to make up friction losses) is required; the mechanical impedance to such a motion is small. To maintain a motion approximating an exponentially decaying sinusoid of just the right frequency, *no* force is required; for this motion, velocity is possible with no applied force. In other words, to this motion mechanical impedance is *zero!*

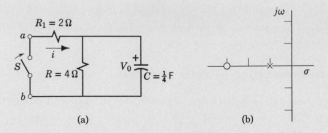

(a)   (b)

Fig. 4.17 Example 9. Circuit and impedance pole-zero diagram.

If the impedance is zero, a current can exist with no external forcing voltage. Therefore, the natural behavior is defined by $s = -3$ or

$$i = Ae^{-3t}$$

As before, A is evaluated from initial data. At the instant the switch is closed, V_0 appears across R_1 (tending to cause a current opposite to that assumed) and

$$i_0 = Ae^0 = A = -\frac{V_0}{R_1}$$

Hence,

$$i = -\frac{V_0}{R_1} e^{-3t}$$

is the natural response current.

If an impedance zero indicates the possibility of a current without a voltage, what is the significance of an impedance pole? Since $v = Zi$, if the impedance is very large, a given voltage can exist with only a small current flowing. Carrying this idea to the limit, under conditions of infinite impedance a voltage can exist with *no current flow*, in other words, a natural voltage. We conclude that each pole, $s = s_a$, of the impedance function of a circuit designates a possible component, $V_a e^{s_a t}$, of the natural voltage response of that circuit.

EXAMPLE 10

Returning to Example 9, assume that energy is stored in the form of an initial voltage V_0 on the capacitor (perhaps by means of the voltage source shown in Fig. 4.18). Predict the voltage v which will appear across terminals ab when the switch S is opened.

SOLUTION. With the external energy source removed, only a natural behavior voltage can appear. Such a voltage can exist with no current flow only if the impedance is infinite. For a pole at $s = -1$, the natural response is

$$v = V_a e^{-t}$$

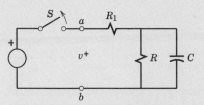

Fig. 4.18 Example 10.

V_a is evaluated from initial data. At the instant the switch is opened, the current in R_1 goes to zero and the voltage across terminals ab is just $v_R = v_C = +V_0$. Hence,

$$v = V_0 e^{-t}$$

is the natural response voltage. This result can be checked by letting $v = i_2 R$ where i_2 is the natural current which would flow in R if R were suddenly connected across the charged capacitor.

The General Impedance Function

Typical impedance functions (for the circuits of Figs. 4.15 and 4.14) are

$$Z(s) = R_1 + \frac{R(1/sC)}{R + (1/sC)} = \frac{sR_1RC + R_1 + R}{sRC + 1}$$

and

$$Z(s) = sL + R + \frac{1}{sC} = \frac{s^2LC + sRC + 1}{sC}$$

The impedance function for any network, no matter how complicated, consisting of resistances, inductances, and capacitances, can be reduced to the ratio of two polynomials in s. In general, we can write

$$Z(s) = K \frac{s^n + \cdots + k_2 s^2 + k_1 s + k_0}{s^m + \cdots + c_2 s^2 + c_1 s + c_0} \qquad (4\text{-}33)$$

While it may not be easy, this can always be factored into

$$Z(s) = K \frac{(s - s_1)(s - s_2) \cdots (s - s_n)}{(s - s_a)(s - s_b) \cdots (s - s_m)} \qquad (4\text{-}34)$$

When $s = s_1, s_2, \ldots, s_n$, $Z(s) = 0$; therefore, these are zeros.
When $s = s_a, s_b, \ldots, s_m$, $Z(s) = \infty$; therefore, these are poles.

If the network is known, the impedance function can be written and factored and the pole-zero diagram constructed. Conversely, from the pole-zero diagram the impedance function can be formulated (except for scale factor K in Eq. 4-34). Theoretically, a network can then be designed or "synthesized," but practically this is not always easy. The complicated problems are so difficult that entire books have been written on the subject of network synthesis. In this book, however, we are concerned primarily with network analysis and the problems are more straightforward.

The General Admittance Function

Impedance is defined for exponentials as the ratio of voltage to current. The reciprocal of impedance is *admittance*, a useful property defined as the ratio of exponential current in amperes to voltage in volts so that

$$Y = \frac{i}{v} = \frac{1}{Z} \tag{4-35}$$

measured in mhos ($\mho$, reciprocal of ohms). For exponential voltages and currents, the admittances of ideal circuit elements are:

$$Y_R = \frac{i_R}{v_R} = \frac{i}{Ri} = \frac{1}{R} = G$$

$$Y_L = \frac{i_L}{v_L} = \frac{i}{L(di/dt)} = \frac{i}{sLi} = \frac{1}{sL} \tag{4-36}$$

$$Y_C = \frac{i_C}{v_C} = \frac{C(dv/dt)}{v} = \frac{sCv}{v} = sC$$

Admittance is particularly useful in analyzing circuits which contain elements connected in parallel. Since current is directly proportional to admittance ($i = Yv$), admittances in parallel can be added directly just as conductances in parallel are added.

The admittance function $Y(s)$ for any network consisting of lumped passive elements also can be reduced to the ratio of two polynomials in s. In the standard factored form this becomes

$$Y(s) = \frac{1}{Z(s)} = \frac{1}{K} \frac{(s - s_a)(s - s_b) \, \cdot \, \cdot \, \cdot \, (s - s_m)}{(s - s_1)(s - s_2) \, \cdot \, \cdot \, \cdot \, (s - s_n)} \tag{4-37}$$

Note that the admittance function has poles where the impedance function has zeros, and vice versa. The pole-zero diagram for the admittance function contains the same information as the pole-zero diagram for the impedance function, but they are labeled differently.

General Procedure for Using Poles and Zeros

The pole-zero concept is a powerful tool in determining the natural behavior (and, as we shall see in Chapter 5, the forced behavior) of any linear physical system. Modified to take advantage of this concept, the general procedure for determining the natural behavior of an electrical circuit is:

1. Write the impedance function for the terminals of interest.
2. Determine the poles and zeros, and plot the pole-zero diagram.
3. (*a*) For the terminals short-circuited, the natural behavior current is

$$i = I_1 e^{s_1 t} + I_2 e^{s_2 t} + \cdots + I_n e^{s_n t} \tag{4-38}$$

where $s_1, s_2, \ldots, s_n$ are zeros of the impedance function.

    (*b*) For the terminals open-circuited, the natural behavior voltage is

$$v = V_a e^{s_a t} + V_b e^{s_b t} + \cdots + V_m e^{s_m t} \tag{4-39}$$

where $s_a, s_b, \ldots, s_m$ are poles of the impedance function.

4. Evaluate the coefficients from the initial conditions.

An analogous procedure can be formulated, using the admittance function.

EXAMPLE 11

In the circuit of Fig. 4.19, the current source has been connected to terminals *ab* for a time long enough for steady-state conditions to be reached. At time $t = 0$, the switch S is thrown so that the current source is simultaneously disconnected from terminal *a* and connected to terminal *c*. Predict the open-circuit voltage *v* across terminals *ab*.

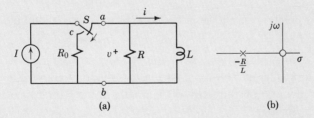

Fig. 4.19 Example 11. Circuit and impedance pole-zero diagram.

SOLUTION.

1. $Y_{ab}(s) = Y_R + Y_L = \dfrac{1}{R} + \dfrac{1}{sL} = \dfrac{sL + R}{sLR} = \dfrac{1}{R} \dfrac{s + (R/L)}{s}$

Therefore, in the form of Eq. 4.34

$$Z_{ab}(s) = \frac{1}{Y(s)} = R \frac{s}{s + (R/L)} = R \frac{(s - 0)}{(s - [-R/L])}$$

2. The impedance function has a zero at $s = 0$ and a pole at $s = -R/L$.

3. For the terminals open-circuited,

$$v = V_a\, e^{-(R/L)t}$$

4. Under steady conditions, the current in the inductance is constant, $di/dt = 0$, and $v_L = v_R = 0$. Therefore, $i_R = v_R/R = 0$ and all the current I flows in the inductance L.

At $t = 0^+$, $I_R = -i_L = -I$; therefore, $v = V_a\, e^0 = V_a = -IR$. Hence, the open-circuit voltage is

$$v = -IRe^{-(R/L)t}$$

What would happen if, at the instant the current source is disconnected, terminals ab were short-circuited (by means of another switch not shown)?
For the terminals short-circuited (and an impedance zero at $s = 0$),

$$i = I_1\, e^{0t} = I_1 = I$$

a steady current.
An ideal inductor connected to an ideal short circuit constitutes an ideal circuit with no resistance; therefore, the initial current I continues to flow undiminished. Such a situation can only be approximated in a practical circuit.

SUMMARY

♦ Forced behavior is the response to external energy sources.

♦ Natural behavior is the response to internal stored energy.

♦ Many physical systems with one energy-storage element can be described adequately by first-order integrodifferential equations. The general procedure for determining the natural behavior of a linear system is:
1. Write the governing integrodifferential equation.
2. Reduce this to a homogeneous differential equation.
3. Assume an exponential solution with undetermined constants.
4. Determine the exponents from the homogeneous equation.
5. Evaluate the coefficients from the given conditions.

♦ In a second-order system with two energy-storage elements, the character of the natural response is determined by the discriminant.

♦ If the discriminant is positive, the response is *overdamped* and is represented by the sum of two decaying exponentials:

$$a = A_1\, e^{s_1 t} + A_2\, e^{s_2 t}$$

If the discriminant is negative, the response is *oscillatory* and is represented by the damped sinusoid:

$$a = Ae^{-\alpha t} \sin(\omega t + \theta)$$

If the discriminant is zero, the response is *critically damped* and is represented by the sum of two different terms with the same exponent:

$$a = A_1 e^{st} + A_2 te^{st}$$

◆ Impedance Z and admittance Y are defined for exponentials.

    In general,

      $v = Zi$ where $Z =$ impedance in ohms

      $i = Yv$ where $Y =$ admittance in mhos

    Specifically,

$$Z_R = R \qquad Y_R = G$$
$$Z_L = sL \qquad Y_L = 1/sL$$
$$Z_C = 1/sC \qquad Y_C = sC$$

◆ Impedances and admittances in complicated networks are combined in the same way as resistances and conductances, respectively.

◆ The impedance function $Z(s)$ and the admittance function $Y(s)$ contain the same information as the characteristic equation.

◆ The pole-zero diagram contains the essential information of the impedance function or the admittance function.

A zero of the impedance function indicates the possibility of a current without an applied voltage, therefore a natural current.

A pole of the impedance function indicates the possibility of a voltage without an applied current, therefore a natural voltage.

◆ Using the pole-zero concept, the general procedure for determining natural behavior of an electrical circuit is:

    1. Write the impedance or admittance function for the terminals of interest.

    2. Determine the poles and zeros of impedance or admittance.

    3. Use the poles and zeros to identify possible components of natural voltage or current.

    4. Evaluate the coefficients from the given conditions.

REVIEW QUESTIONS

1. Cite an example of natural behavior in each of the following branches of engineering: aeronautical, chemical, civil, industrial, and mechanical.

2. To what extent is the natural behavior of a system influenced by the waveform of the forcing function which stores energy in the system?

3. Discuss the possibility of a positive exponent appearing in the natural response of a passive network. In any physical system.

4. Outline the procedure for determining the natural behavior of a mechanical system in translation.

5. In contrast to the exponential behavior of its idealized model, an actual coasting automobile comes to a complete stop long before an infinite time. Why?

6. Measurements on a very rapid transient are difficult and the results include large random errors. In determining the time constant for this system, would a linear or a semilog plot of experimental values be preferable? Why?

7. What is the physical difference between a "first-order" system and a "second-order" system?

8. In what sense is the "characteristic equation" characteristic of the circuit?

9. In what sense does the "discriminant" discriminate?

10. What important initial information is available from an inductor in a circuit? From a capacitor? Explain.

11. In the case of a practical resistor, can the current be changed instantaneously? Can the voltage? Explain.

12. What is the difference in the waveform represented by $i_1 = I_0 e^{j4t}$ and $i_2 = I_0(e^{j4t} + e^{-j4t})$? Could both be plotted on the same graph? Explain.

13. A damped sinusoid has a period, but is it a "periodic" wave? Explain.

14. Why is the natural response determined by the homogeneous equation instead of by the governing integrodifferential equation?

15. What is the meaning of a "complex" frequency?

16. Give three reasons why so much attention is devoted to exponential functions in network analysis?

17. If, for exponentials, si corresponds to di/dt, what is the significance of $(1/s)i$?

18. What is the value of $|Z|$ (height of the "tent") in Fig. 4.16 for large real values of s? For large imaginary values? What is the limit of $|Z|$ as s approaches infinity?

19. In regard to *natural* response, is there any information available in the impedance function (Fig. 4.16c) that is not in the pole-zero diagram (Fig. 4.16d)? Explain.

20. Devise and sketch a physical system in which there is force without velocity (corresponding to an infinite mechanical impedance) and in which the force decays exponentially with time.

EXERCISES

1. In Fig. 4.20, switches A and C have been closed for a long time, and switch B has been open for a long time. At time $t = 0$, A and C are opened and B is closed simultaneously. Predict:
  (a) The current i_L immediately after $t = 0$.
  (b) The current i_R immediately after $t = 0$.
  (c) The current i_R at $t = \infty$.

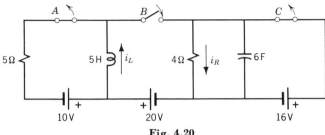

Fig. 4.20

2. An initial charge V_0 exists on the capacitor in Fig. 4.21. At time $t = 0$, switch S is closed.

(a) Apply Kirchhoff's law to establish the voltage relation around the loop *abcd*. (Do not solve.)

(b) Repeat for loop *dcef*.

(c) Repeat for loop *feba*.

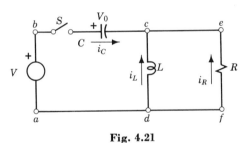

Fig. 4.21

3. The governing equation for a certain parallel circuit is:

$$I_1 + I_2 \sin \omega t = \frac{v}{R} + C\frac{dv}{dt} + \frac{1}{L}\int v\, dt$$

Derive the homogeneous differential equation for this circuit.

4. In Fig. 4.22, switch S has been in position 1 a long time; C_2 is uncharged. At $t = 0$, the switch is thrown to position 2.

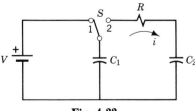

Fig. 4.22

(a) Calculate the energy stored in C_1 just before $t = 0$.

(b) Write the integrodifferential equation governing the behavior of the circuit for $t > 0$.

(c) Convert the governing equation into a first-order homogeneous differential equation in i.

(d) Let $C_1 = C_2 = C$ and express $i(t)$ for $t > 0$.

(e) For $C_1 = C_2 = 10 \ \mu F$, $R = 10 \ k\Omega$, and $V = 20$ V, plot enough points to draw a graph of $i(t)$.

(f) Using a dotted line, plot the graph of $i(t)$ if V and R are both doubled.

5. In Fig. 4.23, switch S has been closed for a long time.

(a) If steady-state conditions have been reached, what is the voltage across L? The current through R? The current through L?

(b) If switch S is now opened at $t = 0$, derive an expression for the current through L as a function of time.

(c) Express the voltage across L as $f(t)$.

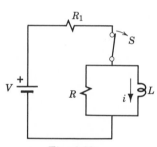

Fig. 4.23

6. In an RC circuit undergoing natural behavior, where is energy stored? Where is energy dissipated? Using the expression for current, show that the total energy dissipated during natural behavior is just equal to the energy stored initially.

7. A coil of inductance L and resistance R carrying a current I is short-circuited at time $t = 0$. Derive an expression for the total energy dissipated in the resistance. How is this related to the energy initially stored in the magnetic field of the inductance? For $L = 2$ H, $R = 10 \ \Omega$, and $I = 10$ A, calculate the energy dissipated in the resistance and the energy initially stored in the inductance.

8. The rate of radioactive disintegration (mass per unit of time) is directly proportional to the amount of material present.

(a) Derive an expression for the amount of material M remaining at any time t.

(b) If the half-life (see p. 57) of radium is 1600 yr, write a specific expression for the amount of radium remaining of an original 2 mg sample.

9. A flywheel has a radius $r = 10$ cm and a moment of inertia $J = \frac{1}{2}Mr^2 = 0.1$ kg-m^2. It is being driven at 300 rpm against a friction torque $\tau_f = \pi/2$ N-m. At time $t = 0$, the driving torque is removed and the flywheel coasts to a standstill under the influence of the friction torque which can be assumed to be proportional to the angular velocity in radians per second.

(a) Applying d'Alembert's principle, write the differential equation governing the angular velocity ω of the flywheel after $t = 0$.

(b) Assuming an exponential solution, solve the equation to obtain ω as $f(t)$.

(c) Calculate the total number of revolutions before the flywheel comes to rest.

10. For the flywheel of Exercise 9,

(a) Calculate the energy initially stored.

(b) Write an equation for the instantaneous power dissipation in friction (by analogy to the corresponding electrical system) and calculate the total energy dissipated in friction.

11. A 3220-lb car 15 ft long is moving with a velocity of 50 ft/sec. At time $t = 0$, the car is shifted into neutral and allowed to coast. Assuming the friction force in pounds is equal to 4 times the velocity in feet per second, find the distance the car will coast on a level road.

12. In a given system, transient effects are negligible when they are "95% over." Define the period of time for a transient effect to become negligible in terms of the time constant of the system.

13. How can the time constant be increased in a mass-friction system? In a spring-damper system?

14. Given the curve of a function $a = Ae^{-t/T}$, show that the tangent drawn to the curve at $t = t_1$ always intersects the t axis at $t = t_1 + T$.

15. An inductance L carrying a current I is suddenly shorted through a resistance R (and the current source simultaneously removed).

(a) Derive the equation of current as a function of time after the switching and calculate di/dt at $t = 0^+$.

(b) If the current continued to decrease at its initial rate, calculate the time required for the current to reach zero; compare this time with the "time constant."

16. On p. 88 it is pointed out that the total charge transferred during the decay of an RL circuit approaches a finite limit. Derive an expression for charge transferred as a function of elapsed time and compare your result with the graph of Fig. 4.6.

17. Show that RC, the time constant in a resistance-capacitance circuit, has the units of seconds. Repeat for a resistance-inductance circuit.

18. A 30-μF capacitor is charged by means of a battery. A high-resistance voltmeter is then connected across the capacitor and the following data recorded:

v (V)	5.85	5	4	3	2	1
t (sec)	0	1.2	2.7	4.4	7.3	12.2

(a) Plot voltage as a function of time on linear scales and estimate the time constant.

(b) Replot the curve of (a) in terms of dimensionless ratios.

(c) Plot the data with voltage on a logarithmic scale, using printed semilog paper.

(d) Derive an expression for the time constant in terms of the slope of the curve (ln v vs t) in (c) and calculate the time constant from the curve.

(e) Estimate the resistance of the voltmeter.

19. Explain the natural response of an oscillatory RLC circuit on a physical basis in terms of the energy interchanges which occur. You may wish to reason by analogy with an oscillating pendulum.

20. In a series RLC circuit, energy is initially stored in the form of a voltage V_0 on the capacitor. Write an energy balance for the system, indicating that the rate of change of stored energy must be just equal to the rate of energy dissipation. From the energy balance derive the homogeneous equation (Eq. 4-12).

21. In a series RLC circuit, the capacitor has an initial voltage $V_0 = 60$ V; $R = 20\ \Omega$, $L = 5$ H, and $C = 0.01$ F.

(a) Calculate the numerical values of i, v_C, v_R, and v_L at $t = 0^+$.

(b) Calculate di/dt and d^2i/dt^2 at $t = 0^+$.

(c) For this system, write the "governing" equation, the "homogeneous" equation, and the "characteristic" equation.

(d) Will the natural response be under, over, or critically damped?

(e) Solve for $i(t)$, evaluating all constants from initial conditions, and plot enough points to sketch, approximately to scale, the current as a function of time.

22. In the circuit of Fig. 4.24, the capacitor has an initial voltage $V_0 = 12$ V; $C = 1\ \mu$F, $R = 1\ \mathrm{k}\Omega$ and $L = 6.25$ H. The switch is closed at $t = 0$.

(a) Determine the numerical values of v, i_R, i_L, and i_C just after the switch is closed, i.e. at $t = 0^+$.

(b) Calculate dv/dt and d^2v/dt^2 at $t = 0^+$.

(c) For this system, write the "governing" equation, the "homogeneous" equation, and the "characteristic" equation.

(d) Will the response be under, over, or critically damped?

(e) Solve for $v(t)$ and evaluate all constants from initial conditions.

(f) Plot enough points to sketch, approximately to scale, the voltage as a function of time. (You may prefer to do this in terms of the components.)

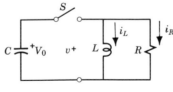

Fig. 4.24

23. The circuit of Exercise 22 is modified so that $L = 3.45$ H; all other values remain the same.

(a) Write the differential equation and determine the character of the response.

(b) Solve for $v(t)$ and evaluate all constants from initial conditions.

24. Determine and sketch the root locus for a series RLC circuit in which:
(a) C is the changing parameter.
(b) L is the changing parameter.

25. A practical series circuit consists of a coil ($L = 20$ mH, $R = 5\,\Omega$) and a nearly ideal capacitor ($C = 0.5\,\mu$F). Calculate the percentage difference between ω and ω_n for this circuit.

26. An RLC series circuit with an initial voltage V_0 on the capacitor (see Fig. 4.9a) is closed with a switch at time $t = 0$.

(a) For the case of critical damping, derive a general expression for the natural current response.

(b) For $V_0 = 10$ V and the circuit values of Example 5 on p. 95, determine and plot to scale the response current as a function of time.

27. Repeat Exercise 26 for the case of no initial voltage on the capacitor but with an initial current I_0 in the inductor.

28. Draw a "map of s-land" (similar to but larger than the sketch in Fig. 4.25), indicating the response expected for a root of the characteristic equation located at each of the 15 regions indicated by a rectangle. Follow the example drawn for $s = +\sigma + j\omega$, showing an exponentially increasing sinusoidal func-

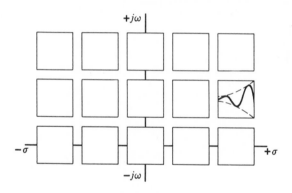

Fig. 4.25

tion of time, $e^{(\sigma+j\omega)t}$. Clearly indicate changes in the expected response corresponding to changes in σ and ω.

29. Given that $i = 2e^{-5t}$ A in the circuit of Fig. 4.26, calculate v_L, the voltage across the 1-H inductance.

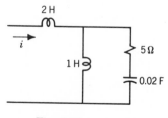

Fig. 4.26

30. Given that $i = 6e^{-2t}$ A in the circuit of Fig. 4.27, calculate v_C the voltage across the capacitance.

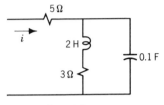

Fig. 4.27

31. A current $i = 5e^{-2t}$ A is flowing in a circuit consisting of $R = 10\ \Omega$, in series with $L = 3$ H.

(a) Calculate v_L and v_R and sketch approximately to scale.

(b) Explain on a physical (not mathematical) basis the sign of v_L.

(c) Combine the data for v_L and v_R to obtain $v(t)$.

(d) Calculate $Z(s)$, determine $v(t)$ from $Z(s)$, and compare with the result for Part 3.

32. In the circuit of Fig. 4.28, $R_1 = 2\ \Omega$, $R = 4\ \Omega$, and $L = 2$ H.

(a) Determine enough points to plot $Z(s)$.

(b) What is the impedance of this circuit to direct current?

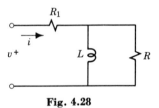

Fig. 4.28

(c) If a voltage $v = V_0 e^{st}$ is acting where $V_0 = 1$ V, what current i flows for $s = -3$? For $s = -2$? For $s = -4$?

(d) Assume current $i = 2e^{-4t}$ A is flowing and calculate the necessary voltage $v(t)$.

33. For the two mechanical circuits shown in Fig. 4.29, determine the "motional" impedance, i.e., the ratio of force to velocity for exponential functions.

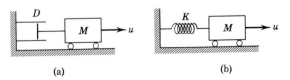

(a)   (b)

Fig. 4.29

34. A two-terminal network consists of a capacitance C in parallel with a series combination of resistance R and capacitance C. Sketch the pole-zero diagram of impedance for this network.

35. Sketch the pole-zero diagram of admittance for the network of Exercise 34.

36. A two-terminal network consists of an inductance $L = 2$ H in series with a parallel combination of $R = 1\ \Omega$ and $C = 1$ F. Plot the pole-zero diagram of impedance for this network.

37. Plot the pole-zero diagram of admittance for the network of Exercise 36.

38. The pole-zero diagrams of impedance for two systems are shown in Fig. 4.30. What conclusions can be drawn about the two systems described?

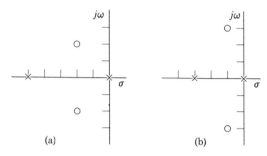

Fig. 4.30

39. Energy is stored in the circuit of Fig. 4.31 and the terminals are short circuited at $t = 0$. Derive an expression for current i as a function of time t,

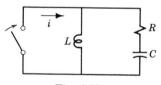

Fig. 4.31

leaving the coefficients undetermined. What information would be required to determine the coefficients?

40. A two-terminal network consists of a capacitance in parallel with a series combination of resistance and inductance.

(a) Write the general impedance function as a ratio of two polynomials.

(b) Draw the pole-zero diagram of impedance if $C = 0.2$ F, $L = 1$ H, and $R = 4\ \Omega$.

41. Energy is stored in the circuit whose pole-zero admittance diagram is shown in Fig. 4.32 and the terminals are short-circuited. Write an expression for the resulting current as a function of time, leaving constants undetermined.

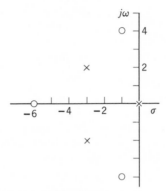

Fig. 4.32

42. It is desired to obtain the natural response current i upon closing switch S in Fig. 4.33.

    (a) Outline a step-by-step procedure for doing this, employing the pole-zero diagram approach.

    (b) If $V_0 = 12$ V, $C = 1$ μF, $L = 3.45$ H, and $R = 1$ kΩ, determine $i(t)$.

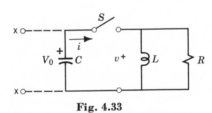

Fig. 4.33

43. Find the admittance $Y(s)$ of the circuit of Exercise 42 (with the switch closed), looking in at terminals xx. Plot the pole-zero diagram of admittance and use this information to determine the equation of $v(t)$ for the values of part (b).

44. The circuit of Exercise 42 has the values indicated in part (b).

    (a) Determine and plot the pole-zero diagram of impedance, looking in at the terminals of the *switch*.

    (b) If there is a current in L and a voltage on C at the instant the switch is *opened*, determine the voltage $v_s(t)$ across the switch (leaving coefficients undetermined).

    (c) Explain *physically* the components of voltage v_s.

45. Determine $i(t)$ for the circuit of Exercise 21, using the pole-zero approach.

46. Determine $v(t)$ for the circuit of Exercise 22, using the pole-zero approach.

PROBLEMS

1. In a printing process (Fig. 4.34), a lightweight plate P is depressed a distance X_0 and then released. Its return to the rest position, caused by the spring compliance K m/N, is slowed by the two friction devices for each of which $D = 10$ N-s/m.

(a) State the idealizing assumptions necessary to reduce this to a simple two-element system, and determine the velocity of the plate as a function of time and the constants of the system.

(b) Specify the spring compliance K so that within 0.6 sec the plate will return to a distance from its rest position equal to 5% of X_0.

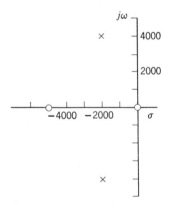

Fig. 4.34

2. A vacuum-insulated bottle contains W lb of a liquid of specific heat C_p (Btu/lb-°F) at a temperature τ_0 (°F above the outside temperature). The effective thermal conductance of the container is U (Btu/sec-°F temperature difference).

(a) Stating all assumptions and checking your equations dimensionally, express the heat stored in the liquid and the rate of heat conduction through the container.

(b) Predict the temperature of the liquid as a function of time.

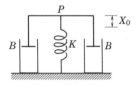

Fig. 4.35

3. An electrical circuit with the pole-zero diagram of admittance shown in Fig. 4.35 is needed.

(a) Design a possible circuit with these general characteristics.

(b) Specify values for the circuit elements in your design.

4. In the practical circuit of Fig. 4.36, the capacitor is marked $\frac{1}{12}$ μF, the resistor 3 kΩ, and the inductor 4 H. The capacitor is charged to a voltage $V_0 = 24$ V and then the switch is closed. Following a logical procedure and stating all assumptions, predict the current i as a function of time after the switch is closed.

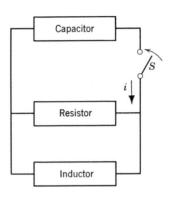

Fig. 4.36

- ◆ **FORCED RESPONSES**
- ◆ **PHASOR METHODS**
- ◆ **A-C CIRCUIT ANALYSIS**
- ◆ **ANALOGS AND DUALS**

CHAPTER **5**

Forced Response

Internal energy storage gives rise to natural behavior; regardless of how the energy is stored or where, the natural response of a circuit is determined by the characteristics of the circuit itself. In contrast, the form of the forced response due to an external energy source is dependent on the form of the forcing function; for example, a sinusoidal voltage always produces sinusoidal currents. Having mastered the technique of predicting natural behavior, we are now ready to tackle the problem of determining the response to some important forcing functions or waveforms. Then in Chapter 6 we shall use our knowledge of natural and forced response to determine the complete response of an electrical circuit, employing an approach which is applicable to nonelectrical problems as well.

In limiting consideration to just the forced response, we are assuming that natural behavior is absent. Either there was no natural response, or sufficient time has elapsed since the initiation of any transient effect for the natural response to become negligibly small. This condition exists in many practical problems.

The material in this chapter represents another step in a cumulative process. We use the accepted definitions, the fundamental element and connection laws, the methods of representing signal waveforms, and the impedance concept to solve a new set of problems. While impedance was defined for exponentials, a more general interpretation permits its application to continuous and sinusoidal waves as well. To simplify the analysis of circuits involving sinusoidal voltages and currents, we use the phasor.

RESPONSE TO FORCING FUNCTIONS

By definition, impedance is the ratio of voltage to current for exponentials of the form $i = I_0 e^{st}$. In general,

$$v = Z(s)i \qquad (5\text{-}1)$$

a special form of Ohm's law where impedance $Z(s)$ is in ohms.

For resistance, $v_R = Ri$ and $Z_R(s) = v/i = R$.

For inductance, $v_L = L\,di/dt = sLi$ and $Z_L(s) = v/i = sL$.

For capacitance, $i_c = C\,dv/dt = sCv$ and $Z_C(s) = v/i = 1/sC$.

Impedances to exponentials can be combined in series and parallel just as resistances are.

Response to Exponentials

In the circuit of Fig. 5.1a, an exponential forcing function $i = I_0 e^{-\alpha t}$ flows in the series combination of R and L. There is no information on

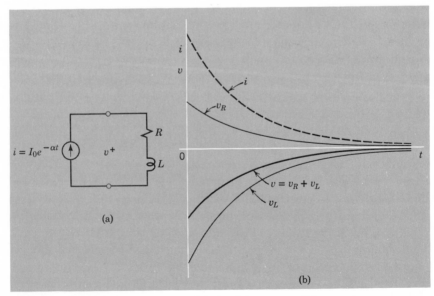

Fig. 5.1 Response of RL circuit to exponential current.

how the current was initiated; we only know that such a current could not be established by closing a switch at $t = 0$. (Why not?) Assuming such a current does exist, what is the response of the circuit in terms of voltages across the elements?

Since $Z_R(s) = R$,

$$v_R = Z_R(s)i = RI_0 e^{-\alpha t}$$

Since $Z_L(s) = sL = -\alpha L$,

$$v_L = Z_L(s)i = -\alpha L I_0 e^{-\alpha t}$$

The total voltage is the sum of the two in series or

$$v = v_R + v_L = (R - \alpha L)I_0 e^{-\alpha t}$$

As expected, the response to an exponential forcing function is itself exponential of the same "frequency" α or the same time constant $T = 1/\alpha$. The negative sign of v_L is due to the tendency of an inductance to oppose a change in current. Assuming that $\alpha L > R$, the total voltage is negative as shown in Fig. 5.1b.

The impedance $Z(s) = R + sL$ and, therefore, the response $v(t)$ vary widely with changes in parameter s. For a given magnitude I_0, the inductive voltage v_L is directly proportional to s and changes sign with s. For the special case of $s = -R/L$, $Z(s) = 0$, or the circuit presents no opposition to this particular current function; our interpretation is that since current is possible with no forcing voltage, this is a natural response current. Two other interesting cases are for $s = 0$ and $s = j\omega$.

Response to Direct Currents

A unidirectional current of constant magnitude is called a continuous or direct current, abbreviated dc. In common usage a voltage of the same form is called a "d-c† voltage," and we sometimes talk of "d-c currents" in contrast to alternating or "a-c currents." Direct-current energy supplied by chemical batteries, thermocouples, solar cells, or rotating d-c generators is used for a wide variety of purposes including ship propulsion, electrolytic refining, electron beam acceleration, and transistor operation. In circuit diagrams d-c voltage sources appear so often that the special symbol of Fig. 5.2 is used; the longer line indicates the positive terminal.

---

† When used as an *adjective*, the abbreviation should be hyphenated.

For the special case of $s = 0$ (see Fig. 4.12), the general exponential becomes

$$i = I_0 e^{0t} = I_{dc} = I†$$ (5-2)

The d-c values of impedance $Z(s)$, for the case of $s = 0$, we designate $Z(0)$. For resistance, inductance, and capacitance these impedances are:

$$Z_R(0) = R \qquad Z_L(0) = 0 \qquad Z_C(0) = \infty$$ (5-3)

The same results are obtained by considering the fundamental element equations. In a resistance, $v = Ri$ for all waveforms; for a direct current I, a direct voltage $V = RI$ appears across a resistance. The impedance $v/i = V/I = R$ as expected.

When a direct current $i = I$ flows in an inductance, $di/dt = 0$ and, therefore, $v = L(di/dt) = 0$. The impedance $v/i = 0$, or an inductance, has the characteristic of a short circuit. We say "an inductance looks like a short circuit to a d-c current." When a direct voltage is applied to an inductance carrying no initial current,

$$i = \frac{1}{L} \int_0^t v \, dt = \frac{V}{L} t$$ (5-4)

and the current increases linearly with time.

When a direct voltage $v = V$ appears across a capacitance, $dv/dt = 0$ and, therefore, $i = C(dv/dt) = 0$. The impedance $v/i = \infty$ or we say, "a capacitance looks like an open circuit to a d-c voltage." When a direct current $i = I$ flows in an initially uncharged capacitance,

$$v = \frac{1}{C} \int_0^t i \, dt = \frac{I}{C} t$$ (5-5)

and the voltage increases linearly with time.

EXAMPLE 1

Switch S in Fig. 5.2a has been closed for a long time. Determine the current i and the voltages across R_1, R_2, and R_3.

SOLUTION. We assume that after the "long time" specified all natural response has died away and only a forced response exists. For a direct forcing voltage the response is a direct current. To a direct current, inductance L looks like a short circuit effectively removing R_2 from the circuit; the voltage across R_2 is zero. To a direct voltage, capacitance C looks like an open circuit and it can be removed from the circuit; all the current i flows through R_3. For the d-c case, the circuit looks like Fig. 5.2b. The total series resistance is $R_1 + R_3$ and

---

† Capital I and V are used to designate constant values, such as phasors or d-c magnitudes, and lower case i and v to designate functions of time.

$$i = I = \frac{V}{R_1 + R_3}$$

Hence,

$$v_1 = R_1 i = \frac{R_1}{R_1 + R_3} V \quad \text{and} \quad v_3 = R_3 i = \frac{R_3}{R_1 + R_3} V$$

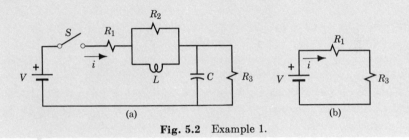

(a)   (b)

Fig. 5.2   Example 1.

Response to Sinusoids

The representation of sinusoids by exponentials leads to the phasor concept whereby functions of time are transformed into constant quantities for easy manipulation and display.   Also, we know that in dealing with exponentials the impedance concept provides a convenient method for finding forced response.   Therefore, we expect exponential representation of sinusoids to lead to a convenient method for analyzing circuits with sinusoidal sources and for displaying the results.

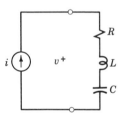

Fig. 5.3   *RLC* circuit.

To confirm our expectation, let us consider the series *RLC* circuit of Fig. 5.3 where $i = I_m \cos \omega t$. Applying Kirchhoff's voltage law to obtain the connection equation,

$$v = Ri + L \frac{di}{dt} + \frac{1}{C} \int i \, dt \tag{5-6}$$

Under steady-state conditions, v is the forced response and will be sinusoidal for a sinusoidal forcing current.   Anticipating the result, let us assume that $v = \text{Re} \{Ae^{j\omega t}\}$ where constant $A = V_m e^{j\theta} = \mathbf{V}$.   Letting $i = \text{Re} \{I_m e^{j0} e^{j\omega t}\} = \text{Re} \{\mathbf{I}e^{j\omega t}\}$, the terms in Eq. 5-6 are:

$$Ri = R \, \text{Re} \{\mathbf{I}e^{j\omega t}\} = \text{Re} \{R\mathbf{I}e^{j\omega t}\}$$

$$L \frac{di}{dt} = L \frac{d}{dt} \text{Re} \{\mathbf{I}e^{j\omega t}\} = L \, \text{Re} \{\mathbf{I}(j\omega)e^{j\omega t}\} = \text{Re} \{j\omega L\mathbf{I}e^{j\omega t}\}$$

and†

$$\frac{1}{C} \int i \, dt = \frac{1}{C} \int \text{Re } \{\mathbf{I}e^{j\omega t}\} \, dt = \frac{1}{C} \text{Re } \left\{\frac{\mathbf{I}}{j\omega} e^{j\omega t}\right\} = \text{Re } \left\{\frac{1}{j\omega C} \mathbf{I}e^{j\omega t}\right\}$$

Substituting in Eq. 5-6,

$$\text{Re } \{\mathbf{V}e^{j\omega t}\} = \text{Re } \{R\mathbf{I}e^{j\omega t}\} + \text{Re } \{j\omega L\mathbf{I}e^{j\omega t}\} + \text{Re } \left\{\frac{1}{j\omega C} \mathbf{I}e^{j\omega t}\right\}$$

$$= \text{Re } \left\{\left(R\mathbf{I} + j\omega L\mathbf{I} + \frac{1}{j\omega C} \mathbf{I}\right) e^{j\omega t}\right\}$$

following the rule for the addition of complex quantities. By the rule
for equality, if the real parts of these two complex quantities are to be
equal at all times (assuming that t is the only variable), then the complex quantities themselves are equal. This requires that

$$\mathbf{V} = R\mathbf{I} + j\omega L\mathbf{I} + \frac{1}{j\omega C} \mathbf{I} = \left(R + j\omega L + \frac{1}{j\omega C}\right) \mathbf{I} \qquad (5\text{-}7)$$

This is a reassuring result because the quantity in parentheses looks like
$Z(s) = R + sL + 1/sC$ for a series RLC circuit if s has the value $j\omega$.

From Eq. 5-7 we conclude that phasor voltage and phasor current are
related by a *complex impedance* $\mathbf{Z} = Z(j\omega)$ or

$$\mathbf{V} = \mathbf{Z}\mathbf{I} \qquad (5\text{-}8)$$

which is sometimes referred to as the Ohm's law of sinusoidal circuits.

Impedance $\mathbf{Z}$ is measured in ohms when phasors $\mathbf{V}$ and $\mathbf{I}$ are in volts
and amperes, respectively. Note that $\mathbf{Z}$ is a complex quantity, like a
phasor, but $\mathbf{Z}$ is *not* a phasor. The term phasor is reserved for quantities
representing sinusoidal varying functions of time. The chief virtue of
complex impedance is that while it expresses the relation between two
time-varying quantities, $\mathbf{Z}$ itself is *not* a function of time.

PHASOR METHODS

Circuit Laws in Terms of Phasors

The element equations define the voltage-current characteristics of
passive elements. From Eq. 5-7 we can form the set of steady-state

---

† It can be shown that, with respect to a real variable such as time,

$$\frac{d}{dt} \text{Re } \{\mathbf{W}\} = \text{Re } \left\{\frac{d\mathbf{W}}{dt}\right\} \qquad \text{and} \qquad \int \text{Re } \{\mathbf{W}\} \, dt = \text{Re } \left\{\int \mathbf{W} \, dt\right\}$$

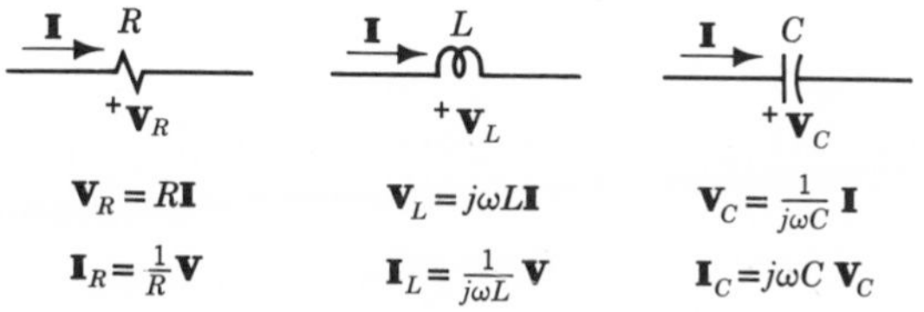

$$\mathbf{V}_R = R\mathbf{I} \qquad \mathbf{V}_L = j\omega L\mathbf{I} \qquad \mathbf{V}_C = \frac{1}{j\omega C}\mathbf{I}$$

$$\mathbf{I}_R = \frac{1}{R}\mathbf{V} \qquad \mathbf{I}_L = \frac{1}{j\omega L}\mathbf{V} \qquad \mathbf{I}_C = j\omega C\,\mathbf{V}_C$$

Fig. 5.4 Element equations in terms of phasors.

relations shown in Fig. 5.4. The sign convention indicates that for the assumed reference direction of positive current the corresponding reference polarity for voltage is as shown. Such a convention is necessary because the actual current and voltage are both changing sign periodically, but not simultaneously.

The connection equations for sinusoidal forced response are based on Kirchhoff's laws. Assuming that all sources in a linear circuit are sinusoids of the same frequency, all steady-state voltages and currents are sinusoids of that same frequency. Kirchhoff's voltage law

$$\Sigma v = 0 = v_1 + v_2 + \cdots + v_k$$

becomes, in terms of phasors,

$$\Sigma v = 0 = \mathrm{Re}\,\{\mathbf{V}_1 e^{j\omega t}\} + \mathrm{Re}\,\{\mathbf{V}_2 e^{j\omega t}\} + \cdots + \mathrm{Re}\,\{\mathbf{V}_k e^{j\omega t}\} \quad (5\text{-}9)$$

By the rule of equality, if Eq. 5-9 is to hold for all values of t,

$$0 = \mathbf{V}_1 + \mathbf{V}_2 + \cdots + \mathbf{V}_k = \Sigma\mathbf{V} \qquad (5\text{-}10)$$

In other words, for steady-state sinusoidal functions, Kirchhoff's voltage law holds for voltage phasors and $\Sigma\mathbf{V} = 0$ around any closed loop. Following a similar line of reasoning, Kirchhoff's current law holds for current phasors and $\Sigma\mathbf{I} = 0$ into any node.

EXAMPLE 2

A voltage $v = 120 \cos (1000t + 90°)$ V is applied to the circuit of Fig. 5.5a where $R = 15\ \Omega$, $C = 83.3\ \mu F$, and $L = 30$ mH. Find $i(t)$.

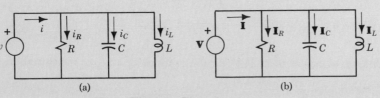

(a)   (b)

Fig. 5.5 Example 2.

SOLUTION. The first step is to transform $v(t)$ into phasor $\mathbf{V} = 120 \underline{/90°}$ V.
Then

$$\mathbf{I}_R = \frac{1}{R}\mathbf{V} = \frac{1}{15}120 \underline{/90°} = 8 \underline{/90°} = 0 + j8 \text{ A}$$

$$\mathbf{I}_C = j\omega C\mathbf{V} = (0.0833 \underline{/90°})(120 \underline{/90°}) = 10 \underline{/180°} = -10 + j0 \text{ A}$$

$$\mathbf{I}_L = \frac{1}{j\omega L}\mathbf{V} = \frac{120 \underline{/90°}}{30 \underline{/90°}} = 4 \underline{/0°} = 4 + j0 \text{ A}$$

By Kirchhoff's current law, $\Sigma\mathbf{I} = 0$ or

$$\mathbf{I} = \mathbf{I}_R + \mathbf{I}_C + \mathbf{I}_L = (0 - 10 + 4) + j(8 + 0 + 0) = -6 + j8 = 10 \underline{/127°} \text{ A}$$

The final step is to transform $\mathbf{I}$ into $i = 10 \cos (1000t + 127°)$ A

A-C Impedance and Admittance

While an "alternating" current can be nonsinusoidal, unless otherwise
stated we assume that an alternating current or an "a-c voltage" is
sinusoidal. Most electrical energy is generated, transmitted, and consumed in the form of alternating current. Also, much of the d-c energy
used in power and communication applications is first generated as a-c
energy and then converted to d-c form. The number of applications of
a-c circuits is so great that we can justify taking time to learn some short
cuts in solving such circuits.

Taking another look at Eq. 5-7, repeated here for convenience,

$$\mathbf{V} = R\mathbf{I} + j\omega L\mathbf{I} + \frac{1}{j\omega C}\mathbf{I} = \left(R + j\omega L + \frac{1}{j\omega C}\right)\mathbf{I} \qquad (5\text{-}7)$$

we see that the total complex impedance of a series RLC circuit consists
of the sum of the impedances of the elements. Just as each passive
circuit element has associated with it an impedance to exponentials $Z(s)$
and an impedance to direct currents $Z(0)$, it also has an impedance to
sinusoids $Z(j\omega)$.

For resistance, $\mathbf{Z}_R(j\omega) = \mathbf{Z}_R = R = R \underline{/0°}$

For inductance, $\mathbf{Z}_L(j\omega) = \mathbf{Z}_L = j\omega L = \omega L \underline{/90°}$ (5-11)

For capacitance, $\mathbf{Z}_C(j\omega) = \mathbf{Z}_C = \frac{1}{j\omega C} = \left(\frac{1}{\omega C}\right)\underline{/-90°}$

The quantity R is called the *a-c resistance*† and is measured in ohms.

---

† The a-c resistance of a physical resistor may be different from the d-c resistance.

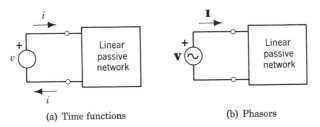

(a) Time functions   (b) Phasors

Fig. 5.6   A two-terminal network.

The corresponding term for an inductance is called the *inductive reactance* $X_L = \omega L$ in ohms.   For a capacitance, the corresponding term is called *capacitive reactance* $X_C = 1/\omega C$ in ohms.   Note that $Z_C(j\omega) = -jX_C$; a minus sign is always associated with X_C.

In Fig. 5.6a, a linear passive network is energized by a voltage source applied to two terminals brought out for the purpose. · The current out of the lower terminal is just equal to the current into the upper terminal. (Why?)   Such a *two-terminal* network can be represented by Fig. 5.6b if voltage v is sinusoidal.

The steady-state sinusoidal response of any two-terminal network is completely defined by the impedance $\mathbf{Z} = \mathbf{V}/\mathbf{I}$ at the terminals.   Another way of characterizing a network is in terms of the admittance $Y(s)$, defined in Chapter 4 as the ratio of exponential current to voltage.   For sinusoidal current and voltage,

$$Y(j\omega) = \mathbf{Y} = \frac{\mathbf{I}}{\mathbf{V}}$$

where $\mathbf{Y}$ is the complex admittance in mhos.

In general, $\mathbf{Z}$ and $\mathbf{Y}$ are complex and can be written as

$$\mathbf{Z} = Z \underline{/\phi_Z} = R + jX \tag{5-12}$$

$$\mathbf{Y} = Y \underline{/\phi_Y} = G + jB$$

The real part of $\mathbf{Z}$ is called *resistance* in ohms and is designated R; in the RLC circuit described by Eq. 5-8, the real part of $\mathbf{Z}$ is the resistance of a particular element, but in general this is *not* true.   The imaginary part of $\mathbf{Z}$ is called *reactance* in ohms and is designated X; for the RLC circuit, $X = X_L - X_C = \omega L - 1/\omega C$.   The real part of $\mathbf{Y}$ is called *conductance* in mhos and is designated G; in general, G is *not* the conductance of a particular element.   The imaginary part of $\mathbf{Y}$ is called *susceptance* in

mhos and is designated B. A positive B is associated with a predominantly capacitive circuit.

Since **Z** and **Y** are complex quantities, they obey the rules of complex
algebra and can be represented by plane vectors.   In contrast to phasors,
Z and **Y** can only lie in the first and fourth quadrants of the complex
plane because R and G are always positive for passive networks.   Since
Z = 1/**Y**,

$$R + jX = \frac{1}{G + jB} = \frac{G}{G^2 + B^2} - j\frac{B}{G^2 + B^2} \qquad (5\text{-}13)$$

Similarly,

$$G + jB = \frac{1}{R + jX} = \frac{R}{R^2 + X^2} - j\frac{X}{R^2 + X^2} \qquad (5\text{-}14)$$

It must be emphasized that R and G, and X and B are the real and
imaginary parts of quantities defined at the terminals and, in general,
are not associated with particular elements of a network.   Failure to
realize this is sure to result in mistakes in the solution of complicated
circuits.   First, however, let us use the admittance concept in a simple
example.

EXAMPLE 3

Given the problem of Example 2, (see Fig. 5.7) where **V** = 120 $\underline{/90°}$ V, ω =
1000 rad/sec, R = 15 Ω, C = 83.3 μF, and L = 30 mH, find **I**.

SOLUTION.   The admittance concept is particularly useful in dealing with
parallel circuits since admittances of parallel elements are added directly.   From
the element equations displayed in Fig. 5.4,

$$\mathbf{Y}_R = \frac{\mathbf{I}}{\mathbf{V}} = \frac{1}{R} = \frac{1}{15} = 0.0667 \; \text{℧}$$

$$\mathbf{Y}_C = j\omega C = jB_C = j1000 \times 83.3 \times 10^{-6} = j0.0833 \; \text{℧}$$

$$\mathbf{Y}_L = \frac{1}{j\omega L} = -jB_L = -j\frac{1}{\omega L} = -j\frac{1}{1000 \times 0.03} = -j0.0333 \; \text{℧}$$

Then the admittance at the terminals of the one-port is

$$\mathbf{Y} = \mathbf{Y}_R + \mathbf{Y}_C + \mathbf{Y}_L = 0.0667 + j(0.0833 - 0.0333) = 0.0667 + j0.05 \; \text{℧}$$

In polar form,

$$\mathbf{Y} = \sqrt{(0.0667)^2 + (0.05)^2} \; \underline{/\arctan \frac{0.05}{0.0667}} = 0.0833 \; \underline{/37°} \; \text{℧}$$

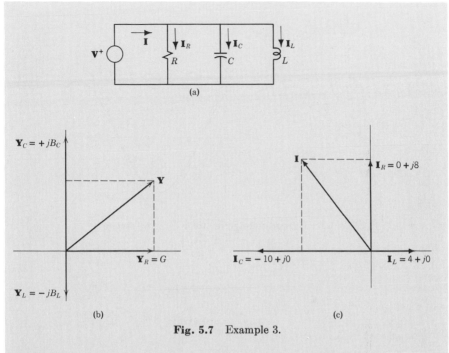

Fig. 5.7 Example 3.

and

$$I = YV = (0.0833\ \underline{/37°})(120\ \underline{/90°}) = 10\ \underline{/127°}\ A$$

The components of Y are shown in Fig. 5.7b; for comparison the component currents calculated in Example 2 are shown in Fig. 5.7c.

Voltage and Current Relations

By definition, impedance $Z(j\omega)$ is the ratio of the voltage phasor to the current phasor or $Z = V/I$ where all quantities are complex. For a resistance (Fig. 5.8), $Z_R = V_R/I = R\ \underline{/0°}$; therefore, the voltage and current phasors are drawn at the same angle. The voltage and current are shown as functions of time in Fig. 5.8c; the voltage and current waves reach maximum and zero values simultaneously. We say that *the voltage across a resistance is in phase with the current through it.*

For an inductance (Fig. 5.9), $Z_L = V_L/I = \omega L\ \underline{/90°}$; therefore, the voltage phasor is 90° *ahead* of the current phasor. When the voltage and current are shown as functions of time (Fig. 5.9c), it is clear that the voltage wave reaches its maximum and zero values at an *earlier* time than the current wave. We say that *the voltage across an inductive reactance leads by 90° the current through it.*

For a capacitance (Fig. 5.10), $Z_C = V_C/I_C = (1/\omega C)\ \underline{/-90°}$; therefore the voltage phasor is 90° *behind* the current phasor. When the voltage

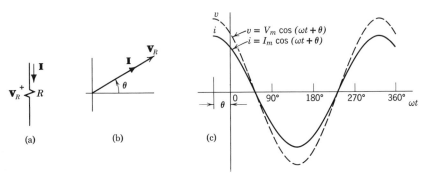

Fig. 5.8   Current-voltage relations for a resistance.

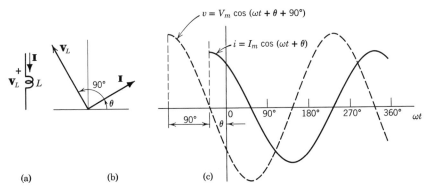

Fig. 5.9   Current-voltage relations for an inductance.

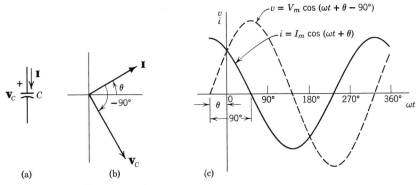

Fig. 5.10   Current-voltage relations for a capacitance.

and current are shown as functions of time (Fig. 5.10c), it is clear that the voltage wave reaches its maximum and zero values at a *later* time than the current wave. We say that *the voltage across a capacitive react-ance lags by 90° the current through it.* (These phrases emphasize that the *voltage across an element* is specified with respect to the *current through that element* and not with respect to any other current.)

A-C CIRCUIT ANALYSIS

By using the impedance concept, differential equations are replaced by algebraic equations. By using the phasor concept, continuously varying quantities are replaced by complex constants. With these aids the analy-sis of a-c circuits becomes a relatively simple process.

Series *RL* and *RC* Circuits

The process is illustrated by the analysis of the circuit in Fig. 5.11. For the series combination of R and L,

$$\mathbf{Z} = R + jX_L = R + j\omega L = Z \underline{/\phi} = \sqrt{R^2 + (\omega L)^2} \underline{/\arctan \frac{\omega L}{R}}$$

(5-15)

Assuming that $\mathbf{V}$ is given as $V_m \underline{/\theta}$,

$$\mathbf{I} = \frac{\mathbf{V}}{\mathbf{Z}} = \frac{V_m \underline{/\theta}}{Z \underline{/\phi}} = \frac{V_m}{Z} \underline{/\theta - \phi} = I_m \underline{/\theta - \phi}$$

(5-16)

As shown in Fig. 5.11c,† the total voltage phasor leads the current phasor by *phase angle* ϕ, something less than 90°. The voltage across the resist-ance is in phase with the current and the voltage across the inductive reactance is 90° ahead of the current. These are components of the total applied voltage and the phasor sum of $\mathbf{V}_R$ and $\mathbf{V}_L$ is equal to $\mathbf{V}$.

For the series combination of R and C (Fig. 5.12),

$$\mathbf{Z} = R - jX_C$$
$$= R - j\left(\frac{1}{\omega C}\right) = Z \underline{/\phi} = \sqrt{R^2 + \left(\frac{1}{\omega C}\right)^2} \underline{/\arctan \frac{-1/\omega C}{R}}$$

(5-17)

where ϕ is a negative angle. Assuming that $\mathbf{I}$ is given as $I_m \underline{/\theta}$,

$$\mathbf{V} = \mathbf{Z}\mathbf{I} = (Z \underline{/\phi})(I_m \underline{/\theta}) = ZI_m \underline{/\phi + \theta} = V_m \underline{/\phi + \theta}$$

(5-18)

---

† In drawing phasor diagrams, all voltages are drawn to one scale and all currents are drawn to one scale (which may be quite different from the voltage scale).

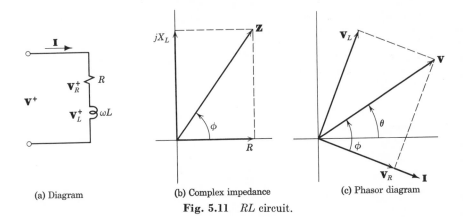

(a) Diagram   (b) Complex impedance   (c) Phasor diagram

Fig. 5.11   *RL* circuit.

As shown in Fig. 5.12c, the voltage across the resistance R is in phase with the current $\mathbf{I}$.   The voltage across the capacitive reactance X_C lags behind the current by 90°.   The resulting total voltage lags behind the current by an angle less than 90°.

EXAMPLE 4

In the circuit of Fig. 5.12a, $\mathbf{V} = 20 \underline{/45°}$ V, $R = 5$ Ω, and $X_C = 1/\omega C = 8.66$ Ω.   Find $\mathbf{I}$, $\mathbf{V}_R$, and $\mathbf{V}_C$.

SOLUTION.   By Eq. 5-17,

$$\mathbf{Z} = R - j\left(\frac{1}{\omega C}\right) = 5 - j8.66 = 10 \underline{/-60°}\ \Omega$$

Then

$$\mathbf{I} = \frac{\mathbf{V}}{\mathbf{Z}} = \frac{20 \underline{/45°}}{10 \underline{/-60°}} = 2 \underline{/105°}\ \text{A}$$

$$\mathbf{V}_R = R\mathbf{I} = (5 \underline{/0°})(2 \underline{/105°}) = 10 \underline{/105°}\ \text{V}$$

and

$$\mathbf{V}_C = -jX_C\mathbf{I} = (8.66 \underline{/-90°})(2 \underline{/105°}) = 17.32 \underline{/15°}\ \text{V}$$

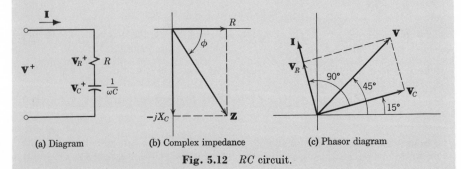

(a) Diagram   (b) Complex impedance   (c) Phasor diagram

Fig. 5.12   *RC* circuit.

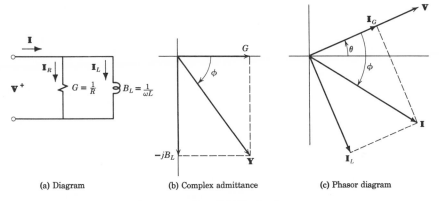

(a) Diagram   (b) Complex admittance   (c) Phasor diagram

Fig. 5.13   Parallel GL circuit.

These results are plotted in Fig. 5.12c.   Assuming ω is known, the phasors could be transformed into time functions, but this is seldom necessary.   For reasons discussed in Chapter 7, the values of interest in steady-state circuit analysis are proportional to the phasor magnitudes, and ammeters and voltmeters are calibrated to read these values directly.

Parallel GL and GC Circuits

It was pointed out earlier that in dealing with parallel circuits the admittance approach is particularly useful.   The process is illustrated by the analysis of the circuit in Fig. 5.13a.   For the parallel combination of G and L,

$$\mathbf{Y} = G - jB_L = G - j\left(\frac{1}{\omega L}\right) = Y \underline{/\phi} = \sqrt{G^2 + \left(\frac{1}{\omega L}\right)^2} \Big/ \arctan \frac{-1/\omega L}{G}$$

$$(5\text{-}19)$$

where ϕ is a negative angle.   Assuming that $\mathbf{V}$ is given as $V_m \underline{/\theta}$,

$$\mathbf{I} = \mathbf{Y}\mathbf{V} = (Y \underline{/\phi})(V_m \underline{/\theta}) = YV_m \underline{/\phi + \theta} = I_m \underline{/\phi + \theta} \quad (5\text{-}20)$$

As shown in Fig. 5.13c, the current in the conductance G is in phase with the voltage $\mathbf{V}$.   The current in the inductive susceptance B_L lags behind the voltage by 90°.   The resulting total current I lags behind the voltage by an angle less than 90°.

For the parallel combination of G and C (Fig. 5.14),

$$\mathbf{Y} = G + jB_C = G + j\omega C = Y \underline{/\phi} = \sqrt{G^2 + (\omega C)^2} \Big/ \arctan \frac{\omega C}{G} \quad (5\text{-}21)$$

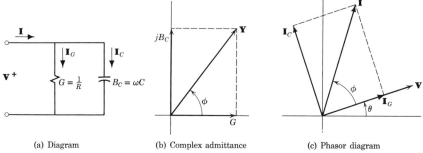

(a) Diagram   (b) Complex admittance   (c) Phasor diagram

Fig. 5.14 Parallel GC circuit.

Equation 5-20 applies for this circuit as well, but here phase angle ϕ is positive and the total current phasor *leads* the voltage by something less than 90°.

While the admittance approach is usually easier, parallel circuits can also be analyzed in terms of impedances properly combined. In general, for parallel elements,

$$\mathbf{Y} = \mathbf{Y}_1 + \mathbf{Y}_2 + \cdots + \mathbf{Y}_n \qquad (5\text{-}22)$$

or

$$\frac{1}{\mathbf{Z}} = \frac{1}{\mathbf{Z}_1} + \frac{1}{\mathbf{Z}_2} + \cdots + \frac{1}{\mathbf{Z}_n} \qquad (5\text{-}23)$$

For the special case of two parallel elements,

$$\frac{1}{\mathbf{Z}} = \frac{1}{\mathbf{Z}_1} + \frac{1}{\mathbf{Z}_2} \quad \text{or} \quad \mathbf{Z} = \frac{\mathbf{Z}_1 \mathbf{Z}_2}{\mathbf{Z}_1 + \mathbf{Z}_2} \qquad (5\text{-}24)$$

For a parallel GL circuit, the impedance at the terminals is

$$\mathbf{Z} = \frac{\mathbf{Z}_G \mathbf{Z}_L}{\mathbf{Z}_G + \mathbf{Z}_L} = \frac{R(j\omega L)}{R + j\omega L}$$

Then

$$\mathbf{I} = \frac{\mathbf{V}}{\mathbf{Z}} = \frac{R + j\omega L}{jR\omega L}\,\mathbf{V} = \left(\frac{1}{j\omega L} + \frac{1}{R}\right)\mathbf{V} = \left(G - j\frac{1}{\omega L}\right)\mathbf{V}$$

which agrees with Eqs. 5-19 and 5-20.

In talking about circuit analysis in general, we need a term which includes both impedance and admittance. For this purpose we shall use the word *immittance* derived from *im*pedance and ad*mittance*.

General Circuit Analysis

We are now ready to formulate a general procedure applicable to a variety of problems in steady-state sinusoidal circuits. While the exact sequence depends on the particular problem, the following steps are usually necessary:

1. Transform time functions to phasors and convert element values to complex immittances.
2. Combine immittances in series or parallel to simplify the circuit.
3. Determine the desired response in phasor form, using connection equations.
4. Draw a phasor diagram to check computations and to display results.
5. Transform phasors to time functions if required.

EXAMPLE 5

The circuit of Fig. 5.15a represents a "load" consisting of C, R, and L supplied by a generator over a transmission line approximated by L_T. What generator voltage is required if the load voltage is to be $v = 283 \cos{(500t + 45°)}$ V?

SOLUTION.

1. In phasor form, $v(t)$ becomes $\mathbf{V} = 283\ \underline{/45°}$ V.

$$\mathbf{Z}_T = j\omega L_T = j500 \times 3 \times 10^{-3} = j1.5\ \Omega$$

$$\mathbf{Y}_C = j\omega C = j500 \times 10^{-3} = j0.5\ \mho \quad \text{and} \quad \mathbf{Z}_C = \frac{1}{\mathbf{Y}_C} = -j2\ \Omega$$

$$\mathbf{Z}_L = j\omega L = j500 \times 4 \times 10^{-3} = j2\ \Omega$$

The circuit diagram of Fig. 5.15b displays these values. If current $\mathbf{I}$ is determined, voltage $\mathbf{V}_g$ can be calculated from a loop equation.

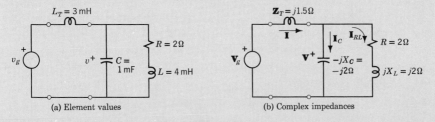

(a) Element values   (b) Complex impedances

Fig. 5.15 Example 5.

2. Since $\mathbf{I} = \mathbf{YV}$, we need the admittance of the parallel circuit constituting the load.

$$\mathbf{Y}_{RL} = \frac{1}{\mathbf{Z}_{RL}} = \frac{1}{2 + j2} = \frac{1}{2\sqrt{2}\;\underline{/45°}} = 0.25\sqrt{2}\;\underline{/-45°} = 0.25 - j0.25\;\mho$$

$$\mathbf{Y} = \mathbf{Y}_C + \mathbf{Y}_{RL} = j0.5 + (0.25 - j0.25) = 0.25 + j0.25 = 0.25\sqrt{2}\;\underline{/+45°}\;\mho$$

3. Then

$$\mathbf{I} = \mathbf{YV} = (0.25\sqrt{2}\;\underline{/45°})(283\;\underline{/45°}) = 100\;\underline{/90°}\;\text{A}$$

The phasor diagram should be drawn as the calculations proceed, to provide a continuous check as well as a final display of results.

4. In addition to the given V and the calculated I we know that:

$$\mathbf{I}_C = \mathbf{Y}_C\mathbf{V} = (0.5\;\underline{/90°})(283\;\underline{/45°}) = 141.5\;\underline{/135°}\;\text{A}$$

$$\mathbf{I}_{RL} = \mathbf{Y}_{RL}\mathbf{V} = (0.25\sqrt{2}\;\underline{/-45°})(283\;\underline{/45°}) = 100\;\underline{/0°}\;\text{A}$$

$$\mathbf{V}_R = \mathbf{RI}_{RL} = (2\;\underline{/0°})(100\;\underline{/0°}) = 200\;\underline{/0°}\;\text{V}$$

$$\mathbf{V}_L = \mathbf{Z}_L\mathbf{I}_{RL} = (2\;\underline{/90°})(100\;\underline{/0°}) = 200\;\underline{/90°}\;\text{V}$$

These are shown on the phasor diagram of Fig. 5.16a. The construction lines indicate consistency with the connection equations, $\mathbf{I} = \mathbf{I}_C + \mathbf{I}_{RL}$ and $\mathbf{V} = \mathbf{V}_R + \mathbf{V}_L$. Other checks are also available: $\mathbf{I}_C$ leads $\mathbf{V}$ by 90°, $\mathbf{V}_R$ is in phase with $\mathbf{I}_{RL}$, and $\mathbf{V}_L$ leads $\mathbf{I}_{RL}$ by 90°. To determine the generator voltage, we write a loop equation, $\Sigma \mathbf{V} = 0 = \mathbf{V}_g - \mathbf{IZ}_T - \mathbf{V}$ and solve for

$$\mathbf{V}_g = \mathbf{Z}_T\mathbf{I} + \mathbf{V} = (1.5\;\underline{/90°})(100\;\underline{/90°}) + 283\;\underline{/45°} = 150\;\underline{/180°} + 283\;\underline{/45°}$$

$$= -150 + j0 + 200 + j200 = 50 + j200 = 206\;\underline{/76°}\;\text{V}$$

This result is confirmed by the phasor diagram of Fig. 5.16b.

5. The final step, if required, is to transform phasors into functions of time. By inspection.

$$v_g = 206\cos(500t + 76°)\;\text{V}.$$

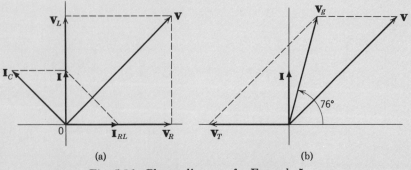

(a)   (b)

Fig. 5.16   Phasor diagrams for Example 5.

ANALOGS AND DUALS

One justification for this intensive study of electrical circuit analysis is that the techniques developed are equally applicable to analogous situations in other fields. By definition, *analogous systems are described by the same integrodifferential equation* or set of equations. The solution of the equation describing one physical system automatically yields the solution for any analogous system. The solution of an electrical circuit provides results which are directly applicable to analogous mechanical, hydraulic, or thermal circuits.

Analogs

As an illustration, consider the mass M sliding with a friction coefficient D on a surface as shown in Fig. 5.17a (same as Fig. 4.3). By d'Alembert's principle, the governing equation is

$$Du + M\frac{du}{dt} = f \tag{5-25}$$

This looks familiar; in form it is similar to the equation resulting from the application of Kirchhoff's voltage law to the circuit of Fig. 5.11 (repeated here as Fig. 5.17b)

$$Ri + L\frac{di}{dt} = v \tag{5-26}$$

Mathematically, these two integrodifferential equations are the same and, therefore, the circuits are analogous; the solutions of the two equations are identical if simple symbol substitutions are permitted.

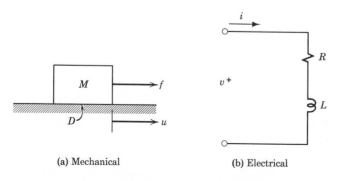

(a) Mechanical   (b) Electrical

Fig. 5.17 Analogous circuits.

For exponential functions we expect a *motional impedance* $Z(s) = D + sM$. The natural behavior is defined by $Z(s) = 0$ or $s = -D/M$ and $u = Ue^{-(D/M)t}$. A steady pull on the mass corresponds to a "direct" force and $f = F$; then $Z(O) = D$ and $U = F/D$ is the forced response to a direct force.

For a sinusoidal pull, $f = F_m \cos(\omega t + \theta)$, a phasor approach is indicated where $\mathbf{F} = F_m \,\underline{/\theta}$. Then

$$Z(j\omega) = \mathbf{Z} = D + j\omega M = Z_m \,\underline{/\phi} \qquad (5\text{-}27)$$

where

$$Z_m = \sqrt{D^2 + (\omega M)^2} \quad \text{and} \quad \phi = \arctan \frac{\omega M}{R} \qquad (5\text{-}28)$$

Then

$$\mathbf{U} = \frac{\mathbf{F}}{\mathbf{Z}} = \frac{F_m \,\underline{/\theta}}{Z_m \,\underline{/\phi}} = U_m \,\underline{/\theta - \phi} \qquad (5\text{-}29)$$

and

$$u(t) = U_m \cos(\omega t + \theta - \phi) \qquad (5\text{-}30)$$

In this case we have solved the mechanical circuit by using the techniques developed for electrical circuits. Recognizing that the two circuits are analogous, we could have gone directly to the solution by making appropriate substitutions in Eqs. 5-15 and 5-16. The analogous terms are identified by a comparison of Eqs. 5-25 and 5-26; the results are tabulated in the first two rows of Fig. 5.18.

The mechanical analog for capacitance C is obtained by comparing Eq. 2-49 with Eq. 5-6. Recalling that displacement $x = \int u \, dt$ and charge $q = \int i \, dt$, we see that x and q are analogous.

Mechanical	M	D	K	f	u	x
Electrical	L	R	C	v	i	q
Thermal		R_τ	C_p	τ	q_τ	w_τ
Electrical II	C	G	L	i	v	λ

Fig. 5.18 A table of analogs.

Two important equations in heat transfer by conduction are

$$q_\tau = \frac{\tau}{R_\tau} \quad \text{and} \quad q_\tau = C_p \frac{d\tau}{dt} = \frac{dw_\tau}{dt} \qquad (5\text{-}31)$$

where q_τ = rate of heat flow in calories/sec,

$\quad R_\tau$ = thermal resistance in sec-°K/cal,

$\quad \tau$ = temperature difference in °K,

$\quad C_p$ = thermal capacitance in cal/°K,

$\quad w_\tau$ = thermal energy in cal.

The first equation expresses the fact that the rate of heat transfer by conduction is directly proportional to the temperature difference. The second provides for the heat absorbed by a body under conditions of changing temperature. Comparison of these equations with those describing electric circuit components leads to the thermal analogs shown in Fig. 5.18. Note that in this analog there is no term analogous to mass or inductance; heat flow does not exhibit any momentum or inertia effect.

Equations 5-31 have little practical value because they imply lumped thermal effects, whereas heat conduction is always a distributed phenomenon. (Why?) A further complication is that R_τ and C_p vary widely with temperature. In spite of these limitations, writing the equations and identifying the analogous terms are valuable because of the insights gained when the techniques of circuit theory are applied (see Problem 6).

Electrical analogs have been used to study heat flow in power transistors, the production and absorption of neutrons in a nuclear reactor, and the behavior of diverse acoustical and hydraulic systems. In recognition of the ease and effectiveness of the electronic analog computer, an entire chapter in this book is devoted to the principles and operation of this versatile engineering tool.

Duals

At this time an alert student should be aware of a certain amount of repetition in the discussion of electrical circuits. The equations and diagrams for the series RL circuit of Fig. 5.11 are similar to those for the parallel GC circuit of Fig. 5.14. With some changes in symbols, the equations and diagrams for the series RC circuit of Fig. 5.12 are just like those for the parallel GL circuit of Fig. 5.13. Apparently, when we solve one electrical circuit, we automatically obtain the solution to another. How can we take advantage of this interesting fact?

In drawing up the table of mechanical-electrical analogs, we used the series RLC circuit of Fig. 5.3. If, instead, we write the integrodifferential

L	R	C	v	i	Z	X
C	G	L	i	v	Y	B

Fig. 5.19   A table of dual quantities.

equation for the parallel *GCL* circuit of Fig. 5.7, we get the different set of analogs shown in the fourth row of Fig. 5.18.† It is always possible to draw two electrical circuits analogous to a given physical system, and the corresponding terms in the two circuits are related in accordance with the principle of *duality*.

The series *RLC* circuit and the parallel *GCL* circuit are said to be *duals* because *the set of transforms which converts the first into the second also converts the second into the first.* By using the set of transforms indicated in Fig. 5.19, either circuit can be converted into the other. In general, the loop equations of a planar network have the same form as the node equations of its dual.‡ Some of the dual relationships which exist in electrical networks are listed in Fig. 5.20.

A knowledge of duality enables us to double the benefit from any circuit analysis we perform. As an illustration, the paragraph which includes Eqs. 5-17 and 5-18 transforms directly into the paragraph which includes Eqs. 5-19 and 5-20. To test your understanding of the principle, write out the dual of the discussion of the series *RL* circuit (the paragraph including Eqs. 5-15 and 5-16) and see how well it describes the circuit of Fig. 5.14.

Sometimes it is advantageous to construct the dual of a given circuit instead of working with the given circuit itself. The first step is to place a dot in each loop of the given circuit and one more dot outside; these dots are the nodes of the dual circuit. Then, through each element of the given circuit, draw a line terminating on the dots. Finally, on each

---

† The term λ (lambda) is called flux linkage and is equal to $\int v\,dt$. See Eq. 16.1.
‡ In the language of network topology, a *planar* network is one which can be drawn on a sphere; every planar network has a dual.

Loop current	Node voltage
Kirchhoff's voltage law	Kirchhoff's current law
Series connection	Parallel connection
Current source	Voltage source
Short circuit	Open circuit

Fig. 5.20   A table of dual relations.

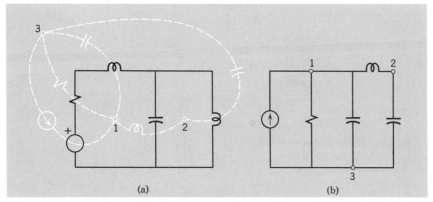

Fig. 5.21 Construction of a dual circuit.

line place the dual of the element through which the line is drawn; these lines are the branches of the dual circuit. The procedure is illustrated in Fig. 5.21.

EXAMPLE 6

The "voltage divider" of Fig. 5.22a is a useful device. Derive an expression for v_2 in terms of v. Draw the dual circuit and state (without derivation) the dual relation.

SOLUTION.

$$v_2 = iR_2 = \frac{v}{R_1 + R_2} R_2$$

or

$$\frac{v_2}{v} = \frac{R_2}{R_1 + R_2} \tag{5-32}$$

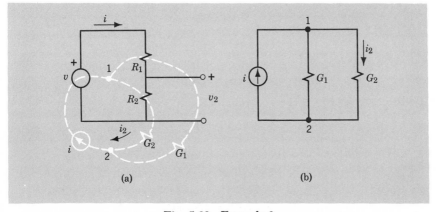

Fig. 5.22 Example 6.

The *voltage* across R_2 is to the total *voltage* as the *resistance* R_2 is to the sum of the *resistances*.

For the "current divider" (Fig. 5.22b), the dual relation is

$$\frac{i_2}{i} = \frac{G_2}{G_1 + G_2} \tag{5-33}$$

The *current* through G_2 is to the total *current* as the *conductance* G_2 is to the sum of the *conductances*.

The Generality of the Impedance Approach

The impedance approach is a good illustration of the power of a general method. While the impedance concept was developed for use in determining natural response, it turns out to be applicable to forced response as well. Though defined in terms of exponential functions, with a proper interpretation impedance can also be used with direct and sinusoidal currents. When an electrical circuit has been solved, we automatically have the solution to its dual. Through the analysis of an electrical circuit, we gain insight into the behavior of other analogous systems. Mastery of this important concept and the associated techniques is well worthwhile.

SUMMARY

◆ The waveform of the forcing function determines the waveform of the forced response.

◆ Impedance is defined for exponentials of the form $i = I_0 e^{st}$.
Impedances are combined in series and parallel, just as resistances. In general, the forced response is governed by

$$v = Z(s)i$$

where

$$Z_R(s) = R \qquad Z_L(s) = sL \qquad Z_C(s) = \frac{1}{sC}$$

◆ For $s = 0$, $i = I_0 = I$, a direct current. In this case,
$$Z_R(0) = R \qquad Z_L(0) = 0 \qquad Z_C(0) = \infty$$

A capacitance looks like an open circuit to a direct voltage.

An inductance looks like a short circuit to a direct current.

◆ Since $i = I_m \cos(\omega t + \theta) = \text{Re}\{I_m e^{j\theta} e^{j\omega t}\} = \text{Re}\{\mathbf{I} e^{j\omega t}\}$ sinusoids are conveniently represented by phasors.

Phasor voltage and current are related by the complex impedance $\mathbf{Z} = Z(j\omega)$ or the complex admittance $\mathbf{Y} = Y(j\omega)$.

$$\mathbf{V} = \mathbf{ZI} \qquad \text{and} \qquad \mathbf{I} = \mathbf{YV}$$

where

$$Z_R(j\omega) = R \qquad Z_L(j\omega) = j\omega L \qquad Z_C(j\omega) = 1/j\omega C$$
$$Y_R(j\omega) = G \qquad Y_L(j\omega) = 1/j\omega L \qquad Y_C(j\omega) = j\omega C$$

For phasors, Kirchhoff's laws are written:

$$\Sigma \mathbf{V} = 0 \qquad \text{and} \qquad \Sigma \mathbf{I} = 0$$

◆ The steady-state sinusoidal response of a two-terminal network is completely defined by $\mathbf{Z}$ or $\mathbf{Y}$ at the terminals where

$$\mathbf{Z} = Z \underline{/\phi_Z} = R + jX \qquad \text{and} \qquad \mathbf{Y} = Y \underline{/\phi_Y} = G + jB$$

The voltage $\mathbf{V}_R$ is in phase with the current $\mathbf{I}_R$.

The voltage $\mathbf{V}_L$ leads the current $\mathbf{I}_L$ by $90°$.

The voltage $\mathbf{V}_C$ lags the current $\mathbf{I}_C$ by $90°$.

◆ To determine the forced response to sinusoids:

1. Transform time functions to phasors and evaluate complex immittances.
2. Combine immittances in series or parallel to simplify the circuit.
3. Determined the desired response in phasor form.
4. Draw a phasor diagram to check and display results.
5. Transform phasors to time functions if required.

◆ Analogous systems are described by similar integrodifferential equations.

Corresponding terms in the equations are analog quantities.

The solution of a problem is applicable to all analogous problems.

◆ Two networks are duals if the set of transforms which converts the first into the second also converts the second into the first.

The loop equations of a planar network have the same form as the node equations of its dual.

The solution of any network automatically provides the solution to its dual.

REVIEW QUESTIONS

1. Define impedance.
2. Given $v = V_m \cos \omega t$ and $i = I_m \cos (\omega t + \phi)$, derive an expression for v/i. Is this an "impedance"? Does v/i look useful?

3. Why could not the current in Fig. 5.1 be established by closing a switch at $t = 0$?

4. Derive the d-c element impedances for R, L, and C from the values of $Z(j\omega)$, letting ω approach zero as a limit. In the s plane where $s = \sigma + j\omega$, what is the geometrical interpretation of letting σ approach zero or letting ω approach zero?

5. In terms of steady-state response to a direct current or voltage, what is the effect of an inductance? Of a capacitance?

6. What is meant by a "long time" after closing a switch?

7. What two major advantages result from representing sinusoids by exponentials?

8. Outline in words the steps taken in arriving at the conclusion that phasor voltage and phasor current are related by a complex impedance.

9. Compare the dimensions of $Z_L(j\omega)$ and $Z_C(j\omega)$ with those of ohms.

10. What is the distinction between a phasor and a complex quantity?

11. Outline in words the reasoning which leads to $\Sigma \mathbf{I} = 0$ into any node.

12. Define admittance, reactance, susceptance, and immittance.

13. A two-terminal circuit consists of a capacitance C in parallel with a series combination of resistance R and inductance L. In the admittance $\mathbf{Y} = G + jB$, is $G = 1/R$? What is the value of G?

14. Starting with element immittances on the complex plane, show the graphical determination of $\mathbf{Y}$ and $\mathbf{Z}$ for the circuit in the preceding question.

15. Sketch a sinusoidal voltage wave $v(t)$ and a current $i(t)$ which *leads* the voltage by 45°. Draw the corresponding phasors. If v and i are the inputs to a two-terminal circuit, is it predominantly capacitive or inductive?

16. Given $\mathbf{I} = 10 \,\underline{/150°}$ and $\mathbf{V} = 200 \,\underline{/-150°}$. Is the associated $\mathbf{Z}$ inductive or capacitive? What is the phase angle ϕ?

17. Draw up a table summarizing the voltage-current phase angle relations for inductive and capacitive reactances and susceptances.

18. Define analog and dual.

19. Describe a hydraulic system and draw its electrical analog.

20. Draw a mechanical dual of the D-M combination in Fig. 5.17. It may help to write the dual equation first.

21. Draw a phasor diagram showing $\mathbf{U}$ and $\mathbf{F}$ of Eq. 5-29.

22. Why is practical heat conduction "always a distributed phenomenon"?

23. Without reference to the text, list 6 electrical quantities or phrases and their duals.

24. Write out the dual of the discussion of the series RL circuit and see how well it describes the circuit of Fig. 5.14.

EXERCISES

1. In Fig. 5.23, $R = 10 \,\Omega$, $L = 3$ H, and $i = 5e^{-2t}$ A.
   (a) Determine v_R and v_L and plot approximately to scale.
   (b) Explain the sign of v_L on a physical (not mathematical) basis.

(c) Combine the results for v_L and v_R to obtain $v(t)$.

(d) Calculate $Z(s)$, determine $v(t)$, and compare to answer (c).

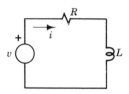

Fig. 5.23

2. Repeat Exercise 1 for $i = 5e^{-4t}$ A.

3. If $R_1 = 5\ \Omega$, $R = 3\ \Omega$, $L = 2$ H, and $C = 0.1$ F in Fig. 5.24, determine the forced voltage v_C in response to a current $i = 6e^{-2t}$ A.

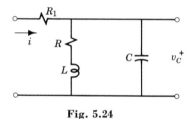

Fig. 5.24

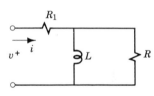

Fig. 5.25

4. In Fig. 5.25, $R_1 = 2\ \Omega$, $R = 4\ \Omega$, and $L = 2$ H.

(a) Calculate sufficient points to plot $Z(s)$ versus s.

(b) What is the response i to a voltage $v = 10e^{st}$ V where $s = -3$? Where $s = -2$? Where $s = -4$?

(c) What is the response $v(t)$ to a current $i = 2e^{-4t}$ A?

(d) What is the impedance of this circuit to direct current?

5. In Fig. 5.24, $R_1 = 5\ \Omega$, $R = 3\ \Omega$, $L = 2$ H, and $C = 0.1$ F. Determine the current i a "long" time after applying a direct voltage $v = 12$ V to the terminals by:

(a) calculating $Z(s)$ and letting s approach 0 as a limit;

(b) modifying the circuit in accordance with the rules in quotation marks on p. 124.

6. In Exercise 5, what is the voltage on C after a "long" time?

7. In Fig. 5.25, $R_1 = 2\ \Omega$, $R = 4\ \Omega$, and $L = 2$ H. By means of a switch and battery (not shown), a direct voltage $v = 12$ V is applied. Determine the current i a "long" time after closing the switch. Explain.

8. In Fig. 5.23, $i = I_m \cos \omega t$. Using basic element and connection equations (and no phasors), derive a literal expression for the steady-state voltage v in terms of the given quantities only. Compare your answer with the result obtained by transforming Eq. 5-9 into a time function incorporating Eq. 5-15.

9. In Fig. 5.26, $i = I_m \cos \omega t$. Using basic element and connection equations (no phasors), derive a literal expression for the steady-state voltage v in terms of the given quantities only. Compare your answer with the result obtained by transforming Eq. 5-8 into a time function.

10. In Fig. 5.26, $R = 10\ \Omega$, $L = 10$ mH, $C = 20\ \mu$F, and $i = 2 \cos (2000t - 30°)$ A.

    (a) Determine phasors $\mathbf{V}_R$, $\mathbf{V}_L$, $\mathbf{V}_C$, and $\mathbf{V}$.

    (b) Show $\mathbf{I}$ and the calculated phasors on a labeled phasor diagram.

    (c) Determine $v(t)$.

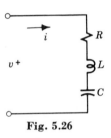

Fig. 5.26

11. In Fig. 5.26, $R = 6\ \Omega$, $L = 10$ mH, $C = 500\ \mu$F, and $v = 120 \cos (1000t + 90°)$ V.

    (a) Determine individual and total impedances, and calculate phasors $\mathbf{I}$, $\mathbf{V}_R$, $\mathbf{V}_L$, and $\mathbf{V}_C$.

    (b) Show calculated quantities on a labeled phasor diagram drawn approximately to scale.

    (c) Determine $i(t)$.

12. In Fig. 5.27, $X_C = 2\ \Omega$, $X_L = 2\ \Omega$, $R = 2\ \Omega$, $\omega = 1000$ rad/sec, and $\mathbf{V}_L = 0 + j20$ V. Calculate and show on a phasor diagram with $\mathbf{V}_L$ the phasors $\mathbf{I}_L$, $\mathbf{V}_R$, $\mathbf{V}_C$, $\mathbf{I}_C$, and $\mathbf{I}$. Determine $i(t)$.

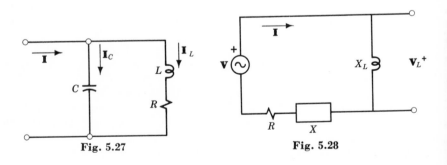

Fig. 5.27   **Fig. 5.28**

13. In Fig. 5.28, the applied voltage $\mathbf{V} = 50\ \underline{/-90°}$ V and $\mathbf{V}_L = 70\ \underline{/53°}$ V across $X_L = 35\ \Omega$. Drawing a phasor diagram as you go along, find R and X. Is X inductive or capacitive?

14. In Fig. 5.28 the applied voltage $\mathbf{V} = 100 \,\underline{/90°}$ V and $\mathbf{I} = 5 \,\underline{/30°}$ A. The magnitude of $\mathbf{V}_L$ is measured to be 40 V. Drawing a phasor diagram as you go along, find R and X. Is X inductive or capacitive?

15. A sinusoidal current with a magnitude of 1 A flows in a series combination of $R = 35$ Ω and an unknown impedance Z. Voltmeter readings indicate a voltage of 75 V across the unknown impedance, and a voltage of 100 V across R and Z together. Find the impedance $\mathbf{Z}$.

16. In Fig. 5.29, $G = 1$ ℧, $B_C = 1$ ℧, and $B_L = 2$ ℧. Devise a series circuit consisting of R and X with the same $\mathbf{V}$-$\mathbf{I}$ characteristics at the terminals.

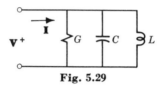

Fig. 5.29

17. In Fig. 5.29, $G = 200$ μ℧, $C = 0.05$ μF, and $L = 0.1$ mH. Devise a series circuit with the same $\mathbf{V}$-$\mathbf{I}$ characteristics at the terminals at $\omega = 10,000$ rad/sec.

18. In Fig. 5.27, it is desired to make $\mathbf{I}_L$ lag behind $\mathbf{I}_C$ by 120°. If $X_C = 20$ Ω and $X_L = 20$ Ω, what should be the value of R?

19. In Fig. 5.30, meter readings give the following magnitudes: $I_G = 8$ A, $V_G = 60$ V, $I_L = 10$ A, $V_L = 50$ V. Assuming $\mathbf{I}_G = 8 \,\underline{/0°}$, draw a phasor diagram consistent with these values and determine $\mathbf{I}_C$ and total $\mathbf{V}$. Show construction lines dotted.

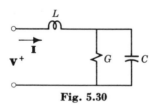

Fig. 5.30

20. In Fig. 5.30, $\mathbf{I}_G = 10 \,\underline{/0°}$ A, $X_L = 20$ Ω, $R = 1/G = 30$ Ω, and $X_C = 10$ Ω.

   (a) Determine $\mathbf{I}_C$, $\mathbf{I}$, $\mathbf{V}_G$, $\mathbf{V}_L$, and $\mathbf{V}$ and show all voltages and currents on a phasor diagram.

   (b) Calculate the input impedance $\mathbf{Z}$ (at the terminals) and compare with $\mathbf{V}/\mathbf{I}$ from part (a).

21. In Fig. 5.28, X consists of a 500 pF capacitance, $L = 2$ mH, and $R = 50$ Ω. Find the frequency ω at which the voltage $\mathbf{V}$ and current $\mathbf{I}$ are (a) in phase, (b) 45° out of phase.

22. In Fig. 5.31, $G = 0.02$ ℧, $B_C = 0.02$ ℧, $R = 30$ Ω, and $X_L = 40$ Ω.

   (a) Calculate the total admittance $\mathbf{Y}$.

   (b) Determine the current $\mathbf{I}$ for $\mathbf{V} = 120 \,\underline{/30°}$ V.

(c) Determine the real and imaginary parts of the input impedance **Z** (at the terminals).

23. In Fig. 5.31, $G = 0.01$ ℧, $R = 30\,\Omega$, and $X_L = 40\,\Omega$. Determine the value of B_C to make the input impedance Z a pure resistance.

24. In Fig. 5.31, $G = 1$ m℧, $C = 1\,\mu$F, $R = 1$ kΩ and $L = 0.5$ H. A voltage $v = 50 \cos 2000t$ V is applied.
   (a) Calculate the input admittance and the input current $i(t)$.
   (b) Calculate the voltages $v(t)$ across R and L.
   (c) Show all currents on a labeled phasor diagram.

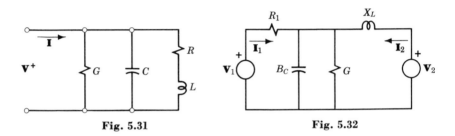

Fig. 5.31   Fig. 5.32

25. A load consisting of $G = 0.04$ ℧ in parallel with $B_C = 0.03$ ℧ (Fig. 5.32) is fed by two voltage sources $V_1 = 180\;\underline{/0°}$ V and $V_2 = 76\;\underline{/0°}$ V. If $R_1 = 5\,\Omega$ and $X_L = 2\,\Omega$, calculate I_1 and I_2.

26. A combination of spring $(f_K = x/K)$ and dashpot $(f_D = Du)$ is shown in Fig. 5.33.
   (a) Write the equation of motion under an applied force f.
   (b) Write an analogous equation for an electrical circuit and draw the circuit.
   (c) Write an analogous equation for a different electrical circuit and draw the circuit.

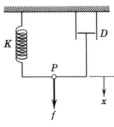

Fig. 5.33

27. (a) For the spring-dashpot combination of Exercise 26, derive an expression for motional impedance Z_m.

(b) Determine the displacement x for a steady pull $f = F$, reasoning by analogy.

(c) Determine the displacement x for a pull $f = F_m \cos \omega t$.

(d) Determine the force f required to impart a velocity $u = U_m \cos \omega t$ to the point P.

28. A disk of inertia J and radius r (Fig. 5.34) is supported by an elastic shaft ($\tau_s = \theta/K$) and damped by a friction brake ($F_b = D\, d\theta/dt$). Apply d'Alembert's principle and write the equation of motion under an applied torque τ. Draw up a table similar to Fig. 5.18, showing analog relations between mechanical translation, mechanical rotation, and series electrical circuits.

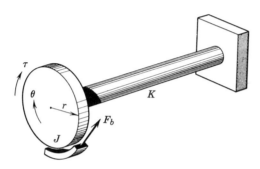

Fig. 5.34

29. A metal sphere of thermal capacity C_p is surrounded by a uniform insulating layer of thermal resistance R_τ (Fig. 5.35).

(a) Express the fact that the rate of thermal energy absorption by the object must be equal to the rate of heat flow through the resistance and derive the equation governing temperature τ_2.

(b) For an external temperature variation $\tau_1 = \tau_m \cos \omega t$, determine the internal temperature τ_2.

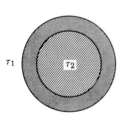

Fig. 5.35

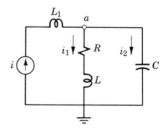

Fig. 5.36

30. For the circuit in Fig. 5.36,

(a) Write the governing equations.

(b) Construct the dual circuit.

(c) Write the governing equations of the dual.

31. Repeat Exercise 30 for the circuit of Fig. 5.37.

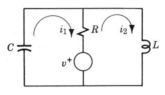

Fig. 5.37

PROBLEMS

1. In deriving Eq. 5-9, use was made of the relation

$$(d/dt) \text{ Re } \{\mathbf{W}\} = \text{Re } \{d\mathbf{W}/dt\}$$

Recalling that differentiation is basically a process of division, demonstrate the validity of this relation.

2. A circuit consisting of R and L in parallel (Fig. 5.38) is to be replaced by a series circuit which is "equivalent" at angular frequency ω. Define "equivalent" and evaluate R_s and L_s.

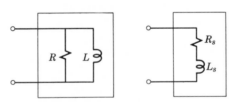

Fig. 5.38

3. In a series RLC circuit, $R = 100 \, \Omega$, $L = 2.5 \, \text{mH}$, and $C = 100 \, \text{pF}$. Calculate and plot a graph of the magnitude of Z versus ω with ω on a logarithmic scale. Be sure to include any interesting region of ω.

4. In Fig. 5.29, $G = 200 \, \mu\mho$ and $C = 0.05 \, \mu\text{F}$. With a certain value of L, the parallel circuit can be replaced at $\omega = 20,000 \, \text{rad/sec}$ by a resistance R. Find L and R. Draw a phasor diagram that shows $\mathbf{Y}$, $\mathbf{I}$, $\mathbf{I}_G$, $\mathbf{I}_C$, and $\mathbf{I}_L$ for this condition.

5. A certain piece of electronic equipment works best when it "sees" a pure resistance load of $600 \, \Omega$. The load resistance available is $1000 \, \Omega$. An engineer suggests the coupling circuit of Fig. 5.39 where $R = 1000 \, \Omega$. Design the

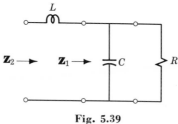

Fig. 5.39

coupling circuit by first finding the value of C to make $\mathbf{Z}_1 = 600 + jX_1$ Ω and then finding the proper value of L to make $\mathbf{Z}_2 = 600 + j0$ Ω for $f = 10^3$ cps.

6. An unheated house has an effective overall thermal resistance

$$R_r = 0.001°\text{F-hr/Btu.}$$

The effective overall thermal capacitance of the contents of the house is $C_p = 6000$ Btu/°F. The outside temperature varies from 100°F at 2 P.M. to 50°F at 2 A.M. Making and stating any necessary assumptions, predict the minimum temperature of the interior and the time at which it will occur.

- ◆ **GENERAL PROCEDURE**
- ◆ **FIRST-ORDER CIRCUITS**
- ◆ **SECOND-ORDER CIRCUITS**
- ◆ **IMPULSE RESPONSE**

CHAPTER **6**

Complete Response

The natural response of a circuit is due to energy stored in inductances or capacitances. Working from the differential equation, we developed a method of using the poles and zeros of the impedance function to indicate the character of the natural response. The forced response is produced by external energy sources such as batteries or generators. Expanding the impedance concept, we then used exponential representation to reduce integrodifferential equations to algebraic equations, and finding the forced response was reduced to a routine procedure.

In our previous work only one of these responses was considered at a time. In determining natural response (Fig. 6.1a), we assumed energy had been stored by an external source and then that source was removed. In determining forced response (Fig. 6.1b), we assumed that a sufficient time had elapsed so that all natural response components had died away,

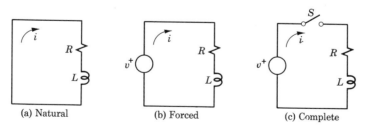

(a) Natural   (b) Forced   (c) Complete

Fig. 6.1   Circuit response.

or at least had become negligibly small. In general, however, there is a transient period during which behavior is not so simple; to determine the current which flows after switch S in Fig. 6.1c is closed we must determine the *complete response*.

Components of the Complete Response

Considering the problem from an energy viewpoint, we note that the natural response tends to decay exponentially as the stored energy is dissipated. The forced response continues indefinitely because energy is supplied to make up any losses. Since we are interested in the transient period in which both effects are present, we conclude that the complete response is some combination of natural and forced response.

To provide a firm basis for analysis we write the differential equation, using the element equations and the connection equation. Assuming a linear circuit and a sinusoidal forcing function, at all times after closing the switch,

$$L \frac{di}{dt} + Ri = V_m \cos \omega t \tag{6-1}$$

Any expression which satisfies this equation is a solution of the equation; one such solution is

$$i_f = I_m \cos (\omega t + \phi) \tag{6-2}$$

where i_f is the forced response current. For the related homogeneous equation

$$L \frac{di}{dt} + Ri = 0 \tag{6-3}$$

a solution is

$$i_n = I_n e^{-(R/L)t} \tag{6-4}$$

But if the value of i_n from Eq. 6-4 makes the left-hand side of Eq. 6-1 just equal to zero, then

$$i = i_f + i_n = I_m \cos (\omega t + \phi) + I_n e^{-(R/L)t} \tag{6-5}$$

must also be a solution of Eq. 6-1. We conclude that the complete response is the *sum* of the forced and natural response.†

Having reached this conclusion, we are in the fortunate position of being able to solve a new group of problems without developing any new

---

† Mathematicians call these the *particular* solution and the *complementary* solution, respectively. These two components can be added only if the circuit is linear; see p. 242.

theory. The techniques of finding forced and natural response can be applied directly to finding the complete response of a variety of circuits with a variety of driving functions or *excitations*.

In this group are some very practical and important engineering problems. In the design of some systems, the transient behavior is the critical factor; for example, whether the control system of a supersonic aircraft is satisfactory may depend upon its ability to respond smoothly to a sudden disturbance. In other systems, only the transient behavior has any significance; as an illustration, a radar system must generate, transmit, receive, and interpret sharp pulses of energy which never reach a steady state. The plan of this chapter is first to develop a general procedure, then to apply it to some first-order circuits with d-c and sinusoidal driving functions, and then to consider the complete response of circuits with more than one energy-storage element.

A GENERAL PROCEDURE

Our general procedure consists of finding the forced and natural response components and then combining them properly. What are the essential characteristics of each component and how are they determined?

Characteristics of the Components

Each component has a distinctive *form* to be discovered and an *amplitude* to be determined. For any exponential excitation, the form of the forced response is the same as the form of the forcing function; a direct voltage causes a direct current and a sinusoidal current produces a sinusoidal voltage. The amplitude of the forced response is determined by the magnitude of the forcing function and the impedance of the circuit; for direct currents the impedance of interest is $Z(0)$, for sinusoids $Z(j\omega)$.†

The form of the natural response is governed by the circuit itself. Basically, the form is obtained from the homogeneous differential equation, but our approach is to use the poles and zeros of an immittance function to identify the natural components of voltage and current. The amplitude of the natural response is determined from energy considerations. From this viewpoint, the amplitude is just that required to pro-

---

† Exponential forcing functions are not common in practical problems and they are not discussed in detail here.

vide for the difference between the initial energy storage (in L and C) and that indicated by the forcing function. This idea will become more clear when applied to specific examples.

The General Procedure

The complete response of any linear two-terminal circuit to exponentials is obtained as follows:

1. *Write the appropriate impedance or admittance function.* The function $Z(s)$ or $Y(s)$ carries all the information of the integrodifferential equation based on element and connection equations. Choose the terminals across which the desired voltage appears or into which the desired current flows.

2. *Determine the forced response from the forcing function and the proper immittance.* The form of the forcing function indicates the value of s in $Z(s)$ or $Y(s)$ and the approach used in determining the forced response. For direct currents, apply Ohm's law and $V = RI$. For sinusoids, use phasor methods and $\mathbf{V} = \mathbf{ZI}$.

3. *Identify the natural components from poles or zeros of $Z(s)$ or $Y(s)$.* Working with impedance, for example, use the poles to obtain possible components of natural response voltage and the zeros to obtain possible current components. Write these components with undetermined amplitudes.

4. *Add the forced and natural responses and evaluate the undetermined constants.* Obtain the necessary information from initial conditions. From energy considerations we know that inductance currents and capacitance voltages cannot change instantaneously; the energy distribution just after a switch is closed, for example, must be the same as just before the switch was closed.

FIRST-ORDER CIRCUITS

The general procedure is outlined in electrical terms and the emphasis in the following examples is primarily on electric circuits. It should be apparent, however, that the method is applicable to nonelectrical problems as well. The step function which is produced by closing an electrical switch is analogous to suddenly opening a valve, applying a force, or igniting a flame; the complete responses of hydraulic, mechanical, and thermal circuits are similar to those of electric circuits.

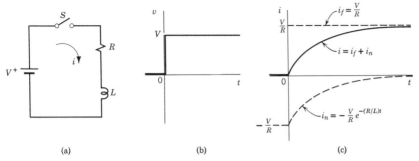

Fig. 6.2 RL circuit with step voltage applied.

Step Response of an *RL* Circuit

Closing switch S in Fig. 6.2 at time $t = 0$ results in the application of a step voltage of magnitude V to the series combination of resistance R and inductance L.   To obtain the complete response current i during the transient period we follow the procedure outlined.

1. *Write the impedance function.*
   For this series circuit, $Z(s) = R + sL$.
2. *Determine the forced response.*
   For a direct voltage source, $s = 0$ and $Z(0) = R$.
   Then $i_f = V/R$ is the forced response.
3. *Identify the natural components.*
   Setting $Z(s) = 0$, $s = -R/L$.
   ·Therefore, $i_n = Ae^{-(R/L)t}$ is a possible natural response.
4. *Evaluate the undetermined constants.*
   In general, $i = i_f + i_n = V/R + Ae^{-(R/L)t}$.   Just *before* closing the switch the current in the inductance was zero; therefore, just *after* closing the switch the current must still be zero.   (We call this time $t = 0^+$.)   At $t = 0^+$

$$i = I_0 = 0 = \frac{V}{R} + Ae^{-(R/L)(0)} = \frac{V}{R} + Ae^0 = \frac{V}{R} + A$$

Therefore, $A = 0 - V/R = -V/R$ and

$$i = i_f + i_n = \frac{V}{R} - \frac{V}{R}\,e^{-(R/L)t} \text{ is the complete response} \qquad (6\text{-}6)$$

Forced, natural, and complete responses are plotted in Fig. 6.2c.   The forced response, a current step, has the same form as the forcing function, a voltage step.   The natural response is a decaying exponential; the sign is negative because the actual initial energy storage is less than that called for by the forcing function. The complete response current is a continuous function as are all inductance currents. The initial slope di/dt can be obtained from the differential equation

$$L \frac{di}{dt} + Ri = V$$

by noting that at $t = 0^+$, $i = 0$, $Ri = 0$, and

$$\frac{di}{dt} = \frac{V - Ri}{L} = \frac{V}{L}$$

As the current increases, Ri increases and the slope decreases. After several time constants, Ri approaches V and di/dt approaches zero, or the current approaches the steady-state value V/R.

EXAMPLE 1

In Fig. 6.3a, switch S_1 is open and S_2 is closed. At $t = 0$, switch S_1 is closed and a short time later at $t = t'$ switch S_2 is opened. Determine and plot $i(t)$ for the transient period.

SOLUTION. Since natural response is initiated at two different times, the problem will be solved in two parts following the four-step procedure.

For $0 < t < t'$,

1. The impedance function is $Z(s) = R + sL$.
2. The forced response is $i_f = V/R$.
3. The natural response is $i_n = Ae^{-(R/L)t}$.
4. The complete response is $i = i_f + i_n = V/R + Ae^{-(R/L)t}$.
   At $t = 0^+$

$$i = 0 = \frac{V}{R} + A \qquad \therefore \quad A = -\frac{V}{R}$$

and

$$i = \frac{V}{R} - \frac{V}{R} e^{-(R/L)t} \tag{6-7}$$

as shown in Fig. 6.3b.

For $t' < t < \infty$,

1. The impedance function is $Z'(s) = R + R' + sL$.
2. The forced response is $i_f' = V/(R + R')$.
3. The natural response is $i_n' = A'e^{-[(R+R')/L](t-t')}$.
4. The complete response is

$$i' = i_f' + i_n' = \frac{V}{R + R'} + A'e^{-[(R+R')/L](t-t')} \tag{6-8}$$

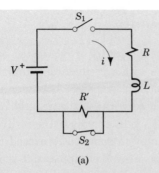

(a)

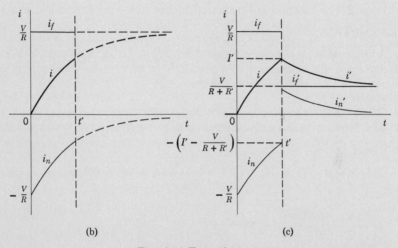

(b)   (c)

Fig. 6.3 Example 1.

At $t = t'$ just *before* opening switch S_2, by Eq. 6-7

$$i = \frac{V}{R} (1 - e^{-(R/L)t'}) = I'$$

At $t = t'^+$ just *after* opening S_2, the current must be the same; by Eq. 6-8,

$$i' = I' = \frac{V}{R + R'} + A'e^0 \qquad \therefore \quad A' = I' - \frac{V}{R + R'}$$

When this value is substituted in Eq. 6-8

$$i' = \frac{V}{R + R'} + \left(I' - \frac{V}{R + R'}\right) e^{-[(R+R')/L](t-t')} \qquad (6\text{-}9)$$

This response is plotted in Fig. 6.3c, assuming $R' \cong R$ and $t' \cong L/R$, one time constant. Note that the amplitude of the natural response in each case is determined by the difference between the actual current and the current called for by the forcing function.

A-C Switching Transients

A long time after an a-c source is connected to a circuit, the current reaches the steady state with a predictable amplitude and phase relation. In a practical situation, the transient behavior just after the switch is closed cannot be predicted because the natural response depends on the particular point in the cycle. at which the switch is closed.   Since the "switching transient" may in some cases exceed the rating of the generator and associated transmission equipment, it is essential that the power engineer be able to predict the response under the worst possible conditions.   The method is illustrated in the following numerical example.

EXAMPLE 2

A load consisting of a series combination of $R = 5\,\Omega$ and $C = 306\,\mu\text{F}$ (Fig. 6.4) is connected to a voltage $v = 6000\cos 377t$ V at time $t = 0$.   Find current i as a function of time after closing the switch.

SOLUTION.

1. The impedance function is $Z(s) = R + 1/sC$.
2. The forced response is determined for $Z(j\omega) = R - j1/\omega C$

   Hence

   $$\mathbf{Z} = 5 - j1/377 \times 306 \times 10^{-6} = 5 - j8.66 = 10\ \underline{/-60°}\ \Omega$$

   and

   $$\mathbf{I}_f = \frac{\mathbf{V}}{\mathbf{Z}} = \frac{6000\ \underline{/0°}}{10\ \underline{/-60°}} = 600\ \underline{/+60°}\ \text{A}$$

   $$i_f = 600\cos(377t + 60°)\ \text{A}$$

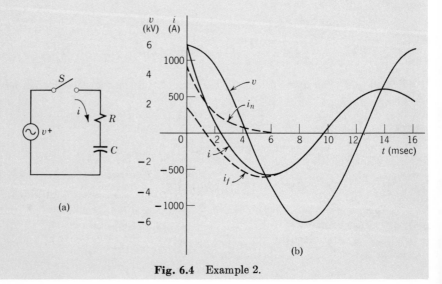

Fig. 6.4   Example 2.

3. The natural response is $i_n = Ae^{-t/RC}$
4. The complete response is $i = i_f + i_n$ as before. However, there is no requirement of continuity of current in a capacitance. Instead, we make use of the
   fact that voltage on a capacitance cannot suddenly change. Assuming that
   the capacitance is initially uncharged (the practical case), at $t = 0^+$ the
   voltage $v_C = 0$ and the full applied voltage appears across R. At $t = 0^+$,

$$i = \frac{V}{R} = \frac{6000 \cos 0}{5} = 1200 \text{ A} = i_f + i_n = 600 \cos 60° + Ae^0$$

Therefore,
$$A = 1200 - 300 = 900 \text{ A}$$

The complete response is

$$i = 600 \cos (377t + 60°) + 900e^{-654t} \text{ A}$$

as plotted in Fig. 6.4b.

Note that in Example 2 the initial current is twice the peak current
reached under steady-state conditions. Is this the worst possible condition? Since the initial current is proportional to the initial voltage
$(i = v/R)$, the largest current will flow if the switch is closed at a voltage
maximum as in the Example. Is there a point during the cycle at which
the switch could be closed with no natural response component? If so,
can you find it?

Series-Parallel Circuits

The step response of the parallel circuit of Fig. 6.5 can be obtained by
applying the principle of duality to the result for the circuit of Fig. 6.2.
By inspection of Eq. 6-6 and reference to Figs. 5.19 and 20, we write

$$v = IR - IRe^{-t/RC} \qquad (6\text{-}10)$$

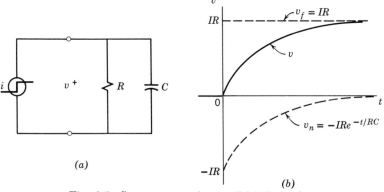

(a)

(b)

Fig. 6.5 Step response of a parallel RC circuit.

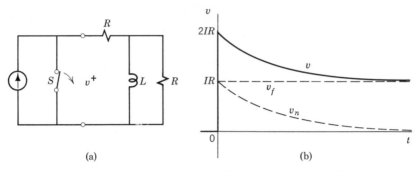

Fig. 6.6 Step response of a series-parallel circuit.

and we have received another dividend from our investment of time and effort in a general principle.

The circuit of Fig. 6.6 contains another element, and the differential equation approach would be more complicated than for a simple series or parallel circuit. Our impedance approach, however, handles such problems easily.

EXAMPLE 3

The step current in Fig. 6.6 is obtained from a d-c source of amplitude I initially shorted by switch S. At $t = 0$, the switch is opened. Predict the voltage v as a function of time.

SOLUTION.

1. The impedance function is

$$Z(s) = R + \frac{R(sL)}{R + sL} = \frac{R^2 + RsL + RsL}{R + sL} = \frac{R^2 + 2RsL}{R + sL}$$

2. The forced response is

$$v_f = IZ(0) = I\frac{R^2}{R} = IR$$

3. The natural response voltage is indicated by the pole of the impedance function. $Z(s) = \infty$ for $R + sL = 0$; therefore, $s = -R/L$ and

$$v_n = Ae^{-(R/L)t}$$

4. The complete response is $v = v_f + v_n = IR + Ae^{-(R/L)t}$. If switch S has been closed a long time, $i_L = 0$. Just after opening the switch, $i_L = 0$ and all the current flows through R and R in series. At $t = 0^+$,

$$v = I(2R) = v_f + v_n = IR + Ae^0$$

Solving,

$$A = IR \quad \text{and} \quad v = IR + IRe^{-(R/L)t}$$

as shown in Fig. 6.6b.

SECOND-ORDER CIRCUITS

For a circuit with two different energy-storage elements, the governing differential equation is of the second order. The characteristic equation has two roots or, in other words, the impedance function has two zeros and two poles (one may be at infinity). Working from either interpretation, we conclude that the natural response contains two components and that there are two arbitrary coefficients to be determined. The general procedure for finding the complete response is applicable, although the determination of the constants from initial conditions may be difficult.

Step Response of *RLC* Series Circuit

As an illustration of the approach to solving second-order circuits, consider the case of a voltage step applied to a series combination of *RLC* (Fig. 6.7). In the typical case, C is initially uncharged and L carries no initial current. The step is obtained from a voltage source V suddenly connected by means of switch S at time $t = 0$. The problem is to find the complete response current i as a function of time. The impedance function is $Z(s) = R + sL + 1/sC$ (step 1) and the forced response is $i_f = V/Z(0) = V/\infty = 0$ (step 2). The natural components (step 3) are obtained by setting $Z(s) = 0$. For

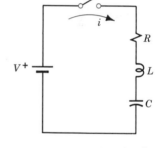

Fig. 6.7 *RLC* series circuit with voltage step applied.

$$s^2L + sR + \frac{1}{C} = 0 \qquad (6\text{-}11)$$

the roots are

$$s = -\frac{R}{2L} \pm \sqrt{\frac{R^2}{4L^2} - \frac{1}{LC}} = -\alpha \pm j\omega \qquad (6\text{-}12)$$

using the nomenclature of Chapter 4. For roots real and distinct (Eq. 4-12),

$$i_n = A_1 e^{s_1 t} + A_2 e^{s_2 t} \qquad (6\text{-}13)$$

For roots real and equal (Eq. 4-18),

$$i_n = A_1 e^{st} + A_2 t e^{st} \qquad (6\text{-}14)$$

For roots complex (Eqs. 4-15, 4-16),

$$i_n = e^{-\alpha t}(B_1 \cos \omega t + B_2 \sin \omega t) \qquad (6\text{-}15)$$

or

$$i_n = A e^{-\alpha t} \sin(\omega t + \theta) \qquad (6\text{-}16)$$

For any case, there are two constants to be determined from initial conditions (step 4). Assuming i_L is initially zero, at $t = 0^+$,

$$i = i_f + i_n = 0 \qquad (6\text{-}17)$$

Assuming v_C is initially zero, at $t = 0^+$, $v_C = 0$ and $v_R = Ri = 0$, and therefore the full applied voltage appears across L or

$$L\frac{di}{dt} = V \quad \text{and} \quad \frac{di}{dt} = \frac{V}{L} \qquad (6\text{-}18)$$

Equations 6-17 and 6-18 provide two conditions for evaluating the constants.

For illustration, consider the case of roots real and distinct. From Eq. 6-13, in general

$$\frac{di}{dt} = s_1 A_1 e^{s_1 t} + s_2 A_2 e^{s_2 t}$$

At $t = 0^+$,

$$\frac{di}{dt} = s_1 A_1 + s_2 A_2 = \frac{V}{L} \qquad (6\text{-}19)$$

and

$$i = i_n = A_1 + A_2 = 0 \qquad (6\text{-}20)$$

Constants A_1 and A_2 are obtained by solving Eqs. 6-19 and 6-20 simultaneously. The slightly different approach when roots are complex is illustrated in the following numerical example.

EXAMPLE 4

In the RLC series circuit of Fig. 6.8 with $V = 70$ V, $R = 4\ \Omega$, $L = 2$ H, and $C = 0.01$ F, there is no initial energy storage. Find and plot the complete response current.

SOLUTION. Following the general procedure (the steps should be familiar by now), $Z(s) = R + sL + 1/sC = 4 + 2s + 100/s$.

$Z(0) = \infty$; therefore, $i_f = 0$.

Setting $Z(s) = 0$, $s = -1 \pm j7$ are the two roots. For roots complex (Eq. 6-16),

$$i_n = A e^{-t} \sin(7t + \theta) \qquad (6\text{-}21)$$

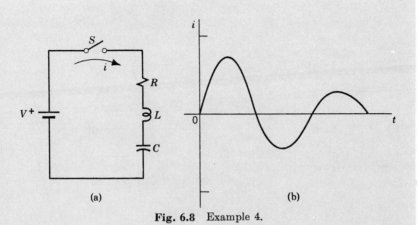

Fig. 6.8 Example 4.

From Eq. 6-17 at $t = 0^+$,

$$i = i_n = 0 = Ae^0 \sin (0 + \theta) \qquad \therefore \quad \theta = 0$$

From Eq. 6-21,

$$\frac{di}{dt} = -Ae^{-t} \sin 7t + 7Ae^{-t} \cos 7t$$

From Eq. 6-18 at $t = 0^+$,

$$\frac{di}{dt} = \frac{V}{L} = \frac{70}{2} = -A(0) + 7A \qquad \therefore \quad A = 5$$

Therefore,

$$i = 5e^{-t} \sin 7t \text{ A} \tag{6-22}$$

The damping coefficient α indicates a time constant of 1 sec and the frequency is 7 rad/sec or 1.1 cycles/sec (see Fig. 6.8b).

A-C Switching Transients

The sudden application of a sinusoidal forcing function to a series-parallel circuit containing two different energy-storage elements represents the most general case of complete response to be treated in this book. While no new principles are involved, the following example is instructive as an illustration of the techniques employed.

EXAMPLE 5

In the circuit of Fig. 6.9a, a current $i = 8.5 \cos 4t$ A is applied to the parallel combination by opening switch S at time $t = 0$. Given that $C = \frac{1}{17}$ F, $R = 2\ \Omega$, and $L = 1$ H, find and plot voltage v as a function of time.

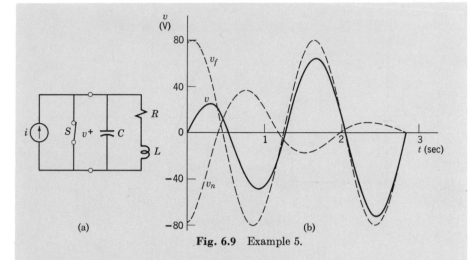

Fig. 6.9 Example 5.

SOLUTION. Following the same general procedure,

$$Y(s) = sC + \frac{1}{R + sL} = \frac{s^2LC + sRC + 1}{R + sL}$$

$$Y(j\omega) = j\omega C + \frac{1}{R + j\omega L} = j\frac{4}{17} + \frac{1}{2 + j4 \times 1}$$

$$= 0.1 + j0.035 = 0.106 \underline{/19.5°} \, \mho$$

$$\mathbf{V}_f = \frac{\mathbf{I}}{\mathbf{Y}} = \frac{8.5 \underline{/0°}}{0.106 \underline{/19.5°}} = 80 \underline{/-19.5°} \, V$$

For $Y(s) = 0$, $LCs^2 + RCs + 1 = 0$ and

$$s = -\frac{R}{2L} \pm \sqrt{\frac{R^2}{4L^2} - \frac{1}{LC}} = -1 \pm \sqrt{1 - 17} = -1 \pm j4$$

Therefore,

$$v_n = Ae^{-t} \cos (4t + \theta)$$

and

$$v = v_f + v_n = 80 \cos (4t - 19.5°) + Ae^{-t} \cos (4t + \theta).$$

At $t = 0^+$, $v_C = v = 0$ or

$$v = 0 = 80 \cos (-19.5°) + A \cos \theta \quad \therefore \quad A \cos \theta = -75.5$$

Also, at $t = 0^+$, $i_L = 0$; therefore, all the current flows in C and

$$\frac{dv}{dt} = \frac{I_m}{C} = -320 \sin (0 - 19.5°) - Ae^0 \cos \theta - 4Ae^0 \sin \theta$$

Substituting the value for $A \cos \theta$ and solving, $A \sin \theta = 9.4$. Then

$$\frac{A \sin \theta}{A \cos \theta} = -\frac{9.4}{75.5} \quad \therefore \quad \theta = \arctan -\frac{9.4}{75.5} = -7.1°$$

and

$$A = \frac{A \cos \theta}{\cos \theta} = \frac{-75.5}{\cos (-7.1°)} = -76$$

Therefore, the complete response is

$$v = 80 \cos (4t - 19.5°) - 76e^{-t} \cos (4t - 7.1°)\text{V}$$

as plotted in Fig. 6.9b. Note that the frequency of the source was selected to be equal to the frequency of the natural response. Under these conditions the voltage oscillations build up from zero and reach their steady-state values in a few cycles.

IMPULSE RESPONSE

It is appropriate at this point to introduce an abstract concept which is of minor importance in a first course but of great importance in advanced courses. The mechanical analog of this electrical effect is the familiar hammer blow on a mass, giving the mass momentum. Because the analog is well understood, because all the necessary electrical foundation has been laid, and because this discussion rounds out the treatment of complete response it is included here. However, mastery of this concept is not essential to study of the material in this book and this section may be omitted.

Pulse Response

An interesting conclusion from Example 4 is that a step voltage can produce a damped sinusoidal response in an RLC circuit. In an analogous way the sudden lateral displacement of a guitar string can produce vibrations which die away exponentially. More commonly the string is rapidly displaced and released or "plucked." The corresponding electrical forcing function is the *pulse*.

As shown in Fig. 6.10, a pulse can be generated by the combination of a positive step and, a short time later, a negative step. This representation is useful because we are familiar with step responses. This is a *rectangular pulse* with an amplitude V and a duration t'.

The response of the RC circuit (Fig. 6.11) to such a forcing function is obtained as the response to two voltage steps. There is no forced response because $Z_C(0) = \infty$ and the complete response to the first step is

$$i = i_n = \frac{V}{R} e^{-t/RC} \qquad 0 < t < t' \qquad (6\text{-}23)$$

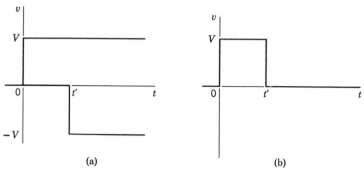

Fig. 6.10 Rectangular pulse formed from two steps.

Assuming the capacitor is initially uncharged, the capacitance voltage at time t is

$$v_C = \frac{1}{C} \int_0^t i \, dt = \frac{1}{C} \int_0^t \frac{V}{R} e^{-t/RC} \, dt = \frac{1}{C} \frac{V}{R} \left. (-RC) e^{-t/RC} \right]_0^t$$

$$= \left. -V e^{-t/RC} \right]_0^t = V(1 - e^{-t/T}) \qquad (6\text{-}24)$$

where $T = RC$ is the time constant.

If a negative step is applied at $t = t'$, the current response has the *form* of Eq. 6-23. Since the capacitance voltage cannot suddenly change, at $t = t'^+$, $v_C = V_C'$ as evaluated from Eq. 6-24 and shown in Fig. 6.11b.

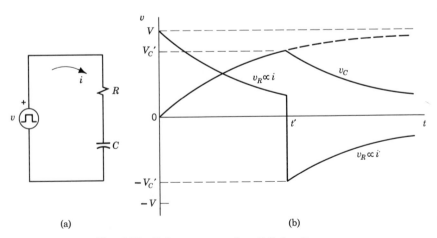

Fig. 6.11 Pulse response of an RC circuit.

The current reverses as the capacitance discharges and

$$i' = i_n' = \frac{V_C'}{R} e^{-(t-t')/RC} \qquad t' < t < \infty \tag{6-25}$$

Since i is proportional to v_R at all times, a separate current curve is not shown.

The Impulse Function

The effect of the pulse in Fig. 6.11 is to charge the capacitor, and the pulse response is an exponential discharge current. The amount of charge stored is dependent upon the amplitude of the pulse V and the duration T_p. The product VT_p is the area of the voltage-time curve and is a significant characteristic of the pulse; the same charge can be stored by a shorter pulse with a greater amplitude.

The effect of varying the pulse dimensions while keeping the area constant is shown in Fig. 6.12. If a steady current $I_0 = V_0/R$ flowed for time $T_p = 0.2T$, the charge stored would be

$$Q_0 = I_0 T_p = \frac{V_0}{R} T_p = \frac{V_0 T_p}{T/C} = \frac{V_0(0.2T)C}{T} = 0.2CV_0 \tag{6-26}$$

Actually, by Eq. 6-24,

$$Q = CV_c = CV_0(1 - e^{-0.2}) = 0.181CV_0 = 0.905Q_0$$

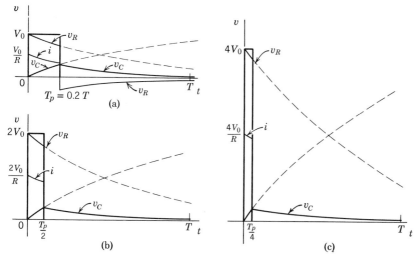

Fig. 6.12   Effect of varying pulse dimensions.

For a duration $T_p/2$ and amplitude $2V_0$ (same area),

$$Q = CV_c = C2V_0(1 - e^{-0.1}) = 0.19CV_0 = 0.95Q_0$$

For a duration $T_p/4$ and amplitude $4V_0$,

$$Q = CV_c = C4V_0(1 - e^{-0.05}) = 0.196CV_0 = 0.98Q_0$$

From these calculations we conclude that as the pulse becomes shorter the actual charge stored approaches the charge stored by a rectangular current pulse I_0T_p. The limiting case of a pulse of area I_0T_p is the *impulse*, a pulse of infinite amplitude for an infinitesimal time but with a finite magnitude. The magnitude of a current impulse is $M_p = \int i\,dt$ and the form of $i(t)$ is not important; in fact, in many problems the exact shape of $i(t)$ is not known, but the response to such an impulse can be determined precisely.

Impulse Response

Three analogous expressions for impulses are:

$$\int f\,dt = Mu \qquad \int i\,dt = Cv \qquad \int v\,dt = Li \qquad (6\text{-}27)$$

In each case it is assumed that initially the element is at "rest" with no initial velocity, charge, or current. The effect of a force impulse on a mass is to impart momentum. What is the effect of a current impulse on a capacitance? What is the effect of a voltage impulse on an inductance? Since there is no forced response to an impulse (Why not?), the complete response is the natural response of the circuit with stored energy.

EXAMPLE 6

The series RL circuit of Fig. 6.13a is "hit" by a voltage impulse of M_p volt-seconds at time $t = 0$. Determine the current response $i(t)$.

SOLUTION. The convention for designating an impulse is a vertical arrow drawn at the appropriate instant, as in Fig. 6.13b; the length of the arrow is not significant since the amplitude of all impulses is infinite. (Note the distinction between the amplitude of the function and the magnitude of the impulse.)

The effect of a voltage impulse is to establish a finite current in L. What fraction of the voltage impulse $v(t)$ appears across L? Since i is finite, $Ri = v_R$ is finite, whereas $v(t)$ is infinite; therefore practically all the voltage impulse appears across L. By Eq. 6-27,

$$I = \frac{1}{L}\int v\,dt = \frac{M_p}{L} = I_0$$

The impulse response is then the natural response consisting of the exponential decay of the initial current I_0, or

$$i = i_n = I_0 e^{-(R/L)t} = \frac{M_p}{L}e^{-(R/L)t} \qquad (6\text{-}28)$$

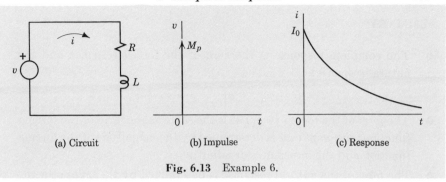

(a) Circuit   (b) Impulse   (c) Response

Fig. 6.13 Example 6.

Practical Impulses

The impulse concept can be used to provide initial energy storage without the use of switches; in general network analysis this is advantageous.† Also, in the analysis of ideal circuits impulses occur as part of the complete response; suddenly connecting an ideal current source to an ideal inductor produces an impulse of voltage. Note that the derivative of a step function is an impulse.

Of more practical significance is the fact that pulses approximating impulses occur in many actual circuits. Sometimes such pulses are unavoidable, as in the case of suddenly applying a voltage generator to a capacitive circuit (see Example 2 in this chapter). Another example is the charge built up on a power transmission line during an electric storm which, when released by a lightning stroke, produces an intense voltage pulse which may destroy the insulation of transformers on the line. In other apparatus, pulses serve valuable functions; a sharp timing pulse is used to trigger the sweep of the electron beam across the screen of a television receiver. If the duration of any pulse is sufficiently short, it can be treated as an impulse by using the approach outlined here.

---

† Another use of impulse functions is in the so-called "operational method" of circuit analysis which is closely related to the Laplace transform method used in more advanced books. See footnote p. 725.

SUMMARY

◆ The complete response is the sum of the forced response and the natural response:

$$i = i_f + i_n \quad \text{or} \quad v = v_f + v_n$$

◆ The *form* of the forced response is the same as the form of the forcing function; the *amplitude* is determined by the magnitude of the forcing function and the impedance or admittance.

◆ The *form* of the natural response is determined by the poles or zeros of the impedance or admittance function; the *amplitude* is determined by the difference between the initial energy storage and that indicated by the forcing function.

◆ The general procedure for finding complete response is:
   1. Write the appropriate impedance or admittance function.
   2. Determine the forced response from the forcing function and the proper immittance.
   3. Identify the natural components from poles and zeros of $Z(s)$ or $Y(s)$.
   4. Add the forced and natural responses and evaluate the undetermined constants from initial conditions.

◆ In determining constants from initial conditions, make use of continuity of current in an inductance and voltage across a capacitance. In second-order circuits, make use of the expressions:

$$\frac{di}{dt} = \frac{v}{L} \quad \text{and} \quad \frac{dv}{dt} = \frac{i}{C}$$

◆ A rectangular pulse can be generated by the combination of a positive step and, a short time later, a negative step.

◆ An impulse is the limiting case of a pulse of area M_p, amplitude M_p/T_p, and duration T_p as T_p approaches zero.
   For a current impulse, the magnitude $M_p = \int i\, dt = Cv$.
   For a voltage impulse, the magnitude $M_p = \int v\, dt = Li$.

◆ The effect of an impulse is to store energy in an energy-storage element; the impulse response of a circuit is the natural response of the circuit with that initial stored energy.

REVIEW QUESTIONS

1. What is the justification for saying that the complete response is equal to the sum of the forced and natural responses?

2. What determines the form of the forced response? The amplitude?

3. What determines the form of the natural response? The amplitude?

4. How are natural response components related to pole-zero diagrams?

5. Is it possible to determine the natural response components completely before determining the forced response? Explain.

6. Draw a circuit consisting of R and L in parallel, indicate some initial energy storage, and outline the procedure you would follow in determining the complete response to a forcing function.

7. Cite two specific examples of step functions occurring in nonelectrical situations.

8. List four commonly employed relations for evaluating undetermined constants from initial conditions.

9. Write the differential equation for obtaining v in Fig. 6.6 and outline the procedure for finding the natural response. Compare the difficulty of this method with that of solving $Z(s) = 0$.

10. Cite two specific examples of short pulses occurring in nonelectrical situations.

11. What is the distinction between a pulse and an impulse?

12. In the Summary to Chapter 5, statements are made regarding how L and C "look" to direct currents; formulate similar statements for impulses.

13. Why is there never a "forced response" to an impulse?

14. Why is the actual function $i(t)$ unimportant in determining the response to the impulse $\int i \, dt$?

EXERCISES

1. Verify that Eq. 6-5 is a solution by substitution in Eq. 6-1.

2. Write the differential equation for Fig. 6.2 and verify that Eq. 6-6 is a solution by substitution in the equation.

3. In the circuit of Fig. 6.14a, S_1 and S_2 are open.

    (a) Upon closing S_1, what is the initial value of i_1?

    (b) After a long time S_1 is opened. What is the value of v_{C1}?

    (c) If S_2 is then closed, what is the initial value of i_2?

    (d) After a long time, what is the value of v_{C2}?

4. In the circuit of Fig. 6.14b, C has an initial voltage of V_0.

    (a) Upon closing S, what are the initial values of i_1 and i_2?

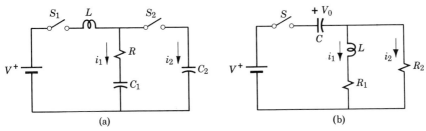

(a)   (b)

Fig. 6.14

(b) What are the initial values of di_1/dt and di_2/dt?

(c) After a long time what is the value of v_C?

5. A step input is applied to a circuit (Fig. 6.15) by closing a switch.

(a) Derive expressions for current i and voltage v_C as functions of time after closing the switch (C is initially uncharged).

(b) Sketch these functions on a labeled graph.

6. Repeat Exercise 5, given that $V = 12$ V, $R = 2$ kΩ, and $C = 2$ μF.

7. Repeat Exercise 6, assuming that C has an initial charge of 6 V with the lower terminal positive.

8. For the circuit of Fig. 6.2, draw a mechanical analog and write the solution, defining all terms.

9. For the circuit of Fig. 6.15, draw a mechanical analog and write the solution, defining all terms.

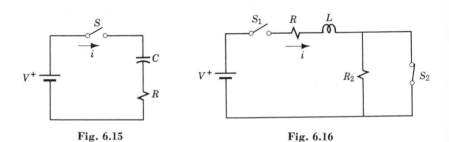

Fig. 6.15   Fig. 6.16

10. By means of the circuit of Fig. 6.16, the current i is to be brought to 1.0 A in 0.1 sec after closing S_1 and then held there by opening S_2. If $L = 10$ H and $R = 20$ Ω, calculate V and R_2.

11. In Fig. 6.17, S_1 is closed at $t_1 = 0$; C is initially uncharged.

(a) Derive an expression for $i(t_1)$ and sketch the graph.

(b) At time $t_2 = 0$ (a long time after $t_1 = 0$), S_2 is closed. Derive an expression for $i(t_2)$ and sketch the graph.

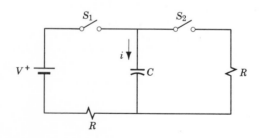

Fig. 6.17

12. In Fig. 6.18, $V_1 = 15$ V, $V_2 = 5$ V, $R = 10$ Ω, and $L = 200$ mH. At time $t = 0$, S_1 is closed; at $t = 20$ msec, S_2 is switched to remove V_2 from the circuit. Determine $i(t)$ and sketch to scale on a labeled graph.

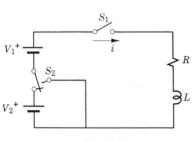

Fig. 6.18

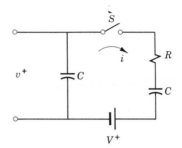

Fig. 6.19

13. In Fig. 6.19, S is closed at $t = 0$.

(a) Write the impedance function for the terminals indicated, draw the pole-zero diagram, and determine voltage $v(t)$.

(b) Check the result for part (a) by first determining current $i(t)$.

14. In Fig. 6.15, the direct voltage V is replaced by $v = 12 \cos (1000t - \pi/2)$ V, $R = 200\ \Omega$, and $C = 5\ \mu$F. S is closed at $t = 0$.

(a) Determine the components of current $i(t)$

(b) Sketch a graph of one cycle of voltage and the associated currents.

(c) Is there a time t_1 at which the switch could be closed so that only a sinusoidal current would flow? If not, why not? If so, what is time t_1?

15. Repeat Exercise 14 for the circuit of Fig. 6.20 where $R = 4\ \Omega$, $L = 7$ mH, and $v = 130 \cos 1745t$ V.

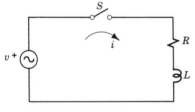

Fig. 6.20

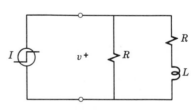

Fig. 6.21

16. Define and calculate the time constant for the circuit of Fig. 6.21.

17. A current step of magnitude I is applied to the circuit of Fig. 6.21. Derive and sketch a graph of the expression for $v(t)$.

18. Define and calculate the time constant for the circuit of Fig. 6.22.

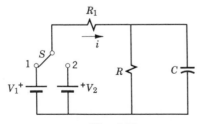

Fig. 6.22

19. In Fig. 6.22, $R_1 = 10\ \Omega$, $R = 20\ \Omega$ and $C = 5\ \mu F$; $V_1 = 30$ V and $V_2 = 60$ V. S has been in position 1 a long time.   Then, at $t = 0$, S is thrown instantaneously to position 2.   Determine and plot the curve of $i(t)$.

20. In Exercise 19, R_1 is replaced by an inductance $L = 22.2$ mH.

(a) Evaluate i and di/dt for time $t = 0^+$, just after switch S is thrown to position 2.

(b) Determine and sketch the curve of $i(t)$.

21. In a series RLC circuit, a step voltage is applied by closing a switch.   If $V = 12$ V, $R = 200\ \Omega$, $L = 5$ mH, and $C = 2\ \mu F$, determine the complete current response, assuming no initial energy storage.

22. Repeat Exercise 21 for $R = 100\ \Omega$; all other values remain the same.

23. In Fig. 6.23, S is closed at $t = 0$.   Considering the right-hand terminal of the switch as a node, derive an expression for $v(t)$.

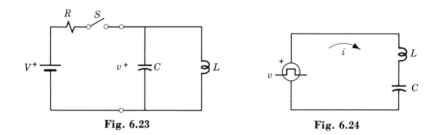

Fig. 6.23   Fig. 6.24

24. In Fig. 6.24, $L = 0.25$ H and $C = 1\ \mu F$; there is no initial energy storage. At $t = 0$, a rectangular pulse of amplitude 1000 V and duration 10 μsec is applied.   *Stating* any simplifying assumptions, determine the current just after $t = 10$ μsec and the current $i(t)$.

25. A parallel combination of $R = 1000\ \Omega$ and $C = 10\ \mu F$ is "hit" by an impulse of 200 A-sec.   Before and after the impulse the current through the terminals is zero or the terminals may be considered to be open circuited.   Determine the current response in the parallel circuit.

26. In Fig. 6.23, switch S is closed and voltage V is replaced by a voltage impulse of M_p volt-seconds at $t = 0$.

(a) Describe the effect of a current impulse on a parallel combination of L and C.

(b) What is the energy distribution in Fig. 6.23 at $t = 0^+$?

(c) Derive an expression for $v(t)$.

PROBLEMS

1. The circuit of Fig. 6.25 is suggested to obtain a flashing light.   The light is nonconducting until v_c reaches 80 V; then it flashes, discharges C completely, and becomes nonconducting again. Design the circuit to provide 10 flashes per second from a supply $V = 120$ V. (Specify R and C.)

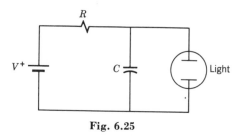

Fig. 6.25

2. A relay is a current-operated switch. A 120-V battery operates the relay of Fig. 6.26 when the switch is closed. The "operating coil" (500-Ω resistance and very small inductance) holds the contacts closed until the relay current decreases to a value called the "dropout current" and equal to 10 mA in this case. It is desired to hold the relay closed for 2 sec after the switch is opened by means of a passive circuit to be connected across the relay as shown. Design this circuit and specify values of the components you suggest.

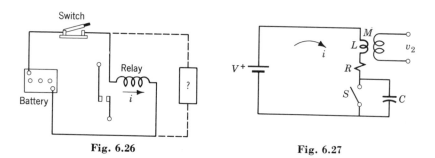

Fig. 6.26   **Fig. 6.27**

3. The secondary voltage in an ignition coil is given by $v_2 = M \, di/dt$ where i is the primary current (Fig. 6.27). In a certain coil $L = 20$ mH, $R = 50 \, \Omega$ and $M = 5$ H. Determine the maximum value of v_2 on the "make" (when S is closed). With a "condenser" $C = 0.2 \, \mu$F across the "breaker points," determine the maximum value of v_2 on the "break." *State* any simplifying assumptions.

4. A large wooden block of mass $M = 2$ kg rests on a horizontal surface with a coefficient of kinetic friction equal to 2.0 N-sec/m. A bullet of mass $m = 0.01$ kg is fired horizontally into the block and the block slides a distance of 2 m. Estimate the velocity of the bullet and the force impulse it imparts. Calculate the initial kinetic energy of the block and compare it with that of the bullet. Explain any discrepancy.

5. Two capacitors of $C_1 = C_2 = 20\ \mu F$ are joined by connectors with an effective resistance of 0.001 Ω and a switch. An ideal model of the combination is shown in Fig. 6.28. C_1 has an initial voltage of 500 V. At $t = 0$, S is closed. Predict the current i and the magnitude of the current pulse which flows. Calculate the initial and final energy in the circuit and explain any discrepancy.

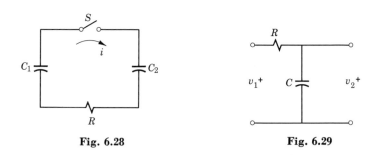

Fig. 6.28   Fig. 6.29

6. In Fig. 6.29, $R = 1$ MΩ and $C = 10\ \mu F$. Determine and plot $v_2(t)$ for the first second after applying v_1 where v_1 is a step of amplitude 10 V. Repeat for an impulse of 1 V-sec. Repeat for $v_1 = 20t$ V where t is in sec. (*Hint:* Approximate this function as the sum of a step and an exponential.) Draw a conclusion regarding the mathematical operation performed by this circuit.

♦ AVERAGE AND EFFECTIVE VALUES
♦ POWER CALCULATIONS
♦ RESONANT CIRCUITS
♦ THREE-PHASE CIRCUITS

CHAPTER 7

Steady-State A-C Circuits

The forced response to a periodic function is a steady-state behavior even though voltages and currents are continuously varying. The great bulk of electrical power is generated, transmitted, and utilized in the form of steady-state alternating currents. Also, much of the communication of information by wire or by radio is in the form of a-c signals ranging in frequency from a few cycles per second to billions of cycles per second. Certainly the most common, but not the most difficult, problems encountered in electrical engineering involve the analysis of a-c circuits, and many books have been written on this important subject.

These are practical problems arising in the design and application of electrical apparatus. They are of concern to the astronautical engineer planning a satellite transmitter installation, the chemical engineer selecting remote process controls, the construction engineer planning a temporary power line, the mechanical engineer building a vibration amplifier, and to the industrial engineer improving plant efficiency.

Previous chapters in this book provide the necessary foundation of basic laws, phasor representation, complex immittance, and circuit analysis. Building on that foundation, we now develop techniques and approaches which transform difficult problems into routine exercises. First we learn how to describe a continuously varying quantity by a single value and use this value in power calculations. Then we consider circuits in which the frequency of the forcing function is varied and study the interesting phenomenon of resonance. Finally we acknowledge the fact that most of the billions of kilowatt-hours of electrical energy used each year is in polyphase form and take a quick look at three-phase circuits.

AVERAGE AND EFFECTIVE VALUES

By definition, a *periodic* function of time is one in which

$$f(t + T) = f(t) \tag{7-1}$$

where T is the period in seconds. The sinusoidal current shown in Fig. 7.1a is periodic with a period of $T = 2\pi/\omega$ sec since

$$i = 10 \cos \omega \left(t + \frac{2\pi}{\omega} \right) = 10 \cos (\omega t + 2\pi) = 10 \cos \omega t$$

Always looking for ways to simplify calculations, we ask: What single value of current could be used to represent this continuously varying current?

The value to be used to represent a varying current depends on the function to be performed by the current. If it is used to actuate a relay, the maximum or *peak* value of 10 A is critical. If it is rectified (so that current flow is always in the same direction) and used to deposit silver in an electrolytic plating operation, the *average* value of 6.36 A is the significant quantity. If it is used to develop power in a resistor, the *effective* value of 7.07 A is the significant quantity. The term "peak value" is self-explanatory, but the other terms deserve consideration.

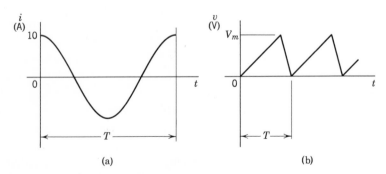

(a)   (b)

Fig. 7.1 Periodic functions.

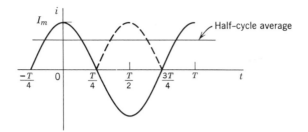

Fig. 7.2 Half-cycle average.

Average Value

The average value of a varying current over the period T is the steady value of current which in period T would transfer the same charge. By definition,

$$I_{av}T = Q = \int_t^{t+T} i(t)\, dt = \int_0^T i\, dt$$

or

$$I_{av} = \frac{1}{T} \int_0^T i\, dt \tag{7-2}$$

In a similar way, average voltage is defined as

$$V_{av} = \frac{1}{T} \int_0^T v\, dt \tag{7-3}$$

In dealing with periodic waves, it is understood that the average is over one complete cycle (or an integral number of cycles) unless a different interval is specified. For example, the average value of any triangular wave (Fig. 7.1b) is equal to half the peak value since the area under the curve ($\int v\, dt$) for one cycle is $\frac{1}{2}V_m T$.

For a sinusoidal wave, the average value over a cycle is zero; the charge transferred during the negative half-cycle is just equal and opposite to that transferred during the positive half-cycle. In certain practical problems we are interested in the *half-cycle* average (Fig. 7.2) given by

$$I_{\text{half-cycle}} = \frac{1}{T/2} \int_{-T/4}^{+T/4} I_m \cos \frac{2\pi t}{T}\, dt = \frac{2I_m}{T}\left(\frac{T}{2\pi}\right) \sin \frac{2\pi t}{T} \bigg]_{-T/4}^{+T/4}$$

$$= \frac{I_m}{\pi}\left[\sin\left(\frac{\pi}{2}\right) - \sin\left(-\frac{\pi}{2}\right)\right] = \frac{2}{\pi} I_m = 0.636 I_m \tag{7-4}$$

Effective Value

In many problems we are interested in the energy-transfer capability of an electric current. By definition, the average value of a varying power is the steady value of power which in period T would transfer the same energy. If

$$P_{av}T = W = \int_t^{t+T} p(t)\, dt = \int_0^T p\, dt$$

then

$$P_{av} = P = \frac{1}{T}\int_0^T p\, dt \tag{7-5}$$

By convention, P always means average power and no subscript is necessary.

If electrical power is transformed into heat in a resistance R,

$$P = \frac{1}{T}\int_0^T p\, dt = \frac{1}{T}\int_0^T i^2 R\, dt = I_{eff}^2 R \tag{7-6}$$

where I_{eff} is defined as the steady value of current which is equally *effective* in transforming power. Solving Eq. 7-6,

$$I_{eff} = \sqrt{\frac{1}{T}\int_0^T i^2\, dt} \tag{7-7}$$

and I_{eff} is seen to be the "square root of the mean squared value" or the *root-mean-square* current I_{rms}.

The effective or rms value of a sinusoidal current can be found from Eq. 7-7. Where $i = I_m \cos (2\pi/T)t$,

$$I_{rms}^2 = \frac{1}{T}\int_0^T I_m^2 \cos^2 \frac{2\pi t}{T}\, dt = \frac{1}{T}\frac{I_m^2}{2}\int_0^T \left(1 + \cos\frac{4\pi t}{T}\right) dt = \frac{I_m^2}{2}$$

and

$$I_{rms} = \frac{I_m}{\sqrt{2}} = 0.707 I_m \tag{7-8}$$

In Fig. 7.3, note that the mean value of $\cos^2 \omega t$ is just equal to 0.5; the average of the $\cos 2\omega t$ term is zero over a full cycle. In words, Eq. 7-8 says that for sinusoids the effective value is $1/\sqrt{2}$ times the maximum value. For all other functions Eq. 7-7 must be used.

Meter Readings

Basically, a measuring instrument converts a physical effect into an observable quantity. The cathode-ray oscilloscope (CRO) converts an

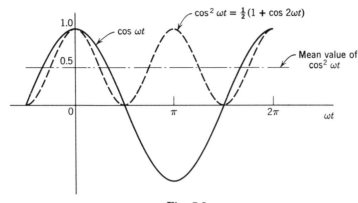

Fig. 7.3

applied voltage into a deflection of the spot of impact of an electron beam. The beam has little inertia and will follow rapid voltage variations, and therefore, the CRO indicates *instantaneous* values.

In the common d-c ammeter, a current in the meter coil (suspended in a magnetic field) produces a torque opposed by a spiral spring (Fig. 7.4a). While the torque is directly proportional to the instantaneous current, the high inertia of the movement (coil, support, and needle) prevents rapid rotation and the observed deflection is proportional to the *average* current.

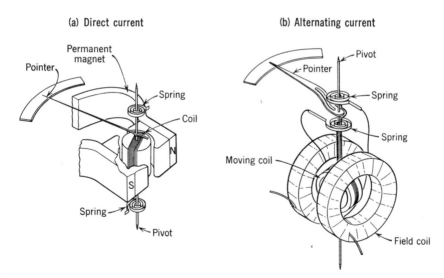

Fig. 7.4 Ammeter construction.

In a common type of a-c ammeter (Fig. 7.4b), the magnetic field is set up by the current itself and the torque produced is proportional to the square of the current. Because of the inertia of the movement, the observed deflection is proportional to the *average squared* current and is calibrated to indicate *rms* values.

If a periodic voltage is applied to a rectifier in series with a capacitance, the capacitance will tend to charge up until the applied voltage reaches its maximum. When the applied voltage decreases, the rectifier prevents a current reversal and the capacitance voltage remains at the *peak* value which can be read by an appropriate d-c instrument. The design and use of such instruments are described in Chapter 21, and this brief mention is just to emphasize the practical nature of the values defined in this section.

Root-Mean-Square Rating

The root-mean-square value has another significance in specifying the "rating" of an electric motor for a varying duty cycle. The interpretation of "rating" depends on the type of device being rated. A fish line rated at "10-lb test" can be expected to fail at slightly over 10 lb of static pull. If an automobile engine is rated at "300 hp," it means that a well-tuned sample operated under ideal conditions free of all accessories develops an output close enough to 300 hp to satisfy the advertising department.† In contrast, a truck engine or an electric motor is usually rated at the power it can produce on a continuous basis over a long period of time without excessive wear.

Actually, most "50-hp" electric motors can develop two or three times this amount of power for short periods of time. If operated with an overload continuously, however, the excessive losses (proportional to i^2R) raise the operating temperature and the insulation deteriorates rapidly. If the rough approximation is made that current drawn is proportional to power output and heat generated is proportional to current-squared, the rms horsepower is the critical rating.

EXAMPLE 1

An electric motor is to be specified for the duty cycle shown in Fig. 7.5. Full power of 10 hp is required for 2 min, the power decreases linearly for the next 3 min, the motor idles for 1 min, and then the cycle repeats.

---

† If a 3220-lb automobile actually had 300 hp available for acceleration it would accelerate from 0 to 60 mph in 2.4 sec!

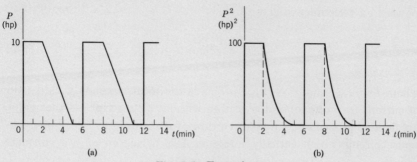

Fig. 7.5 Example 1.

SOLUTION. Making the assumption indicated above, the problem is to find the rms horsepower. From Eq. 7-7,

$$\text{rms hp} = \sqrt{\frac{1}{T} \Sigma (\text{hp}^2 \times \text{time})} \qquad (7\text{-}9)$$

where the integral has been replaced by its equivalent, a summation. The form of Eq. 7-9 indicates a simple approach to this type of problem since Σ (hp^2 × time) is the area under the curve of hp^2 versus time. As shown in Fig. 7.5b, the rectangular area is 100 hp^2 × 2 min. Since the area under a parabola is $\frac{1}{3}$ that of the enclosing rectangle, the parabolic area is 100 hp^2 × 3 min/3. Then

$$\text{rms hp} = \sqrt{\tfrac{1}{6}(100 \times 2 + 100 \times \tfrac{3}{3})} = \sqrt{50} = 7.07 \text{ hp}$$

The next larger standard rating is 7.5 hp and this is specified.

Note that Example 1 is based on the assumption that the thermal capacity of the motor permits an averaging of the heating rate over a short period. If the duty cycle were in hours instead of minutes, a 10-hp motor would be required.

POWER CALCULATIONS

Since voltage is the energy per unit charge and current is the charge per unit time, the basic expression for electrical energy per unit time or power is

$$p = vi = i^2 R = \frac{v^2}{R} \qquad (7\text{-}10)$$

For sinusoidal variation of voltage and current, the instantaneous value of power is a periodic function. Because average power P is usually the important quantity, we have defined the effective or rms current so that power in a resistance is given by

$$P = I^2 R = \frac{V^2}{R} \qquad (7\text{-}11)$$

where $I = I_{\text{rms}}$ and $V = V_{\text{rms}}$. This is the most commonly used value of current (or voltage) and is written without a subscript. Other values are defined in terms of the effective value; for example, a "110-V 60-cycle" house circuit which actually measures 115 V rms on an a-c voltmeter supplies a voltage $v = \sqrt{2}\ 115 \cos 2\pi 60t$ V.

Power is measured with a *wattmeter*. In a common type of wattmeter, the voltage v applied to the "voltage coil" establishes a magnetic field strength directly proportional to v. The current i flowing in the "current coil" reacts with the magnetic field to produce a torque proportional to the instantaneous vi product. The deflection of the needle is proportional to the developed torque and the inertia of the meter movement performs the desired averaging process. The resulting deflection is proportional to the average vi product and the scale is calibrated to read average power in watts. For sinusoidal voltages and currents applied to the proper coils, the wattmeter reading is equal to $VI \cos \theta$ (Eq. 7-16).

Reactive Power

Since power in a resistance is proportional to the square of current or voltage, the power is always positive and energy is dissipated throughout the entire cycle. In contrast, inductance and capacitance store but do not dissipate energy. When current through an inductance is increasing, energy $(w_L = \frac{1}{2}Li^2)$ is transferred from the circuit to the magnetic field; but when the current decreases, this energy is returned. Similarly, when the voltage across a capacitance is increasing, energy $(w_C = \frac{1}{2}Cv^2)$ is transferred from the circuit to the electric field and power is *positive*. When the voltage decreases, this energy is returned and power is *negative*.

From the basic laws, for an inductance carrying an effective current I,

$$p_L = i v_L = iL \frac{di}{dt} = (\sqrt{2}\ I \cos \omega t)(-\omega L \sqrt{2}\ I \sin \omega t)$$

$$= -I^2 X_L \sin 2\omega t \qquad (7\text{-}12)$$

The instantaneous power curve is shown in Fig. 7.6. The amplitude of the power variation is $I^2 X_L$; the $\sin 2\omega t$ factor indicates the periodic

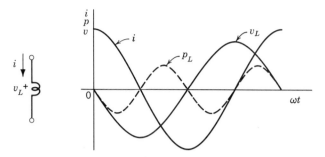

Fig. 7.6 Power in an inductance.

return of energy to the circuit. For a capacitance,

$$p_C = iv_C = i\frac{1}{C} \int i\,dt = (\sqrt{2}\,I \cos \omega t)\left(\frac{1}{\omega C}\,\sqrt{2}\,I \sin \omega t\right)$$

$$= I^2 X_C \sin 2\omega t \tag{7-13}$$

as shown in Fig. 7.7. We conclude that in a reactive element there is no net energy transfer or the average power is zero. However, there is a periodic storage and return of energy and the amplitude of the power variation is

$$P_X = I^2 X \tag{7-14}$$

This useful quantity is called *reactive power* because of its similarity to *active power* $P = I^2 R$.

Power Factor

In the general case of alternating current supplied to a complex impedance (Fig. 7.8), voltage and current differ in phase by an angle θ. In

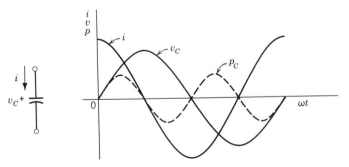

Fig. 7.7 Power in a capacitance.

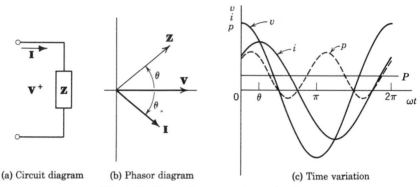

(a) Circuit diagram   (b) Phasor diagram   (c) Time variation

Fig. 7.8   Power in a general a-c circuit.

phasor notation, $\mathbf{V} = \mathbf{Z}\mathbf{I}$; in terms of effective values, $V = ZI$. The instantaneous power is

$$p = vi = \sqrt{2}\,V \cos \omega t \cdot \sqrt{2}\,I \cos (\omega t - \theta) = 2VI \cos \omega t \cos (\omega t - \theta)$$

Recalling that $2 \cos A \cos B = \cos (A - B) + \cos (A + B)$,

$$p = VI \cos \theta + VI \cos (2\omega t - \theta) \qquad (7\text{-}15)$$

Integrating over a cycle, or noting that the term $VI \cos (2\omega t - \theta)$ equals zero over a cycle,

$$P = VI \cos \theta \qquad (7\text{-}16)$$

In a circuit containing resistance only, voltage and current are in phase, $\theta = 0$, and $P = VI$ in watts where V and I are effective values in volts and amperes, respectively.   In general the average power P is VI multiplied by a factor which can never exceed unity.   By definition, the *power factor* is given by

$$\mathrm{pf} = \cos \theta = \frac{P}{VI} \qquad (7\text{-}17)$$

In a typical distribution system, components are connected in parallel across a common voltage.   An inductive component in which the current lags the voltage (as in Fig. 7.8) is said to have a *lagging power factor;* a capacitive component is said to have a *leading power factor* because the current leads the voltage.

Since $X = Z \sin \theta$ (reactance X is the imaginary component of the impedance) and $V = ZI$, Eq. 7-14 becomes

$$P_X = I^2 X = I^2 Z \sin \theta = VI \sin \theta \qquad (7\text{-}18)$$

The quantity sin θ is sometimes called the *reactive factor* because of its resemblance to the power factor. The units of reactive power P_X are *volt-amperes reactive* (abbreviated VAR) to emphasize the difference between this quantity and the power in watts.†

EXAMPLE 2

A coil is to be represented by a linear model consisting of inductance L in series with resistance R. In the laboratory when a 60-cycle current of 2 A (rms) is supplied to the coil (Fig. 7.9), the voltmeter across the coil reads 26 V (rms). A wattmeter indicates 20 W delivered to the coil. Determine L and R.

SOLUTION. By Eq. 7-11,

$$R = \frac{P}{I^2} = \frac{20}{2^2} = 5 \ \Omega$$

By Eq. 7-17,

$$\theta = \text{arc cos} \frac{P}{VI} = \text{arc cos} \frac{20}{2 \times 26} = 67.4°$$

By Eq. 7-18.

$$P_X = VI \sin \theta = 26 \times 2 \sin 67.4° = 48 \ \text{VAR}$$

By Eq. 7-14,

$$X_L = \frac{P_X}{I^2} = \frac{48}{2^2} = 12 \ \Omega$$

$$L = \frac{X_L}{\omega} = \frac{X_L}{2\pi f} = \frac{12}{2\pi 60} = 0.0317 \ \text{H}$$

Check:

$$V = ZI = \sqrt{R^2 + (\omega L)^2} \ I = \sqrt{5^2 + (377 \times 0.0317)^2} \ 2 = 13 \times 2 = 26 \ \text{V}$$

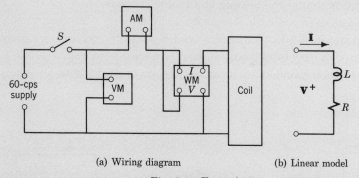

(a) Wiring diagram   (b) Linear model

Fig. 7.9   Example 2.

---

† To quote an early power engineer: "We didn't know what watts were; volt-amperes were a measure of power. If anything happened so that the power did not get into the volt-amperes—well, that was the manufacturer's fault. Nobody raised any questions, and nobody answered any." Paul N. Nunn, *General Electric Review,* Sept. 1956, p. 43.

Effective Value Phasors

The definition of a-c power $VI \cos \theta$ and reactive power $VI \sin \theta$ provides the basis for a new abstract concept which is useful in solving industrial problems in power generation and consumption. To illustrate the concept, we need to draw the phasor diagram for an industrial load. By definition in Chapter 3, where a sinusoidal voltage v is represented as the real part of the complex variable $V_m e^{j(\omega t+\theta)}$, the constant quantity $V_m e^{j\theta}$ has been called the phasor $\mathbf{V}$. The phasor carries information on the phase angle and maximum value of the sinusoid, but the value of importance in power calculations and the value read on a-c meters is the effective value. Therefore, we now redefine $V_m e^{j\theta}$ as the phasor $\mathbf{V}_m$, and we use the phasor $\mathbf{V}$ to represent $\mathbf{V}_m/\sqrt{2}$, the *effective value phasor*. Diagrams drawn henceforth are identical with those drawn previously, except for an indiscernible change in voltage and current scales. Note that phasor $\mathbf{V}$ carries the same information as $\mathbf{V}_m$; given $\mathbf{V} = 10 \underline{/30°}$ V, now $v = 10 \sqrt{2} \cos (\omega t + 30°)$ V. While this change may be confusing at first, the great benefit in problem solving will soon be clear.

Complex Power

Consider an industrial load consisting of heating units and induction motors. The linear model (Fig. 7.10a) consists of a resistance R_H for heating and a series combination of resistance R_M and inductance L_M to represent the motors connected across a common voltage supply. The phasor diagram, using effective values, shows the total plant current $\mathbf{I}$ as the phasor sum of the heating and motor currents.

An *equivalent circuit* with the same v-i characteristics at the terminals is drawn in Fig. 7.10c. Phasors $\mathbf{V}$ and $\mathbf{I}$ and the real and imaginary components of the total plant current are shown in Fig. 7.11b. By dividing the magnitude of each current phasor by V, we obtain a similar

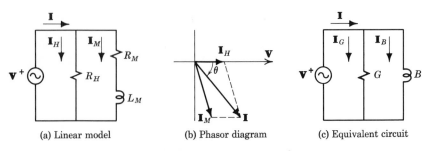

(a) Linear model   (b) Phasor diagram   (c) Equivalent circuit

Fig. 7.10   An industrial load.

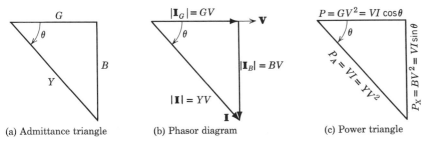

Fig. 7.11 Derivation of the complex power triangle.

triangle, the *admittance triangle*. (For an inductive susceptance, B is a negative quantity and jB is drawn downward on the complex plane.) By multiplying each current magnitude by V, we obtain another similar triangle, the *power triangle*.

The hypotenuse of the power triangle is a new quantity *apparent power* defined by

$$\mathbf{P}_A = VI \cos \theta + jVI \sin \theta = VI \underline{/\theta} \qquad (7\text{-}19)$$

or by

$$\mathbf{P}_A = P + jP_X = P_A \underline{/\theta} \qquad (7\text{-}20)$$

Apparent power is measured in volt-amperes or kilovolt-amperes (abbreviated VA or kVA). In Fig. 7.11c we can visualize apparent power in VA as a complex quantity with a real component equal to power in watts and an imaginary component equal to reactive power† in VAR.

The apparent power is a practical measure of the capacity of a-c equipment. In a transformer used to "step down" the voltage from a distribution potential of 4000 V to a safe handling potential of 120 V, the allowable output is limited by transformer heating due to losses. The losses (discussed in detail in Chapter 16) are determined by voltage and current and are unaffected by power factor. The size of the transformer, for example, required to supply a given industrial load is determined by the apparent power in volt-amperes instead of by the power in watts.

In deriving Eq. 7-17 for power factor and Eq. 7-18 for reactive power, we assumed that "voltage and current differ in phase by an angle θ." To eliminate an ambiguity, we now specify that θ *is the angle associated with the equivalent admittance*. When the current leads the voltage, θ is

---

† Instead of P_X, the conventional symbol for reactive power is Q; but already we use this symbol for charge and in the next section we shall use Q for another important quantity. To reduce (but not eliminate) confusion, we shall be unconventional here.

positive and therefore reactive power $VI \sin \theta$ is positive; the power $VI \cos \theta$ is always positive if $|\theta| \leq 90°$. With this interpretation, leading pf reactive power is positive and lagging pf reactive power is negative. In Example 2, the meter readings do not indicate whether θ is positive or negative; our convention indicates that θ is negative and P_X is identified as a negative 48 VAR.

The concept of complex power provides another approach to solving steady-state a-c problems. Calculations follow the rules of complex algebra and vector techniques and graphical methods are applicable. Powers in different portions of a circuit can be added directly and reactive powers can be added with proper attention to sign. Drawing a power triangle is a valuable aid in visualization. The approach is illustrated in the following example.

EXAMPLE 3

An industrial load consists of the following: 30 kW of heating and 150 kVA (input) of induction motors operating at 0.6 lagging pf. Power is supplied to the plant at 4000 V. Determine the total current and plant power factor.

SOLUTION. In general,

$$\mathbf{P}_A = P + jP_X = P_A \underline{/\theta}$$

Note that if any two of the four quantities are known, the other two can be calculated. To keep track of the quantities involved, set up the table shown in Fig. 7.12a. The given quantites are shown in italics.

Assuming that the pf of the heating load is unity, $\theta_H = 0$ and

$$P_A = \frac{P}{\cos \theta} = \frac{30}{1.0} = 30 \text{ kVA}$$

The power "triangle" for this load is the line labelled 30 kW in Fig. 7.12b. The components of the motor loads are

$$P_M = P_A \cos \theta = 150 \cos (-53.1°) = 90 \text{ kW}$$

$$P_{XM} = P_A \sin \theta = 150 \sin (-53.1°) = -120 \text{ kVAR}$$

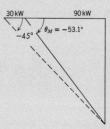

Load	P_A (kVA)	θ	pf	P (kW)	P_X (kVAR)
Heating	30	0°	1.0	30	0
Motors	150	−53.1°	0.6	90	−120
Plant	170	−45°	0.71	120	−120

(a) Table of power quantities   (b) Power triangles

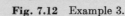

Fig. 7.12 Example 3.

The power triangle for this load is as shown. For the plant

$$P = P_H + P_M = 30 + 90 = 120 \text{ kW}$$

$$P_X = P_{XH} + P_{XM} = 0 - 120 = -120 \text{ kVAR}$$

Then

$$P_A = 120 - j120 = 170 \underline{/-45°} \text{ kVA}$$

The plant power factor is $\cos \theta = 0.71$

The plant current is $\dfrac{P_A}{V} = \dfrac{170 \text{ kVA}}{4 \text{ kV}} = 42.5 \text{ A}$

Power-Factor Correction

To supply the plant in Example 3, the local power company must install a transformer capable of supplying 170 kVA (neglecting provision for overloads) and wire large enough to carry 42.5 A. In addition to the 120 kW of power supplied to the plant, the power company must generate power to supply the I^2R losses in all the generation, transmission, and distribution equipment.

To supply the same power to another plant operating at unity pf would require a transformer rated at only 120 kVA and wire rated at $120/4 = 30$ A. The losses would be only $30^2/42.5^2 = 0.5$ as great. It is reasonable to expect that the charge for supplying power to this second plant would reflect the lower cost to the power company.

One plan for doing this is to include a power factor penalty clause in the rate schedule. The customer with low power factor pays a higher rate per kilowatt-hour (kWh). The usual cause of low power factor is lagging pf equipment such as induction motors, furnaces, and welders. If a power factor penalty is imposed, it may be economically justifiable to "correct" the situation by adding capacitors which draw a leading pf reactive power. Such capacitors operate at nearly zero power factor and are rated in kVAR at a specified voltage rather than in terms of the capacitance provided.

EXAMPLE 4

The power factor of the plant in Example 3 is to be corrected to 0.9 lagging. Specify the necessary auxiliary equipment.

SOLUTION. The power of 120 kW is unaffected by adding reactive power equipment. A table of given (in italics) and calculated values is shown in Fig. 7.13. The apparent power desired is

$$P_A = \frac{P}{\cos \theta} = \frac{120}{0.9} = 133.3 \text{ kVA}$$

and

$$P_X = P_A \sin \theta = 133.3 \sin (-25.8°) = -58 \text{ kVAR}$$

Load	P_A (kVA)	θ	pf	P kW	P_X kVAR
Previous	170	$-45°$	0.71	120	-120
Desired	133.3	$-25.8°$	0.9	120	-58
Correction	62	$90°$	0.0	0	$+62$

(a) Table of power quantities   (b) Power triangles

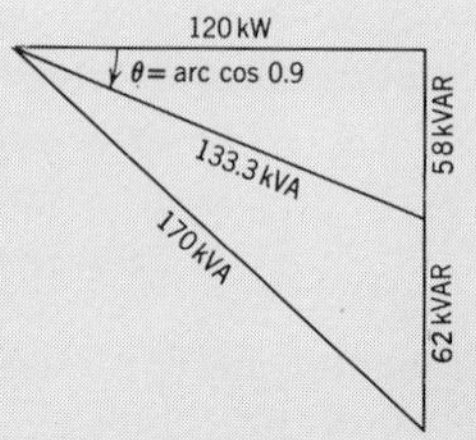

Fig. 7.13 Example 4.

The necessary correction is $-58 - (-120) = +62$ kVAR. The new power triangle is shown in Fig. 7.13b. The nearest commercial unit is 60 kVAR rated at 4000 V. (Note that apparent powers cannot be combined directly.)

RESONANCE

The slender suspension bridge across the Tacoma Narrows in Washington showed tendencies to oscillate up and down during construction and was nicknamed "Galloping Gertie." On November 7, 1940, only a few months after construction was completed, the oscillation began to build up under a moderate wind and then abruptly changed to a writhing motion. Within an hour the violent twisting had torn the 6-million dollar bridge to pieces. Ten years later, after much study, experiment, and wind-tunnel research, a new bridge designed to be stable in winds up to 120 mph was constructed on the same site.

This is an example of *resonance*, a phenomenon characteristic of low-loss second-order structures and systems. At a particular *resonant frequency* the impedance is small and the forced response may be very great even for moderate applied forces or voltages. There are many engineering applications of resonance. In an internal combustion engine with a "tuned" intake manifold, the resonance effect is used to increase the amount of fuel-air mixture delivered to the cylinders at high speed. In a radio receiver, a resonant circuit is used to select a single signal from all the myriad radio waves which impinge on the antenna. The extreme degree of frequency selectivity achievable is one of the key properties of electric circuits.

Frequency Response

The reduction in impedance in a series resonant circuit occurs because inductive reactance and capacitive reactance are of opposite sign and they vary with frequency in inverse fashion.   Inductive reactance ωL is directly proportional to frequency and capacitive reactance $-1/\omega C$ is inversely proportional to frequency.   If an inductance and a capacitance are connected in series, there is always a frequency at which the two reactances just cancel.   A practical circuit for achieving this effect consists of a coil in series with a capacitor; the linear model is the series RLC circuit of Fig. 7.14.

Series Resonance

For this circuit the impedance is

$$\mathbf{Z} = R + j\omega L + \frac{1}{j\omega C} = R + j\left(\omega L - \frac{1}{\omega C}\right) \qquad (7\text{-}21)$$

$$\mathbf{Z} = \sqrt{R^2 + \left(\omega L - \frac{1}{\omega C}\right)^2} \; \underline{/\arctan\,(\omega L - 1/\omega C)/R} \qquad (7\text{-}22)$$

The frequency at which the reactances just cancel and the impedance is a pure resistance is the *resonant frequency* ω_o.   Where $\theta_Z = 0$ and

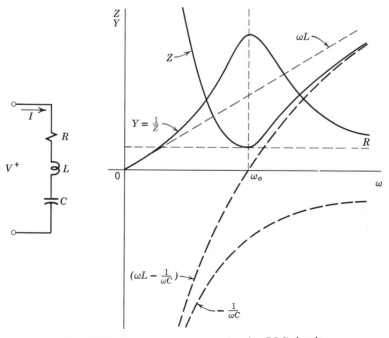

Fig. 7.14   Frequency response of series RLC circuit.

$(\omega_o L - 1/\omega_o C) = 0$, the resonant frequency in radians per second is

$$\omega_o = \frac{1}{\sqrt{LC}} \qquad (7\text{-}23)$$

The corresponding frequency in cycles per second (cps) is

$$f_o = \frac{1}{2\pi \sqrt{LC}} \qquad (7\text{-}24)$$

By definition, at resonance the impedance $Z_o = R$ and $\theta_Z = 0$. At frequencies lower than ω_o, the capacitive reactance term predominates; the impedance increases rapidly as frequency decreases, and θ_Z approaches $-90°$. At frequencies higher than ω_o, the inductive reactance term predominates; the impedance increases rapidly with frequency and θ_Z approaches $+90°$. (Can you visualize the curve of θ_Z as a function of ω?)

Also shown in Fig. 7.14 is the variation with frequency of admittance $Y = 1/Z$. The admittance is high at resonance, where $Y_o = 1/R$, and decreases rapidly as frequency is changed from ω_o. Since $I = YV$, the variation of current with a constant applied voltage has the same shape as the admittance curve. If voltages of various frequencies are applied to a series RLC circuit, a voltage of frequency ω_o will be favored and a relatively large current will flow in response to this particular voltage. The circuit is *frequency selective*.

EXAMPLE 5

The variable capacitor behind a radio dial provides a capacitance of 1 nF when the dial setting is "80." Calculate the inductance of the associated coil.

SOLUTION. A dial setting of "80" means a frequency of 800 kc (kilocycles per second). The coil-capacitor combination provides resonance at this frequency; therefore, $\omega_o L = 1/\omega_o C$ and

$$L = \frac{1}{\omega_o{}^2 C} = \frac{1}{(2\pi f_o)^2 C} = \frac{1}{(2\pi \times 8 \times 10^5)^2 \times 1 \times 10^{-9}} = 39.6 \ \mu\text{H}$$

Pole-Zero Diagram Interpretation

The pole-zero diagram provides the key to the natural response of a circuit; does it tell us anything about the forced response? The admittance function $Y(s)$ for the series RLC circuit is

$$Y(s) = \frac{1}{Z(s)} = \frac{1}{R + sL + 1/sC} = \frac{s}{s^2 L + sR + 1/C} \qquad (7\text{-}25)$$

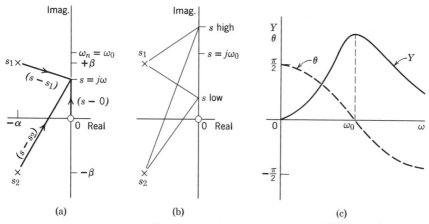

Fig. 7.15 Pole-zero diagram and frequency response of RLC circuit.

In standard factored form, this is

$$Y(s) = \frac{1}{L} \frac{(s - 0)}{(s - s_1)(s - s_2)} \qquad (7\text{-}26)$$

where

$$s_1, s_2 = -\frac{R}{2L} \pm j \sqrt{\frac{1}{LC} - \left(\frac{R}{2L}\right)^2} = -\alpha \pm j\beta \dagger \qquad (7\text{-}27)$$

As shown in Fig. 7.15a, the admittance function has a zero at the origin (and another at infinity) and poles at s_1 and s_2. Since the pole-zero diagram defines the admittance function and the admittance function completely describes the circuit, we should be able to obtain the frequency response from the pole-zero diagram.

If s takes the value $j\omega$, then $Y(s)$ is $Y(j\omega)$, the admittance as a function of frequency. But $s = j\omega$ is a point in the complex plane, a point on the imaginary axis (Fig. 7.15a). The factor $(s - s_1)$ in Eq. 7-26 is the difference between two complex numbers, and therefore $(s - s_1)$ is itself a complex number defined by the length and angle of the line from s_1 to s. Factors $(s - 0)$ and $(s - s_2)$ are defined similarly. Then admittance $Y(s)$ is $(1/L)$ times a complex number divided by the product of

---

† In Chapter 4, this expression was written $s = -\alpha \pm j\omega$, where ω was the natural frequency of the circuit, a constant. Now we wish to let ω be the frequency of the forcing function, a variable. On p. 96, $\omega_n = 1/\sqrt{LC}$ is defined as the undamped natural frequency of a series RLC circuit. The forced response resonant frequency ω_o is just equal to ω_n.

two other complex numbers, and $Y(s)$ could be obtained graphically from the pole-zero diagram by using a scale and protractor.

Of greater importance is the possibility of obtaining the approximate frequency response by inspection. For low frequencies (s close to the origin as in Fig. 7.15b), the numerator ($s - 0$) is small and, therefore, the admittance is low. For high frequencies, ($s - s_2$) is larger than ($s - 0$), ($s - s_1$) increases rapidly with frequency and, therefore, the admittance is low. As the frequency decreases from high values, ($s - s_1$) decreases to a minimum and then increases; since the factors ($s - s_2$) and ($s - 0$) are changing at comparable rates, the factor ($s - s_1$) predominates and the admittance goes through a maximum (Fig. 7.15c).

A similar line of reasoning indicates the shape of the curve showing admittance angle θ as a function of frequency. For low frequencies, the angles associated with ($s - s_1$) and ($s - s_2$) are nearly equal and opposite, and θ is approximately $\pi/2$, the angle of the numerator ($s - 0$). For high frequencies, the angles of ($s - 0$) and ($s - s_2$) are nearly equal, and θ is approximately $-\pi/2$, the angle of $1/(s - s_1)$. At $s = j\omega_o$, the sum of the angles associated with ($s - s_1$) and ($s - s_2$) is just equal to $\pi/2$ and θ is 0.

To the experienced engineer the pole-zero diagram indicates the general shape of the frequency response and puts the critical factors in sharp focus. The diagram also displays the effect of changes in the circuit parameters; for example, a reduction in R moves the poles closer to the imaginary axis, reduces ($j\omega_o - s_1$), and exaggerates the variation of admittance with frequency. Another virtue of the pole-zero diagram is that approximations which simplify calculation without seriously reducing precision may be revealed; for example, if β/α is large and ω is close to ω_o, ($s - s_2$) $\cong 2(s - 0)$ and $Y(s) \cong \frac{1}{2}(s - s_1)$.

Phasor Diagram Interpretation

Additional information about the phenomenon of resonance is revealed by phasor diagrams drawn for various frequencies. Since current is common to each element in this series circuit, phasor $\mathbf{I}$ is drawn as a horizontal reference in Fig. 7.16. The voltage $\mathbf{V}_R$ across the resistance is in phase with the current, and voltages $\mathbf{V}_L$ and $\mathbf{V}_C$ across the inductance and capacitance respectively lead and lag the current. For $\omega = \omega_o$, $\mathbf{V}_L$ and $\mathbf{V}_C$ just cancel (Why?) and the voltage across the resistance is just equal to the applied voltage $\mathbf{V}$. For $\omega < \omega_o$, $\mathbf{V}_C$ is greater than $\mathbf{V}_L$ and the sum of the three voltages is $\mathbf{V}$. In comparison to the case for $\omega = \omega_o$, a larger $\mathbf{V}$ is required for the same current or the admittance is lower; θ_Y is positive indicating a leading power factor. For $\omega > \omega_o$, $\mathbf{V}_L$ is

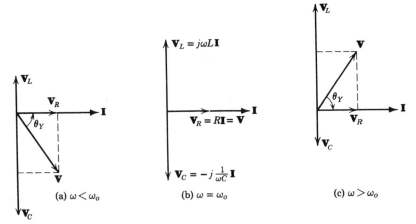

Fig. 7.16 Phasor diagrams for a series *RLC* circuit.

greater than $\mathbf{V}_C$ and the current lags $\mathbf{V}$ (the sum of the three component voltages) by angle θ_Y.

For a given current $\mathbf{I}$, the impedance $\mathbf{Z}$ is directly proportional to the voltage $\mathbf{V}$. Therefore, the voltage diagrams of Fig. 7.16 can be transformed into impedance diagrams. For $\omega < \omega_o$, the impedance is predominantly capacitive. For $\omega = \omega_o$, the impedance is a pure resistance and has a minimum value. For $\omega > \omega_o$, the impedance is predominantly inductive and increases with frequency.

EXAMPLE 6

A generator supplies a variable frequency voltage of constant amplitude = 100 V (rms) to a series *RLC* circuit where $R = 5\ \Omega$, $L = 4$ mH, and $C = 0.1\ \mu$F. The frequency is to be varied until a maximum current flows (a maximum rms value, not an instantaneous maximum). Predict the maximum current, the frequency at which it occurs, and the resulting voltages across the inductance and capacitance.

SOLUTION. For a series *RLC* circuit, maximum current corresponds to maximum admittance at the resonant frequency. At $\omega = \omega_o$, $\omega_o L = 1/\omega_o C$, and $Z = R$. Therefore,

$$I = \frac{V}{Z} = \frac{V}{R} = \frac{100}{5} = 20 \text{ A}$$

and

$$\omega_o = \frac{1}{\sqrt{LC}} = \frac{1}{\sqrt{4 \times 10^{-3} \times 10^{-7}}} = 5 \times 10^4 \text{ rad/sec}$$

Then

$$V_L = \omega L I = 5 \times 10^4 \times 4 \times 10^{-3} \times 20 = 4000 \text{ V}$$

and

$$V_C = \frac{I}{\omega C} = \frac{20}{5 \times 10^4 \times 10^{-7}} = 4000 \text{ V}$$

The phasor diagram is similar to that in Fig. 7.16b.

Quality Factor Q

How can the voltage across one series element be greater than the voltage across all three, as in Example 6? The answer is related to the fact that L and C are energy-storage elements and high *instantaneous* voltages are possible. As indicated in Fig. 7.16b, $\mathbf{V}_L$ and $\mathbf{V}_C$ are 180° out of phase; instantaneous voltages are also 180° out of phase, and a high positive voltage across L is cancelled by a high negative voltage across C. (See Exercise 28.) The voltages do exist, however, and can be measured with practical voltmeters. The possibility of developing high element voltages is a useful property of resonant circuits and we need a convenient measure of this property.

At resonance $\omega_o L = 1/\omega_o C$ and $I = I_o = V/R$. Therefore the react-ance voltages are

$$V_L = \omega_o L I_o = \omega_o L \frac{V}{R} = \frac{\omega_o L}{R} V \qquad (7\text{-}28)$$

and

$$V_C = \frac{I_o}{\omega_o C} = \frac{V}{\omega_o C R} = \frac{\omega_o L}{R} V = V_L \qquad (7\text{-}29)$$

By definition, in a series circuit

$$\frac{\omega_o L}{R} = \frac{1}{\omega_o C R} = Q \qquad (7\text{-}30)$$

where Q is the *quality factor*, a dimensionless ratio.

In a practical circuit, R is essentially the resistance of the coil since practical capacitors have very low losses in comparison to practical inductors. Hence, Q is a measure of the energy-storage property (L) in relation to the energy dissipation property (R) of a coil or a circuit. A well-designed coil may have a Q of several hundred, and an RLC circuit employing such a coil will have essentially the same Q since the capacitor contributes very little to R. In practical coils, the losses (and therefore R in the linear model) increase with frequency and $Q = \omega L/R$ is fairly constant over a limited range of frequencies.

Equation 7-28 indicates that for a given value of current there is a "resonant rise in voltage" across the reactive elements equal to Q times

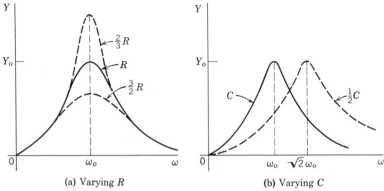

(a) Varying R (b) Varying C

Fig. 7.17 Effect of circuit parameters on frequency response.

the applied voltage. In addition to indicating the magnitude of this resonant rise, Q is a measure of the frequency selectivity of the circuit. A circuit with high Q discriminates sharply; a low-Q circuit is relatively unselective. The solid admittance curve of Fig. 7.17a is redrawn from Fig. 7.14; for the same L and C, the admittance curve near resonance depends on R. Increasing the resistance by 50% reduces Y_o to $\frac{2}{3}$ of its original value and the selectivity is reduced. Decreasing the resistance to $\frac{2}{3}$ of its original value (and thereby increasing Q by a factor of $\frac{3}{2}$) increases Y_o and increases selectivity.

The effect of changing one reactive element while keeping the other and the resistance constant is indicated by Fig. 7.17b. While ω_o is shifted, the general shape of the response curve is still the same. A *universal resonance curve* which would describe series RLC circuits with various parameters and various resonant frequencies would be very valuable. Is it possible that such a universal curve would also describe parallel resonant circuits?

Parallel Resonance

A parallel GCL circuit is shown in Fig. 7.18. For this circuit the admittance is

$$\mathbf{Y} = G + j\omega C + \frac{1}{j\omega L} = G + j\left(\omega C - \frac{1}{\omega L}\right) \tag{7-31}$$

$$\mathbf{Y} = \sqrt{G^2 + \left(\omega C - \frac{1}{\omega L}\right)^2} \; \underline{/\arctan\ (\omega C - 1/\omega L)/G} \tag{7-32}$$

The frequency at which the susceptances just cancel and the admittance

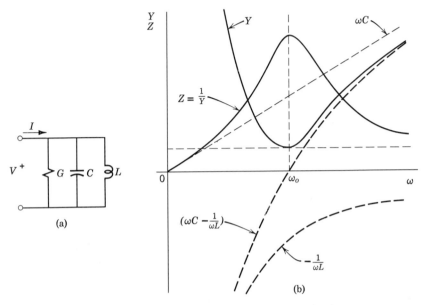

Fig. 7.18 Frequency response of parallel GCL circuit.

is a pure conductance is the resonant frequency ω_o. Where $\theta_Y = 0$ and $(\omega_o C - 1/\omega_o L) = 0$, the resonant frequency in radians/sec is

$$\omega_o = \frac{1}{\sqrt{CL}} \tag{7-33}$$

The corresponding frequency in cycles/sec is

$$f_o = \frac{1}{2\pi \sqrt{CL}} \tag{7-34}$$

By definition, at resonance the admittance $Y_o = G$ and $\theta_Y = 0$. At frequencies lower than ω_0, the inductive susceptance term predominates; the admittance increases rapidly as frequency decreases and θ_Y approaches $-90°$. At frequencies higher than ω_o, the capacitive susceptance term predominates; the admittance increases rapidly with frequency and θ_Y approaches $+90°$.

These equations and descriptive statements look familiar; as a matter of fact, they were written by applying the duality transforms (Figs. 5.19 and 5.20) to the corresponding equations (7-22 to 7-24) and statements for series resonance. Since the circuits are duals, we expect duality in the frequency response curves; Fig. 7.18b is a relabeled version of Fig.

7.14b. (You may wish to translate for yourself the paragraph starting: "Also shown in Fig. 7.14 . . ." on p. 198.)

The phasor diagrams for a parallel *GCL* circuit are shown in Fig. 7.19. In this case there is a resonant rise in current in the reactive elements. At resonance $V = V_o = I/G$. Therefore the reactance currents are

$$I_C = \omega_o C V_o = \omega_o C \frac{I}{G} = \frac{\omega_o C}{G} I = Q_p I \qquad (7\text{-}35)$$

and

$$I_L = \frac{V_o}{\omega_o L} = \frac{I}{\omega_o L G} = \frac{\omega_o C}{G} I = Q_p I \qquad (7\text{-}36)$$

Basic Definition of *Q*

The expressions for *Q* in a parallel circuit are quite different from those in a series circuit; in fact, if the same circuit elements are reconnected, $Q_p = 1/Q_s$. But basically the phenomena described by *Q* are the same in both circuits; apparently we need a more basic definition of *Q*. In essence, quality factor is a measure of the energy storage property of a circuit in relation to its energy dissipation property. A definition based on this concept is

$$Q = 2\pi \frac{\text{Maximum energy stored}}{\text{Energy dissipated per cycle}} \qquad (7\text{-}37)$$

In a pendulum driven at its resonant frequency, the only energy input goes to supply friction losses; the energy stored is transferred back and

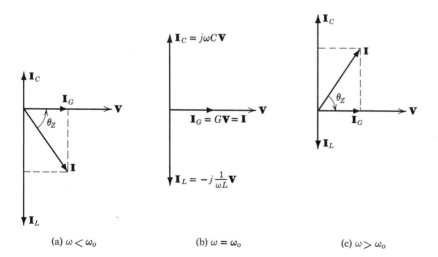

(a) $\omega < \omega_o$ (b) $\omega = \omega_o$ (c) $\omega > \omega_o$

Fig. 7.19 Phasor diagrams for a parallel *GCL* circuit.

forth from potential to kinetic.   In the analogous electric circuit, the input impedance at resonance is a pure resistance and the stored energy is transferred back and forth between the magnetic field of the inductance and the electric field of the capacitance.   It can be shown (see Problem 4) that at the resonant frequency the total stored energy is a constant.   At an instant when the voltage across the capacitance is zero, the current in the inductance is maximum and all the stored energy is in the inductance. At an instant when v_C is maximum, i_L is zero and all the stored energy is in C.   (Is this confirmed by the phasor diagrams of Figs. 7.16 and 7.19?)

Knowing the energy distribution, we can derive specific values of Q from the basic definition.   For a series RLC circuit, the common current is $i = \sqrt{2}\, I \cos \omega t$, and all the stored energy is in L when $i = \sqrt{2}\, I$ or

$$W_{\text{stored}} = W_L = \tfrac{1}{2}Li^2 = LI^2 \tag{7-38}$$

The energy dissipated per cycle is the energy per second (average power) divided by the frequency in cps, or

$$W_{\text{diss/cycle}} = \frac{P}{f_o} = \frac{I^2 R}{f_o}$$

By Eq. 7-37,

$$Q_s = 2\pi \frac{LI^2}{I^2 R/f_o} = 2\pi f_o \frac{L}{R} = \frac{\omega_o L}{R} \tag{7-39}$$

Following a similar line of reasoning, the quality factor for a simple parallel circuit can be obtained (see Exercise 33).   The great advantage of this basic definition of Q is that it is also applicable to more complicated lumped circuits, to distributed circuits such as transmission lines, and to nonelectrical systems.   Note that for a reactive component such as a coil, $Q = \omega L/R$, a function of frequency; for a resonant system, Q is evaluated at ω_o and is a constant.

EXAMPLE 7

A radio receiver usually has several parallel resonant circuits for selecting the desired station.   Using the values from Example 5 ($C = 1$ nF and $L = 39.6\ \mu$H), the resonant frequency is again 800 kc and the dial setting should be "80."   If the GCL linear model has a Q of 100, what is the value of G?   If two signal currents of the same amplitude (50 μA rms) but different frequencies (f_1 at "80" and f_2 at "85" on the dial) are introduced from the antenna, what are the corresponding voltages developed across the tuned circuit?

SOLUTION.   For a Q of 100, Eq. 7-35 yields

$$G = \frac{\omega_o C}{Q_p} = \frac{2\pi \times 8 \times 10^5 \times 10^{-9}}{100} = 50.2\ \mu\mho$$

At the resonant frequency f_1,

$$V_1 = \frac{I_1}{Y_o} = \frac{I_1}{G} = \frac{50 \times 10^{-6}}{50.2 \times 10^{-6}} \cong 1 \text{ V}$$

For a frequency $f_2 = 850$ kc, $\omega = 2\pi \times 8.5 \times 10^5$ rad/sec,

$$Y_2 = \sqrt{G^2 + (\omega C - 1/\omega L)^2} = \sqrt{(50.2)^2 + (5370 - 4720)^2} = 623 \ \mu\mho$$

and

$$V_2 = \frac{I_2}{Y_2} = \frac{50 \times 10^{-6}}{623 \times 10^{-6}} \cong 0.08 \text{ V}$$

For the same impressed current, the voltage response for the desired signal is over 12 times as great as that for the undesired signal, and the power developed in G is over 150 times as great since $P = V^2 G$.

Normalized Response

The frequency selectivity demonstrated in Example 7 is characteristic of all resonant circuits and the response curves of all such circuits have the same general shape. Now we wish to derive a simple but general equation which describes series and parallel circuits, resonant at high and low frequencies, with large and small energy dissipation. To eliminate the effect of specific parameter values, we use dimensionless ratios. For illustration we choose to work with the admittance of a series RLC circuit, but the result has a more general interpretation. For the series circuit of Fig. 7.20a,

$$\mathbf{Z} = R + j\left(\omega L - \frac{1}{\omega C}\right) = \frac{1}{\mathbf{Y}}$$

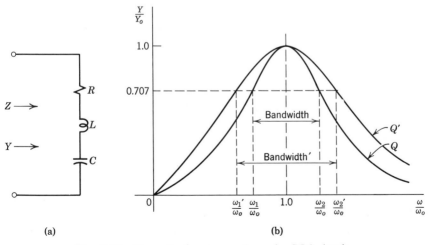

(a)   (b)

Fig. 7.20 Normalized response of a series RLC circuit.

and at resonance,

$$\mathbf{Z}_o = R = \frac{1}{\mathbf{Y}_o}$$

The dimensionless ratio of the admittance at any frequency ω to that at the resonant frequency ω_o is

$$\frac{\mathbf{Y}}{\mathbf{Y}_o} = \frac{\mathbf{Z}_o}{\mathbf{Z}} = \frac{R}{R + j\left(\omega L - \dfrac{1}{\omega C}\right)} = \frac{1}{1 + j\left(\dfrac{\omega L}{R} - \dfrac{1}{\omega CR}\right)} \tag{7-40}$$

Introducing the factor ω_o/ω_o and letting the dimensionless ratio $\omega_o L/R = Q = 1/\omega_o CR$, the admittance ratio for a series RLC circuit is

$$\frac{\mathbf{Y}}{\mathbf{Y}_o} = \frac{1}{1 + j\left(\dfrac{\omega L}{R}\cdot\dfrac{\omega_o}{\omega_o} - \dfrac{1}{\omega CR}\cdot\dfrac{\omega_o}{\omega_o}\right)} = \frac{1}{1 + jQ\left(\dfrac{\omega}{\omega_o} - \dfrac{\omega_o}{\omega}\right)} \tag{7-41}$$

This simple equation also describes the impedance ratio $\mathbf{Z}/\mathbf{Z}_o$ for a parallel GCL circuit; the even simpler reciprocal equation describes the impedance ratio for a series circuit and the admittance ratio for a parallel circuit.

Bandwidth

Figure 7.20b represents the first step toward a universal resonance curve; all variables are dimensionless ratios. The difference in the two curves shown is due to a difference in selectivity. A convenient quantitative measure of selectivity is defined by letting the imaginary term in the denominator of Eq. 7-41 be equal to ± 1. Where

$$\left(\frac{\omega}{\omega_o} - \frac{\omega_o}{\omega}\right) = \pm\frac{1}{Q} \tag{7-42}$$

then

$$\frac{\mathbf{Y}}{\mathbf{Y}_o} = \frac{1}{1 \pm j1} = \frac{1}{\sqrt{2}}\underline{/\mp 45^\circ} \tag{7-43}$$

Imposing this condition defines two frequencies, ω_1 and ω_2, such that

$$\frac{\omega_1}{\omega_o} - \frac{\omega_o}{\omega_1} = -\frac{1}{Q} \quad \text{and} \quad \frac{\omega_2}{\omega_o} - \frac{\omega_o}{\omega_2} = +\frac{1}{Q} \tag{7-44}$$

Frequencies ω_1 and ω_2 are called the lower and upper "70% points," since at these frequencies the magnitude Y/Y_o is $1/\sqrt{2} = 0.707$. For a given applied voltage, current is proportional to admittance and these are also called "70% current points." More generally, these are *half-power fre-quencies* because power is proportional to the square of the current. (Do ω_1 and ω_2 also designate half-power frequencies in parallel circuits?)

The frequency range between the half-power points, $\omega_2 - \omega_1$, is called the *bandwidth*, a direct measure of the selectivity of the circuit. Solving Eqs. 7-44 and selecting the consistent roots, we obtain

$$\omega_1 = \omega_o \sqrt{1 + \left(\frac{1}{2Q}\right)^2} - \frac{\omega_o}{2Q}$$

$$\omega_2 = \omega_o \sqrt{1 + \left(\frac{1}{2Q}\right)^2} + \frac{\omega_o}{2Q}$$

$$\text{(7-45)}$$

Subtracting the first equation from the second,

$$\omega_2 - \omega_1 = \frac{\omega_o}{Q} \qquad \text{(7-46)}$$

Note that the bandwidth $\omega_2 - \omega_1$ is inversely proportional to the quality factor Q, a very convenient result. For frequency in cps, the bandwidth is

$$f_2 - f_1 = \frac{f_o}{Q} \qquad \text{(7-47)}$$

EXAMPLE 8

A circuit with a Q of 100 is resonant at 800 kc. Determine the relative response of an 850-kc signal and calculate the bandwidth.

SOLUTION. This is a general problem of which Example 7 is a specific case. By Eq. 7-41 the magnitude of the relative response is

$$\frac{Y}{Y_o} = \frac{1}{\left[1 + Q^2\left(\frac{\omega}{\omega_0} - \frac{\omega_0}{\omega}\right)^2\right]^{1/2}} = \frac{1}{\left[1 + 100^2\left(\frac{850}{800} - \frac{800}{850}\right)^2\right]^{1/2}} \cong 0.08$$

since $f/f_o = \omega/\omega_o$. In kilocycles per second, the bandwidth is

$$f_2 - f_1 = \frac{f_o}{Q} = \frac{800}{100} = 8 \text{ kc}$$

For an AM radio, this circuit is a little too selective because AM stations broad-cast signals over a 10-kc channel.

Universal Resonance Curve

Equation 7-41 for $\mathbf{Y}/\mathbf{Y}_o$ is simple and general, but it is hard to work with accurately because the factor in parentheses is a small difference between two relatively large quantities. Furthermore, Eqs. 7-45 for ω_1 and ω_2 are complicated. Both difficulties are eliminated if we restrict ourselves to considering practical circuits in which Q is usually 20 or

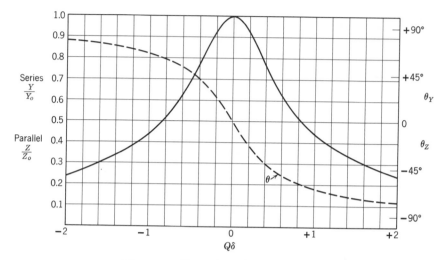

Fig. 7.21   The universal resonance curve.

greater.   Taking into account the precision of typical circuit measurements, the following approach gives satisfactory results in the important region near resonance for circuits in which Q is as low as 10.

First we define a new dimensionless ratio δ (delta) which measures the extent of detuning from resonance.   By definition,

$$\delta = \frac{\omega - \omega_o}{\omega_o} = \frac{\omega}{\omega_o} - 1 \tag{7-48}$$

Then

$$\frac{\omega}{\omega_o} - \frac{\omega_o}{\omega} = \delta + 1 - \frac{1}{\delta + 1} = \delta\frac{\delta + 2}{\delta + 1} \cong 2\delta \tag{7-49}$$

when δ is small, as it is when ω is close to ω_o.   For practical resonant circuits, the important effects occur at small values of δ, and Eq. 7-41 becomes

$$\frac{\mathbf{Y}}{\mathbf{Y}_o} = \frac{1}{1 + j2Q\delta} = \frac{Y}{Y_o}\underline{/\theta_Y} \tag{7-50}$$

This equation is written for the admittance ratio for a series RLC circuit, but it also describes the impedance ratio for a parallel GCL circuit.

The *universal resonance curves* of Fig. 7.21 are obtained from Eq. 7-50 by considering $Q\delta$ as the dimensionless variable.   When Q is incorporated into the independent variable, the two curves of Fig. 7.20 coincide.   For practical circuits where the approximation of Eq. 7-49 is justified, these curves describe the behavior of all series or parallel resonant circuits. This approximation makes the curves symmetric about ω_o where $Q\delta = 0$.

If the half-power points $(Y/Y_o = 0.707)$ are equidistant from ω_o, Eq. 7-46 indicates that

$$\omega_2 - \omega_o = \omega_o - \omega_1 = \frac{\omega_o}{2Q} \tag{7-51}$$

or

$$\omega_1 = \omega_o - \frac{\omega_o}{2Q_o} \quad \text{and} \quad \omega_2 = \omega_o + \frac{\omega_o}{2Q} \tag{7-52}$$

These values are consistent with the fact that on the universal resonance curve the half-power points occur where $Q\delta = \pm 0.5$.

EXAMPLE 9

A parallel circuit with a Q of 100 is resonant at 800 kc, as in Example 8. Using the universal resonance curve, determine the relative response to a frequency of 810 kc.

SOLUTION.

$$Q\delta = Q\frac{\omega - \omega_o}{\omega_o} = Q\frac{f - f_o}{f_o} = 100\frac{810 - 800}{800} = 1.25$$

From the curve,

$$\frac{Z}{Z_o} = 0.37 \quad \text{and} \quad \theta_Z = -68°$$

The minimum spacing of AM broadcast stations is 10 kc, and in a given geographical region they are always much more widely spaced.

Practical Resonant Circuits

In focusing attention on principles, we neglected some practical aspects of resonant circuits. The practical parallel circuit consists of an inductor in parallel with a capacitor, and the only resistance is usually that due to losses in the inductor. The linear model of Fig. 7.22 is the appropriate representation of the actual circuit; if Q is 20 or more, the general equation (Eq. 7-50) and the universal resonance curve give Z/Z_o for this circuit within acceptable limits.

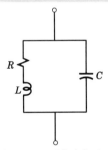

Fig. 7.22 Model of a practical parallel circuit.

The emphasis in this discussion is on a variable frequency ω. In many cases the circuit is "tuned" by varying a capacitor or, less frequently, an inductor. This corresponds to varying ω_o in Eq. 7-41 and the same general resonance behavior is observed.

The specific values of the circuit parameters are usually determined by economic considerations. At audio frequencies (20 to 20,000 cps), inductors with iron cores are used to obtain inductances in the order of henrys. At radio broadcast frequencies (above 500,000 cps), air-core inductors with inductances in the order of microhenrys are resonated with variable air-dielectric capacitors with capacitances in the order of nanofarads. Reasonable values of resistance and quality factor are obtained in properly designed inductors using copper wire. At higher frequencies, undesired resonance may occur due to the inductance of a short lead (a small fraction of a microhenry) and the capacitances between two adjacent conductors (a few picofarads).

THREE-PHASE CIRCUITS

The generation and transmission of electrical power is more efficient in polyphase systems employing combinations of two, three, or more sinusoidal voltages. In addition, polyphase circuits and machines possess some unique advantages; for example, power in a three-phase circuit is constant rather than pulsating as it is in a single-phase circuit. Also three-phase motors start and run much better than single-phase motors. The most common form of polyphase system employs three *balanced* voltages, equal in magnitude and differing in phase by $360°/3 = 120°$. The discussion here is restricted to balanced three-phase circuits. First we see how such voltages are generated and connected, and then we learn to analyze the resulting circuits.

Three-Phase Voltage Generation

The elementary a-c generator of Fig. 7.23 consists of a rotating magnet and a stationary winding. The turns of the winding are spread along the periphery of the machine. The voltage generated in each turn of the four-turn winding is slightly out of phase with the voltage generated in its neighbor because it is cut by maximum magnetic flux density an instant

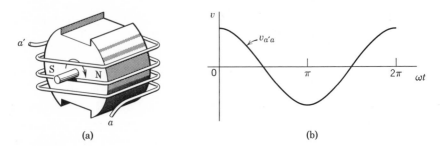

(a)   (b)

Fig. 7.23   Elementary generator and voltage generated in the winding.

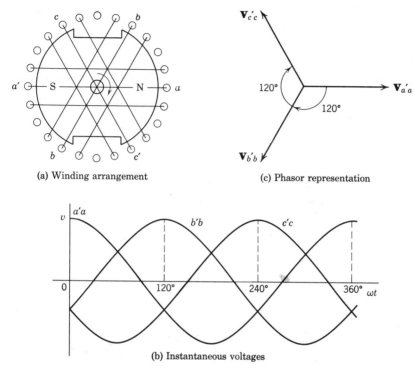

(a) Winding arrangement

(c) Phasor representation

(b) Instantaneous voltages

Fig. 7.24 Balanced three-phase voltages.

earlier or later. (Machine construction and voltage generation are discussed in Chapter 17.) The voltages in the four turns are in series and, therefore, they add to produce voltage $v_{a'a}$.

If the winding were continued around the machine, the voltage generated in the last turn would be 180° out of phase with that in the first and they would cancel, producing no useful effect. For this reason, a winding is commonly spread over no more than one-third of the periphery; the other two-thirds can be used to generate two other similar voltages. The three sinusoids (sinusoids are obtained with a proper winding distribution and magnet shape) generated by the three similar windings are shown in Fig. 7.24. Using double-subscript notation to minimize confusion, the voltages are:

$$v_{a'a} = \sqrt{2}\,V \cos \omega t \qquad\qquad \mathbf{V}_{a'a} = V \underline{/0°}$$

$$v_{b'b} = \sqrt{2}\,V \cos (\omega t - 120°) \qquad \mathbf{V}_{b'b} = V \underline{/-120°} \qquad (7\text{-}53)$$

$$v_{c'c} = \sqrt{2}\,V \cos (\omega t - 240°) \qquad \mathbf{V}_{c'c} = V \underline{/-240°}$$

The three similar portions of a three-phase system are called "phases," a slightly different use of the word. Because the voltage in phase $a'a$ reaches its maximum first, followed by that in phase $b'b$, and then by that in phase $c'c$, we say the *phase rotation* is abc. This is an arbitrary convention; for any given machine the phase rotation may be reversed by reversing the direction of rotation of the magnet or by interchanging the labels on two of the three-phase windings. We shall assume the phase rotation is abc unless otherwise stated.

Delta Connection

Three separate *single-phase* loads can be connected to the three windings of a generator and supplied with power independently. The three-phase system running along the rear property lines in residential areas could be operated in this way. The first customer could be connected across phase a, the second across phase b, and the third across phase c. However, savings in wire and other benefits are gained by interconnecting the three phases.

Consider the terminal board of a three-phase generator as shown in Fig. 7.25a and the corresponding voltage phasors. If terminal c' is connected to terminal a (solid line in Fig. 7.25c), voltage $a'c$, equal to voltage $a'a$ plus voltage $c'c$, appears across terminals $a'c$. In phasor notation,

$$\mathbf{V}_{a'c} = \mathbf{V}_{a'a} + \mathbf{V}_{c'c}$$

If then terminal b' is connected to terminal c (as shown by the dashed line), the voltage appearing across terminals $a'b$ is

$$v_{a'b} = v_{a'a} + v_{c'c} + v_{b'b}$$

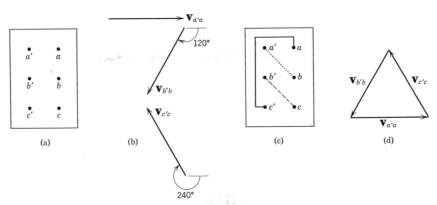

Fig. 7.25 Three-phase generator and Δ connection.

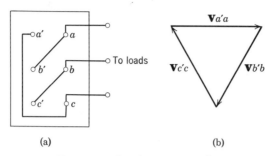

Fig. 7.26 Another Δ connection.

or

$$\mathbf{V}_{a'b} = \mathbf{V}_{a'a} + \mathbf{V}_{c'c} + \mathbf{V}_{b'b}$$

The graph of instantaneous values in Fig. 7.24b shows that $v_{a'b} = 0$ and this is verified by the sum of the balanced phasors in Fig. 7.24c. (The sum of a set of symmetric complex quantities is always zero.)

Since the voltage between terminals a' and b is zero, these terminals can be connected (dotted line) and the result is a system of voltages connected in *delta*. The same three windings can be reconnected as in Fig. 7.26 to yield another delta connection. In either Δ (delta), a voltage appears across each pair of terminals; three wires connected to terminals a, b, and c can supply three single-phase loads. This is the arrangement actually employed to serve residential customers. Can three such wires of a given size carry as much power as six wires of the same size supplying separate single-phase loads? (See Problem 6.)

Wye Connection

The same machine can be reconnected to give a quite different result. If terminals a', b', and c' are connected together (Fig. 7-27a), a, b, and c become the output terminals of a *wye* or *star connection*. Connecting a, b, and c together (Fig. 7.27d) would yield another **Y** (wye). In the Δ connection, the voltage across the output terminals is just equal to the voltage of a winding. In the **Y** connection, however, the voltage across terminals ba is (from Fig. 7.27c)

$$\mathbf{V}_{ba} = \mathbf{V}_{a'a} - \mathbf{V}_{b'b} = \mathbf{V}_{a'a} + \mathbf{V}_{bb'} = 2\mathbf{V}_{a'a}\cos 30° \underline{/30°} = \sqrt{3}\,\mathbf{V}_{a'a}\,\underline{/30°}$$

In general,

$$\mathbf{V}_{\text{line}} = \sqrt{3}\,\mathbf{V}_{\text{phase}}\,\underline{/30°} \tag{7-54}$$

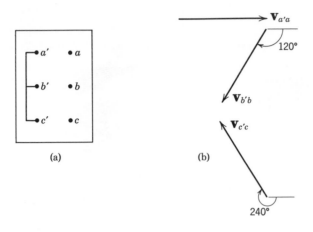

(a)   (b)

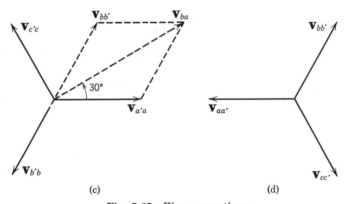

(c)   (d)

Fig. 7.27 Wye connections.

or, in words, *in a Y connection the line-to-line voltage is $\sqrt{3}$ times the phase voltage and is displaced 30° in phase.*

Delta-Circuit Calculations

Given a three-phase source and load, a common problem is to calculate the various currents and voltages and the power supplied to the load. In Fig. 7.28c the load consists of three equal impedances connected in Δ. The internal connection of the source is unimportant; it could be Δ or Y. The only requirement is that there be available at terminals a, b, and c three balanced voltages.

While three-phase circuits are no more difficult to solve than single-phase circuits, there are many opportunities for confusion in dealing with three of everything. A clearly labelled schematic wiring diagram should be drawn and a phasor diagram should be used as a guide and a check. Calculations are simplified and mistakes reduced if, at first, the wiring diagram and the phasor diagram have the same orientation. In Fig. 7.28c if V_{ab} is taken as the horizontal reference, phasor V_{ab} is in the same direction as a line going from a to b. Phasor V_{bc} is in the same direction as a line from b to c and is $120°$ "behind" V_{ab} (Fig. 7.29b). Similarly, V_{ca} is $240°$ behind V_{ab}.

In a delta load the voltages across the three impedances (the phase voltages) are identical with the voltages between the "lines" from source to load (the line voltages). The currents in each phase (labelled consistently with the phase voltages in Fig. 7.29a) are obtained in the cus-

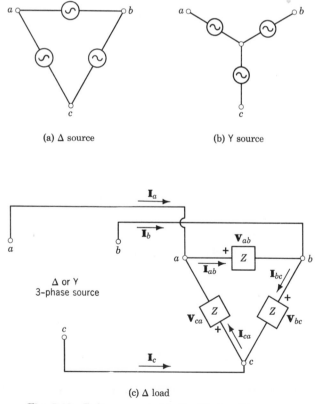

(a) Δ source   (b) Y source

(c) Δ load

Fig. 7.28 Delta connected load with Δ or Y source.

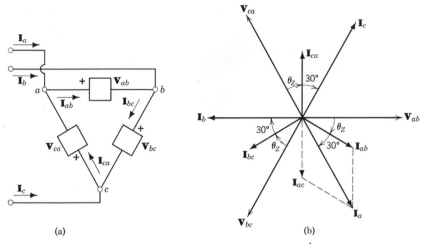

Fig. 7.29   Phasor diagram for a Δ load.

tomary way.   Using phasor representation, the *phase* currents are

$$\mathbf{I}_{ab} = \frac{\mathbf{V}_{ab}}{\mathbf{Z}_{ab}} = \frac{V \,\underline{/0°}}{Z \,\underline{/\theta_Z}} = \frac{V}{Z} \,\underline{/0° - \theta_Z}$$

$$\mathbf{I}_{bc} = \frac{\mathbf{V}_{bc}}{\mathbf{Z}_{bc}} = \frac{V \,\underline{/-120°}}{Z \,\underline{/\theta_Z}} = \frac{V}{Z} \,\underline{/-120° - \theta_Z} \qquad (7\text{-}55)$$

$$\mathbf{I}_{ca} = \frac{\mathbf{V}_{ca}}{\mathbf{Z}_{ca}} = \frac{V \,\underline{/-240°}}{Z \,\underline{/\theta_Z}} = \frac{V}{Z} \,\underline{/-240° - \theta_Z}$$

The *line* currents are not equal to the phase currents.   For example,

$$\mathbf{I}_a = \mathbf{I}_{ab} + \mathbf{I}_{ac} = \mathbf{I}_{ab} - \mathbf{I}_{ca}$$

This addition is indicated in Fig. 7.29b.   Since $\mathbf{I}_{ac} = -\mathbf{I}_{ca}$,

$$\mathbf{I}_a = 2\mathbf{I}_{ab} \cos 30° \,\underline{/-\theta_Z - 30°} = \sqrt{3}\,\mathbf{I}_{ab} \,\underline{/-30°}$$

$\mathbf{I}_b$ and $\mathbf{I}_c$ are obtained similarly and the result is a set of three balanced line currents.   In general,

$$\mathbf{I}_{\text{line}} = \sqrt{3}\,\mathbf{I}_{\text{phase}} \,\underline{/-30°} \qquad (7\text{-}56)$$

or, in words, *in a Δ connection the line current is $\sqrt{3}$ times the phase current and is displaced $-30°$ in phase.*

EXAMPLE 9

A load consisting of three identical impedances $\mathbf{Z} = 10 \,\underline{/-45°}\, \Omega$ in Δ is connected to a three-phase, 220-V source. Determine phase and line currents, and draw a labelled phasor diagram.

SOLUTION. The source is assumed to supply balanced three-phase voltages with a line-to-line value of 220 V rms and phase rotation abc. If $\mathbf{V}_{ab}$ is taken as the horizontal reference, a suitable wiring diagram is shown in Fig. 7.30a. The phase currents are labelled consistently in a clockwise direction and the line currents are all assumed into the load to preserve the balance. Obviously, the phase voltages are just equal to the line voltages. The phase currents are

$$\mathbf{I}_{ab} = \frac{\mathbf{V}_{ab}}{\mathbf{Z}} = \frac{220\,\underline{/0°}}{10\,\underline{/-45°}} = 22\,\underline{/+45°}\ \text{A}$$

$$\mathbf{I}_{bc} = \frac{\mathbf{V}_{bc}}{\mathbf{Z}} = \frac{220\,\underline{/-120°}}{10\,\underline{/-45°}} = 22\,\underline{/-75°}\ \text{A}$$

$$\mathbf{I}_{ca} = \frac{\mathbf{V}_{ca}}{\mathbf{Z}} = \frac{220\,\underline{/-240°}}{10\,\underline{/-45°}} = 22\,\underline{/-195°}\ \text{A}$$

$$\mathbf{I}_a = \mathbf{I}_{ab} + \mathbf{I}_{ac} = 22\,\underline{/+45°} + 22\,\underline{/-15°} = 22\,\sqrt{3}\,\underline{/45° - 30°} = 38\,\underline{/+15°}\ \text{A}$$

By symmetry,

$$\mathbf{I}_b = 38\,\underline{/-105°}\ \text{A} \qquad \text{and} \qquad \mathbf{I}_c = 38\,\underline{/-225°}\ \text{A}$$

The voltages, phase currents, and line currents are shown on the phasor diagram in Fig. 7-30b.

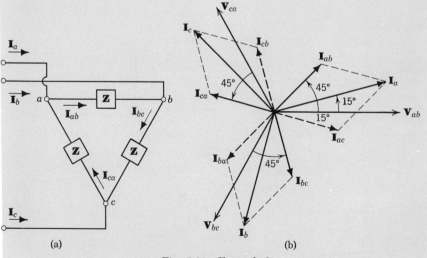

(a) (b)

Fig 7.30 Example 9.

Power Calculations

The total power in a balanced three-phase load is the sum of three equal phase powers or

$$P_{\text{total}} = 3P_p = 3V_pI_p \cos \theta \qquad (7\text{-}57)$$

where $\cos \theta$ is the power factor of the load or θ is the angle between phase voltage V_p and phase current I_p. As illustrated by Example 9, θ is *not* the angle between line voltage and line current. It is easier to measure line quantities, however, so an expression for total power in terms of V_l and I_l is useful.

In a Δ load, $V_l = V_p$ and $I_l = \sqrt{3}\,I_p$; therefore,

$$P_\Delta = 3V_pI_p \cos \theta = 3V_l \frac{I_l}{\sqrt{3}} \cos \theta = \sqrt{3}\,V_lI_l \cos \theta \qquad (7\text{-}58)$$

In a **Y** load, $V_l = \sqrt{3}\,V_p$ and $I_l = I_p$ (see Example 10); therefore,

$$P_{\mathsf{Y}} = 3V_pI_p \cos \theta = 3\frac{V_l}{\sqrt{3}}\,I_l \cos \theta = \sqrt{3}\,V_lI_l \cos \theta \qquad (7\text{-}59)$$

The same expression holds for power in a Δ or a **Y** connected load.

EXAMPLE 10

Three equal impedances of $\mathbf{Z} = 10\;\underline{/+45°}$ Ω are connected in **Y** across a 220-V supply. Determine phase voltages, phase and line currents, and phase and total power. Draw a labeled phasor diagram.

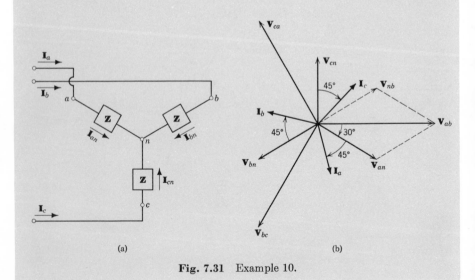

(a)   (b)

Fig. 7.31 Example 10.

SOLUTION. A properly oriented wiring diagram is shown in Fig. 7.31a. By inspection, line current I_a = phase current I_{an}. (Point n is called the "neutral" and is important in unbalanced systems.) From Eq. 7-54,

$$V_p = \frac{V_l}{\sqrt{3}}\,\underline{/-30^\circ} \quad \text{or} \quad V_{an} = \frac{V_{ab}}{\sqrt{3}}\,\underline{/-30^\circ}$$

In this problem,

$$V_{an} = \frac{220\,\underline{/0^\circ} - 30^\circ}{\sqrt{3}} = 127\,\underline{/-30^\circ}\ \text{V}$$

This is consistent with the orientation of the wiring diagram; the other phase voltages are determined by inspection and drawn on the phasor diagram as

$$\mathbf{V}_{bn} = 127\,\underline{/-150^\circ}\ \text{V} \quad \text{and} \quad \mathbf{V}_{cn} = 127\,\underline{/-270^\circ}\ \text{V}$$

Then

$$\mathbf{I}_a = \mathbf{I}_{an} = \frac{\mathbf{V}_{an}}{\mathbf{Z}_{an}} = \frac{127\,\underline{/-30^\circ}}{10\,\underline{/+45^\circ}} = 12.7\,\underline{/-75^\circ}\ \text{A}$$

By symmetry,

$$\mathbf{I}_b = \mathbf{I}_{bn} = 12.7\,\underline{/-195^\circ}\ \text{A} \quad \text{and} \quad \mathbf{I}_c = \mathbf{I}_{cn} = 12.7\,\underline{/-315^\circ}\ \text{A}$$

as shown on the phasor diagram. The phase power is

$$P_p = V_p I_p \cos\theta = 127 \times 12.7(0.707) = 1140\ \text{W}$$

The total power is, by Eq. 7-59,

$$P_t = \sqrt{3}\,V_l I_l \cos\theta = \sqrt{3} \times 220 \times 12.7(0.707) = 3420\ \text{W}$$

Check:

$$P_t = 3P_p = 3 \times 1140 = 3420\ \text{W}$$

Polyphase circuits are complicated, and clearly labeled wiring and phasor diagrams are necessary to minimize confusion. In a given phase, calculations are handled just as in single-phase circuits. The symmetry of balanced three-phase systems reduces the work required.

SUMMARY

◆ In a periodic function of time, $f(t + T) = f(t)$.

◆ The average value of a periodic current is

$$I_{\text{av}} = \frac{1}{T}\int_0^T i\,dt$$

For a sinusoid, the half-cycle average is $\dfrac{2}{\pi} I_m = 0.636 I_m$.

◆ The effective or rms value of a periodic current is

$$I_{rms} = I = \sqrt{\frac{1}{T} \int_0^T i^2 \, dt}$$

For a sinusoid, the rms value $I = \dfrac{I_m}{\sqrt{2}} = 0.707 I_m$.

◆ Phasor diagrams are usually drawn using the effective values read on a-c ammeters and voltmeters.

◆ Rms values are significant whenever the square of a variable is the important quantity. For function curves of simple geometry, the rms value is the average ordinate of the "squared" curve.

◆ Average power (indicated by a wattmeter) is $P = \dfrac{1}{T} \int_0^T vi \, dt$.

◆ For sinusoids,

Power (average) $P = VI \cos \theta = I^2 R = \dfrac{V^2}{R}$ in W

Reactive power $P_X = VI \sin \theta = I^2 X = \dfrac{V^2}{X}$ in VAR

Apparent power $P_A = VI = I^2 Z = \dfrac{V^2}{Z}$ in VA

Complex power $\mathbf{P}_A = P + jP_X$

Power factor $\text{pf} = \cos \theta = \dfrac{P}{VI}$

Reactive factor $= \sin \theta = \dfrac{P_X}{VI}$, positive for leading pf

◆ In determining total apparent power, power components and reactive power components are added separately and combined vectorially; drawing power triangles is helpful.

◆ A circuit containing inductance and capacitance is in resonance if the terminal voltage and current are in phase.
At the resonant frequency the power factor is unity, and the impedance and admittance are purely real.
Phasor diagrams drawn for frequencies near resonance display the variations in V, I, and θ with frequency.

◆ The frequency response of a circuit is also given by $Y(j\omega)$ or $Z(j\omega)$. In pole-zero notation

$$Y(j\omega) = K \frac{(j\omega - s_a)(j\omega - s_b)}{(j\omega - s_1)(j\omega - s_2)}$$

which can be interpreted graphically.

♦ Bandwidth $\omega_2 - \omega_1$ is a general measure of frequency selectivity where ω_1 and ω_2 are half-power frequencies.

♦ The frequency selectivity of a resonant circuit is determined by

$$Q = 2\pi \frac{\text{Maximum energy stored}}{\text{Energy dissipated per cycle}}$$

♦ For series RLC or parallel GCL circuits:

$$\text{Resonant frequency}: \omega_o = \frac{1}{\sqrt{LC}} \quad \text{or} \quad f_o = \frac{1}{2\pi\sqrt{LC}}$$

$$\text{Bandwidth}: \qquad \omega_2 - \omega_1 = \frac{\omega_o}{Q}$$

$$\text{Series}: \quad Q = \frac{\omega_o L}{R} = \frac{1}{\omega_o CR} \quad \text{and} \quad V_L = V_C = QV \text{ at } \omega_o$$

$$\text{Parallel}: \quad Q = \frac{\omega_o C}{G} = \frac{1}{\omega_o LG} \quad \text{and} \quad I_L = I_C = QI \text{ at } \omega_o$$

$$\text{Series } \frac{\mathbf{Y}}{\mathbf{Y}_o} = \text{Parallel } \frac{\mathbf{Z}}{\mathbf{Z}_o} = \frac{1}{1 + jQ\left(\dfrac{\omega}{\omega_o} - \dfrac{\omega_o}{\omega}\right)}$$

♦ For $Q \geq 10$ and $\delta = \dfrac{\omega - \omega_o}{\omega_o}$ small, a good approximation is:

$$\text{Series } \frac{\mathbf{Y}}{\mathbf{Y}_o} = \text{Parallel } \frac{\mathbf{Z}}{\mathbf{Z}_o} = \frac{1}{1 + j2Q\delta}$$

Then

$$\omega_1 = \omega_o - \frac{\omega_o}{2Q} \quad \text{and} \quad \omega_2 = \omega_o + \frac{\omega_o}{2Q}$$

and the response is described by universal resonance curves.

♦ A balanced three-phase source consists of three equal and symmetric single-phase sources connected in Δ or **Y**.

For balanced three-phase systems in

$$\Delta: \mathbf{V}_{\text{line}} = \mathbf{V}_{\text{phase}} \quad \text{and} \quad \mathbf{I}_{\text{line}} = \sqrt{3}\,\mathbf{I}_{\text{phase}} \underline{/-30°}$$

$$\mathbf{Y}: \mathbf{I}_{\text{line}} = \mathbf{I}_{\text{phase}} \quad \text{and} \quad \mathbf{V}_{\text{line}} = \sqrt{3}\,\mathbf{V}_{\text{phase}} \underline{/+30°}$$

♦ In analyzing balanced three-phase circuits, draw a carefully oriented and labelled wiring diagram.

Sketch the phasor diagram as a guide and a check.

Analyze one phase and use symmetry.

Total power $= 3V_{\text{phase}}I_{\text{phase}} \cos\theta = \sqrt{3}\,V_{\text{line}}I_{\text{line}} \cos\theta$.

REVIEW QUESTIONS

1. Distinguish between average and effective values.
2. Why are a-c ammeters calibrated to read rms values?
3. What is the reading of a common d-c ammeter carrying a current $i = 10 \cos 377t$ A?
4. Will an a-c wattmeter read d-c power accurately?
5. Is there a difference in size between a 200-hp automobile engine and a 200-hp truck engine? Explain.
6. What is the frequency of the power pulsations in a 60-cycle circuit?
7. What is the interpretation of "negative instantaneous power p" delivered to a passive circuit?
8. What is the interpretation of "negative reactive power P_X"?
9. Sketch a sinusoidal voltage, a sinusoidal current leading by about 45°, and the corresponding instantaneous power curve.
10. What is an "equivalent circuit"?
11. What is measured in VA? In VAR?
12. Is power a vector or a scalar quantity? What is "complex power"?
13. Outline the steps in adding two apparent powers.
14. Why is the local public utility interested in the pf of a plant?
15. Cite an example of resonance from acoustics, aeronautics, and hydraulics.
16. In terms of energy storage, what is the condition necessary for resonance?
17. Give a definition of resonance which holds for all electrical circuits.
18. What actually happens when you turn the tuning dial of a radio?
19. How is the forced response resonant frequency ω_o related to the undamped natural frequency ω_n?
20. Outline the procedure for obtaining frequency response from a pole-zero diagram.
21. Above ω_o, is a series RLC circuit capacitive or inductive?
22. How can the voltage across one series element in an RLC circuit be greater than the total voltage across all three?
23. Why is Q called the "quality factor"?
24. Using the duality transformations, translate the next full paragraph after Eq. 7.24.
25. How could you determine the Q of a pendulum experimentally?
26. Name two important advantages of resonant circuits.
27. Do ω_1 and ω_2 defined by Eq. 7-37 designate half-power frequencies in parallel circuits?
28. Use a pole-zero diagram to justify the approximation in Eq. 7-43.
29. Why is Y/Y_o called "relative response"?
30. If $\mathbf{I}_1 = I \,\underline{/30°}$ is one current in a balanced three-phase system, what are the other two?
31. Given $\mathbf{V}_{12} = V \,\underline{/90°}$, define the other two voltages of a balanced three-phase system and show them connected in Δ and $\mathbf{Y}$.
32. Explain by phasor diagrams the $\sqrt{3}$ in the voltage and current relations in $\mathbf{Y}$ and Δ circuits.
33. In analyzing a Δ load, why is it unimportant whether the source is connected in Δ or $\mathbf{Y}$?

34. In a "440-V, three-phase" system, what voltage is 440 V?   Is this rms?

35. What is the advantage of using the same orientation for wiring and phasor diagrams?

EXERCISES

1. A periodic waveform of voltage and the associated current is shown in each of the graphs in Fig. 7.32.

(a) For each graph calculate average values of voltage, current, and power.

(b) Is average power always equal to the product of average voltage and average current?   Explain briefly.

(c) For each graph calculate effective values of voltage and current.

(d) Is average power always equal to the product of effective voltage and effective current?   Explain briefly.

2. Repeat Exercise 1 for the waveforms of Fig. 7.33.

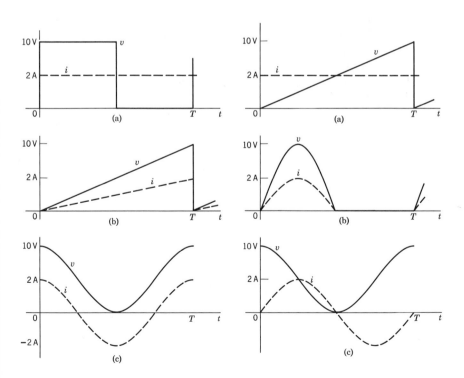

Fig. 7.32 Periodic waveforms.   **Fig. 7.33** Periodic waveforms.

3. The sinusoidal current shown in Fig. 7.34 flows through a series RL circuit where $R = 3\ \Omega$ and $L = 5$ mH.   Frequency $\omega = 1000$ rad/sec.
   (a) Find the average and effective values of current.
   (b) Find the average and effective values of the voltage across the RL combination.

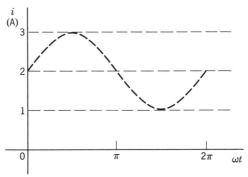

Fig. 7.34

4. If an alternating voltage is applied to a series combination of rectifier and resistor (Fig. 7.35), the resistor current will consist of positive half cycles only. For $I_{\text{peak}} = 5$ A and $f = 60$ cps, calculate:
   (a) The average or d-c current through the resistor.
   (b) The total charge passing the rectifier in one cycle.
   (c) The average power dissipated by the resistor.

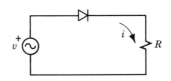

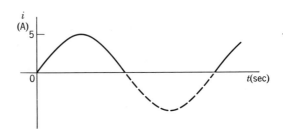

Fig. 7.35

5. Given a voltage consisting of a d-c component of magnitude V_1 and a sinusoidal component having an effective value V_2.

(a) Sketch the total voltage as a function of time for one cycle.

(b) Show that the effective value of the combination is $(V_1^2 + V_2^2)^{1/2}$.

6. The periodic current of Fig. 7.36 is measured simultaneously by a d-c ammeter and an a-c ammeter of the types described in the text. Determine the reading on each.

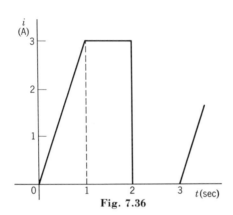

Fig. 7.36

7. The duty cycle of an electric motor is: Idling at $t = 0$ and consuming 5 hp; load increased uniformly over 5 sec to maximum of 30 hp (input); full load of 30 hp held for 5 sec; load removed and motor idling (5 hp) for 10 sec.

(a) Sketch the duty cycle of hp vs time.

(b) List the assumptions necessary in determining the motor required.

(c) Specify the proper motor (available in 15, 20, 30, and 50 hp).

8. The duty cycle of a motor supplying power for an extrusion process (requiring 2 sec) is as shown in Fig. 7.36 with the y axis changed to power in hp. The original motor has burned out and the replacement is rated at 1 hp continuous duty. Specify the number of extrusions allowable per minute. List the assumptions made.

9. Given $i = \sqrt{2}\, I \cos(\omega t + 60°)$ in the current coil of a wattmeter and $v = \sqrt{2}\, V \cos(\omega t - 15°)$ across the voltage coil, predict the wattmeter reading.

10. Given $i = 10 \cos(\omega t - 30°)$ A in the current coil of a wattmeter and $v = 200 \cos(\omega t - 90°)$ V across the voltage coil, predict the wattmeter reading.

11. A current $\mathbf{I} = I \,\underline{/\theta}$ flows through a series combination of R and X_C. Express, in terms of the given quantities, the average power delivered to the combination. Explain your reasoning. Draw a complete phasor diagram.

12. A load connected across a 120-V, 60-cycle line draws 5 kW at a leading pf of 0.6.

(a) Determine the current and the reactive power.

(b) What series combination of circuit elements is equivalent to this load?

13. Repeat Exercise 12 assuming 0.6 pf *lagging*.

14. A 220-V, 60-cycle, single-phase induction motor is represented by a series combination of $R = 10\ \Omega$ and $L = 30$ mH.

(a) Calculate the input power, power factor, reactive power, and apparent power.

(b) If the motor is 74.6% efficient, calculate the output power in hp.

15. An unknown impedance Z is connected as shown in Fig. 7.37. Wattmeter WM indicates 120 W delivered to Z when voltmeter VM_2 indicates 100 V across Z. The current to Z is 2 A on ammeter AM. On the source side of the series reactance $X_L = 10\ \Omega$, VM_1 indicates a source voltage of 85 V.

(a) Calculate pf and resistive and reactive components of Z.

(b) Is Z inductive or capacitive? Draw the power triangle.

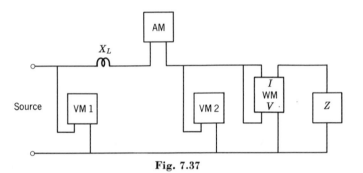

Fig. 7.37

16. A load impedance Z_1 is connected across a voltage source and instrumented as shown in Fig. 7.38. Voltmeter VM reads 400 V, ammeter AM reads 20 A, and wattmeter WM reads 4800 W.

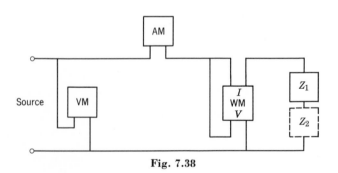

Fig. 7.38

(a) Determine the power, reactive power, apparent power, and pf.

(b) Determine the resistance and reactance components of Z_1. Can you tell if Z_1 is inductive or capacitive?

(c) A second impedance Z_2 known to be purely capacitive reactance is inserted in series with Z_1 and the ammeter now reads 26.7 A. Is Z_1 capacitive or inductive? Calculate the new wattmeter reading.

17. A capacitive load drawing 50 kVA at 0.6 pf is connected in parallel with an inductive load, drawing 10 kW and 10 kVAR, across a 500-V line. Sketch a power diagram and calculate the total line current.

18. Specify the unit to be connected in parallel with the two loads of Exercise 17 to bring the total to 50 kW at unity pf.

19. An induction furnace connected across a 200-V, 60-cycle line draws 10 kVA at 0.5 pf lagging. It is desired to place in parallel a capacitor C so that the total powerfactor of the combination is 0.8 lagging.

(a) Draw a circuit diagram representing the furnace by a resistance R in series with an inductance L.

(b) Draw a phasor diagram showing $\mathbf{V}$ and $\mathbf{I}_f$ and the desired $\mathbf{I}$ of the combination. (Is the power changed by adding C?)

(c) Calculate and show on the phasor diagram the necessary capacitor current $\mathbf{I}_C$.

(d) Construct a power diagram showing power, reactive power, and apparent power of the furnace alone and of the desired combination.

(e) Calculate the reactive power (kVAR) to be supplied by the capacitor and the desired current I_C.

20. Examine the dial of a radio and determine the frequency range of the AM broadcast band. Calculate the range of capacitance needed with a 25-μH inductance to tune over the band.

21. Write the duals of: "impedance," "reactance," "resistance," "inductance," and "capacitance." Write out a statement (50 words or less) describing the behavior of a *series* resonant circuit including each of the above words, underlined. Obtain a statement of the behavior of a *parallel* resonant circuit by substituting the duals.

22. Draw the pole-zero admittance diagram for a series combination of R and C.

(a) Sketch the shape of the curves of Y and θ_Y as functions of ω from inspection of the pole-zero diagram.

(b) For $R = 1\ \Omega$ and $C = 0.25$ F, graphically determine sufficient points to plot Y and θ_Y as functions of ω.

23. The natural response of a series RLC circuit ($R = 10\ \Omega$) is $i = Ae^{-t}\cos(5t + \pi/2)$. Draw the pole-zero diagram of impedance and determine graphically the magnitude and angle of impedance as functions of frequency.

24. For the circuit of Exercise 23, draw the pole-zero diagram of admittance and determine graphically the magnitude and angle of admittance as functions of frequency. (Five carefully selected points are sufficient.)

25. A coil of 20-mH inductance and 40-Ω resistance is connected in series with a capacitor of 0.125 μF. A variable frequency oscillator with constant output of 10 V is connected across the series combination. Calculate and plot sufficient points to show the current response in the range $10{,}000 < \omega < 30{,}000$ rad/sec.

26. Repeat Exercise 25 for resistance increased to 80 Ω.

27. A series RLC circuit has an inductance of 40 mH and a Q of 40 over a fairly wide range of frequency. A source of variable frequency but constant magni-

tude 2 V (rms) is applied to the circuit. A maximum value of current is observed at $\omega = 25{,}000$ rad/sec. Calculate:
  (a) the resonant frequency in cps,
  (b) the maximum value of current,
  (c) the values of R and C,
  (d) the voltage across C at resonance (check by another method).

28. A voltage $v = 2\sqrt{2} \cos 10^7 t$ V is applied to the circuit of Fig. 7.39. C is adjusted (tuned) until the voltage read on the voltmeter is a maximum; for this condition, C is 1 nF and $V_C = 80$ V.
  (a) What voltages would be read across R and L?
  (b) What is the resistance R?

29. The circuit of Fig. 7.39 can be used as a "Q meter." With a current generator supplying a current $i = 20\sqrt{2} \cos 2000t$ mA, C is adjusted until a minimum voltage of 2 V appears across the entire RLC circuit. Under these conditions, VM indicates 40 V across C alone.
  (a) Calculate the Q of the circuit.
  (b) Calculate C, L, and R.

30. A signal generator supplies 2 V at variable frequency to the circuit of Fig. 7.39 where $C = 0.5$ μF. A maximum voltage of 35 V is read on the voltmeter when the generator frequency is 2000 cps. Calculate L and R.

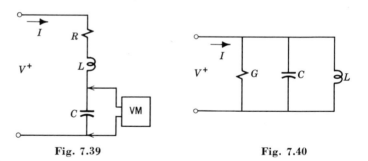

Fig. 7.39   Fig. 7.40

31. In Fig. 7.40, $G = 10^{-4}$ ℧, $C = 2.5$ μF, and $L = 16$ mH.
  (a) Determine the resonant frequency ω_o.
  (b) For $I = 10$ mA at ω_o, determine $\mathbf{I}_G$, $\mathbf{I}_C$, and $\mathbf{I}_L$ and show on a phasor diagram with $\mathbf{V}$.

32. In Fig. 7.40, $I = 12$ mA at $\omega = 10^6$ rad/sec, $G = 10^{-5}$ ℧ and $L = 5$ mH.
  (a) For what value of C is the voltage across G a maximum?
  (b) What is this maximum voltage across G?
  (c) For $I = 12$ mA at $\omega = 2 \times 10^6$ rad/sec (C unchanged), what is V_G?

33. Using the basic definition, derive an expression for Q for the circuit of Fig. 7.40.

34. As shown in Fig. 7.41, the same three elements are connected in two different ways.
  (a) Assuming Q is high, derive an approximate expression for Q of the parallel circuit and compare it to that for Q of the series circuit.

(b) Derive an approximate expression for Z of the parallel circuit at resonance and compare it to that for the series circuit.

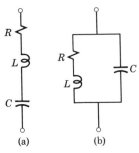

(a)   (b)

Fig. 7.41

35. The natural response of a pendulum in terms of displacement is

$$x = X_m e^{-t/50} \sin 2\pi t$$

Define and determine the Q of this pendulum.

36. Define and determine the Q of an "official" tennis ball.

37. In Fig. 7.41b at 10 kc, $R = 40\ \Omega$, $X_L = 200\ \Omega$, and $X_C = 200\ \Omega$.

(a) Calculate the admittance and impedance at 10 kc.

(b) Define resonance and calculate the resonant frequency in kc.

(c) Sketch a phasor diagram of voltages and currents at resonance.

38. Define and determine the bandwidth of the circuit of Exercise 27.

39. A series resonant circuit is to be designed for a resonant frequency of 20,000 rad/sec and a bandwidth of 400 rad/sec. A capacitor of 0.5 μF capacitance and negligible resistance is available; specify the electrical characteristics of the necessary inductor.

40. An inductor of 159 μH inductance and 100 Ω resistance is to be used in a series circuit resonating at 1.5 Mc.

(a) Determine the bandwidth and the half-power points.

(b) Determine the circuit admittance at 1.7 Mc.

41. The inductor of Exercise 40 is used in a parallel circuit resonating at 2 Mc.

(a) Using the results of Exercise 34, determine the bandwidth.

(b) Determine the circuit impedance at 1.8 Mc.

42. The terminal board of a three-phase generator is shown in Fig. 7.42. Measurements indicate the voltages are as follows:

$$v_{12} = 100 \sqrt{2} \cos \omega t$$

$$v_{34} = 100 \sqrt{2} \cos (\omega t + 60°)$$

$$v_{56} = 100 \sqrt{2} \cos (\omega t + 120°)$$

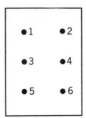

Fig. 7.42

(a) Draw a delta voltage system using these voltages, clearly indicating what connections are to be made on the panel and which are the output terminals.

(b) Repeat for a wye voltage system.

43. Given the circuit of Fig. 7.43 with

$$\mathbf{V_1} = 120 \ \underline{/90°} \ \mathrm{V} \qquad \mathbf{V_3} = 120 \ \underline{/-150°} \ \mathrm{V}$$

$$\mathbf{V_2} = 120 \ \underline{/-30°} \ \mathrm{V} \qquad \mathbf{Z} = 3 + j4 \ \Omega$$

(a) Calculate phasors $\mathbf{I_1}$, $\mathbf{I_2}$, and $\mathbf{I_3}$.

(b) If terminals x are connected together and terminals y are connected together, what will be current $\mathbf{I_{yx}}$?

(c) Under the condition of part b, what will be the voltage $\mathbf{V_{cd}}$?

(d) Draw the phasors of $\mathbf{V_1}$, $\mathbf{V_2}$, $\mathbf{V_3}$, and $\mathbf{I_1}$, $\mathbf{I_2}$, $\mathbf{I_3}$ on a single phasor diagram with all phasors starting from a common point.

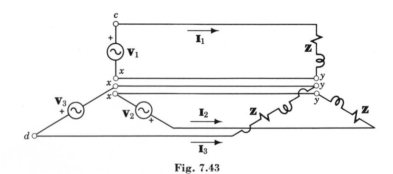

Fig. 7.43

44. Three resistances of 20 Ω each are connected in Δ across a 440-V line. (This means a balanced 3-phase source, 440 V line to line.) Calculate phase and line currents.

45. Repeat Exercise 44 with the resistors connected in Y.

46. Three equal impedances of $10 \ \underline{/-30°} \ \Omega$ are connected in Δ across a 220-V line. (This means a balanced three-phase source, 220-V line to line.)

(a) Draw a clearly labeled wiring diagram properly oriented.

  (b) Calculate phase and line currents.
  (c) Draw a labeled phasor diagram of voltages and currents.
  (d) Calculate the total power.
47. Repeat Exercise 46 with the impedances connected in **Y**.
48. Three equal impedances $Z = 16 + j12$ are connected in Y across a 220-V source; phase rotation is *abc*. Draw a labeled wiring diagram, calculate the line current, and determine the phase angle between voltage V_{ab} and current I_c.
49. Three identical resistors are to be connected in Δ across a 240-V line to make a 6-kW heater. Specify the resistance and power rating of each resistor.
50. Repeat Exercise 49 with the resistors connected in **Y**.
51. Three equal impedances $Z = 6 + j8$ are connected in Δ across a 220-V source.
  (a) Draw a clearly labeled wiring diagram.
  (b) Calculate phase and line currents.
  (c) Draw a labeled phasor diagram of voltages and currents.
  (d) Calculate the total power.
52. Repeat Exercise 51 with the impedances connected in **Y**.
53. A balanced Δ capacitive load is connected as shown in Fig. 7.30. A voltmeter across line *ab* reads 200 V. An ammeter in line *a* reads 17.32A. A wattmeter with voltage coil across *ab* and current coil in line *a* reads 3000 W. Sketch the phasor diagram and determine the complex phase impedance **Z**.

PROBLEMS

1. The duty cycle of the motor driving a punch press consists of pulses of 100-hp amplitude and 1 sec duration every four sec. Specify the motor rating to handle this duty. If a large flywheel is added to the punch press, what is the proper motor rating? Explain your reasoning.
2. During an average month the power bill for an industrial plant indicates consumption of 160,000 kWh and 177,000 kVARh (lagging). The monthly rate schedule is: First 6000 kWh @ 2.5¢/kWh, next 24,000 kWh @ 2.2¢, next 70,000 kWh @ 1.8¢, and the excess @ 1.0¢. The rate schedule contains the provision that the total charge is decreased or increased by 0.5% for each 1% that the average pf is greater or less than 85%.
  (a) Compute the monthly power bill.
  (b) Investigate the possibility of adding capacitors ($15 per kVAR) to improve pf to 85%. Assume 20 h/day operation and 15% fixed charges (depreciation, maintenance, etc.) on the capacitors; *state* any other assumptions.
3. Draw the pole-zero admittance diagram for a series *RLC* circuit and derive an expression for *Q* in terms of α and ω_o.
4. Prove that the energy stored in a series *RLC* circuit excited at its resonant frequency is a constant and not a function of time.
5. Derive an expression for the equivalent series impedance of the circuit in Fig. 7.44. Choose *R* so that $R^2 = L/C$ and simplify the expression for impedance. How does the definition of resonance apply to this circuit? Explain by means of phasor diagrams (or a locus diagram) what happens as ω is varied.

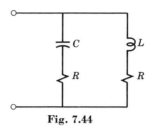

Fig. 7.44

6. For the same line-to-line voltage and the same current per conductor, compare the power transmission capacity of 6 wires supplying 3 single-phase resistive loads with the capacity of 3 wires supplying a three-phase resistive load. Draw a conclusion regarding the economics of three-phase systems.

7. Three equal impedances $\mathbf{Z} = 25 \underline{/+30°}$ Ω are connected in Δ across a 250-V line as shown in Fig. 7.30a. Two wattmeters are used to measure the total power; WM$_1$ responds to V_{ab} and I_a, and WM$_2$ responds to V_{cb} (*not* V_{bc}) and I_c. Draw a labeled wiring diagram and sketch the phasor diagram of voltages and currents. From the phasor diagram predict the wattmeter readings. Compare the sum of the wattmeter readings with the total power.

- ◆ ONE-PORT NETWORKS
- ◆ LINEAR NETWORKS
- ◆ TWO-PORT NETWORKS
- ◆ NONLINEAR NETWORKS

CHAPTER **8**

General Network Analysis

In analyzing specific circuits, we developed some techniques which can be applied to circuits in general. Circuits of considerable complexity or generality we call *networks*, and important principles capable of general application we call *network theorems*. Some of these theorems are useful in reducing complicated networks to simple ones. Other theorems enable us to draw general conclusions about network behavior. In this chapter we state a few of the more useful network theorems, demonstrate their validity, and show how they are applied; general proofs are left to more advanced courses.

We start with linear networks and see how complicated two-terminal circuits can be reduced to simpler circuits which are equivalent. Working with simple equivalents, we draw some interesting conclusions about two-terminal circuits in general. Then we consider three-terminal networks and see how they can be simplified. Finally, we investigate the effects of nonlinearity, see how linear methods can be used in analyzing some nonlinear networks, and learn some new techniques applicable to nonlinear devices.

ONE-PORT NETWORKS

A common problem in a-c circuit analysis is the determination of the forced response of a two-terminal circuit. In Fig. 8.1a there is one "port"

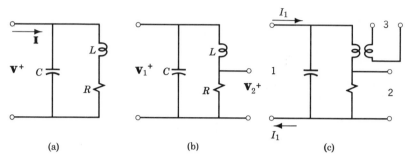

Fig. 8.1 One-port, two-port, and multiport networks.

at which excitation is supplied and response is measured. If the desired response is measured across R as in Fig. 8.1b, this circuit becomes a *three-terminal circuit* (one terminal is common to input and output) or a *two-port circuit*, or simply a *two-port*. Transistors, transformers, and transmission lines are two-ports; in each case there is an input port and a separate output port. The currents into the two terminals of a port are equal and opposite whether the device is a one-port, a two-port, or a multiport (Fig. 8.1c).

Equivalence

Two one-ports are equivalent if they present the same v-i characteristics. Two passive one-ports are equivalent if they have the same input impedance or the same input admittance; for sinusoidal excitation and response, for example, this means the same $\mathbf{Z}$ or $\mathbf{Y}$.

Ordinarily, two real networks are equivalent at one frequency only. At ω_o, the circuit of Fig. 8.1 can be represented by a pure resistance. At $\omega > \omega_o$, the equivalent impedance is a series combination of resistance and capacitive reactance. What simple series circuit is equivalent to this circuit at $\omega < \omega_o$?

Network Reduction

Replacing a complicated network with a relatively simple equivalent is advantageous in network analysis. Already we have used the fact that in passive circuits impedances and admittances are readily combined. For impedances in series,

$$\mathbf{Z}_{eq} = \mathbf{Z}_1 + \mathbf{Z}_2 + \cdots + \mathbf{Z}_n \tag{8-1}$$

and for admittances in parallel,

$$\mathbf{Y}_{eq} = \mathbf{Y}_1 + \mathbf{Y}_2 + \cdots + \mathbf{Y}_n \tag{8-2}$$

For two impedances in parallel and two admittances in series the relations (duals) are:

$$Z_{eq} = \frac{Z_1 Z_2}{Z_1 + Z_2} \quad \text{and} \quad Y_{eq} = \frac{Y_1 Y_2}{Y_1 + Y_2} \quad (8\text{-}3)$$

Equations 8-3 can be extended to cases of more than two elements, but it is usually easier to work with the reciprocals of Eqs. 8-1 and 8-2. Applying these three equations to determine the equivalent impedance of the circuit in Fig. 8.1a,

$$Z_{eq} = \frac{1}{Y_{eq}} = \frac{1}{Y_C + Y_{RL}} = \frac{1}{Y_C + \dfrac{1}{Z_{RL}}} = \frac{1}{j\omega C + \dfrac{1}{R + j\omega L}} = R_{eq} + jX_{eq}$$

When the indicated operations are carried out, it is seen that the resistive and reactive components of the equivalent impedance are both functions of frequency ω.

Another useful tool is the concept of the voltage divider or its dual, the current divider, repeated here for easy reference. Considering the circuits of Fig. 8.2, we see that

$$V_2 = \frac{Z_2}{Z_1 + Z_2} V = \frac{Z_2}{Z_{eq}} V \quad \text{and} \quad I_2 = \frac{Y_2}{Y_1 + Y_2} I = \frac{Y_2}{Y_{eq}} I \quad (8\text{-}4)$$

When a particular voltage or current is desired, using these relations is preferable to writing and solving loop or node equations. Network reduction techniques are also useful in demonstrating general theorems.

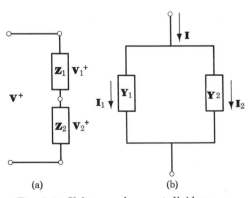

(a)   (b)

Fig. 8.2 Voltage and current dividers.

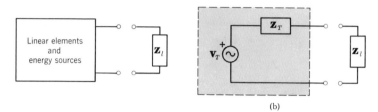

(b)

Fig. 8.3   Linear one-port and Thévenin equivalent.

Thévenin's Theorem

The one-port networks discussed so far have been *passive;* they absorb energy from the source.   In contrast, *active* networks include energy sources.   A valuable method for representing active networks by simpler equivalents is described in the following statement of *Thévenin's theorem:*

Insofar as a load is concerned, any one-port network of linear elements and energy sources can be replaced by a series combination of an ideal voltage source $\mathbf{V}_T$ *and a linear impedance* $\mathbf{Z}_T$ *where* $\mathbf{V}_T$ *is the open-circuit voltage of the one-port and* $\mathbf{Z}_T$ *is the ratio of the open-circuit voltage to the short-circuit current.*

If the two networks of Fig. 8.3 are to be equivalent for all values of load impedance, they must be equivalent for extreme values such as $\mathbf{Z}_l = \infty$ and $\mathbf{Z}_l = 0$.   The value $\mathbf{Z}_l = \infty$ corresponds to the open-circuit condition; by comparison of the two networks, the open-circuit voltage $\mathbf{V}_{oc}$ of the original network is equal to $\mathbf{V}_T$ of the equivalent.   The value $\mathbf{Z}_l = 0$ corresponds to the short-circuit condition; by comparison of the two networks, the short-circuit current $\mathbf{I}_{sc}$ of the original network is equal to $\mathbf{V}_T/\mathbf{Z}_T$ of the equivalent.   Therefore,

$$\mathbf{V}_T = \mathbf{V}_{oc} \quad \text{and} \quad \mathbf{Z}_T = \frac{\mathbf{V}_T}{\mathbf{I}_{sc}} = \frac{\mathbf{V}_{oc}}{\mathbf{I}_{sc}} \tag{8-5}$$

define the components of the Thévenin equivalent network.

Alternatively, $\mathbf{Z}_T$ is the "impedance seen by looking in" at the terminals with all independent† energy sources removed.   Voltage sources must be removed by short-circuiting, and current sources must be removed by open-circuiting.   By way of explanation, the impedance

---

† All energy sources considered up to this point have been *independent* of voltages and currents in other parts of the circuit.   *Controlled* sources, for example those used in representing transistors (Chapter 10), must not be removed in applying Thévenins' theorem.

"seen" by the network in Fig. 8.3b is $\mathbf{Z}_l$; the impedance "looking in" at the terminals of the Thévenin equivalent when $\mathbf{V}_T$ is short-circuited is $\mathbf{Z}_T$.

This theorem is particularly useful when the load is to take on a series of values or when a general analysis is being performed with literal numbers. We shall use it in analyzing such devices as transistor amplifiers and synchronous motors. No general proof of the theorem is given here, but an elementary example is solved to demonstrate its validity.

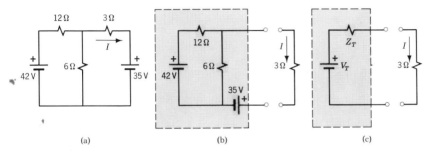

(a)   (b)   (c)

Fig. 8.4 Application of Thévenin's Theorem

EXAMPLE 1

Using Thévenin's theorem, determine the current in the 3-Ω resistance of Fig. 8.4a.

SOLUTION. The load resistance of interest is isolated as a load (Fig. 8.4b), and the Thévenin equivalent is drawn (Fig. 8.4c). Once the components of the equivalent circuit are determined, I is easily calculated. Under open-circuit conditions (Fig. 8.5a), the voltage divider concept indicates that the voltage across the 6-Ω resistance is

$$V_6 = \frac{6}{6 + 12} \, 42 = 14 \text{ V}$$

and, by Eq. 8.5,

$$V_T = V_{oc} = +14 - 35 = -21 \text{ V}$$

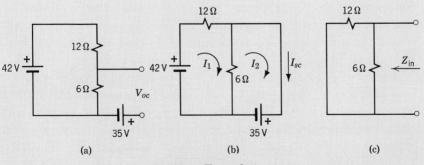

(a)   (b)   (c)

Fig. 8.5 Example 1.

Under short-circuit conditions (Fig. 8.5b), the loop-current equations are:

$$18I_1 - 6I_2 = 42$$

$$-6I_1 + 6I_2 = -35$$

Solving,

$$I_2 = I_{sc} = -\tfrac{21}{4} \text{ A}$$

Hence, by Eq. 8.5,

$$Z_T = \frac{V_{oc}}{I_{sc}} = \frac{-21}{-\frac{21}{4}} = 4 \ \Omega$$

Alternatively, the impedance looking into Fig. 8.5c is

$$Z_T = Z_{\text{in}} = \frac{6 \times 12}{6 + 12} = 4 \ \Omega$$

Therefore (Fig. 8.4c),

$$I = \frac{V_T}{Z_T + 3} = \frac{-21}{4 + 3} = -3 \text{ A}$$

and the current in the 3-Ω resistance is 3 A upward.   (This result can be checked by loop or node analysis.)

The significance of the restriction "insofar as a load is concerned" is revealed if we attempt to use the Thévenin equivalent to determine internal behavior in Example 1.   The power developed internally in the Thévenin equivalent is $P_T = V_T I = 21 \times 3 = 63$ W.   In the original circuit, $I_1 = \tfrac{4}{3}$ A and the total power supplied is $P = 35 \times 3 + 42 \times \tfrac{4}{3} = 161$ W.   The Thévenin circuit is "equivalent" only in a restricted sense.

Norton's Theorem

Our experience with duals leads us to expect that there is a parallel to Thévenin's theorem.   An alternative equivalent is described in the following statement called *Norton's theorem:*

Insofar as a load is concerned, any one-port network of linear elements and energy sources can be replaced by a parallel combination of an ideal current source I_N *and a linear admittance* Y_N *where* I_N *is the short-circuit current of the one-port and* Y_N *is the ratio of the short-circuit current to the open-circuit voltage.*

If the two networks of Fig. 8.6 are to be equivalent for all values of load admittance, they must be equivalent for extreme values such as $Y_l = \infty$ and $Y_l = 0$.   The value $Y_l = \infty$ corresponds to the short-circuit condition; by comparison of the two networks, the short-circuit current I_{sc} of the original is equal to I_N of the equivalent.   The value $Y_l = 0$ corresponds to the open-circuit condition; by comparison of the

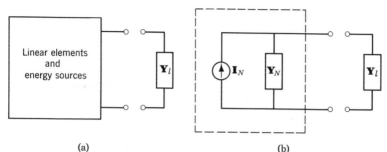

(a)   (b)

Fig. 8.6 Linear one-port and Norton equivalent.

two networks, the open-circuit voltage $\mathbf{V}_{oc}$ of the original network is equal to $\mathbf{I}_N/\mathbf{Y}_N$ of the equivalent. Therefore,

$$\mathbf{I}_N = \mathbf{I}_{sc} \quad \text{and} \quad \mathbf{Y}_N = \frac{\mathbf{I}_N}{\mathbf{V}_{oc}} = \frac{\mathbf{I}_{sc}}{\mathbf{V}_{oc}} \tag{8-6}$$

define the components of the Norton equivalent network. Note that $\mathbf{Y}_N = 1/\mathbf{Z}_T$.

EXAMPLE 2

Using Norton's theorem, determine the current in the 3-Ω resistance of Fig. 8.4a.

SOLUTION. The circuit is redrawn in Fig. 8.7a to isolate the load.

$$V_{oc} = -21 \text{ V} \quad \text{and} \quad I_{sc} = -\tfrac{21}{4} \text{ A}$$

as before. Hence, by Eqs. 8.6,

$$I_N = I_{sc} = -\frac{21}{4} \text{ A} \quad \text{and} \quad Y_N = \frac{I_{sc}}{V_{oc}} = \frac{-\frac{21}{4}}{-21} = \frac{1}{4}$$

By the current-divider principle,

$$I = \frac{Y_l}{Y_l + Y_N} I_N = \frac{\frac{1}{3}}{\frac{1}{3} + \frac{1}{4}}\left(-\frac{21}{4}\right) = \frac{4}{4+3}\left(-\frac{21}{4}\right) = -3 \text{ A}$$

as before.

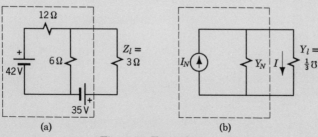

(a)   (b)

Fig. 8.7 Example 2.

As a by-product of the development of Thévenin's and Norton's theorems, we have obtained another general principle: *Any voltage source* **V** *with its associated impedance* **Z** *can be replaced by an equivalent current source* **I** *with an associated admittance* **Y** *where* **I** = **V**/**Z** *and* **Y** = 1/**Z**. This principle can be very useful in network analysis; for example, it permits the analyst to choose either an ideal voltage source or an ideal current source in representing a real energy source.

LINEAR NETWORKS

The emphasis so far has been on linear elements which combine to form linear networks governed by linear integrodifferential equations. Usually we have analyzed the response of circuits to a single excitation, but in considering the frequency selectivity of a resonant circuit, we assumed the simultaneous application of many signals of different frequencies and amplitudes.   It is time to justify this approach.

The concept of linearity is illustrated in Fig. 8.8; an element of force ΔF produces the same element of deflection Δy at any point in the linear region.   In the nonlinear region, however, an equal element of force ΔF produces a different element of deflection $\Delta y'$.

Superposition Theorem

In any situation where effect is directly proportional to cause, it is permissible to consider several causes individually and then combine the resulting individual effects to find the total effect.   It is common practice to calculate the deflection of beams in this way.   If a cantilever beam, such as the springboard of Fig. 8.9, carries three loads, the total deflec-

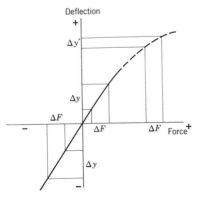

Fig. 8.8   The concept of linearity.

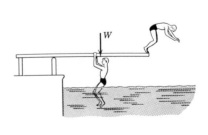

Fig. 8.9   A linear beam.

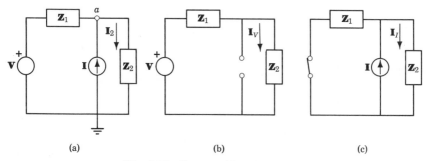

Fig. 8.10 Superposition components.

tion is the sum of the separate deflections due to the weight of the board itself, the swimmer hanging below, and the diver standing on the tip. The general principle is called the *superposition theorem* and may be stated as follows:

If cause and effect are linearly related, the total effect of several causes acting simultaneously is equal to the sum of the effects of the individual causes acting one at a time.

In electrical circuits, the causes are excitation voltages and currents and the effects are response voltages and currents. A typical case is the circuit of Fig. 8.10a. If the base of the current source is chosen as the reference node, the potential of node a is $I_2 Z_2$ and the sum of the currents out is

$$\frac{I_2 Z_2 - V}{Z_1} - I + I_2 = 0 \qquad (8\text{-}7)$$

Then

$$I_2 Z_2 - V - IZ_1 + I_2 Z_1 = 0$$

or

$$I_2 = \frac{V + IZ_1}{Z_1 + Z_2} = \frac{V}{Z_1 + Z_2} + \frac{Z_1}{Z_1 + Z_2} I \qquad (8\text{-}8)$$

Equation 8-8 indicates that the current I_2 consists of two parts, one due to V and the other due to I. If the current source is removed (by open circuiting) as in Fig. 8.10b, a component of current $I_V = V/(Z_1 + Z_2)$ flows in Z_2. If the voltage source is removed (by short-circuiting) as in Fig. 8.10c, a component of current $I_I = IZ_1/(Z_1 + Z_2)$† flows in Z_2.

---

† This is another form of the current divider equation:

$$I_2 = \frac{Y_2}{Y_1 + Y_2} I = \frac{1/Z_2}{(1/Z_1) + (1/Z_2)} I \cdot \frac{Z_1 Z_2}{Z_1 Z_2} = \frac{Z_1}{Z_2 + Z_1} I \qquad (8\text{-}9)$$

As indicated by the superposition theorem, $I_2 = I_V + I_I$, the effects produced by the two causes separately. Note that ideal voltage sources are removed by short-circuiting and ideal current sources by open-circuiting. Real energy sources always have internal impedances which must remain in the circuit.

EXAMPLE 3

A load of 6 Ω is fed by a parallel combination of two batteries. Battery A has an open-circuit voltage of 42 V and an internal resistance of 12 Ω; battery B has an open-circuit voltage of 35 V and an internal resistance of 3 Ω. Determine the current supplied and the power dissipated internally by battery B.

SOLUTION. If the batteries are represented by linear models, the circuit (Fig. 8.11a) is that of Examples 1 and 2. With the 35-V source removed (Fig. 8.11b), the component of current due to battery A can be written in one step as

$$I_A = \frac{6}{6+3}\left(\frac{42}{12+\dfrac{3 \times 6}{3+6}}\right) = \frac{2}{3}\left(\frac{42}{12+2}\right) = 2 \text{ A downward}$$

if the principles of current division (Eq. 8-9) and resistance combination (Eqs. 8-1 and 8-3) are applied simultaneously. If the 42-V source is removed (the internal resistance of the battery is left), the component of current due to battery B (Fig. 8.11c) is

$$I_B = \frac{35}{3+\dfrac{6 \times 12}{6+12}} = \frac{35}{3+4} = 5 \text{ A upward}$$

Then, by superposition,

$$I = -I_A + I_B = -2 + 5 = 3 \text{ A upward}$$

as before. To determine the power dissipated in the 3-Ω resistance, we might note that with the 35-V source removed, the power is

$$P_A = I_A{}^2 R = 2^2 \times 3 = 12 \text{ W}$$

With the 42-V source removed, the power is

$$P_B = I_B{}^2 R = 5^2 \times 3 = 75 \text{ W}$$

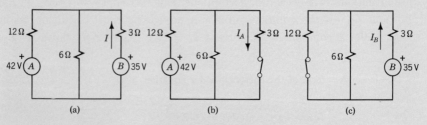

(a)   (b)   (c)

Fig. 8.11   Example 3.

But the actual power dissipated is *not* $12 + 75 = 87$ W. Why not? What principle would be violated in such a calculation? The answer is that power is not linearly related to voltage or current and therefore superposition cannot be applied in power calculations. Superposition is applicable only to linear effects such as the current response. Having found the current by superposition, we can calculate the power in the 3-Ω resistance as

$$P = I^2R = (-I_A + I_B)^2R = 3^2 \times 3 = 27 \text{ W}$$

Maximum Power Transfer

One of the distinguishing characteristics of the engineer is his concern with optimization. The engineer solves real problems and his solutions are always compromises. Efficiency costs money; safety increases complexity; performance adds weight; improvement takes time. In striving for the optimum design, the engineer provides the highest efficiency per dollar, the most powerful performance per pound, or the best results within the deadline.

Frequently the engineer has the problem of "matching" one component of a system to another to obtain optimum results. For example, an automobile transmission must be matched to the engine and, in another sense, the passing gear provides a match between the engine and the load represented by acceleration up a steep hill. The bicycle-gear ratio represents a simple solution to the problem of matching a load to a source. Why does a racing bicycle have 10 gear ratios? Why is the gear ratio different on a boy's model and a girl's model?

The optimum load for an electric source depends on the desired result. A d-c generator (Fig. 8.12a) has certain *fixed losses* which are present whether or not a load is connected and *variable losses* which are directly

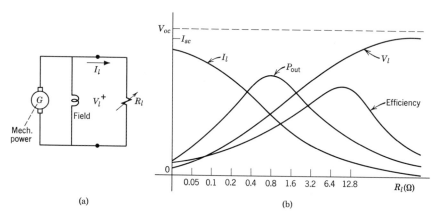

(a) (b)

Fig. 8.12 D-C generator with variable load resistance.

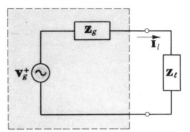

Fig. 8.13   Power transfer.

related to the output current. As shown in the graph, for R_ℓ small, the output current I_ℓ is high, but the output voltage V_ℓ is low; for R_ℓ large, the output voltage is high, but the current is low. At an intermediate value of R_ℓ the power output is a maximum. The efficiency, output/ input, increases as the load resistance increases from zero. Because of the fixed losses, however, a maximum efficiency occurs at a particular value of R_ℓ. If the available power is large and efficiency is the important criterion, a relatively large value of load resistance is optimum; this is true in most applications of electrical power equipment. If efficiency is less important and the power available is limited, then a lower value of load resistance is optimum; this is true in many communications applications.

With the aid of Thévenin's theorem we can draw a general conclusion about the conditions for maximum power transfer. We know that any network of linear elements and energy sources (and, approximately, any real generator and its associated circuitry) can be represented by a series combination of an ideal voltage **V** and an impedance **Z**. In the simplest case, these are the open-circuit generator voltage $\mathbf{V}_g$ and the internal impedance $\mathbf{Z}_g$ (Fig. 8.13). The current delivered to the load is

$$I_\ell = \frac{V_g}{|\mathbf{Z}_g + \mathbf{Z}_\ell|} = \frac{V_g}{\sqrt{(R_g + R_\ell)^2 + (X_g + X_\ell)^2}}$$

The power transferred to the load is

$$P_\ell = I_\ell^2 R_\ell = \frac{V_g^2 R_\ell}{(R_g + R_\ell)^2 + (X_g + X_\ell)^2} \tag{8-10}$$

For a given generator, V_g, R_g, and X_g are fixed; R_ℓ and X_ℓ can be adjusted for optimum results. For maximum power transfer, Eq. 8-10 is to be maximized. The general procedure is to differentiate with respect to the variable and set the derivative equal to zero, but Eq. 8-10 indicates that for any value of R_t, P_t is maximum for $X_t = -X_g$. Hence, the first requirement for maximum power transfer is that the reactance of the load be made equal and opposite to the equivalent reactance of the source. Under this condition,

$$P_t = \frac{V_g{}^2 R_t}{(R_g + R_t)^2} = V_g{}^2 R_t (R_g + R_t)^{-2}$$

and for maximum P_t,

$$\frac{dP_t}{dR_t} = V_g{}^2 [(R_g + R_t)^{-2} - 2R_t(R_g + R_t)^{-3}] = 0$$

Solving,

$$R_t = R_g$$

Hence, the second requirement is that the resistance of the load be made equal to the equivalent resistance of the source. In general, for maximum power transfer the impedance of the load should be adjusted so that

$$\mathbf{Z}_t = R_t + jX_t = R_g - jX_g = \mathbf{Z}_g{}^* \qquad (8\text{-}11)$$

In words, *for maximum power transfer the impedance of the load should be made equal to the complex conjugate of the Thévenin equivalent impedance of the source.*

Under the conditions for maximum power transfer, the efficiency is just 50% since $I^2 R_t = I^2 R_g$ and half the power is dissipated internally in the source. No electrical appliance is designed to draw maximum power from a wall-outlet which has an equivalent internal impedance of a small fraction of an ohm. Instead, an electrical load is usually designed to draw a definite amount of power and, for high efficiency and low voltage drop, the impedance of the source is made as low as is economically feasible. Note that the source impedance is never made equal to the load impedance.

EXAMPLE 4

A generator represented by a voltage $\mathbf{V}_g = 100 \underline{/0°}$ V and an internal impedance $\mathbf{Z}_g = 10 + j20\ \Omega$ is connected to a load ($\mathbf{Z}_t = 20 + jX_t$) by means of a transmission network ($\mathbf{Z}_t = R_t - j15\ \Omega$). Specify the values of R_t and X_t for maximum power transfer to the load.

SOLUTION. In this unusual case (Fig. 8.14), the source has one variable element R_t, and the load has one variable element X_t. If P_t is to be maximized, then I_t must be maximized and R_t must be *zero* because the addition of any resistance can only decrease I_t.

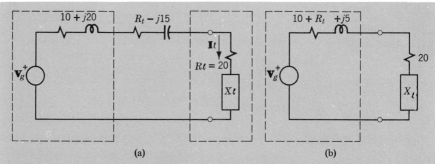

(a)   (b)

Fig. 8.14   Example 4.

Insofar as the load is concerned, the equivalent source impedance is then

$$\mathbf{Z}_{eq} = \mathbf{Z}_g + \mathbf{Z}_t = 10 + j20 + 0 - j15 = 10 + j5 \; \Omega$$

By Eq. 8-11, for maximum I_t and maximum P_t,

$$X_t = -X_{eq} = -5 \; \Omega$$

If a variation in R_t were permitted, then, for maximum power transfer from this source, R_t would be made equal to $R_{eq} = 10 \; \Omega$.

Reciprocity Theorem

Another interesting principle (which we need for a development later in this chapter) can be demonstrated by the circuit of Example 3 (Fig. 8.11b redrawn here as Fig. 8.15a for convenience). A voltage of 42 V applied in branch 1 caused a current of 2 A to flow in branch 2. Suppose the 42-V source and the ammeter are interchanged as in Fig. 8.15b. Will the current indicated by the ammeter be larger or smaller than 2 A? Let us calculate I_1 by applying the principles of current division and

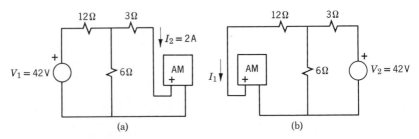

(a)   (b)

Fig. 8.15   Reciprocity in linear bilateral networks.

resistance combination. By inspection,

$$I_1 = \frac{6}{6 + 12}\left(\frac{42}{3 + \dfrac{6 \times 12}{6 + 12}}\right) = \frac{1}{3}\left(\frac{42}{3 + 4}\right) = 2 \text{ A}$$

The current is exactly the same! This calculation illustrates a principle, called the *reciprocity theorem*, which can be proved in general form. One statement of the theorem is as follows:

In any passive, linear, bilateral network, if a voltage **V** *applied in branch 1 causes a current* **I** *to flow in branch 2, then voltage* **V** *applied in branch 2 will cause current* **I** *to flow in branch 1.*

The reciprocity principle holds only for linear *passive* networks; here V is the only energy source. Also, the network elements must be *bilateral;* in other words, cause and effect must proceed equally well in both directions. All the components considered so far have been bilateral; many practical devices are not. For example, an audio signal applied to the loudspeaker of a radio will not produce a radio signal in the antenna.

The ratio of a voltage V_1 in one part of a network to a current I_2 in another part is called the *transfer impedance* $Z_{12} = V_1/I_2$. This network parameter has all the properties of an impedance; for example, the pole-zero diagram of the transfer impedance Z_{12} determines the character of the response i_2 to an excitation v_1. (In a similar way, the frequency response of an amplifier is determined by a *transfer function* relating output to input variables.) An important conclusion of the reciprocity theorem is that *in passive, linear, bilateral networks, the transfer impedance* Z_{12} *is just equal to* Z_{21}. (What is the value of Z_{12} in Fig. 8.15?)

TWO-PORT NETWORKS

If we attempt to find the equivalent series resistance of the circuit in Fig. 8.16a by network reduction methods, we find that there are no resistances in series or parallel to be combined. There is something different about this circuit. What is it? The network reduction formulas previously derived are applicable to two-terminal networks only; in this circuit there is a *three-terminal network* which cannot be replaced by a two-terminal equivalent. However, if the three-terminal network shaded in Fig. 8.16b is transformed into a properly selected three-terminal equivalent network, the difficulty is removed and the equivalent series resistance can be found.

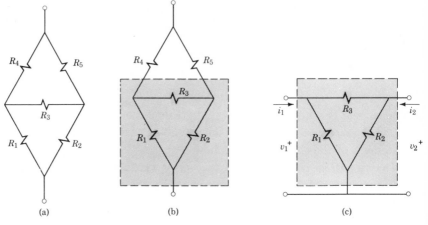

Fig. 8.16 Bridge circuit analysis.

Two-Ports

The three-terminal network is a special case of the general *two-port* suggested by Fig. 8.16c. By convention, $+i_1$ and $+i_2$ are assumed *into* the network. Note that the current at third terminal is defined by i_1 and i_2, and the third voltage is defined by v_1 and v_2. In general, of the four variables only two are independent and we may write

$$\begin{cases} v_1 = f_1(i_1, i_2) \\ v_2 = f_2(i_1, i_2) \end{cases} \quad \text{or} \quad \begin{cases} i_1 = \varphi_1(v_1, v_2) \\ i_2 = \varphi_2(v_1, v_2) \end{cases} \tag{8-12}$$

Equations similar to Eqs. 8-12 are useful in characterizing real devices such as transistors and motors. For the special case of ideal elements, the functions are linear and Eqs. 8-12 become

$$\begin{cases} v_1 = k_1 i_1 + k_2 i_2 \\ v_2 = k_3 i_1 + k_4 i_2 \end{cases} \quad \text{or} \quad \begin{cases} i_1 = k_5 v_1 + k_6 v_2 \\ i_2 = k_7 v_1 + k_8 v_2 \end{cases} \tag{8-13}$$

For sinusoidal excitation, the voltages and currents are represented by phasors, the constants are complex impedances or admittances, and Eqs. 8-13 become

$$\begin{cases} \mathbf{V}_1 = \mathbf{Z}_{11}\mathbf{I}_1 + \mathbf{Z}_{12}\mathbf{I}_2 \\ \mathbf{V}_2 = \mathbf{Z}_{21}\mathbf{I}_1 + \mathbf{Z}_{22}\mathbf{I}_2 \end{cases} \quad \text{or} \quad \begin{cases} \mathbf{I}_1 = \mathbf{Y}_{11}\mathbf{V}_1 + \mathbf{Y}_{12}\mathbf{V}_2 \\ \mathbf{I}_2 = \mathbf{Y}_{21}\mathbf{V}_1 + \mathbf{Y}_{22}\mathbf{V}_2 \end{cases} \tag{8-14}$$

For bilateral elements, $\mathbf{Z}_{12} = \mathbf{Z}_{21}$ and $\mathbf{Y}_{12} = \mathbf{Y}_{21}$ by the theorem of reciprocity, and we conclude that any linear bilateral two-port can be characterized by a set of three parameters.

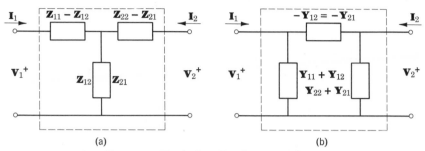

(a)   (b)

Fig. 8.17 Equivalent T and π networks.

Comparing Eq. 8-14a with the circuit of Fig. 8.17a, we see that one possible arrangement of the impedance parameters is in a T configuration as shown. Writing loop equations for Fig. 8.17a,

$$V_1 = (Z_{11} - Z_{12} + Z_{12})I_1 + Z_{12}I_2 = Z_{11}I_1 + Z_{12}I_2$$

$$V_2 = Z_{21}I_1 + (Z_{22} - Z_{21} + Z_{21})I_2 = Z_{21}I_1 + Z_{22}I_2$$

as required. Comparing Eq. 8-14b with the circuit of Fig. 8.17b, we see that one possible arrangement of the admittance parameters is in a π configuration as shown. This can be confirmed by writing the appropriate node equations. Other circuit arrangements are possible and will be developed when needed.

T-π Transformation

For our present purposes, let us consider the T and π configurations as three-terminal networks. As redrawn in Fig. 8.18, these can also be

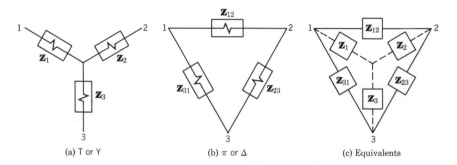

(a) T or Y   (b) π or Δ   (c) Equivalents

Fig. 8.18 Equivalent three-terminal networks.

called **Y** and Δ networks. Here all elements are designated by their impedances (rather than admittances) and lettered in a consistent scheme.

We specified that two passive two-terminal networks are equivalent if they have the same terminal impedance; if this is true, one can be substituted for the other. Extending this concept of equivalence to three-terminal networks, we say that the **T** and π networks are equivalent if the impedance at any pair of terminals of one network is just equal to the impedance at the corresponding pair of terminals of the other. On the basis of this equality we can determine the conditions under which one network can be substituted for the other. As noted previously, in practical networks the equivalence may hold for only a single frequency.

The procedure is straightforward, but the algebra is laborious. Equating the impedances of the two networks between terminals 1 and 2:

$$Z_1 + Z_2 = \frac{Z_{12}(Z_{23} + Z_{31})}{Z_{12} + Z_{23} + Z_{31}} \tag{8-15}$$

Between terminals 2 and 3:

$$Z_2 + Z_3 = \frac{Z_{23}(Z_{31} + Z_{12})}{Z_{12} + Z_{23} + Z_{31}} \tag{8-16}$$

Between terminals 3 and 1:

$$Z_3 + Z_1 = \frac{Z_{31}(Z_{12} + Z_{23})}{Z_{12} + Z_{23} + Z_{31}} \tag{8-17}$$

Note the symmetry of these three equations; it is due to the inherent symmetry of the networks. The second equation can be written directly from the first by a cyclical change in subscripts.

To solve for the **T** (or **Y**) elements in terms of the π (or Δ) elements, we first eliminate Z_3 by subtracting Eq. 8-17 from Eq. 8-16. Then this result is subtracted from Eq. 8-15 to eliminate Z_2. The result is:

$$Z_1 = \frac{Z_{12}Z_{31}}{Z_{12} + Z_{23} + Z_{31}} \tag{8-18}$$

By symmetry we conclude that the impedance of the equivalent **Y** element is the product of the adjacent Δ elements divided by the sum of the Δ elements (Fig. 8.18c). This is called the Δ-**Y** (delta-wye) or π-**T** (pi-tee) transformation.

If instead we solve for the equivalent Δ (or π) elements in terms of the **Y** (or **T**) elements, the result is:

$$Z_{12} = \frac{Z_1Z_2 + Z_2Z_3 + Z_3Z_1}{Z_3} \tag{8-19}$$

Again we invoke symmetry and conclude that the impedance of the equivalent Δ element is the sum of the products of the Y elements divided by the opposite Y element.

EXAMPLE 5

Determine the equivalent series resistance of the bridge network of Fig. 8.19a. SOLUTION. First, the Δ in the dashed circle is replaced by an equivalent Y (Fig. 8.19b), using Eq. 8.18.

$$Z_1 = \frac{Z_{12}Z_{31}}{Z_{12} + Z_{23} + Z_{31}} = \frac{10 \times 6}{10 + 6 + 4} = \frac{60}{20} = 3 \ \Omega$$

$$Z_2 = \frac{Z_{23}Z_{12}}{Z_{12} + Z_{23} + Z_{31}} = \frac{4 \times 10}{10 + 6 + 4} = \frac{40}{20} = 2 \ \Omega$$

$$Z_3 = \frac{Z_{31}Z_{23}}{Z_{12} + Z_{23} + Z_{31}} = \frac{6 \times 4}{10 + 6 + 4} = \frac{24}{20} = 1.2 \ \Omega$$

When this substitution is made, resistances in series and parallel can be combined to give

$$Z_{ab} = \frac{(3 + 3)(1 + 2)}{(3 + 3) + (1 + 2)} + 1.2 = \frac{6 \times 3}{6 + 3} + 1.2 = 2 + 1.2 = 3.2 \ \Omega$$

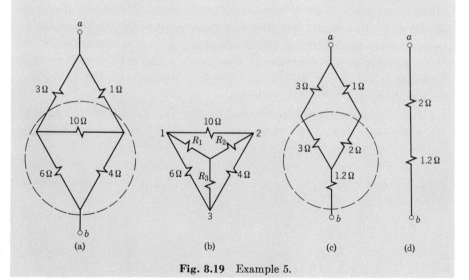

Fig. 8.19 Example 5.

Another formulation of Eq. 8-19 is obtained if we recognize and take advantage of the duality relation between the Y and Δ networks. From Eq. 8-18 we can write directly

$$\mathbf{Y}_{12} = \frac{\mathbf{Y}_1\mathbf{Y}_2}{\mathbf{Y}_1 + \mathbf{Y}_2 + \mathbf{Y}_3} \tag{8-19a}$$

These are not equations to be memorized; rather they are formulas to be applied in specific problems. A common application is in the simplification of networks where two-terminal network reduction methods do not work.

EXAMPLE 6

Three equal impedances $\mathbf{Z} = 10 \underline{/60°}\ \Omega$ are connected in $\mathbf{Y}$ to form a three-phase load. Determine the impedances of the equivalent Δ.

SOLUTION. For this balanced network, Eq. 8-19a yields

$$\mathbf{Y}_{ab} = \frac{\mathbf{Y}_a\mathbf{Y}_b}{\mathbf{Y}_a + \mathbf{Y}_b + \mathbf{Y}_c} = \frac{(\mathbf{Y}_a)^2}{3\mathbf{Y}_a} = \frac{\mathbf{Y}_a}{3}$$

and

$$\mathbf{Z}_{ab} = \frac{1}{\mathbf{Y}_{ab}} = \frac{3}{\mathbf{Y}_a} = 3\mathbf{Z}_a = 30 \underline{/60°}\ \Omega$$

The impedances of the equivalent Δ load are just equal to three times the corresponding impedances of the balanced $\mathbf{Y}$ load. (The same result is obtained more directly from Eq. 8.19.)

Coupling Circuits

The two-port is frequently used as a *coupling circuit* to tie one component of a system to another in an optimum way. The π circuit of Fig. 8.20a is used to couple two stages of amplification; the input voltage v_1 contains a-c signals and a d-c component inherent in the operation of the amplifier (a vacuum tube or transistor). The output voltage contains only a-c signals because the coupling capacitor C_C blocks the d-c component.

The inverse function is performed by the *filter* (Fig. 8.20b), a special coupling circuit which blocks a-c components but permits direct currents to flow unimpeded. Electronic power supplies which transform a-c power into direct currents to supply electronic apparatus ordinarily contain filters of this type. The frequency response of these coupling circuits is interesting and will be investigated later on.

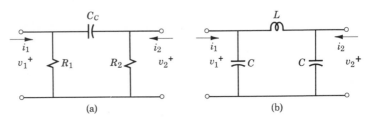

Fig. 8.20 Coupling circuit and filter.

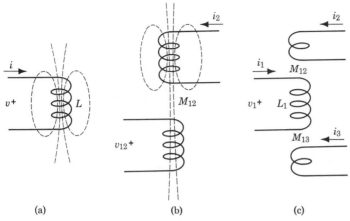

(a)   (b)   (c)

Fig. 8.21 Self- and mutual inductance.

The two-ports examined so far provide *conductive* coupling, so called because there is a direct electrical connection between the output and the input. Another possibility is to employ a magnetic field to couple energy from one component to another; in this important category are trans- formers and induction motors. In the transformer, the output is electri- cally isolated from the input. In the induction motor, the rotating wind- ing is mechanically and electrically isolated from the stationary winding. From a circuit viewpoint, these important practical features are described in terms of the circuit parameter called "mutual inductance."

Mutual Inductance

As you recall from physics, the voltage in volts induced in a coil of n turns encircling a changing magnetic flux ϕ in webers is

$$v = n\frac{d\phi}{dt} \qquad (8\text{-}20)$$

If the flux is due to current flowing in the coil itself (Fig. 8.21a), the flux is proportional to the current and the number of turns or $\phi = kni$ and

$$v = n\frac{d(kni)}{dt} = kn^2\frac{di}{dt} = L\frac{di}{dt} \qquad (8\text{-}21)$$

where L is the self-inductance in henrys. Up to this point, only this form of inductance has been discussed, so we have referred to L simply as "inductance."

If the changing flux is due to a current i_2 in a second coil (Fig. 8.21b), the voltage v_{12} induced in coil 1 is

$$v_{12} = M_{12} \frac{di_2}{dt} \qquad (8\text{-}22)$$

where M_{12} is the *mutual inductance* in henrys. In the same way, a voltage can be induced in coil 1 due to a changing current i_3 in a third coil. For a linear system, superposition applies and the voltage appearing across coil 1 in Fig. 8.21c is

$$v_1 = v_{11} + v_{12} + v_{13} = L_1 \frac{di_1}{dt} + M_{12} \frac{di_2}{dt} + M_{13} \frac{di_3}{dt} \qquad (8\text{-}23)$$

The magnitude and sign of mutual inductance M_{12} depend on the proximity and the orientation of the two coils. If the orientation is such that the flux contributed by current i_2 subtracts from that due to current i_1, the corresponding voltage term v_{12} is negative. If it is desired that mutual inductance M_{12} always be a positive quantity, then a negative sign must be used with the $M_{12}(di_2/dt)$ term in Eq. 8-23. There are conventional methods of designating coil terminals so that this sign is determined automatically.[†]

Inductive Coupling

A practical form of magnetic or inductive coupling is shown in Fig. 8.22a. To increase the coupling, that is, to increase the mutual inductance M, the two real coils represented by this linear model may be wound on a common core with favorable magnetic properties, but the two coils are electrically isolated. This inductively coupled two-port appears in a wide variety of practical forms. In a radio receiver, a few turns of

---

[†] See p. 332 of H. H. Skilling: *Electrical Engineering Circuits*, 2nd ed., John Wiley and Sons, New York, 1965.

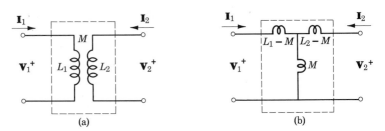

(a)   (b)

Fig. 8.22 Inductively coupled circuit and equivalent T circuit.

fine wire on an insulating form couple the antenna to the first amplifier stage.   In a power system, many turns of heavy wire wound on an iron core 10 ft tall couple the generator to the high-voltage transmission line.

For purposes of analysis it may be desirable to replace the inductively coupled two-port by the equivalent T circuit of Fig. 8.22b.   For sinusoids, the voltage V_{12} coupled into the input by a current I_2 is $V_{12} = j\omega M_{12}I_2$ where $j\omega M_{12}$ is a mutual impedance Z_{12}.   By the reciprocity theorem, for bilateral networks $Z_{12} = Z_{21}$ or $M_{12} = M_{21} = M$ as shown.   Then

$$V_1 = j\omega L_1 I_1 + j\omega M I_2 = Z_{11}I_1 + Z_{12}I_2$$
$$V_2 = j\omega M I_1 + j\omega L_2 I_2 = Z_{21}I_1 + Z_{22}I_2$$

(8-24)

Comparing Eqs. 8-24 with the circuit of Fig. 8.22b, we see that the T circuit shown is an equivalent.   In the equivalent circuit, the common element is a self-inductance of magnitude M.

EXAMPLE 7

A series RLC circuit is inductively coupled to an input circuit consisting of R_1 and L_1 (Fig. 8.23).   Determine the total input impedance.

SOLUTION.   The "primary" voltage is the sum of the I_1Z_{11} voltage drop and the voltage induced by the "secondary" current or

$$V_1 = I_1Z_{11} + j\omega M I_2 = I_1(R_1 + j\omega L_1) + j\omega M I_2 \qquad (8\text{-}25)$$

For the secondary loop, self impedance Z_{22} consists of L_2, R_2, and C_2

$$\therefore\ V_2 = 0 = j\omega M I_1 + Z_{22}I_2 = j\omega M I_1 + \left(R_2 + j\omega L_2 - j\frac{1}{\omega C_2}\right)I_2 \quad (8\text{-}26)$$

Solving Eq. 8-26 for I_2 and substituting in Eq. 8-25,

$$V_1 = I_1Z_{11} + j\omega M\left(-\frac{j\omega M}{Z_{22}}\right) = I_1\left[Z_{11} + \frac{(\omega M)^2}{Z_{22}}\right]$$

Then the input impedance is

$$Z_{in} = \frac{V_1}{I_1} = Z_{11} + \frac{(\omega M)^2}{Z_{22}} \qquad (8\text{-}27)$$

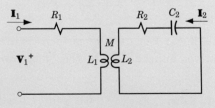

Fig. 8.23   Example 7.

The effect of the secondary circuit on the input impedance in Example 7 is as if an impedance $(\omega M)^2/Z_{22}$ were connected in series with the primary. At resonance, Z_{22} is a relatively small pure resistance, but the impedance coupled into the primary may be a relatively large resistance.

NONLINEAR NETWORKS

In the preceding discussions we assumed linearity, but real devices are never strictly linear. In some cases, nonlinearity can be disregarded; linear approximation yields results which predict the behavior of the real devices within acceptable limits. In other cases, nonlinearity is annoying and special steps must be taken to avoid or eliminate its effect; later we shall learn how to use feedback to minimize the distortion introduced in electronic amplifiers. Sometimes nonlinearity is desirable or even essential; the distortion which is annoying in an amplifier is the basis of operation of the harmonic generator for obtaining output signals at frequencies which are multiples of the input signal.

It has been pointed out† that as technology advances, there is increasing emphasis on nonlinearity. As the precision of measurement improves, nonlinearities become apparent in systems which were presumed to be linear; in the precise calculation of satellite orbits, minor nonlinearities have significant effects. As the frontiers of operation are pushed to new extremes, nonlinear behavior may be encountered; the shock waves produced in supersonic flight are highly nonlinear. New devices with superior characteristics find immediate application, even if their nonlinearity makes analysis difficult; the ubiquitous transistor is a good example. For work in the world of tomorrow's technology, an education limited to the study of linear systems is inadequate.

Nonlinear Circuits

The general linear differential equation of the second order is illustrated by the relation governing the behavior of an RLC series circuit. In terms of charge,

$$L\frac{d^2q}{dt^2} + R\frac{dq}{dt} + \frac{1}{C}q = F(t) \qquad (8\text{-}28)$$

By definition, this is linear because the coefficients are constant and q and its time derivatives appear only to the first power. In a circuit

---

† J. K. Hale and J. P. La Salle: "Analyzing Nonlinearity," *International Science and Technology*, June, 1963.

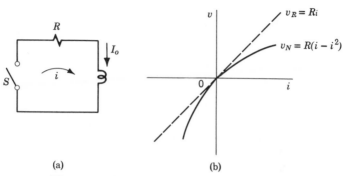

(a)   (b)

Fig. 8.24 Nonlinear first-order circuit.

governed by such an equation, the theorem of superposition applies and we can make use of the other general theorems. The fact that superposition applies leads to two important conclusions. First, the complete response is the sum of natural and forced responses, and for exponentials the forced response is of the same form as the forcing function. Second, there are no restrictions on amplitude; from the response to small excitations we can predict the response to large excitations. Neither of these conclusions apply in nonlinear networks.

As an illustration,† consider the first-order circuit of Fig. 8.24a. The The governing equation is

$$L \frac{di}{dt} + Ri = 0 \qquad (8\text{-}29)$$

and the solution is

$$i = I_0 e^{-(R/L)t} \qquad (8\text{-}30)$$

an exponentially decaying function. Regardless of the initial amplitude (I_0', I_0'', or I_0'''), the circuit soon comes to rest (Fig. 8.25a); the circuit is said to be "stable."

Suppose now that the dissipative element is nonlinear; as indicated in Fig. 8.24b for small values of i, the $v\text{-}i$ characteristic of this element is

$$v_N = R(i - i^2) \qquad (8\text{-}31)$$

Letting $R/L = 1$, the differential equation is

$$\frac{di}{dt} + i - i^2 = 0 \qquad (8\text{-}32)$$

---

† Hale and La Salle, *loc. cit.*

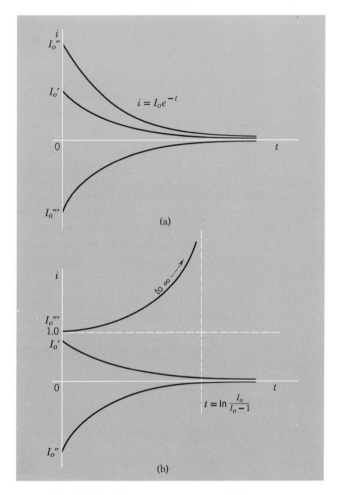

Fig. 8.25 Natural response of (a) linear and
(b) nonlinear RL circuits for various values of
initial amplitude.

The solution of this equation is

$$i = \frac{I_0 e^{-t}}{1 - I_0 + I_0 e^{-t}} \tag{8-33}$$

as can be verified by substitution in Eq. 8-32.   The solutions for various
values of initial amplitude are shown in Fig. 8.25b.   For small values of i,
the nonlinearity term i^2 is very small and the response is similar to that
for a linear circuit.

As I_0 approaches unity, the behavior becomes entirely different.   Letting $i = 1 + x$, Eq. 8-32 becomes

$$\frac{dx}{dt} + (1 + x) - (1 + x)^2 = \frac{dx}{dt} - x - x^2 = 0 \qquad (8\text{-}34)$$

and the interesting region is near $x = 0$. If we neglect x^2 in comparison to x for values near $x = 0$, Eq. 8-34 becomes

$$\frac{dx}{dt} - x = 0 \qquad (8\text{-}35)$$

a linear equation whose solution is

$$x = X_0 e^{+t}$$

an exponentially *increasing* function of time. This linear approximation gives some valuable information, but it fails to predict the highly unstable behavior at $t = \ln [I_0/(I_0 - 1)]$.

Nonlinear Elements

From the preceding example we conclude that an innocent-appearing nonlinearity may greatly affect the behavior of a circuit or system. Also, while there are definite limitations, we conclude that linear methods of analysis can provide useful information about nonlinear networks. Before discussing methods, let us look at some of the nonlinear elements which are important in practical problems.

A dissipative element for which voltage is not proportional to current is a *nonlinear resistor*. An ordinary incandescent lamp has a characteristic similar to that in Fig. 8.26a; the "resistance" of the filament increases with temperature and, therefore, under steady-state conditions, with current.

Vacuum tubes and semiconductor devices are inherently nonlinear (see Chapter 9). Because of its *v-i* characteristic (Fig. 8.26b), the semi-conductor *diode* is useful in discriminating between positive and negative voltages. If a sinusoidal voltage is applied to such a diode, the resulting current has a large d-c component and the diode is functioning as a *rectifier*.

To increase the energy-storage capability of an inductor, an iron core with favorable magnetic properties is used. (These properties are discussed in Chapter 15.) In such an inductor, the magnetic flux ϕ is not proportional to current (Fig. 8.26c); at large values of current, a given increment of current produces only a small increment of flux. A sinusoidal current causes a nonsinusoidal variation in flux; since $v = n(d\phi/dt)$, the voltage variation is nonsinusoidal. Another interpretation is that "inductance" is not constant. This nonlinearity is troublesome in a power transformer, but it may be useful in a control system.

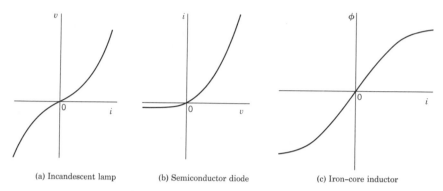

(a) Incandescent lamp   (b) Semiconductor diode   (c) Iron–core inductor

Fig. 8.26   Characteristics of nonlinear elements.

Methods of Analysis

The method employed depends on the nature of the problem, the form of the data, and the computation aids available.   The modern digital computer and analog computer permit the ready solution of problems which were hopelessly time consuming a few years ago, but here we are concerned only with simple series and parallel circuits.

Analytical Solution.   If an analytical expression for the v-i character-istic can be obtained from physical principles or from experimental data, some simple problems can be solved algebraically.   A useful represen-tation is the power series

$$i = a_0 + a_1v + a_2v^2 + a_3v^3 + \cdots \qquad (8\text{-}36)$$

The first two terms provide a linear approximation.   The first three terms give satisfactory results in many practical problems, although more terms may be necessary in some cases.

EXAMPLE 8

A voltage $v = V_m \cos \omega t$ is applied to the semiconductor diode of Fig. 8.26b. Determine the nature of the resulting current.

SOLUTION.   Assuming that the v-i characteristic can be represented by the first three terms of the power series of Eq. 8-36, the current is

$$i = a_0 + a_1v + a_2v^2$$

But we note that for $v = 0$, $i = 0$; therefore, $a_0 = 0$.   For the given voltage,

$$i = a_1V_m \cos \omega t + a_2V_m{}^2 \cos^2 \omega t$$

or

$$i = a_1V_m \cos \omega t + \frac{a_2V_m{}^2}{2} (1 + \cos 2\omega t)$$

$$= \frac{a_2V_m{}^2}{2} + a_1V_m \cos \omega t + \frac{a_2V_m{}^2}{2} \cos 2\omega t \qquad (8\text{-}37)$$

Equation 8-37 indicates that the resulting current consists of a steady or d-c component, a "fundamental" component of the same frequency as the applied voltage, and a "second-harmonic" component at frequency 2ω.

Depending on the relative magnitudes of a_1 and a_2 and the associated circuitry, the diode of Example 8 could be used as a rectifier, an amplifier, or a harmonic generator. In a specific problem, the coefficients in the power series can be determined by choosing a number of points on the v-i characteristic equal to the number of terms to be included, substituting the coordinates of each point in Eq. 8-36, and solving the resulting equations simultaneously.

Piecewise Linearization. Where approximate results are satisfactory, a convenient approach is to represent the actual characteristic by a series of linear "pieces." The characteristic of the iron-core inductor of Fig. 8.27 can be divided into two regions, each approximated by a straight line. Below the "knee" of the curve, the behavior is adequately described by $\phi = k_1 i$; above the knee, a different expression must be used. Usually a trial solution will indicate in which region operation is occurring, and the problem is reduced to one in linear analysis. (This approach is used in developing models for electronic devices in Chapter 10.)

Graphical Solution. In piecewise linearization we use graphical data to obtain linear analytical expressions which hold over limited regions. Sometimes it is desirable to plot given analytical functions to obtain a solution graphically. The equation $e^{-x} - \sin x = 0$ is difficult to solve analytically. When the functions $y = e^{-x}$ and $y = \sin x$ are plotted as in Fig. 8.28, the simultaneous solutions of these two equations are represented by points whose coordinates satisfy both equations. Therefore, the intersections of the two curves are the solutions to the original equation and can be read directly from the curves. The precision of this

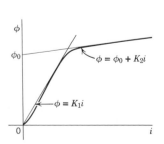

Fig. 8.27 Piecewise linearization of an iron-core inductor.

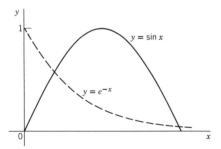

Fig. 8.28 Graphical solution.

method is limited only by the time available for plotting on successively larger scales. This method is also useful when the characteristic of some portion of the circuit is available in graphical form or in a table of experimental data.

Networks With One Nonlinear Element

If there is a single nonlinear resistance in an otherwise linear resistive network, and if the v-i characteristic of the nonlinear element is known, a relatively simple method of solution is available. This situation occurs frequently in practice and the method of attack deserves emphasis.

Assuming d-c sources, the first step is to replace all except the nonlinear element with the Thévenin equivalent shown in Fig. 8.29a as V_T and R_T. The combination of V_T and R_T is equivalent "insofar as a load is concerned." For any value of load resistance, the terminal voltage is

$$V = V_T - R_T I \qquad (8\text{-}38)$$

This is the equation of a straight line, the *load line*, with intercepts V_T and V_T/R_T and slope $-R_T$. (Alternatively, the intercepts are V_{oc}, and I_{sc} for the original network.) The graph of the nonlinear characteristic is v as a function of i for the load. The simultaneous satisfaction of these two relations, which yields the values of V and I at the terminals, is the intersection of the two curves.

For transistors, vacuum tubes, and some control system components, the v-i characteristics are represented by a family of curves. The "load" may be the linear element represented by R_T with power supplied by a battery of voltage V_T. Once the load line is drawn, the effect of variations in operating conditions (signals) is clearly visible. Note that if V_T varies during operation, the load line moves parallel to itself.

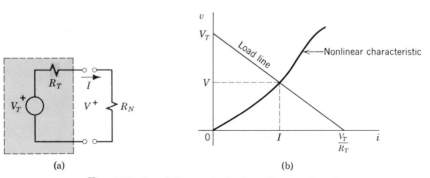

(a)   (b)

Fig. 8.29 Load-line analysis of nonlinear network.

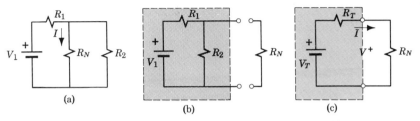

Fig. 8 30 Example 9.

EXAMPLE 9

The nonlinear element whose characteristic is given in Fig. 8.29b is connected in the circuit of Fig. 8.30a. Determine the current I.

SOLUTION. First, the nonlinear element is isolated (Fig. 8.30b) and the Thévenin equivalent determined. Considering R_1 and R_2 as a voltage divider,

$$V_T = V_{oc} = \frac{R_2}{R_1 + R_2} V_1$$

The short-circuit current is just V_1/R_1. The equivalent resistance is

$$R_T = \frac{V_{oc}}{I_{sc}} = \frac{R_2 V_1}{R_1 + R_2} \frac{R_1}{V_1} = \frac{R_1 R_2}{R_1 + R_2}$$

which is also the resistance seen looking in at the terminals with the voltage source removed.

Next, the load line is drawn with intercepts V_T and V_T/R_T as shown in Fig. 8.29b. The intersection of the load line with the nonlinear characteristic gives the desired current I.

SUMMARY

◆ Two one-port networks are equivalent if they present the same v-i characteristics.

Two passive one-ports are equivalent if they have the same input impedance or the same input admittance.

In general, two real networks are equivalent at one frequency only.

◆ For impedances in series,
$$Z_{eq} = Z_1 + Z_2 + \cdots + Z_n$$

For admittances in parallel,
$$Y_{eq} = Y_1 + Y_2 + \cdots + Y_n$$

♦ Insofar as a load is concerned, any one-port network of linear elements and energy sources can be replaced by a series combination of an ideal voltage source V_T and a linear impedance Z_T (Thévenin's equivalent), or by a parallel combination of an ideal current source I_N and a linear admittance Y_N (Norton's equivalent), where $V_T = V_{oc}$, $Z_T = V_{oc}/I_{sc}$, $I_N = I_{sc}$, and $Y_N = I_{sc}/V_{sc} = 1/Z_T$.

♦ Any series combination of voltage source V and impedance Z can be replaced by an equivalent parallel combination of current source $I = V/Z$ and admittance $Y = 1/Z$.

♦ If cause and effect are linearly related, the principle of superposition applies and the total effect of several causes acting simultaneously is equal to the sum of the effects of the individual causes acting one at a time.

♦ For maximum power transfer, the impedance of the load should be made equal to the complex conjugate of the Thévenin equivalent impedance of the source.

♦ In any passive, linear, bilateral network, if a voltage V applied in branch 1 causes a current I to flow in branch 2, then voltage V applied in branch 2 will cause current I to flow in branch 1.
  In such a network the transfer impedance $Z_{12} = V_1/I_2$ is equal to the transfer impedance Z_{21}.

♦ Any linear, bilateral, two-port network can be characterized by a set of three parameters and represented by an equivalent T (Y) or π (Δ) network.

♦ Coupling circuits are two-ports used to connect one component of a system to another in an optimum way.

♦ If two ideal coils are inductively coupled, mutual inductance exists and the voltage across coil 1 is

$$v_1 = L_1 \frac{di_1}{dt} + M \frac{di_2}{dt}$$

♦ Real devices are never strictly linear and may, due to nonlinearity, exhibit behavior not expected in linear devices.
  Within limitations, however, linear analysis can provide useful information about nonlinear networks.

♦ Simple networks involving nonlinear elements can be solved in various ways, depending on the nature of the problem and the form of the data.
  If there is a single nonlinear element in an otherwise linear network, construction of a load line is helpful.

REVIEW QUESTIONS

1. What is the difference between a "dual" and an "equivalent"?
2. If two passive one-ports are equivalent, is the same power dissipated in both? Prove your answer.
3. What is the difference between "passive" and "active" networks?
4. Under what circumstances is Thévenin's theorem useful?
5. Is the same power dissipated in an active circuit and the Norton equivalent?
6. How are the Norton and Thévenin components related?
7. Cite two nonelectrical examples where superposition applies.
8. Under what circumstances is the superposition principle useful?
9. How are voltage and current sources "removed"?
10. Energy is to be added to a ball by throwing. For maximum energy would you choose a marble, a golf ball, a baseball, or a medicine ball? Why?
11. Why is the gear ratio different on boys' and girls' bicycles?
12. Why is maximum power transfer sometimes undesirable?
13. Cite nonelectrical examples of bilateral and unilateral devices.
14. How is the fact that $Z_{12} = Z_{21}$ related to the reciprocity theorem?
15. Draw a T network of resistances and add a resistance between terminals 1 and 2. Outline the procedure for reducing this to a π.
16. Is the same power dissipated in a Δ three-phase load and the equivalent Y load?
17. Sketch, qualitatively, the frequency response curve of V_2/V_1 versus ω for the coupling circuit of Fig. 8.20a.
18. Why is inductive coupling advantageous in a motor?
19. For the circuit of Fig. 8.23, sketch the magnitude of the input impedance as a function of frequency near the series resonant frequency of the secondary.
20. Give two engineering examples where nonlinearity is desirable.
21. If transistors are inherently nonlinear, how can they be used for linear ("undistorted") amplification?
22. The v-i characteristic of an active device is $v = 100 - 2i - i^2$. Outline two methods for determining the current which flows when a resistance R is connected to the device.
23. What is meant by "piecewise linearization"? A "load line"?

EXERCISES

1. A one-port consists of $Z_1 = 5 \underline{/53.1°}\ \Omega$ and $Z_2 = 12 \underline{/-30°}\ \Omega$ connected in series.
    (a) Find R and X of an equivalent series combination.
    (b) Find G and B of an equivalent parallel combination.
    (c) For $V = 100 \underline{/0°}$ V applied across the one-port, find V_1 and V_2.
2. A one-port consists of $Z_1 = 15 \underline{/-53.1°}\ \Omega$ and $Z_2 = 10 \underline{/+60°}\ \Omega$ connected in parallel.
    (a) Find R and X of an equivalent series combination.
    (b) Find G and B of an equivalent parallel combination.
    (c) For $I = 10 \underline{/0°}$ A into the one-port, find I_1 and I_2.

3. A one-port consists of $R = 5\ \Omega$, $X_L = 2\ \Omega$, and $X_C = 4\ \Omega$ connected in parallel.
 (a) Find G and B of an equivalent parallel combination.
 (b) Find R and X of an equivalent series combination.
 (c) For $\mathbf{I} = 12\ \underline{/30°}$ A into the one-port, find $\mathbf{I}_L$ and $\mathbf{I}_C$.

4. Determine current $\mathbf{I}_1$ in Fig. 8.31 using Thévenin's theorem.

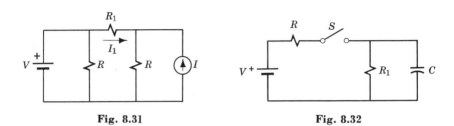

<table>
<tr><td>**Fig. 8.31**</td><td>**Fig. 8.32**</td></tr>
</table>

5. In Fig. 8.32, C is initially uncharged and switch S is closed at $t = 0$. Use Thévenin's theorem to simplify the circuit and find v_C as a function of time. What is the time constant for this circuit?

6. An a-c generator and underground transmission cable are represented by the circuit of Fig. 8.33, where $v = 260 \cos \omega t$ V, $X_L = 500\ \Omega$, $R = 50\ \Omega$, and $R_C = 1100\ \Omega$. Determine the parameters of an equivalent generator consisting of $\mathbf{V}_g$ in series with $\mathbf{Z}_g$.

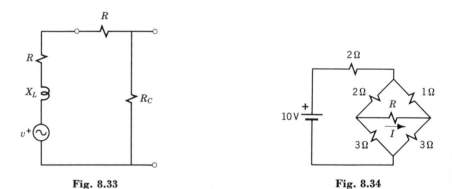

<table>
<tr><td>**Fig. 8.33**</td><td>**Fig. 8.34**</td></tr>
</table>

7. It is desired to determine current I as a function of resistance R in Fig. 8.34. Simplify the circuit to permit ready calculation of I as R is changed. Calculate I for $R = 3\ \Omega$.

8. In Fig. 8.35, a current generator ($I_1 = 2$ A, $R_1 = 60\ \Omega$) and a voltage generator ($V_2 = 120$ V, $R_2 = 30\ \Omega$) supply a variable load R_ℓ through a transmission line ($R = 10\ \Omega$).
 (a) Replace generator 2 with an equivalent current generator.
 (b) Combine the two current generators into a single generator.

(c) Replace the entire circuit to the left of R_ℓ with an equivalent voltage generator.

(d) Calculate the power delivered to $R_\ell = 20\ \Omega$.

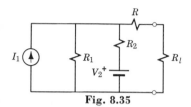

Fig. 8.35

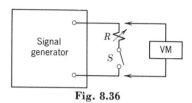

Fig. 8.36

9. The internal impedance of the electronic signal generator in Fig. 8.36 is nearly pure resistance. Measurement indicates an open-circuit voltage of 10 V. Then R is connected and varied until VM indicates 5 V, at which point $R = 600\ \Omega$. Determine, sketch, and label the Norton equivalent for this generator.

10. Considering R as a load, determine the Norton equivalent of the circuit in Fig. 8.34.

11. Determine current I_1 in Fig. 8.31, using Norton's theorem; evaluate Y_N by two different methods.

12. Determine current I_1 in Fig. 8.31, using superposition.

13. For the circuit of Exercise 8, calculate the power delivered to $R_\ell = 20\ \Omega$, using the superposition principle. Clearly indicate partial circuits used.

14. In Fig. 8.37, $v = 20 + 20 \cos 1000t$ V, $R = 10\ \Omega$, $C = 1\ \mu$F, and $L = 1$ H. Find the steady-state current $i(t)$.

15. Calculate the voltage across the 2-Ω resistance in Fig. 2.26, using superposition.

16. For the circuit of Exercise 8 (Fig. 8.35), predict the value of R_ℓ to absorb maximum power. Plot four points on a graph of P_ℓ versus R_ℓ and check your prediction.

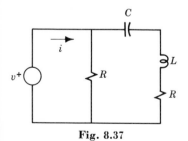

Fig. 8.37

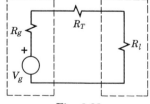

Fig. 8.38

17. In Fig. 8.38 a load ($R_\ell = 10\ \Omega$) is supplied from a generator ($V_g = 120$ V and $R_g = 15\ \Omega$) through a transmission line (R_T). Determine the value of R_T for:

(a) Maximum power transferred *to* the load.

(b) Maximum power supplied *by* the generator.

(c) Maximum power dissipated *in* R_T.

18. A generator is connected to a load (Fig. 8.39). To maximize the power transmitted to the load, an additional $\mathbf{Z}_t$ is to be added. Determine:

(a) The optimum value of $\mathbf{Z}_t$.

(b) The maximum power transmitted.

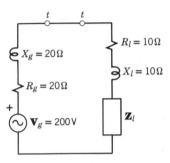

Fig. 8.39

19. Instead of adding Z_t in Exercise 18, it is decided to insert a "transmission impedance" $\mathbf{Z}_t$ between terminals tt. What value of $\mathbf{Z}_t$ will maximize the power transmitted to the load consisting of $R_t + jX_t$?

20. In a complicated linear network a voltage of 12 V applied between terminals 1 and 2 produces a current of 6 mA in an ammeter connected between terminals 3 and 4. If a voltage of 20 V is applied between terminals 3 and 4, what current will be read if the ammeter is connected between terminals 1 and 2? State theorems used.

21. In Fig. 8.35, voltage source V_2 is removed and replaced by a very high resistance voltmeter. $I_1 = 3$ A, $R_1 = 60$ Ω, $R_2 = 30$ Ω, $R = 10$ Ω, and $R_t = 20$ Ω.

(a) Approximately what current flows in R_2?

(b) Approximately what is the reading of the voltmeter?

(c) If current source I_1 and the voltmeter are interchanged, approximately what will be the voltmeter reading? Check analytically.

22. Given the two-port of Fig. 8.40, evaluate k_1, k_2, k_3, and k_4 in Eqs. 8.13. Following the scheme of Fig. 8.17a, determine the parameters of an equivalent T network.

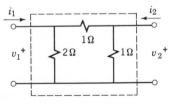

Fig. 8.40

23. Derive Eq. 8.18 from Eqs. 8.15, 8.16, and 8.17.
24. Derive Eq. 8.19a from Eq. 8.19.
25. For $R = 3\ \Omega$ in Fig. 8.34, find I, using network reduction principles. Draw labelled circuits to illustrate each step.
26. In Fig. 8.41, replace the passive network with an equivalent T. Use the superposition principle to find I, clearly indicating the partial circuits used.

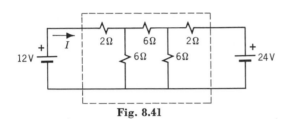

Fig. 8.41

27. The symmetrical "bridged-T" network shown in Fig. 8.42 is supplied by a current source $\mathbf{I} = 2\ \underline{/0°}$ A. Using network theorems to reduce the labor required, determine the voltage across the right-hand capacitor.

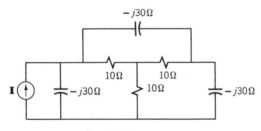

Fig. 8.42

28. Calculate the element values of an equivalent T circuit to replace the coupling circuit of Fig. 8.20a at frequency ω.
29. When two coils are connected in series, the total inductance is measured to be 19 mH. When the connections to one coil are reversed, the total series inductance is 31 mH.
    (a) What is the mutual inductance?
    (b) If the coils are similar, except that coil 2 has twice as many turns as coil 1, what are L_1 and L_2?
30. In Fig. 8.22a, $L_1 = 1$ H, $L_2 = 2$ H, and $M = 0.5$ H. A resistance $R = 500\ \Omega$ is connected across the output and a voltage $\mathbf{V_1} = 100\ \underline{/0°}$ V at $\omega = 500$ rad/sec is applied. Determine the current $\mathbf{I_1}$ and the input impedance $\mathbf{Z_1}$.
31. In Fig. 8.22a, a capacitance C is connected across the output. Derive an expression for the input impedance $\mathbf{Z_1}$.

32. In Fig. 8.23, $C_2 = 1$ nF and the secondary circuit is series resonant at $f_o = 2$ Mc with a Q of 50. Coil 1 has an inductance $L_1 = 40$ μH and a Q of 50. If $M = 40$ μH, determine the input impedance Z_1 at $f = 2$ Mc.

33. The v-i characteristic of a certain semiconductor diode is approximately $i = I_s(e^{bv} - 1)$, where I_s and b are constants.

(a) Expand the exponential in a power series and express $i(v)$, using the first three terms of Eq. 8-36.

(b) The diode is in series with a 200-Ω resistance. Predict the current if a voltage of $+1.0$ V is applied to the series combination, assuming $I_s = 0.1$ mA and $b = 40$ V^{-1}. (Try to repeat for an applied voltage of -1.0 V).

(c) Check the accuracy of this approach by comparing the sum of the voltage drops across the diode and the resistance at the predicted current with the given voltage applied.

34. Solve Exercise 33b by a graphical method.

35. The v-i characteristic of a vacuum diode is approximately $i = Kv^{3/2}$ for positive values of v.

(a) For $K = 2 \times 10^{-4}$ (i in A and v in V), express $i(v)$, using the first three terms of Eq. 8.36.

(b) The diode is in series with a 3-kΩ resistance. Predict the current for an applied voltage of 100 V.

36. Solve Exercise 35b by a graphical method.

37. The following data describe two nonlinear devices:

$v(V)$	0	3	5	7	10	15	20	25
i_A(mA)	0	1.1	2.0	2.8	3.8	4.2	4.4	4.6
i_B(mA)	0	0.3	0.5	0.7	1.2	3.0	5.0	7.1

(a) Plot the v-i characteristic of device A and represent it by piecewise linearization.

(b) Predict the current in device A in response to an applied voltage $v = 20 + 4 \cos \omega t$ V.

(c) Repeat part (b) for $v = 5 + 4 \cos \omega t$ V.

38. Repeat Exercise 37 for device B.

39. Device A of Exercise 37 is connected in series with a 20-V battery and a 4-kΩ resistance; predict the current.

40. Device B of Exercise 37 is connected in parallel with a 5-kΩ resistance and a current source supplying 2 mA; predict the current in device B.

41. Device B of Exercise 37 is connected in the circuit of Fig. 8.43.

(a) Draw the v-i characteristics of device B and R_1 to scale.

(b) Construct the composite characteristic of device B and R_1.

(c) Express $i(v)$ for the left-hand portion of the circuit.

(d) Plot the characteristic of part (c) and determine i, v, and i_B.

42. Replace all except device B (see Exercise 37) in Fig. 8.43 with a Thévenin equivalent and determine i_B by the load-line method.

43. Devices A and B of Exercise 37 are connected as in Fig. 8.44.

(a) Plot the v-i characteristics of A and B.

(b) Plot the composite characteristic of A and B in series.

(c) Determine i, v_A, and v_B by the load-line method.

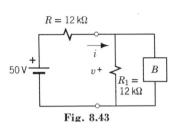

Fig. 8.43

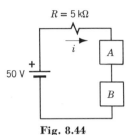

Fig. 8.44

PROBLEMS

1. In Fig. 8.45, the capacitive reactance $X_C = 12\ \Omega$ and the voltage $V_C = 60$ V (rms). Taking advantage of network theorems, determine the rms value of the applied voltage V.

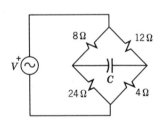

Fig. 8.45

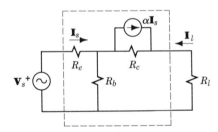

Fig. 8.46

2. One possible linear model for a transistor is shown (within the dotted lines) in Fig. 8.46 where $R_e = 25\ \Omega$, $R_b = 1$ kΩ, $R_c = 1$ MΩ, and $\alpha = 0.98$. Replace the model and the voltage source with a Thévenin equivalent and calculate the voltage amplification V_l/V_s for $R_l = 10$ kΩ.

3. A voltage $v = 10 + 5e^{-100t}$ V is suddenly applied (by closing a switch) at $t = 0$ to a series combination of $R = 5$ kΩ and $C = 1\ \mu$F. Find the current i as a function of time (be sure to include all components), and plot component and total currents approximately to scale.

4. A high-resistance voltmeter across a battery reads 12 V. A low-resistance ammeter shorted across the terminals (momentarily!) reads 300 A. *Stating* all assumptions, determine the maximum power that can be obtained from this battery.

5. In Fig. 8.47, $v_1 = 12 + 12 \cos 1000t$ V, $R_1 = 1\ \Omega$, $R = 2\ \Omega$, $L = 1$ mH, $C = 500\ \mu$F, and $i_2 = 6 \cos 1000t$ A. Taking advantage of network theorems and clearly indicating the method used, determine the steady-state current i.

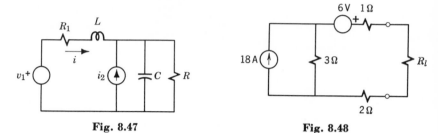

Fig. 8.47   Fig. 8.48

6. For the circuit of Fig. 8.48, plot power in R_l as a function of R_l in ohms.

7. The output characteristics of two d-c generators are:

I(A)	0	20	40	60	80
V_1(V)	120	119	117	113	105
V_2(V)	120	118	113	105	90

The two generators are connected in parallel to supply power to a load resistance $R_l = 0.8$ Ω. Plot the characteristics and determine, graphically, the current and power supplied by each generator.

8. An ordinary 50-W incandescent lamp is connected in *series* with a 200-W lamp across a 110-V line. *Stating* all assumptions, estimate the relative brightness of the two lamps.

PART II　　　ELECTRONIC DEVICES

- ♦ ELECTRON MOTION
- ♦ VACUUM DIODES
- ♦ CONDUCTION IN SOLIDS
- ♦ SEMICONDUCTOR DIODES
- ♦ TWO-PORT DEVICES
- ♦ ELEMENTARY AMPLIFIERS

CHAPTER **9**

Principles of Electronics

The history of the development of electronics is a fascinating story extending over a century.   It starts with the first observations of cathode rays and extends into tomorrow.   There is no single thread to the story; it is more like a tapestry woven from the interrelated contributions of mathematicians, physicists, engineers, and inventors.

Two parallel paths of development are fairly clear.   While Hittorf and Crookes were studying cathode rays (1869), Maxwell was developing his mathematical theory of electromagnetic radiation.   Soon after Edison observed electronic conduction in a vacuum (1883), Hertz demonstrated (1888) the existence of the radio waves predicted by Maxwell.   At the time of J. J. Thomson's measurement of e/m (1897), Marconi was becoming interested in wireless and succeeded in spanning the Atlantic (1901). While Einstein was generalizing from the photoelectric effect, Fleming was inventing the first electron tube (1904) a sensitive diode detector utilizing the Edison effect.   De Forest's invention of the triode (1906) made it possible to amplify signals electronically and led to Armstrong's sensitive regenerative detector (1912) and the important oscillator.

Electronic progress reflects the brilliant achievements of individuals and the painstaking contributions of research teams.   It has been affected by war, as in the development of radar in World War II; in turn, it affects the course of future wars through the control of defense and offense systems.   Its influence extends from the battlefield to the living room and from outer space to inner man.   In 1933 Jansky proved that certain radio signals originate outside our star system, and now implanted electronic pacemakers stimulate defective hearts.

In this chapter we take a first look at the physical principles which underlie the operation of all electronic devices. To design new devices much more study of fundamental principles will be necessary. Our aim here is to gain the understanding necessary for effective use of existing devices in conventional applications. First, we examine the motion of individual electrons in a vacuum, and then we consider the effect of many electrons, as in a practical vacuum tube. Next, we consider conduction in solids where electron motion is influenced by the fixed ions of a metal or the impurity atoms added to a semiconductor. Finally, we analyze the characteristics of some important electronic devices and see how amplification is achieved by tubes and transistors.

ELECTRON MOTION

The model of the electron as a charged particle of negligible size is satisfactory for many purposes. Based on many careful measurements, the accepted values for charge and mass of the electron are

$$e = 1.6019 \times 10^{-19} \text{ C} \cong 1.6 \times 10^{-19} \text{ C}$$

$$m = 9.1072 \times 10^{-31} \text{ kg} \cong 9.1 \times 10^{-31} \text{ kg}$$

In contrast, the hydrogen ion which carries a positive charge of the same magnitude has a mass approximately 1840 times as great. If the mass, charge, and initial velocity are known, the motion of individual electrons and ions in electric and magnetic fields can be predicted using Newton's laws of mechanics.

Motion in a Uniform Electric Field

A uniform electric field of strength $\mathcal{E}$ is established between the parallel conducting plates of Fig. 9.1a by applying a potential difference or voltage. By definition (Eq. 2-5)

$$\mathcal{E} = -\frac{dv}{dl} = -\frac{V_b - V_a}{L} \text{ volts/meter} \tag{9-1}$$

if the spacing is small compared to the dimensions of the plates. Note that if $V_b > V_a$, $V_b - V_a$ is a positive quantity and the electric field is negative (directed to the left in Fig. 9.1b).

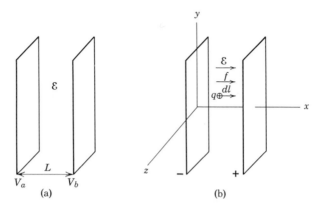

Fig. 9.1 Uniform electric field.

By definition (Eq. 2-4), the electric field strength is the force per unit positive charge. Therefore, the force in newtons on a charge q in coulombs is

$$\mathbf{f} = q\mathcal{E} \tag{9-2}$$

Considering the energy gained by a charge q moving a distance dl against the force of the electric field, the voltage of point b with respect to point a is

$$V_{ba} = \frac{1}{q} \int_a^b dw = \frac{1}{q} \int_a^b (-f)\, dl = -\frac{1}{q} \int_a^b q\mathcal{E}\, dl = -\int_a^b \mathcal{E}\, dl \tag{9-3}$$

In words, the voltage between any two points in an electric field is the line integral of the electric field strength. Equation 9-3 is the corollary of Eq. 9-1.

For the orientation of Fig. 9.1b, the electric field $\mathcal{E}$ is a negative quantity. An electron of charge $-e$ in the space between the plates experiences a force

$$f_x = (-e)(\mathcal{E}) = -e\mathcal{E} = ma_x$$

or

$$a_x = -\frac{e\mathcal{E}}{m} \tag{9-4}$$

We see that an electron in a uniform electric field moves with a constant acceleration. We expect the resulting motion to be similar to that of a freely falling mass in the earth's gravitational field. The equations of motion are:

$$u_x = \int_0^t a_x \, dt = a_x t + U_0 = -\frac{e\mathcal{E}}{m} t + U_0 \tag{9-5}$$

$$x = \int_0^t u_x \, dt = \frac{a_x t^2}{2} + U_0 t + X_0 = -\frac{e\mathcal{E}}{2m} t^2 + U_0 t + X_0 \tag{9-6}$$

EXAMPLE 1

A voltage V_d is applied across two horizontal plates of length L separated a distance d, as in Fig. 9.2. An electron with initial velocity U_0 in the positive x direction is introduced at the origin. Determine the path of the electron and the vertical displacement at the time it leaves the region between the plates.

SOLUTION. Assuming no electric field in the x direction and a uniform field of magnitude $\mathcal{E}_y = -V_d/d$ in the negative y direction, the accelerations are:

$$a_x = 0 \quad \text{and} \quad a_y = -\frac{e\mathcal{E}_y}{m} = \frac{eV_d}{md}$$

There is no acceleration in the x direction and the electron moves with constant velocity to the right. There is a constant upward acceleration and the electron gains a vertical component of velocity. The path is determined by:

$$x = U_0 t \quad \text{and} \quad y = -\frac{e\mathcal{E}}{2m} t^2 = \frac{eV_d}{2md} t^2$$

Eliminating t,

$$y = \frac{eV_d}{2mdU_0{}^2} x^2 \tag{9-7}$$

or the electron follows a parabolic path.

At the edge of the field, $x = l$ and the vertical displacement is

$$y = \frac{eV_d}{2mdU_0{}^2} l^2$$

If V_d exceeds a certain value, the displacement y exceeds $d/2$ and the electron strikes the upper plate. (What is the critical value of V_d?)

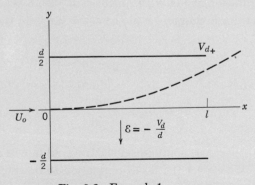

Fig. 9.2 Example 1.

Energy Gained by an Accelerated Electron

When an electron is accelerated by an electric field it gains kinetic energy at the expense of potential energy, just as does a freely falling mass. Since voltage is energy per unit charge, the potential energy lost by an electron in "falling" from point a to point b is, in joules,

$$PE = W = q(V_a - V_b) = -e(V_a - V_b) = eV_{ba} \qquad (9\text{-}8)$$

The kinetic energy gained, evidenced by an increase in velocity, is just equal to the potential energy lost or

$$KE = \tfrac{1}{2}mu_b{}^2 - \tfrac{1}{2}mu_a{}^2 = PE = eV_{ba} \qquad (9\text{-}9)$$

This important equation indicates that the kinetic energy gained by an electron in an electric field is determined only by the voltage difference between the initial and final points; it is independent of the path followed and the electric field configuration. (We assume that the field does not change with *time*.)

Frequently we are interested in the behavior resulting from a change in the energy of a single electron. Expressed in joules, these energies are very small; a more convenient unit is suggested by Eq. 9-8. An *electron volt* is the potential energy lost by 1 electron falling through a potential difference of 1 volt. By Eq. 9-8,

$$1 \text{ eV} = eV = (1.6 \times 10^{-19} \text{ C})(1 \text{ V}) = 1.6 \times 10^{-19} \text{ J} \qquad (9\text{-}10)$$

For example, the energy required to remove an electron from a hydrogen atom is about 13.6 eV. The energy imparted to an electron in a linear accelerator may be as high as 20 BeV (20 billion electron volts).

For the special case of an electron starting from rest ($u_a = 0$) and accelerated through a voltage V, Eq. 9-9 can be solved for $u_b = u$ to yield

$$u = \sqrt{2(e/m)V} = 5.93 \times 10^5 \sqrt{V} \text{ m/sec} \qquad (9\text{-}11)$$

In deriving Eq. 9-11 we assume that mass m is a constant; this is true only if the velocity is small compared to the velocity of light $c \cong 3 \times 10^8$ m/sec.

EXAMPLE 2

Find the velocity reached by an electron accelerated through a voltage of 3600 V.

SOLUTION. Assuming that the resulting velocity u is small compared to the velocity of light c, Eq. 9-11 applies and

$$u = 5.93 \times 10^5 \sqrt{3600} = 3.56 \times 10^7 \text{ m/sec}$$

In this case,

$$\frac{u}{c} = \frac{3.56 \times 10^7}{3 \times 10^8} \cong 0.12$$

At the velocity of Example 2 the increase in mass is appreciable, and the actual velocity reached is about 0.5% lower than that predicted. For voltages above 4 or 5 kV, a more precise expression should be used (see Problem 1).

Motion in a Uniform Magnetic Field

One way of defining the strength of a magnetic field (Eq. 2-6) is in terms of the force exerted on a unit charge moving with unit velocity normal to the field. In general, the force in newtons is

$$\mathbf{f} = q\mathbf{u} \times \mathbf{B} \qquad (9\text{-}12)$$

where q is charge in coulombs and B is magnetic flux density in teslas (or webers/meter^2). The vector cross product is defined by the right-hand screw rule illustrated in Fig. 9.3. Rotation from the direction of $\mathbf{u}$ to the direction of $\mathbf{B}$ advances the screw in the direction of $\mathbf{f}$. The magnitude of the force is $quB \sin \theta$ and the direction is always normal to the plane of $\mathbf{u}$ and $\mathbf{B}$.

Equation 9-12 is consistent with three observable facts:

1. A charged particle at rest in a magnetic field experiences no force ($u = 0$).

2. A charged particle moving parallel with the magnetic flux experiences no force ($\theta = 0$).

3. A charged particle moving with a component of velocity normal to the magnetic flux experiences a force which is normal to u and therefore the magnitude of velocity (or speed) is unchanged.

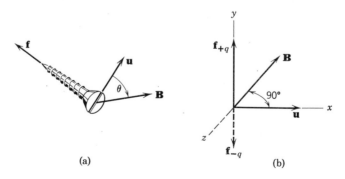

(a)   (b)

Fig. 9.3   Vector cross product.

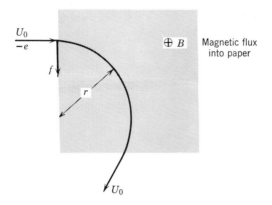

Fig. 9.4   Electron motion in magnetic field.

From the third statement we conclude that no work is done by a magnetic field on a charged particle and its kinetic energy is unchanged.

Figure 9.4 shows an electron entering a finite region of uniform flux density. For an electron ($q = -e$) moving in the plane of the paper ($\theta = 90°$), the force is in the direction shown with a magnitude

$$f = eU_0B \qquad (9\text{-}13)$$

Applying the right-hand rule, we see that the initial force is downward and, therefore, the acceleration is downward and the path is deflected as shown. A particle moving with constant speed and constant normal acceleration follows a circular path. The centrifugal force due to circular motion must be just equal to the centripetal force due to the magnetic field or

$$m\frac{U_0{}^2}{r} = eU_0B$$

and the radius of the circular path is

$$r = \frac{mU_0}{eB} \qquad (9\text{-}14)$$

The dependence of radius on the mass of the charged particle is the principle underlying the *mass spectrograph* for studying isotopes.

The fact that electrons moving parallel to a magnetic field are unaffected while those with components of velocity normal to the field are deflected is cleverly exploited in the *magnetic focusing* scheme of Fig. 9.5. A beam of electrons passes through a small hole and travels to a fluorescent screen. To minimize the divergence (exaggerated in the

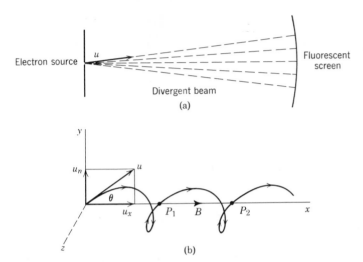

Fig. 9.5   Magnetic focusing of electron beam.

drawing), a uniform magnetic field (supplied by direct current in a long coil around the axis of the beam) is provided. A particular electron emerging from the hole with velocity u at an angle θ with respect to B is shown in Fig. 9.5b. The component of velocity $u_n = u \sin \theta$ is normal to B, and the electron experiences a force which produces a circular component of motion with a radius given by Eq. 9-14. The time to complete one revolution is the circumference divided by the velocity or

$$T = \frac{2\pi r}{u_n} = \frac{2\pi m u_n}{eB u_n} = \frac{2\pi m}{eB} \qquad (9\text{-}15)$$

and T, the *period*, is independent of the velocity.

The component of velocity $u_x = u \cos \theta$ is parallel to B; therefore, it is unaffected by B, and the axial velocity is constant. The superposition of circular motion on axial translation results in motion along a helical path as shown. The axial distance traveled in one cycle is p, the *pitch* of the helix, where

$$p = u_x T = \frac{2\pi m u_x}{eB} \qquad (9\text{-}16)$$

is independent of u_n. Electrons with various initial directions travel along helices with various radii and various orientations. We conclude, however, that all electrons with the same axial velocity u_x return to the same point P_1 on the x axis after one revolution and to the same point P_2 after two revolutions. When B is adjusted so that the distance from the hole to the screen is a multiple of p, a sharply focused spot appears on the screen.

Motion in Combined ε and B Fields

In the general case, both electric and magnetic fields are present and exert forces on a moving charge. The total force is

$$f = q(\varepsilon + u \times B) \qquad (9\text{-}17)$$

The special cases previously described can be derived from this general relation. If both ε and B are present, the resulting motion depends on the relative orientation of ε and B, and also on the initial velocities. An interesting case is that in which an electron starts from rest in a region where ε and B are mutually perpendicular. The electron is accelerated in the direction of $-\varepsilon$, but as soon as it is in motion there is a reaction with B and the path starts to curve. Curving around, the electron is soon travelling in the $+\varepsilon$ direction and experiences a decelerating force which brings it to rest. Once the electron is at rest, the cycle starts over; the resulting path is called a *cycloid* and resembles the path of a point on a wheel as it rolls along a line (see Problem 2).

If the fields are not uniform, mathematical analysis is usually quite difficult. A case of practical importance is the "electron lens" used in electron microscopes and for electric field focusing of the electron beam in the cathode-ray tube.

The Cathode-Ray Tube

The television picture tube and the precision electron display tube used in oscilloscopes are modern versions of the evacuated tubes used by Crookes and Thompson to study cathode rays. The electrons constituting a "cathode ray" have little mass or inertia and, therefore, they can follow rapid variations; their ratio of charge to mass is high, so they are easily deflected and controlled. The energy of high-velocity electrons is easily converted into visible light; therefore, their motion is easily observed. For these reasons the "C-R tube" is a unique information processing device; from our standpoint it is also an ingenious application of the principles of electron motion. The essential components are shown in Fig. 9.6; an *electron gun* produces a focused beam of electrons, a *deflection system* changes the direction of the beam, and a *fluorescent screen* converts the energy of the beam into visible light.

Electron Gun. Electrons are emitted from the hot cathode (Fig. 9.7a) and pass through a small hole in the cylindrical control electrode; a nega-

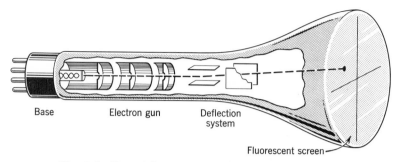

Fig. 9.6   Essential components of a cathode-ray tube.

tive voltage (with respect to the cathode) on this electrode tends to repel the electrons and, therefore, the voltage applied controls the intensity of the beam.   Electrons passing the control electrode experience an accelerating force due to the electric field established by the positive voltages V_f and V_a on the focusing and accelerating anodes.   The space between these anodes constitutes an electron lens (Fig. 9.7b); the electric flux lines and equipotential lines resulting from the voltage difference $V_a - V_f$ provide a precise focusing effect.   A diverging electron is accelerated forward by the field, and at the same time it receives an inward component of velocity which brings it back to the axis of the beam at the screen.

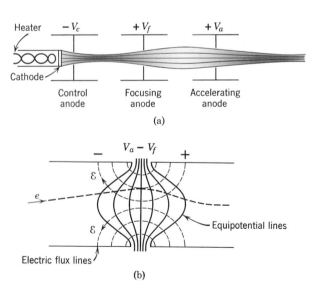

Fig. 9.7   Elementary electron gun with electric field focusing.

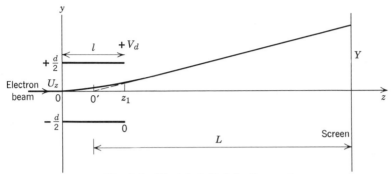

Fig. 9.8 Electric field deflection system.

Deflection System. In a television picture tube, the beam is moved across the screen 15,750 times per second, creating a picture consisting of 525 horizontal lines of varying intensity. The deflection of the beam may be achieved by a magnetic field or an electric field. Figure 9.8 shows the beam produced in the electron gun entering the vertical deflection plates of an electric field system.

The beam deflection at the screen can be calculated using our knowledge of electron motion. For the coordinate system of Fig. 9.8, Eq. 9-11 gives an axial velocity

$$U_z = \sqrt{2eV_a/m} \tag{9-18}$$

where V_a is the total accelerating potential. Within the deflecting field, the parabolic path (Eq. 9-7) is defined by

$$y = \frac{eV_d}{2mdU_z{}^2} z^2 = kz^2 \tag{9-19}$$

The slope of the beam emerging from the deflecting field at $z = z_1 = l$ is

$$\frac{dy}{dz} = 2kz = 2kl \tag{9-20}$$

The equation of the straight-line path followed by the beam to the screen is

$$y - y_1 = m(z - z_1)$$

where $y_1 = kz_1{}^2 = kl^2$ and $m = dy/dz = 2kl$. Substituting these values and solving,

$$y = 2kl(z - l) + kl^2 = 2kl\left(z - \frac{l}{2}\right) \tag{9-21}$$

Since for $y = 0$, $z = l/2$, Eq. 9-21 leads to the conclusion that the electron beam appears to follow a straight-line path from a virtual source at $0'$. At the screen $z = L + l/2$ and (by Eqs. 9-19 and 9-18) the deflection is

$$Y = 2klL = \frac{eV_dlL}{mdU_z^2} = \frac{eV_dlL}{md} \cdot \frac{m}{2eV_a} = \frac{lL}{2dV_a} V_d \qquad (9\text{-}22)$$

or the vertical deflection at the screen is directly proportional to V_d, the voltage applied to the vertical deflecting plates. A second set of plates provides horizontal deflection.

Fluorescent Screen. Part of the kinetic energy of the electron beam is converted into luminous energy at the screen. Absorption of kinetic energy results in an immediate *fluorescence* and a subsequent *phosphorescence*. The choice of screen material depends on the application. For laboratory oscilloscopes, a medium persistence phosphor with output concentrated in the green region is desirable; the eye is sensitive to green and the persistence provides a steady image of a repeated pattern. For a television tube, a balanced mixture of phosphors is used to provide a white glow of short persistence. For radar screens a very long persistence is desirable.

The cathode-ray oscilloscope as a laboratory instrument is discussed in Chapter 21, but one feature merits mention here. If voltages varying with time are applied to the x- and y-deflecting plates of the tube, a pattern is traced out on the screen; if the voltages are periodic and one period is an exact multiple of the other, a stationary pattern is obtained. If a sawtooth wave (usually provided by a *sweep generator* within the oscilloscope) is applied to the horizontal-deflection plates, the projection of the beam on the x axis is directly proportional to time. If a signal voltage wave is applied to the vertical-deflection plates, the projection of the beam on the y axis is directly proportional to the amplitude of this signal. If both voltages are applied simultaneously, the pattern displayed on the screen is the signal as a function of time (Fig. 9.9).

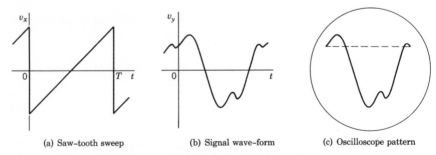

(a) Saw–tooth sweep   (b) Signal wave–form   (c) Oscilloscope pattern

Fig. 9.9   Display of a repeated waveform.

EXAMPLE 3

Determine the deflection sensitivity in centimeters of deflection per volt of signal, for a *C-R* tube in which $l = 2$ cm, $L = 30$ cm, $d = 0.5$ cm, and the total accelerating voltage is 2 kV.

SOLUTION. From Eq. 9-22, the deflection sensitivity is

$$\frac{Y}{V_d} = \frac{lL}{2dV_a} = \frac{0.02\text{m} \times 0.3\text{m}}{2 \times 0.005\text{m} \times 2000\text{V}} \times 100 = 0.03 \text{ cm/V}$$

To obtain a reasonable deflection, say, 3 cm, a voltage of 100 V would be necessary. In a practical oscilloscope, amplifiers are provided to obtain reasonable deflections with less than 0.1-V input signals.

VACUUM DIODES

The cathode-ray tube can be analyzed in terms of the effect of electric and magnetic fields on a single electron in space. As a next step we now consider the case of an evacuated space containing many electrons, as in an ordinary vacuum tube. First, we look at the process for obtaining large quantities of electrons, then we consider the effect of the resulting *space charge*, and on this basis we determine the behavior of a two-electrode vacuum tube in terms of its *v-i* characteristics.

Electron Emission

The Bohr model is satisfactory for describing how free electrons can be obtained in space. As you recall, starting with the hydrogen atom consisting of a single proton and a single orbital electron, models of more complex atoms are built up by adding protons and neutrons to the nucleus and electrons in orbital groups or shells. In a systematic way, shells are filled and new shells started. The chemical properties of an element are determined by the *valence* electrons in the outer shell. Good electrical conductors like copper and silver have only one electron in the outer shell.

Only certain orbits are allowed, and atoms are stable only when the orbital electrons have certain discrete energy levels. Transfer of an electron from an orbit corresponding to energy W_1 to an orbit corresponding to energy W_2 results in the radiation of a *quantum* of electromagnetic energy of frequency f given by

$$W_1 - W_2 = hf \tag{9-23}$$

where h is Planck's constant $= 6.625 \times 10^{-34}$ J-sec.

The energy possessed by an orbital electron consists of the kinetic energy of motion in the orbit and the potential energy of position with respect to the positive ion representing all the rest of the neutral atom. If other atoms are close (as in a solid), the energy of an electron is affected by the charge distribution of the neighboring atoms. In a crystalline solid, there is an orderly arrangement of atoms and the permissible electron energies are grouped into *energy bands*. Between the permissible bands there may be ranges of energy called *forbidden bands*.

For an electron to exist in space it must possess the energy corresponding to motion from its normal orbit out to an infinite distance; the energy required to move an electron against the attractive force of the net positive charge left behind is the *surface barrier energy* W_B. Within a metal at absolute zero temperature, electrons possess energies varying from zero to a maximum value W_M. The minimum amount of work that must be done on an electron before it is able to escape from the surface of a metal is the *work function* W_W where

$$W_W = W_B - W_M \tag{9-24}$$

For copper $W_W = 4.1$ eV, while for cesium $W_W = 1.8$ eV.

The energy required for electron emission may be obtained in various ways. The "beta rays" given off spontaneously by *radioactive* materials (along with alpha and gamma rays) are emitted electrons. In *photoelectric* emission, the energy of a quantum of electromagnetic energy is absorbed by an electron. In *high-field* emission, the potential energy of an intense electric field causes emission. In *secondary* emission, a fast-moving electron transfers its kinetic energy to one or more electrons in a solid surface. All these processes have possible applications, but the most important process is *thermionic* emission in which thermal energy is added by heating a solid conductor.

The temperature of an object is a measure of the kinetic energy stored in the motion of the constituent molecules, atoms, and electrons. The energies of the individual constituents vary widely, but an average energy corresponding to temperature T can be expressed as kT, where $k = 1.38 \times 10^{-23}$ J/°K is the Boltzmann constant. At a temperature above absolute zero, the distribution of electron energy in a metal is modified and some electrons possess energies appreciably above W_M. Statistical analysis shows that the probability of an electron receiving sufficient energy to be emitted is proportional to $e^{-W_W/kT}$. At high temperatures, many electrons possess energies greater than W_B and emission current densities of the order of 1 ampere per square centimeter are practical. Commercial cathodes make use of special materials which combine low work function with high melting point.

Space Charge

The construction of a typical vacuum diode is shown in Fig. 9.10. A cylindrical *anode* or *plate* is mounted in an evacuated glass envelope. A cylindrical *cathode* is heated by a high-resistance *heater* supplied by a voltage V_a. The plate is maintained at a positive potential V_b with respect to the cathode. Negative electrons emitted from the cathode are drawn to the positive plate; after flowing through an external load circuit, the electrons return to the cathode.

We are interested in the *v-i* characteristics of this electronic device. To simplify the analysis, let us consider the idealized diode of Fig. 9.11a in which the electrodes are parallel planes, and only a few electrons are present in the evacuated space. Superimposed on the sketch of Fig. 9.11b is a graph of potential v in the cathode-plate space. There is a corresponding uniform negative electric field intensity $\mathcal{E}$. An electron emitted from the cathode with zero velocity experiences an accelerating force equal to $-e\mathcal{E}$, and its velocity u at any point is proportional to $\sqrt{v}$ (Eq. 9-11).

If the cathode temperature is raised, more and more electrons are emitted, some with appreciable initial velocity, and there are many in the space at all times. (A current of 10 mA corresponds to 6×10^{16} electrons/sec.) Repulsive forces cause the electrons close to the cathode to accelerate more slowly and those close to the plate to accelerate more rapidly; the final velocity is determined by V_b since the kinetic energy gained is $\frac{1}{2}(mu_b{}^2 - mu_o{}^2) = eV_b$. Up to a point, the plate current in electrons per second is just equal to the rate of emission. A further

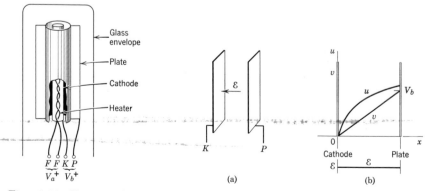

Fig. 9.10 Vacuum diode construction.

Fig. 9.11 Potential, field, and velocity distributions in an idealized vacuum diode.

increase in cathode temperature increases the rate of emission, but some electrons are repelled by the space charge and "fall" back into the cathode; the plate current is said to be *space-charge limited*.

The conditions existing in the cathode-plate space are described by the graphs in Fig. 9.12.   The governing equations are:

$$u = \sqrt{u_o^2 + 2ev/m} \tag{9-25}$$

$$\varepsilon = -\frac{dv}{dx} \tag{9-26}$$

$$\rho u = J \tag{9-27}$$

$$\rho = \epsilon \frac{d\varepsilon}{dx} \tag{9-28}$$

Equations 9-25 and 9-26 are familiar.   Equation 9-27 expresses the fact that the current density $J(\text{A/m}^2)$ is the product of charge density ρ (rho) (C/m^3) and velocity u (m/sec); the current density is constant across the space since the electrons passing one intermediate plane must pass any other plane.   Equation 9-28 is based on Gauss' law which says that the total electric flux passing through any closed surface is equal to the total charge enclosed by the surface.†

Vacuum tubes are always operated with cathode temperatures high enough to provide excess emission, and the actual voltage distribution is as shown by the solid line in Fig. 9.12a.   The electric field distribution $(\varepsilon = -dv/dx)$ is as shown in Fig. 9.12b; the negative field at the cathode repels all but the most energetic emitted electrons.   As shown in Fig. 9.12c, even the fast-moving electrons are slowed down by the negative field, reach a minimum velocity at the point of minimum voltage (Eq. 9-25), and then are accelerated.   The region of minimum velocity is a region of maximum charge density (Fig. 9.12d) since current density is constant (Eq. 9-27).   The effect is as if electrons were being emitted at low velocity from a region outside the cathode, so we say that a *virtual cathode* exists there.

$†\ \psi = \oint D dA = \epsilon \oint \varepsilon dA = \int dq = \int \rho A\ dx$

where ψ = electric flux (psi),
   D = electric flux density = ψ/A,
     ϵ = permittivity (epsilon) = D/ε,
   $A\ dx$ = element of volume.
Solving this equation for ρ yields Eq. 9-28.

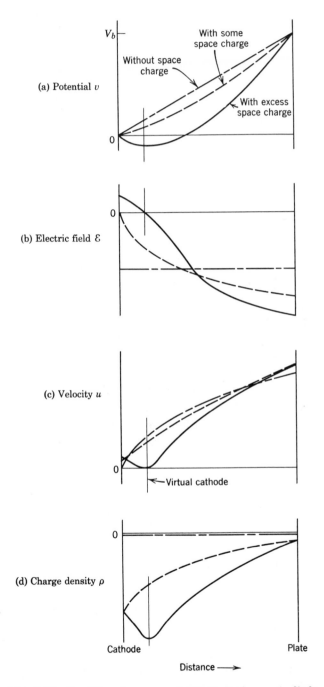

V_b

With some
space charge

Without space
charge

(a) Potential v

With excess
space charge

0

0

(b) Electric field $\mathcal{E}$

(c) Velocity u

0

←Virtual cathode

0

(d) Charge density ρ

Cathode   Plate

Distance ——➤

Fig. 9.12   Conditions in a space-charge limited vacuum diode

Vacuum Diode Characteristics

The shape of the v-i characteristic of a vacuum diode can be predicted if we assume a voltage distribution of the form $v(x) = V_b(a_0 + a_1x + a_2x^2 + \cdot \cdot \cdot)$. By Eqs. 9-28 and 9-26, for space-charge limited operation the charge density near the plate is

$$\rho_b = \epsilon \frac{d\mathcal{E}}{dx} = -\epsilon \frac{d^2v}{dx^2} = k_1 V_b$$

since for any voltage distribution $v(x)$, the second derivative at any point is directly proportional to the maximum value V_b. By Eq. 9-25, the velocity near the plate is

$$u_b \cong k_2 V_b^{1/2}$$

if the initial velocity is neglected or if V_b is measured with respect to the potential of the virtual cathode. Then, by Eq. 9-27,

$$I_b = J_b A \cong k_1 k_2 A V_b V_b^{1/2} \cong K V_b^{3/2} \tag{9-29}$$

The results of a more precise analysis and also of careful experiment agree closely with the "$\frac{3}{2}$ power law" predicted by Eq. 9-29 for parallel-plane electrodes. Experimental results for practical tubes with electrodes in the form of concentric cylinders (Fig. 9.10) also agree quite well with Eq. 9-29, but design calculations are usually based on graphical data supplied by the manufacturer.

The effects of cathode temperature and plate voltage on plate current are displayed in Fig. 9.13. The electron emission (proportional to $e^{-W_w/kT}$) rises rapidly with cathode temperature; if the plate voltage is sufficiently high, all the electrons are drawn across the space and the

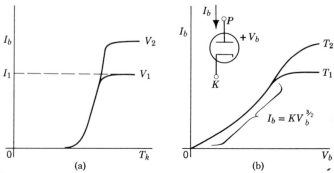

Fig. 9.13 Effect of cathode temperature and plate voltage on plate current.

plate current rises correspondingly (Fig. 9.13a). Due to space charge, however, the plate current is limited to I_1 for a given V_1 (Eq. 9-29), and a further increase in cathode temperature does not result in increased current. Raising the plate voltage to V_2 raises the possible current. As shown in Fig. 9.13b, for a given cathode temperature T_1, plate current increases with plate voltage according to the $\frac{3}{2}$ power law until all the emitted electrons are being drawn across the space. Operation under this condition is said to be "temperature limited"; a further increase in current requires an increase in cathode temperature. Vacuum tubes are ordinarily operated in the "space-charge limited" region in which $I_b \cong K V_b^{\frac{3}{2}}$.

EXAMPLE 4

A vacuum diode is operated with a heater voltage $V_a = 6$ V and a plate voltage $V_b = 100$ V; the plate current I_b is 12 mA. Increasing V_a to 6.5 V produces no change in I_b. Predict the value of I_b for $V_a = 7$ V and $V_b = 25$ V.

SOLUTION. The fact that increasing V_a, and therefore cathode temperature, produces no change in I_b indicates that the tube is operating in the space-charge limited region. Therefore, the increase in V_a above 6 V is not significant and

$$\frac{I_b'}{I_b} = \frac{K V_b'^{\frac{3}{2}}}{K V_b^{\frac{3}{2}}} = \left(\frac{V_b'}{V_b}\right)^{\frac{3}{2}}$$

Solving,

$$I_b' = I_b \left(\frac{V_b'}{V_b}\right)^{\frac{3}{2}} = 12 \left(\frac{25}{100}\right)^{\frac{3}{2}} = 12 \times \tfrac{1}{8} = 1.5 \text{ mA}$$

Gas Diodes

The effect of large numbers of negative electrons in the cathode-plate space is to limit the current. What is the effect of positive ions in this space? If a small amount of a gas, such as argon or mercury vapor, is introduced, the effect at low plate voltages is small; electrons crossing the space may collide with one or more atoms of gas, give up some kinetic energy, and then proceed to the plate. If, however, the electron imparts sufficient energy to ionize the gas atoms, there are two significant effects. First, ionization produces a free electron which adds to the current flow. Second, the positive ion moves toward the cathode and tends to neutralize the negative space charge. The resulting increased flow of electrons increases the probability of ionization, decreases the space charge further, and increases the current still more. The space charge becomes positive due to the presence of many slow-moving ions and the current is limited solely by cathode emission. The resulting gas diode characteristic is

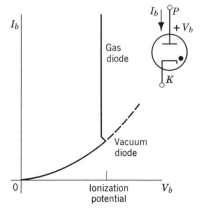

Fig. 9.14 Gas diode characteristics.   **Fig. 9.15** Phototube characteristics.

shown in Fig. 9.14; in such a tube containing mercury vapor (ionization potential = 10.4 V), a large current can flow with just a small applied voltage and, therefore, with just a small power loss.

Photo-Emissive Diodes

In thermionic diodes, emission is obtained by heating the cathode. A diode in which electrons are obtained by photoelectric emission is called a "phototube." In one type, the cathode is a half-cylinder with the inside surface coated with a material sensitive to visible light. The emitted electrons are collected at a slender anode mounted in front. As shown in Fig. 9.15, for a given luminous flux the current increases with voltage until all the electrons are drawn to the anode. For voltages above a certain value, the current is proportional to the luminous flux. For example, such tubes are used in motion picture projectors to convert illumination from the sound track into electric currents for amplification and reproduction.

CONDUCTION IN SOLIDS

Conduction occurs in a vacuum if free electrons are available to carry charge under the action of an applied field. In an ionized gas, positively charged ions as well as electrons contribute to the conduction process. In a liquid, the charge carriers are positive and negative ions moving under the influence of an applied field. Solids vary widely in the type and number of charge carriers available, and in the ease with which the carriers move under the action of applied fields. In electrical engineering we are interested in *insulators* which have practically no available charge carriers, *conductors* which have large numbers of mobile charge carriers, and *semiconductors* which have conductivities intermediate between those of insulators and conductors.

Metallic Conductors

In a typical metal such as copper or silver, the atoms are arranged in a systematic array to form a *crystal*. The atoms are in such close proximity that the outer, loosely bound electrons are attracted to numerous neighboring nuclei and, therefore, are not closely associated with any one nucleus (Fig. 9.16). These *conduction electrons* are visualized as being free to wander through the crystal structure or *lattice*. At absolute zero temperature, the conduction electrons encounter no opposition to motion and the resistance is zero.

At ordinary temperatures, the electron-deficient atoms or *ions* possess kinetic energy in the form of vibration about neutral positions in the lattice; this vibrational energy is measured by temperature. There is a continual interchange of energy between the vibrating ions and the free electrons in the form of elastic and inelastic collisions. The resulting electron motion is random, there is no net motion, and the net current is zero (Fig. 9.17a).

If a uniform electric field of intensity ε V/m is applied, the electrons are accelerated; superimposed on the rapid random motion, there is a small component of velocity in the direction of $-\varepsilon$. At each inelastic collision with an ion, the electron loses its kinetic energy; it then accelerates again, gains a component of velocity in the $-\varepsilon$ direction, and loses its energy at the next inelastic collision (Fig. 9.17b). The time between collisions is determined by the random velocity and the length of the

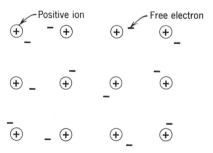

Fig. 9.16 Simplified representation of a metallic crystal.

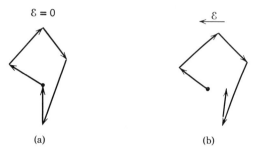

$\varepsilon = 0$

ε

(a)   (b)

Fig. 9.17   Motion of an electron in a metallic crystal.

mean free path. On the average, the electrons gain a directed *drift velocity* u m/sec which is directly proportional to ε (since the acceleration is constant for an average increment of time), and

$$u = \mu \varepsilon \qquad (9\text{-}30)$$

where μ (mu) is the *mobility* in meters squared per volt-second.

The resulting flow of electrons carrying charge $-e$ at drift velocity u constitutes a current. If there are n free electrons per cubic meter, the current density $J(\text{A/m}^2)$ is

$$J = neu = ne\mu \varepsilon = \sigma \varepsilon \qquad (9\text{-}31)$$

where

$$\sigma = ne\mu$$

is the *conductivity* of the material in mhos per meter. The reciprocal of σ (sigma) is the *resistivity* ρ (rho) in ohm-meters. Equation 9-31 is another formulation of Ohm's law; it says that the current density is directly proportional to the voltage gradient. For a conductor of area A and length l,

$$I = JA = \sigma A \varepsilon = \sigma A \frac{V}{l} = \sigma \frac{A}{l} V \qquad (9\text{-}32a)$$

where $\sigma A / l$ is the conductance G in mhos. Alternatively,

$$R = \frac{V}{I} = \frac{1}{G} = \frac{l}{\sigma A} = \rho \frac{l}{A} \qquad (9\text{-}32b)$$

is the resistance in ohms.

EXAMPLE 5

The resistivity of copper at 20°C is 1.73×10^{-8} Ω-m. Find the average drift velocity in a copper conductor with a cross-sectional area of 10^{-6} m^2 carrying a current of 4 A.

SOLUTION. For copper with an atomic weight of 63.6 and a density of 8.9 g/cm³, by Avogadro's law the number of atoms per meter³ is

$$n_A = \frac{6.025 \times 10^{23} \text{ atoms/g-atom} \times 8.9 \times 10^6 \text{ g/m}^3}{63.6 \text{ g/g-atom}} = 8.43 \times 10^{28}$$

Assuming that there is one free electron per atom, $n = n_A$. By Eq. 9-31,

$$u = \frac{J}{ne} = \frac{I/A}{ne} = \frac{4 \times 10^6}{8.43 \times 10^{28} \times 1.6 \times 10^{-19}} \cong 3 \times 10^{-4} \text{ m/sec}$$

The average drift velocity in a good conductor is very slow compared to the random thermal electron velocities of the order of 10^5 m/sec at room temperatures. As temperature increases, random thermal motion increases, the time between energy-robbing collisions decreases, mobility decreases, and therefore conductivity decreases. It is characteristic of metallic conductors that resistance increases with temperature.

Semiconductors

The two semiconductors of greatest importance in electronics are germanium and silicon. These elements are located in the fourth column of the periodic table and have four valence electrons. The crystal structure of germanium or silicon follows a tetrahedral pattern with each atom sharing one valence electron with each of four neighboring atoms. The *covalent bonds* are shown in the two-dimensional representation of Fig. 9.18. At temperatures close to absolute zero, the electrons in the outer

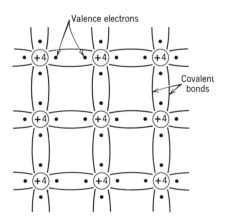

Fig. 9.18 Two-dimensional representation of germanium crystal.

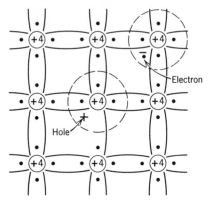

Fig. 9.19 Germanium crystal with one covalent bond broken.

shell are tightly bound, there are no free carriers, and germanium is an insulator.

The energy required to break a covalent bond is about 0.7 eV for germanium and about 1.1 eV for silicon.   At room temperature (300°K), a few electrons have this amount of thermal energy and are excited into the conduction band, becoming free electrons.   When a covalent bond is broken (Fig. 9.19), a vacancy or *hole* is left.   The region in which this vacancy exists has a net positive charge; the region in which the freed electron exists has a net negative charge.   In such semiconductors *both electrons and holes contribute to electrical conduction*.   If a valence electron from another covalent bond fills the hole (without gaining sufficient energy to become "free"), the vacancy appears in a new place and the effect is as if a positive charge (of magnitude e) has moved to the new location.†

Consideration of hole behavior as the motion of a positively charged particle of definite mass and mobility is consistent with the quantum mechanical properties of valence electrons.   Attempting to describe this behavior in terms of classical physics leads to results which are contrary to the observed facts.   For our purposes we shall consider conduction in semiconductors as due to two separate and independent particles carrying

---

† There is an analogy in our economic system.   In payment for a sweater, you may give a retailer $10 in cash or accept from him a bill for $10.   You feel the same with $10 *subtracted* from your wallet or with $10 *added* to your debts.   If you send the bill to your father for payment, the "vacancy appears in a new place" and the effect is as if your father had sent you $10.   The sum of cash to you and bills to your father constitutes the net financial "current" from your father to you.

opposite charges and drifting in opposite directions under the influence of an applied electric field.

With two charge-carrying particles, the expression for current density is

$$J = (n\mu_n + p\mu_p)e\mathcal{E} = \sigma\mathcal{E} \qquad (9\text{-}33)$$

where n and p are the concentrations of electrons and holes (number/m^3) and μ_n and μ_p are the corresponding mobilities. Therefore, the conductivity is

$$\sigma = (n\mu_n + p\mu_p)e \qquad (9\text{-}34)$$

Some of the properties of germanium and silicon are shown in Table 9-1.

TABLE 9-1 Properties of Germanium and Silicon†

	Germanium	Silicon
Energy gap at 300°K (eV)	0.67	1.1
Electron mobility μ_n (m^2/V-sec)	0.39	0.135
Hole mobility μ_p (m^2/V-sec)	0.19	0.048
Intrinsic carrier density n_i (/m^3)	2.4×10^{19}	1.5×10^{16}
Intrinsic resistivity ρ_i (Ω-m)	0.46	2300

† Quoted by E. M. Conwell in "Properties of Silicon and Germanium II," *Proc. IRE,* p. 1281, June 1958.

In a pure semiconductor, the number of holes is just equal to the number of conduction electrons, or

$$n = p = n_i \qquad (9\text{-}35)$$

where n_i is the *intrinsic* concentration. New electron-hole pairs are generated continuously and, under equilibrium conditions, they are removed by recombination at the same rate. At ordinary operating temperatures, only a very small fraction of the valence electrons are in the conduction state at any instant.

EXAMPLE 6

Estimate the relative concentration of germanium atoms and electron-hole pairs at room temperature, and predict the intrinsic resistivity.

SOLUTION. By Avogadro's law, the concentration of atoms is

$$n_A = \frac{6.025 \times 10^{23} \text{ atoms/g-atom} \times 5.32 \times 10^6 \text{ g/m}^3}{72.6 \text{ g/g-atom}} \cong 4.4 \times 10^{28} \text{ atoms/m}^3$$

From Table 9-1, the intrinsic concentration at 300°K is 2.4×10^{19} electron-hole pairs per cubic meter; therefore, there are

$$\frac{n_A}{n_i} \cong \frac{4.4 \times 10^{28}}{2.4 \times 10^{19}} \cong 2 \times 10^9 \text{ germanium atoms per electron-hole pair}$$

Since in the pure semiconductor $n = p = n_i$, by Eq. 9.34

$$\sigma_i = (n\mu_n + p\mu_p)e = (\mu_n + \mu_p)n_i e$$

$$= (0.39 + 0.19) \times 2.4 \times 10^{19} \times 1.6 \times 10^{-19} = 2.2 \ \mho/m$$

and the resistivity is

$$\rho_i = \frac{1}{\sigma_i} = \frac{1}{2.2} \cong 0.45 \ \Omega\text{-m}$$

The result of Example 6 confirms the fact that intrinsic germanium is a poor conductor as compared to copper ($\rho = 1.73 \times 10^{-8} \ \Omega$-m); semiconductors are valuable, not for their conductivity, but for two unusual properties. First, the concentration of free carriers, and consequently the conductivity, increases exponentially with temperature (approximately 5% per degree centigrade at ordinary temperatures). The *thermistor*, a temperature-sensitive device that utilizes this property, is used in instrumentation and control, and also may be used to compensate for the *decrease* in conductivity with temperature in the metallic parts of a circuit. Second, the conductivity of a semiconductor can be increased greatly, and to a precisely controlled extent, by adding small amounts of impurities in the process called *doping*. Since there are two types of mobile charge carriers, of opposite sign, extraordinary distributions of charge carriers can be created. The semiconductor diode and the transistor utilize this property.

Doped Semiconductors

The startling effect of doping can be illustrated by adding to germanium or silicon an impurity element from the adjacent third or fifth column of the periodic table. Assume that a small amount of a *pentavalent* element (antimony, phosphorous, or arsenic) is added to otherwise pure germanium. Such a doping element has five valence electrons and the effective ionic charge is $+5e$. When a pentavalent atom replaces a germanium atom in the crystal lattice (Fig. 9.20), only four of the valence electrons are used to complete the covalent bonds; the remaining electron, with the addition of a small amount of thermal energy, becomes a free electron available for conduction. The resulting material is called an *n-type* semiconductor because of the presence of negative charge carriers in an electrically neutral crystal. The net positive charges left behind are immobile and cannot contribute to current.

If a small amount of a *trivalent* element (aluminum, boron, gallium, or indium) is added to otherwise pure germanium, a *p-type* semiconductor is obtained. When a trivalent atom replaces a germanium atom in the

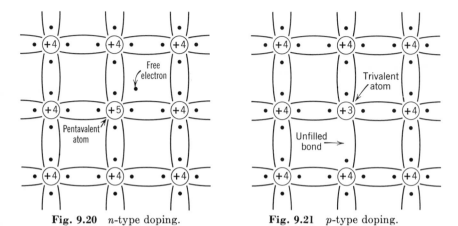

Fig. 9.20 *n*-type doping.   **Fig. 9.21** *p*-type doping.

crystal lattice (Fig. 9.21), only three valence electrons are available to complete covalent bonds. If the remaining unfilled covalent bond is filled by a valence electron from a neighboring atom, a mobile hole is created and there is the possibility of current conduction by the motion of positive charges. Used in this way, a trivalent atom is called an *acceptor* atom because it accepts an electron. (The net negative charge created is immobile.) In the same sense, a pentavalent atom is called a *donor* atom.

By adding donor or acceptor atoms in small amounts, the conductivity of a semiconductor can be increased enormously. To predict the magnitude of this effect we must understand quantitatively the process of generation and recombination. The *thermal generation rate g* (electron-hole pairs/sec-m^3) depends on the properties of the material and is a function of temperature. The energy required for a valence electron to become a free electron, or the energy needed in the "generation" of a conduction electron, can be expressed in electron volts as eV_g. The average energy corresponding to temperature T can be expressed as kT. Statistical analysis shows that the probability of a valence electron receiving sufficient energy to become free is proportional to $e^{-eV_g/kT}$; the rate of thermal generation (and also the rate of thermionic emission) involves this factor and, therefore, is highly temperature-dependent.

In a semiconductor containing mobile electrons and holes, they tend to recombine and disappear. If there are few electron-hole pairs in existence, the *rate of recombination* is low; if there are many, the rate is high. If, as in *n*-type material, there are few holes but many electrons, the rate of recombination is high due to the large number of electrons. In general,

$$R = rnp \qquad (9\text{-}36)$$

where R = recombination rate (electron-hole pairs/sec-m^3) and
      r = a proportionality constant for the material.
This version of the *mass-action law* says that the rate of recombination is dependent on the numbers of reacting elements present.†

Under equilibrium conditions, the rate of generation is just equal to the rate of recombination or

$$g = R = rnp \qquad (9\text{-}37)$$

In the pure crystal the intrinsic concentrations of electrons and holes are equal or $n_i = p_i$ and

$$g = R = rn_ip_i = rn_i^2 \qquad (9\text{-}38)$$

Even in a doped crystal, the great bulk of the atoms are still germanium (or silicon) and the thermal generation rate is unchanged from the intrinsic value. Therefore, Eq. 9-38 is a general relation and

$$np = n_i^2 \qquad (9\text{-}39)$$

in doped semiconductors as well.

A second fundamental relation is based on the fact that the total crystal must be electrically neutral. In n-type material with a donor atom concentration of N_d atoms per cubic meter, practically all the donor atoms are ionized, leaving N_d immobile positive charges. The mobile positive charge density is p_n; therefore, the total positive charge density is $N_d + p_n$. In n-type material, the total negative charge density is just the electron density n_n. For electrical neutrality

$$n_n = N_d + p_n \cong N_d \qquad (9\text{-}40)$$

in the practical case where $N_d \gg p_n$. The concentration of holes in n-type material is, by Eq. 9-39,

$$p_n = \frac{n_i^2}{n_n} \cong \frac{n_i^2}{N_d} \qquad (9\text{-}41)$$

The corresponding equations for p-type material are:

$$p_p \cong N_a \qquad \text{and} \qquad n_p \cong \frac{n_i^2}{N_a} \qquad (9\text{-}42)$$

---

† As a crude analogy, consider a dance in which couples dance together for awhile, then separate and wander through the other couples until they find a new partner. The rate of recombination depends on the number of unattached partners available.

EXAMPLE 7

Determine how replacing approximately every millionth germanium atom with an atom of antimony affects the properties of a germanium crystal.

SOLUTION. Since there are about 4.4×10^{28} germanium atoms per cubic meter (see Example 6), the necessary concentration of donor atoms is

$$N_d = 4.4 \times 10^{28} \times 10^{-6} = 4.4 \times 10^{22} \cong n_n$$

The corresponding intrinsic concentration is $n_i = 2.4 \times 10^{19}$; therefore, this tiny amount of impurity has increased the concentration of free electrons by a factor of nearly 2000. Substituting this value in Eq. 9-41, the new hole concentration is

$$p_n = \frac{n_i^2}{n_n} \cong \frac{n_i^2}{N_d} = \frac{(2.4 \times 10^{19})^2}{4.4 \times 10^{22}} = 1.3 \times 10^{16}$$

or the hole concentration has been *reduced* by a factor of about 2000.† (Is the approximation in Eq. 9-40 justified?) The new conductivity is

$$\sigma = (n\mu_n + p\mu_p)e \cong N_d\mu_n e \cong 4.4 \times 10^{22} \times 0.39 \times 1.6 \times 10^{-19}$$

$$= 2740 \ \mho/m$$

The conductivity of the doped crystal is vastly different from the intrinsic conductivity of 2.2 $\mho/m$ calculated in Example 6.

We conclude from Example 7 that a small concentration of impurity greatly modifies the electrical properties of a semiconductor. Even more startling effects occur in regions where the impurity concentration is highly nonuniform, as it is at a junction of n-type and p-type materials.

Diffusion

If the doping concentration is nonuniform, the concentration of charged particles is also nonuniform, and it is possible to have charge motion by the mechanism called *diffusion*. In an analogous situation, if a bottle of perfume is opened at one end of an apparently still room, in a short time some of the perfume will have reached the other end. For mass transfer by diffusion, two factors must be present: there must be random motion of the particles and there must be a concentration gradient. The thermal energy of apparently still air provides the first, and opening a bottle of concentrated perfume provides the second. Note that no force is required for this type of transport; the net transfer is due to a statistical redistribution.

If a nonuniform concentration of randomly moving electrons or holes exists, diffusion will occur. If, for example, the concentration of elec-

---

† To carry the previous analogy a little further, if the dance floor is flooded with male stags, the number of girls looking for partners is drastically reduced.

trons on one side of an imaginary plane is greater than that on the other, and if the electrons are in random motion, after a finite time there will be a net motion of electrons from the more dense side. This net motion of charge which constitutes a diffusion current is proportional to the concentration gradient dn/dl. The diffusion current density due to electrons is given by

$$J_n = eD_n \frac{dn}{dl} \qquad (9\text{-}43)$$

where D_n = the diffusion constant for electrons (m^2/sec). The corresponding relation for holes is

$$J_p = -eD_p \frac{dp}{dl} \qquad (9\text{-}44)$$

Note that in each case the charged particles move away from the region of greatest concentration, but the motion is not due to any force of repulsion. Like mobility, diffusion is a statistical phenomenon and it is not surprising to find that they are related by the Einstein equation

$$\frac{\mu_n}{D_n} = \frac{\mu_p}{D_p} = \frac{e}{kT} \qquad (9\text{-}45)$$

or that the factor e/kT, which appeared in thermionic emission and thermal generation, shows up again here.

SEMICONDUCTOR DIODES

Semiconductors, pure or doped, p-type or n-type, are bilateral; current flows in either direction with equal facility. If, however, a p-type region exists in close proximity to an n-type region, there is a carrier density gradient which is unilateral; current flows easily in one direction only. The resulting device, a *semiconductor diode*, exhibits a very useful control property.

pn Junction Formation

The fabrication of semiconductor diodes is a developing technological art. For satisfactory results, the entire diode must have a common crystalline structure. The pure crystals necessary may be "grown" by touching a "seed" crystal to the surface of molten germanium and then slowly raising it (Fig. 9.22a). The germanium crystallizes onto the seed and "grows" in the same crystalline orientation as the seed. If the

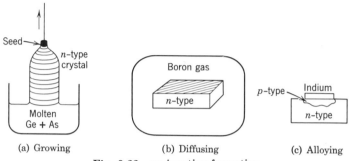

(a) Growing (b) Diffusing (c) Alloying

Fig. 9.22 *pn* junction formation.

melt contains a donor element such as arsenic, *n*-type semiconductor is obtained. If at a certain point in the growing process an excess of acceptor element is added to the melt, the subsequent crystal will be *p*-type. The metallurgical boundary between the two materials is called a *grown junction*.

An *n*-type crystal could be obtained by heating a germanium crystal in the presence of a pentavalent element (such as phosphorus) and allowing the donor atoms to diffuse into the host crystal. If the resulting *n*-type crystal is heated in the presence of a trivalent element such as boron gas, acceptor atoms in a sufficient quantity to override the donor atoms may diffuse into the crystal (Fig. 9.22b). The resulting device is called a *diffused-junction* diode.

If a dot of trivalent indium is placed on an *n*-type crystal and heated to the proper temperature, a small drop of molten mixture will form. Upon cooling, the drop solidifies into *p*-type material that follows the crystalline pattern of the host crystal (Fig. 9.22c). The resulting device is an *alloy-junction* diode. By careful control of the alloying procedure it is possible to obtain diodes in which the transition from *p*-type to *n*-type material occurs in a distance corresponding to a few atomic layers.

pn Junction Behavior

The external behavior of a typical *pn* junction diode is shown in Fig. 9.23. To use a diode effectively, we must understand (at least qualitatively) the internal mechanism which results in these remarkable properties; an understanding of diode behavior is directly transferable to the analysis of more complicated devices, such as the transistor, so a detailed study at this point is justified. We assume that the diode consists of a single crystal with an abrupt change from *p*- to *n*-type at the junction in the *y-z* plane; only variations with respect to *x* are significant.

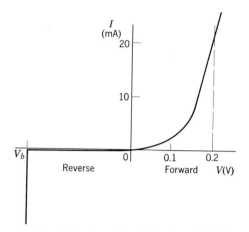

Fig. 9.23   Junction diode characteristic.

The distribution of charges in such a diode is represented in Fig. 9.24. The circles represent immobile ions with their net charges; the separate + and − signs represent mobile holes and electrons.   We imagine that a junction is created instantaneously; because of the density gradient at the junction, holes diffuse from the *p*-type material to the right across the junction and recombine with some of the many free electrons in the *n*-type material.   Similarly, electrons diffuse from the *n*-type material to the left across the junction and recombine.   The diffusion of holes

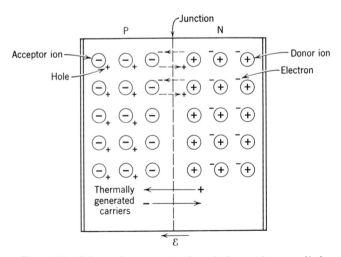

Fig. 9.24   Schematic representation of charges in a *pn* diode.

leaves *uncovered* bound negative charges on the left of the junction, and the diffusion of electrons leaves *uncovered* bound positive charges on the right. To avoid repeating every statement, we call holes in the *p*-region and electrons in the *n*-region *majority carriers*. Thus the result of the diffusion of majority carriers is the uncovering of bound charge in the *transition region* and the creation of an internal electric field. Electrons in the *p*-region and holes in the *n*-region are called *minority carriers*. Under the action of the electric field, minority carriers (perhaps generated thermally) drift across the junction. With two types of carriers (reduced from four by the use of the terms "majority" and "minority") and two different conduction mechanisms (drift and diffusion) we expect the explanation of Fig. 9.23 to be complicated.

Open Circuit. The simpler representation of the diode in Fig. 9.25 shows only the uncovered charge in the transition region; the remainder of the open-circuited diode is electrically neutral. With the distribution of charge density shown, there is an electric field (see Eq. 9-28)

$$\varepsilon = \frac{1}{\epsilon} \int \rho \, dx \qquad (9\text{-}46)$$

Since $\varepsilon = -dv/dx$ (Eq. 9-26), the potential distribution across the junc-

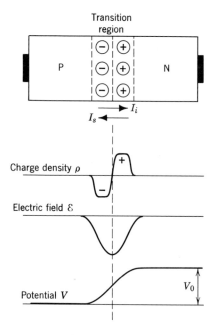

Fig. 9.25 Open-circuited *pn* diode.

tion is obtained by integrating the field. The potential barrier or "potential hill" of height V_0 acts to oppose diffusion of majority carriers (holes to the right and electrons to the left) and to encourage drift of minority carriers across the junction.

The diffusion of majority carriers across the junction constitutes an *injection* current I_i; the drift of thermally generated minority carriers constitutes a *saturation* current I_s. Since any minority carriers which arrive at the edge of the transition region are forced across by the field (holes "roll down" a potential hill; electrons "roll up"), I_s depends only on the rate of thermal generation and is independent of the height of the barrier. In contrast, the injection current I_i is very sensitive to the barrier height; only those majority carriers having kinetic energies in excess of eV_0, diffuse across the junction.

Under open-circuit conditions the net current is zero; therefore, $I_i = I_s$. The magnitude of I_i determines the amount of charge uncovered. This determines V_0 which, in turn, limits I_i in a self-regulating process. The height of the potential barrier is determined by the necessity for equilibrium; for no net current, the diffusion current must be just equal to the drift component. The equilibrium value V_0 is also called the *contact potential* for the junction. This potential cannot be used to cause external current flow. Connecting a conductor across the terminals creates two new contact potentials which just cancel that at the junction.†

Forward Bias. If equilibrium is upset by a decrease in the junction potential to $V_0 - V$ (Fig. 9.26), the probability of majority carriers possessing sufficient energy to pass the potential barrier is greatly increased. An increase in I_i represents a net current since I_s is unaffected by a small change in the potential barrier. (Why?) The net external current $I = I_i - I_s$ represents electrons entering the n-region and holes entering the p-region. These have the effect of partially neutralizing the uncovered charge, thereby reducing the junction potential. This is consistent with the assumed condition; in other words, a net current through the diode is consistent with a reduction in the junction potential. If the junction potential is reduced by the application of an external *biasing* voltage V, as shown in Fig. 9.26, a net current I flows. (The small voltage drop across the diode body at moderate currents is neglected in this discussion.)

---

† An analogy may be helpful. In a column of gas, molecules drift downward under the action of gravity, but diffuse upward due to their random thermal energy. A pressure difference exists between top and bottom, but there is no net flow. The pressure difference cannot be used to cause any external flow.

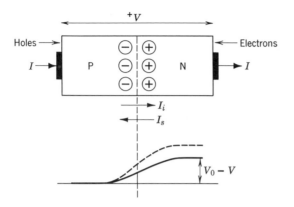

Fig. 9.26 Forward-biased *pn* diode.

The calculation of the magnitude of the net current is based on the fact that electrons crossing the junction become minority carriers in the *p*-region and must be transported toward the terminal by diffusion since the electric field in the body of the diode is small. Similarly, the holes crossing the junction become minority carriers in the *n*-region. The current flow, therefore, depends on the density gradient of the minority carriers at the edge of the transition region. (See Eq. 9-43.) As we expect from our previous experience with thermionic emission of electrons and thermal generation of electron-hole pairs, the transport process is related to the statistical probability of electrons and holes possessing sufficient energy. The injection current I_i is of the form $Ae^{eV/kT}$ and, for a given temperature, I_s is nearly constant. The total current is

$$I = I_i - I_s = Ae^{eV/kT} - I_s \qquad (9\text{-}47)$$

But under open-circuit conditions where $V = 0$,

$$I = 0 = Ae^0 - I_s \qquad \therefore A = I_s$$

In general, then, the junction diode current is

$$I = I_s(e^{eV/kT} - 1) \qquad (9\text{-}48)$$

Reverse Bias. If the junction potential is increased to $V_0 + V$ (Fig. 9.27), the probability of majority carriers possessing sufficient energy to pass the potential barrier is greatly reduced. Because I_s is unaffected by a small change in the barrier height, a reduction in I_i below the equilibrium value represents a net current in the reverse direction. The effect of such a current is to extract holes from the *p*-region and electrons from the *n*-region, thereby increasing the uncovered charge and increasing the junction potential. Again, this is consistent with the

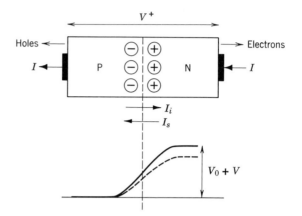

Fig. 9.27   Reverse-biased pn diode.

assumed condition.   In other words, if the junction potential is raised by the application of a *reverse-biasing* voltage as shown in Fig. 9.27, a current flows in the reverse direction, the direction of I_s. But the largest possible value of this reverse current is just I_s when $I_i = 0$.

This is consistent with Eq. 9-48.   At room temperature (say, $T = 20°C = 293°K$), $e/kT \cong 40$ and a convenient form of this equation is

$$I = I_s(e^{40V} - 1) \qquad (9\text{-}49)$$

For $V = -0.1$ V, $e^{40V} = e^{-4} \cong 0.02$, and $I \cong -I_s$.   The name for I_s comes from the fact that the current due to reverse bias reaches "saturation" at a low value of bias voltage.   This saturation current is due to thermally generated carriers and, at ordinary temperatures, is very small (measured in μA).   Ideally, the reverse current should be zero; actually, I_s is an important diode parameter which is very sensitive to temperature. It is directly proportional to the thermal generation rate $g = rn_i{}^2$ which varies exponentially with temperature.   As a rough but convenient rule, I_s doubles with each increase of approximately 10°C.   (Strictly speaking, this rule holds only for germanium near room temperature.)

EXAMPLE 8

The current of a diode at room temperature is 100 μA at a voltage of -1 V. Predict the magnitude of the current for voltages of -0.2 V and $+0.2$ V at room temperature and at 20°C above room temperature.

SOLUTION.   The current at -1 V can be assumed to be the reverse saturation current or $I_s = 100 \mu A$.

At $V = -0.2$ V, $e^{40V} = e^{-8} \cong 0$ $\therefore$ $I \cong I_s = 100 \mu A$

At $V = +0.2$ V, $e^{40V} = e^8 \cong 3000$

Therefore,

$$I = 100(e^8 - 1) \times 10^{-6} = 100(3000 - 1) \times 10^{-6} \cong 300 \text{ mA}$$

At 20°C above room temperature, I_s will be approximately four times as great. The two values of current will be $I_s = 400 \ \mu A$ and $I = 1.2$ A, respectively.

Breakdown Phenomena

Along with the change in junction potential due to forward and reverse biasing, there is a significant change in the width of the transition region. For a given junction potential, a definite number of bound charges must be uncovered; therefore, the width of the transition (or "space charge") region depends on the density of doping. Under forward bias, the junction potential is reduced and the transition region narrows; under reverse bias, the transition region widens.

If the reverse bias is increased sufficiently, a sudden increase in reverse current is observed (see Fig. 9.23). This is due to the *Zener* effect or the *avalanche* effect. In Zener breakdown, the electric field in the junction becomes high enough to pull electrons directly out of covalent bonds. The electron-hole pairs thus created then contribute a greatly increased reverse current. The avalanche effect occurs at voltages higher than Zener breakdown voltages. At these high voltages, carriers gain sufficient energy between collisions to knock electrons from covalent bonds; these too can reach ionizing energies in a cumulative process.

In either type of breakdown, the reverse current is large and nearly independent of voltage. If the power dissipated is within the capability of the diode, there is no damage; reduction of the reverse bias voltage below V_b reduces the current to I_s. By controlling doping densities, it is possible to manufacture Zener diodes† with breakdown voltages from a few volts to several hundred. These are valuable because of their ability to maintain a nearly constant voltage under conditions of widely varying current.

TWO-PORT ELECTRONIC DEVICES

The vacuum or semiconductor diode exhibits a useful control property; it permits appreciable current flow under forward-bias voltage and tends to prevent current flow when the voltage is reversed. Such a one-port

---

† In commercial practice, the term "Zener diodes" includes devices employing both effects.

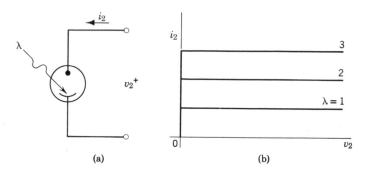

Fig. 9.28   Phototube as a transducer.

device is sometimes called a "switch."   Electrically speaking, a phototube is also a diode, but the current flow for a given voltage is influenced
by the light signals introduced at a second port.   In idealized form, the
characteristic curves of Fig. 9.28b represent the phototube as a two-port
transducer.

An *amplifier* is an important example of an electronic two-port.   As a
result of voltage or current signals applied to the input, larger voltage or
current signals are available at the output.   In the idealized current
amplifier of Fig. 9.29, the output current for any output voltage is A
times as great as the input current.†   In the idealized voltage amplifier

---

† A truly "ideal" amplifier would function just as well for negative currents and
voltages, and the characteristic curves would extend into all four quadrants.

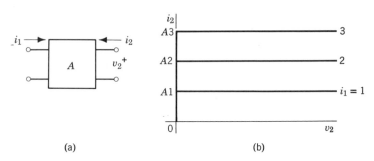

Fig 9.29   Idealized current amplifier.

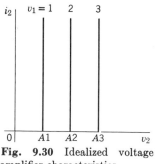

Fig. 9.30 Idealized voltage amplifier characteristics.

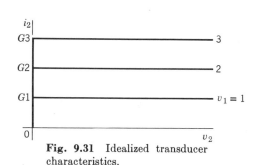

Fig. 9.31 Idealized transducer characteristics.

of Fig. 9.30, the output voltage is A times the input voltage for any output current. In the idealized transducer of Fig. 9.31, the output current is G times the input voltage; such a device can be converted into a voltage amplifier by sending the output current through a load resistance.

Vacuum tubes and transistors have characteristics which approximate these idealized curves. In this chapter we describe their operation in terms of characteristic curves, in Chapter 10 we derive convenient linear models of the actual devices, and in Chapter 11 we use curves and models in the design of practical amplifiers.

The Vacuum Triode

Perhaps Lee de Forest did not have Fig. 9.30 in mind in 1906, but he did invent a device whose characteristics approach those shown. The vacuum diode was already in use as a detector of radio signals. De Forest inserted an open mesh *grid* between the cathode and plate and called the resulting triode an "audion" because of its ability to amplify audio signals. The conventional symbol for a triode is shown in Fig. 9.32a; the heater is usually omitted from circuit diagrams.

The operation of the triode can be explained in terms of the effect of the grid on the potential distribution in the cathode-plate space. Assuming space-charge limited operation, the potential distribution in a diode is as shown by the solid line in Fig. 9.32b. Because of the excess electrons emitted from the cathode, a space charge exists and tends to repel the emitted electrons back to the cathode; only the more energetic electrons pass the potential barrier and are drawn to the plate.

If an open-wire grid is placed in the space, it tends to assume the potential of that place but does not impede electron flow because of the low ratio of wire width to grid opening. If a positive potential v_c is placed on the grid, the potential distribution is modified as shown. The

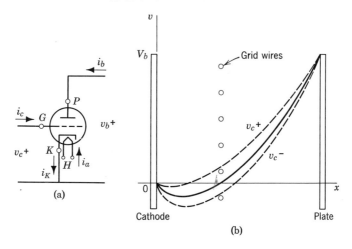

Fig. 9.32   Triode notation and potential distribution.

effect can be described as a lowering of the potential barrier or as a reduction in the negative field strength (the slope of the potential curve). In either case, the result is an increased net current from the cathode. Some of the electrons are attracted to the positive grid, but most of the current goes through the grid to the plate.   If a negative potential $-v_c$ is placed on the grid, the potential barrier is raised and the plate current is reduced.   The negative grid repels electrons and there is no grid current.

For a given plate voltage, the variation of current with grid voltage is as shown in Fig. 9.33.   For positive grid voltages, the cathode current is

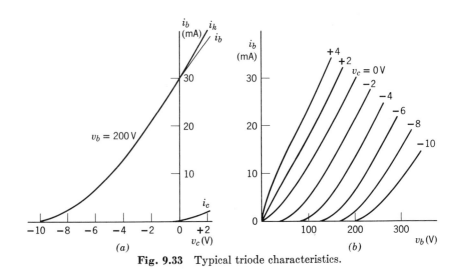

Fig. 9.33   Typical triode characteristics.

divided between plate and grid. At $v_c = 0$, a small grid current i_c flows due to electrons striking the grid wires. A small negative potential on the grid repels even the most energetic electrons and reduces this current to zero. As the grid is made more negative, the plate current i_b is reduced and becomes zero at a grid voltage called the *cutoff* value. A family of such curves drawn for various values of plate voltage constitutes the i_b versus v_c characteristics.

An alternative method of displaying triode characteristics is shown in Fig. 9.33b. Here plate current i_b is shown as a function of plate voltage v_b for various values of grid voltage v_c. The cathode current can be approximated by the theoretical relation

$$i_k = K(\mu v_c + v_b)^{3\!/_2} \tag{9-50}$$

For negative grid operation, $i_k = i_b$ and the curves resemble the $\frac{3}{2}$ power curve of the diode. The grid, being closer to the cathode, is more effective than the plate by the factor μ in Eq. 9-50. Note the resemblance between these curves and those of the idealized amplifier of Fig. 9.30. With a variation in grid voltage, an input signal, there is a variation in plate voltage, an output signal. Also note that if the grid is negative, no grid current flows and the power input is zero. This is a desirable feature in an amplifier. In fact, one of the great virtues of the triode is its ability to control an appreciable output power with no input power.

Tetrodes and Pentodes

The relations shown in Fig. 9.33 are called *static* characteristics because they are obtained from d-c measurements. In radio-frequency amplification, the signals consist of voltage variations at megacycle frequencies. Since $i = C \, dv/dt$, at these frequencies the very small capacitances between grid and cathode, grid and plate, and plate and cathode draw appreciable current. These *interelectrode capacitances* may be the limiting factors in the high-frequency performance of the tube. The grid-plate capacitance, only a few picofarads, is particularly annoying because it not only decreases the possible amplification but it also provides a path whereby some of the output signal is fed back into the input and unwanted oscillations may occur.

One way to reduce the grid-plate capacitance is to insert a second grid (Fig. 9.34a, b) which provides an electrostatic shield between *control grid* ($c1$) and plate. This *screen grid* ($c2$) is maintained at a fixed positive potential with respect to the cathode. It draws a small current, but the bulk of the current flows through the screen grid to the plate. One result of the screen grid, an advantage, is that variations in plate voltage (for example, from v_b to $v_b{}'$) have little effect on the potential distribution near the cathode and, therefore, have little effect on the plate current (Fig. 9.34b). The relative effect of the grid voltage is increased, i.e., the value of μ in Eq. 9-50, and therefore the voltage amplification capability.

A second result, a disadvantage in amplification, is that the plate characteristics become highly nonlinear. The dips in the plate current curves of Fig. 9.34c can be explained in terms of the potential distribution between the screen grid and the plate. In any vacuum tube, electrons accelerated by more than a few volts gain sufficient kinetic energy to knock electrons out of the plate in the process called *secondary emission*. In a diode or triode, the electric field near the plate forces the secondary electrons back to the plate. In a tetrode at low plate voltages ($v_b{}'$ in Fig. 9.34b), the electric field is reversed, secondary electrons are attracted to the more positive screen grid, and the plate current is effectively reduced.

The kinks in the plate characteristics of a tetrode can be removed by inserting another grid between the screen grid and the plate (Fig. 9.35a). Normally connected to the cathode, and therefore at zero potential, this *suppressor grid* ($c3$) depresses the potential distribution curve (Fig. 9.35b) and restores the negative electric field in front of the plate. Secondary emission from the plate is suppressed and the plate characteristics, shown in Fig. 9.35c, approach those of the idealized current amplifier (Fig. 9.31). Another method of obtaining the desired depression of the potential distribution in front of the plate is to use the space charge produced by a concentrated beam of electrons. Such a *beam power* tube has characteristics which even more closely approach those of the idealized current amplifier.

The evolution of multielectrode vacuum tubes from the simple diode is a good illustration of skilled invention guided by basic knowledge and

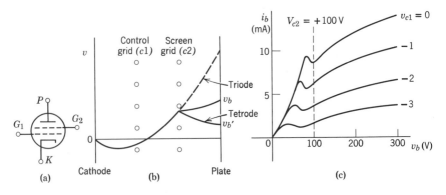

Fig. 9.34 Tetrode potential distribution and plate characteristics.

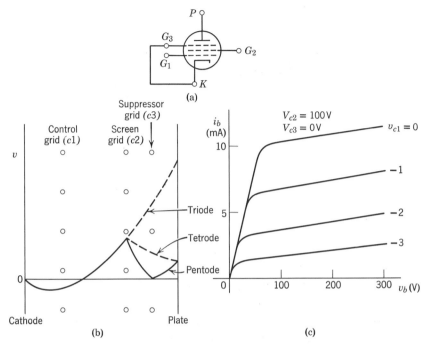

Fig. 9.35 Pentode potential distribution and plate characteristics.

stimulated by practical need. The diode acts as an efficient switch. The triode and pentode provide great amplification. The cathode-ray tube is a sensitive instrument. The linear accelerator imparts enormous energies to tiny electrons. The key ingredient in each is the engineer's ability to provide electric fields which precisely and predictably control the motion of charged particles.

The Transistor

The high power required to obtain thermionic emission and the large surfaces necessary for practical operation are two of the chief disadvantages of the vacuum tube. In contrast, the transistor requires no cathode power and the dimensions are very small. On the other hand, the transistor is more sensitive to temperature changes, and it is limited to lower voltages than the vacuum tube. However, for many purposes the advantages of semiconductor devices far outweigh their disadvantages, and the vacuum tube is being displaced from many applications in which it was formerly preeminent.

Essentially, a transistor consists of two *pn* junctions in close proximity.

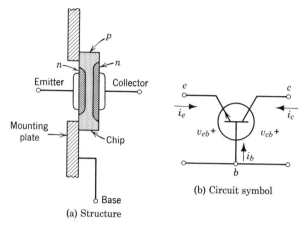

(b) Circuit symbol

(a) Structure

Fig. 9.36 *Npn* transistor.

Like the diode, it is formed of a single crystal with the doping impurities distributed so as to create two abrupt changes in carrier density.

The structure of an *npn* alloy-junction transistor is shown in Fig. 9.36a. A *p*-type germanium chip less than 1 mm square serves as the *base* and is supported by a metal mounting plate.   An *n*-type *emitter* region is alloyed to one side and another *n*-type *collector* region is alloyed to the other. The two *pn* junctions are separated by a base region which is thinner than this paper.   In the conventional symbol (Fig. 9.36b), the emitter lead is identified by the arrow which points in the direction of normal hole (positive charge) flow.   A *pnp* transistor is equally effective.   (The arrow in the symbol always points toward *n*-type material.)   While a transistor will work with either alloy contact serving as the emitter, it should be connected as labeled because doping densities and geometries are intentionally asymmetric.

The operation of a transistor can be explained qualitatively in terms of the potential distributions across the junctions (Fig. 9.37b).   The emitter junction is forward-biased; the effect of bias voltage V_{EB} is to reduce the potential barrier at the emitter junction and facilitate the injection of electrons (in this example) into the base where they are minority carriers. The collector junction is reverse-biased; the effect of bias voltage V_{CB} is to increase the potential barrier at the collector junction.   The base is so thin that almost all the electrons injected into the base from the emitter diffuse across the base and are swept up the potential hill into the collector where they recombine with holes "supplied" by the external battery. (Actually, electrons are "removed" by the external battery, leaving a

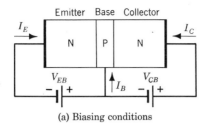

(a) Biasing conditions

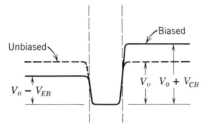

(b) Potential distribution

Fig. 9.37 Potential distribution in *npn* transistor.

supply of holes available for recombination.)   The net result is the transfer from the emitter circuit to the collector circuit of a current which is nearly independent of the collector-base voltage.   As we shall see, this permits the insertion of a large load resistance in the collector circuit to obtain voltage amplification.   The modulation of the emitter-junction potential barrier by a small-signal voltage produces a corresponding variation in emitter and collector currents and a relatively large output voltage across the load resistance.   Alternatively, variation of the base current (the small difference between emitter and collector currents) can be used to control the relatively larger collector current to achieve current amplification.

Transistor Characteristics

The d-c behavior of a transistor can be predicted on the basis of the motion of charge carriers across the junctions and into the base.   With the emitter junction forward-biased and the collector junction reverse-biased, in so-called *normal* operation, the carrier motion of an *npn* transistor is as shown in the symbolic diagram of Fig. 9.38.   The emitter current i_E consists of electrons injected across the *np* junction and holes injected from the base.   To optimize transistor performance, the base is doped relatively lightly, the factor γ is almost unity, and most of the

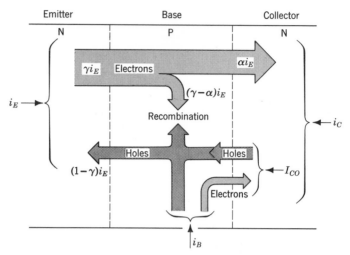

Fig. 9.38   Carrier motion in normal operation of npn transistor.

current consists of electrons injected from the emitter. Some of the injected electrons recombine with holes in the p-type base, but the base is made very narrow so that most of the electrons (minority carriers in this p-region) diffuse across the base and are swept across the collector junction (up the potential hill). The factor α varies from 0.90 to 0.999; a typical value is 0.98.

The electron current αi_E constitutes the major part of the collector current. In addition, there is a reverse saturation current across the collector junction due to thermally generated minority carriers, just as in a diode (see Eq. 9-48). This current is

$$-I_{CO}(e^{eV/kT} - 1) \cong I_{CO} \qquad (9\text{-}51)$$

when the reverse biasing exceeds a few tenths of a volt. The collector current is then

$$i_C = -\alpha i_E + I_{CO} \qquad (9\text{-}52)$$

where α, the *forward current-transfer ratio*, increases slightly with increased collector biasing voltage v_{CB}.

The base current (Fig. 9.38) consists of holes diffusing to the emitter, positive charges to supply the recombination which occurs in the base, and the reverse saturation current to the collector. By Kirchhoff's law,

$$i_B = -i_E - i_C \qquad (9\text{-}53)$$

and i_B is the small difference between two nearly equal currents.

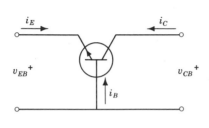

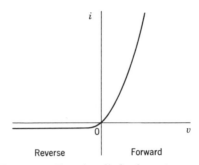

Fig. 9.39 Common-base configuration.

Fig. 9.40 Junction diode characteristic.

Common-Base Characteristics. The transistor connection of Fig. 9.39 is called the *common-base* configuration because the base is common to input and output ports. The *v-i* characteristics of a transistor in this configuration can be derived from our knowledge of diode character-istics and transistor operation. The emitter-base section is essentially a forward-biased diode so the input characteristics in Fig. 9.41a are simi-lar to those of the first quadrant of Fig. 9.40; the effect of collector-base voltage v_{CB} is small. With the emitter open-circuited, $i_E = 0$ and the base-collector section is essentially a reverse-biased junction. For $i_E = 0$, $i_C \cong I_{CO}$ and the collector characteristic (Fig. 9.41b) is similar to the third quadrant of Fig. 9.40. For $i_E = -5$ mA, the collector current is increased by an amount $-\alpha i_E \cong +5$ mA (see Eq. 9-52) and the curve is as shown. The slope of the curves is due to an effective increase in α as v_{CB} increases. Note the similarity of the common-base characteristics

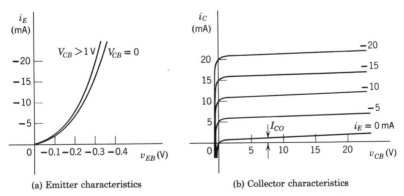

(a) Emitter characteristics

(b) Collector characteristics

Fig. 9.41 Common-base characteristics of an *npn* transistor.

to those of the idealized current amplifier in Fig. 9.29. The common-base configuration is not good for current amplification, however, because the factor α is always less than 1.

Common-Emitter Characteristics. If the *npn* transistor is reconnected in the *common-emitter* configuration of Fig. 9.42, current amplification is possible. The input current is now base current i_B, and emitter current $i_E = -(i_C + i_B)$; therefore, collector current is (by Eq. 9-52)

$$i_C = -\alpha i_E + I_{CO} = +\alpha(i_C + i_B) + I_{CO}$$

Solving,

$$i_C = \frac{\alpha}{1 - \alpha} i_B + \frac{I_{CO}}{1 - \alpha} \qquad (9\text{-}54)$$

To simplify Eq. 9-54 we define a new factor

$$\beta = \frac{\alpha}{1 - \alpha} \qquad (9\text{-}55)$$

and note that

$$\frac{I_{CO}}{1 - \alpha} = (1 + \beta)I_{CO} = I_{CEO}$$

The simplified equation for output (collector) current in terms of input (base) current is

$$i_C = \beta i_B + I_{CEO} \qquad (9\text{-}56)$$

The common-emitter characteristics are shown in Fig. 9.43. The input current i_B is small and, for a collector-emitter voltage of more than a volt or so, depends only on the emitter-base junction voltage. The collector characteristics are in accordance with Eq. 9-56; for $i_B = 0$, the collector current is small and nearly constant at a value I_{CEO}. For each increment of current i_B, the collector current is increased an amount βi_B. For $\alpha = 0.98$, $\beta = \alpha/(1 - \alpha) = 0.98/(1 - 0.98) = 49$, and a small increase in i_B corresponds to a large increase in i_C. A small increase in α produces a much greater change in β, and the effect of v_{CE} is more

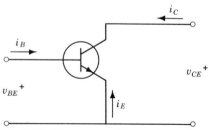

Fig. 9.42 Common-emitter configuration.

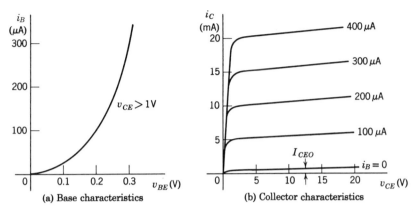

Fig. 9.43 Common-emitter characteristics of an *npn* transistor.

pronounced. Note that $v_{CE} \cong v_{CB}$ since v_{BE} is so small. Comparison of the collector characteristics with those of the idealized current amplifier indicates the possibility of current amplification.

Comparison of Fig. 9.43b with Fig. 9.35b reveals the similarity between transistor and pentode as two-port devices. There is a rough analogy between the cathode of a vacuum tube and the emitter of a transistor; both act as a source of charge carriers. The control grid voltage and the base current are analogous in that each serves to control the output current. The plate and the collector perform analogous functions in receiving the controlled current. In spite of their vast internal differences, in view of these external similarities we expect the analysis of circuits containing tubes or transistors to follow a common pattern.

ELEMENTARY AMPLIFIERS

An electronic amplifier consists of a device having the proper external characteristics, power supplies to place the device in the proper operating condition, a means for introducing the input signal, and a means for extracting the output signal. A sophisticated approach to predicting the behavior of amplifiers is presented in Chapter 10. As preparation for that discussion, let us consider the analysis of two elementary forms of electronic amplifiers by using the graphical approach of Chapter 8.

Triode Voltage Amplifier

In Fig. 9.44, batteries V_{cc} and V_{bb} supply power to the triode tube whose characteristics are shown. The input signal is applied in series with the negative grid-bias voltage of magnitude V_{cc}. It is convenient

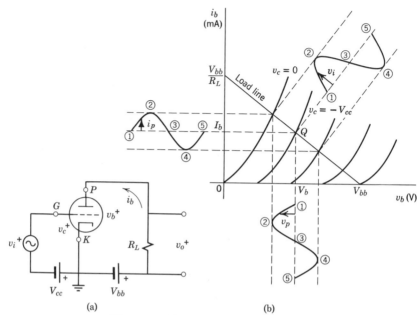

Fig. 9.44   Elementary triode amplifier.

to consider a sinusoidal input voltage v_i since any periodic wave can be represented by a series of sinusoids of various frequencies and amplitudes. The plate supply voltage V_{bb} maintains the plate at a positive potential with respect to the cathode. We anticipate that a signal voltage v_i will cause a variation in grid voltage v_c, which will produce a variation in plate current i_b, developing, in turn, an amplified output voltage across the load resistance R_L.

By Kirchhoff's voltage law around the output loop,

$$v_b = V_{bb} - i_b R_L \tag{9-57}$$

This is the equation of the *load line*, a straight line (Fig. 9.44b) with intercepts V_{bb} (for $i_b = 0$) and V_{bb}/R_L (for $v_b = 0$), and a slope of $-1/R_L$. The intersections of the load line with the characteristic curves of the nonlinear triode represent graphical solutions of Eq. 9-57 and define the operating values of v_b, i_b, and v_c.

By Kirchhoff's law around the input loop,

$$v_c = -V_{cc} + v_i \tag{9-58}$$

With no signal, $v_i = 0$ and $v_c = -V_{cc}$. The intersection of the load line with the characteristic curve for $v_c = -V_{cc}$ locates Q, the *quiescent point*.

The quiescent plate current is labeled I_b and the quiescent plate voltage is V_b.

With a sinusoidal signal applied, the grid voltage takes successive values corresponding to points 1, 2, 3, 4, 5 on the waveform. The corresponding values of plate voltage and current are obtained graphically from the load line. The signal output v_o is the sinusoidal component of the voltage across R_L, or

$$v_o = v_p = i_p R_L \tag{9-59}$$

where v_p and i_p are instantaneous values of the sinusoidal components of plate voltage and current as shown in Fig. 9.44b. The voltage amplification, or voltage *gain* of the amplifier, is

$$A_v = \frac{v_o}{v_i} = \frac{V_{om}}{V_{im}} = \frac{V_o}{V_i} \tag{9-60}$$

depending on whether the voltage ratio is expressed in terms of instantaneous, maximum, or rms values. Numerical values for a typical triode are shown in Fig. 9.45.

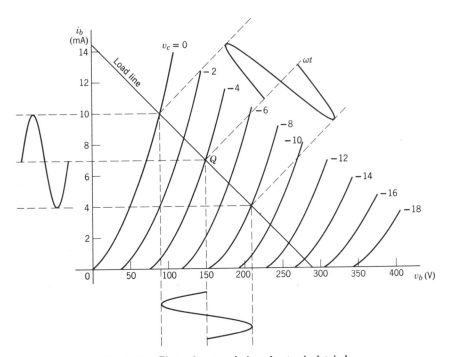

Fig. 9.45 Plate characteristics of a typical triode.

EXAMPLE 9

The triode whose characteristics are given in Fig. 9.45 is used in the circuit of Fig. 9.44a where $V_{cc} = 4$ V, $V_{bb} = 290$ V, and $R_L = 20$ kΩ. Predict the output voltage and voltage gain for $v_i = 4 \sin \omega t$ V.

SOLUTION. The intercepts of the load line are determined to be $V_{bb} = 290$ V and $V_{bb}/R_L = 290$ V/20 kΩ $= 14.5$ mA, and the load line is drawn. The intersection of the load line with the $v_c = -4$ V curve indicates a Q point at $I_b = 7$ mA and $V_b = 150$ V.

For $\omega t = \pi/2$, the signal voltage is $v_i = +4$ V, the grid voltage $v_c = -V_{cc} + v_i = -4 + 4 = 0$, and the corresponding plate current is $i_b = 10$ mA. For $\omega t = 3\pi/2, v_i = -4$ V$, v_c = -4 - 4 = -8$ V, and the corresponding $i_b = 4$ mA. A signal voltage swing of ± 4 V causes a plate current swing of ± 3 mA, and (by Eq. 9-59) the corresponding output signal is

$$V_{o_m} = I_{p_m}R_L = 3 \text{ mA} \times 20 \text{ kΩ} = 60 \text{ V}$$

This value could also be obtained graphically as a change in v_b from 210 to 150 V. The voltage gain is

$$A_v = \frac{V_{o_m}}{V_{i_m}} = \frac{60}{4} = 15$$

Transistor Current Amplifier

The graphical analysis of a transistor amplifier is similar to that of a vacuum-tube amplifier. In Fig. 9.46, batteries V_{BB} and V_{CC} supply power to the *npn* transistor whose collector characteristics are shown. The input signal (assumed sinusoidal) is applied in parallel with the emitter biasing circuit. The reverse bias on the collector is maintained by battery V_{CC}; note that most of this voltage appears across the collector junction since the voltage across the forward-biased emitter junction is quite small. (Why?) We anticipate that a signal current i_i will cause a variation in base current i_B which will produce a variation in collector current i_C; the varying component of i_C constitutes an amplified output current.

For linear amplification, the quiescent point Q should be in the linear region on the characteristic curves. In this elementary amplifier, let us assume that the characteristics are known precisely and that the Q point has been selected. For no signal input, $i_i = 0$, and $i_B = I_B$, the quiescent value. Application of Kirchhoff's voltage law around the input loop yields

$$V_{BB} - I_B R_1 - v_{BE} = 0 \qquad (9\text{-}61)$$

But for a forward-biased junction, v_{BE} is only a few tenths of a volt and may be neglected in comparison to V_{BB}. Under this assumption,

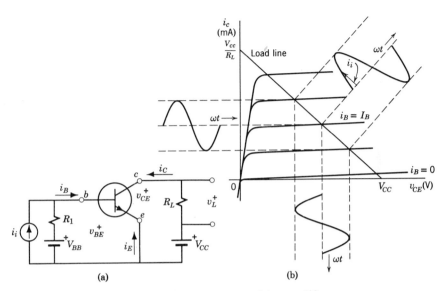

Fig. 9.46 Elementary transistor amplifier.

$$I_B \cong \frac{V_{BB}}{R_1} \qquad (9\text{-}62)$$

With a signal current i_i applied, the base current becomes

$$i_B = I_B + i_i \qquad (9\text{-}63)$$

an a-c component superimposed on a d-c component.

By Kirchhoff's voltage law around the output loop,

$$v_{CE} = V_{CC} - i_C R_L \qquad (9\text{-}64)$$

This is the equation of the load line shown in Fig. 9.46b. The quiescent point lies at the intersection of the load line and the characteristic curve for $i_B = I_B$. The intersections of the load line and the characteristic curves of the nonlinear transistor represent graphical solutions of Eq. 9-64 and define the instantaneous values of i_C and v_{CE} corresponding to values of the input signal current i_i. The signal output i_o is the sinusoidal component of i_C, the current in R_L. The current amplification, or current gain, is

$$A_i = \frac{i_o}{i_i} = \frac{I_{om}}{I_{im}} = \frac{I_o}{I_i} \qquad (9\text{-}65)$$

depending on whether the current ratio is expressed in terms of instantaneous, maximum, or rms values.

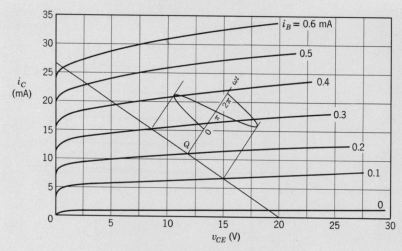

Fig. 9.47   Example 10.

EXAMPLE 10

The transistor whose characteristics are given in Fig. 9.47 is used in the circuit of Fig. 9.46a. The Q point is to be at $I_B = 0.2$ mA, and $V_{CE} = 12$ V. Supply batteries available provide $V_{BB} = 3$ V, and $V_{CC} = 20$ V. Specify R_1 and R_L and determine the current gain and output voltage for an input current $i = 0.1 \sin \omega t$ mA.

SOLUTION. By Eq. 9-62,

$$R_1 \cong \frac{V_{BB}}{I_B} = \frac{3 \text{ V}}{0.2 \text{ mA}} = 15 \text{ k}\Omega$$

For quiescent operation at $I_B = 0.2$ mA and $v_{CE} = V_{CE} = 12$ V, $I_C = 11$ mA. By Eq. 9-64,

$$R_L = \frac{V_{CC} - V_{CE}}{I_C} = \frac{20 - 12 \text{ V}}{11 \text{ mA}} \cong 730 \, \Omega$$

The resulting load line is as drawn in Fig. 9.47.

For $\omega t = \pi/2$, the signal current is 0.1 mA, the base current is $I_B + i_i = 0.2 + 0.1 = 0.3$ mA, and the corresponding collector current is 15 mA. A signal current swing of 0.1 mA causes a collector current swing of 4 mA. The current gain is

$$A_i = \frac{I_{o_m}}{I_{i_m}} = \frac{4 \text{ mA}}{0.1 \text{ mA}} = 40$$

The sinusoidal component of voltage across R_L is

$$V_{o_m} = I_{o_m}R_L = 0.004 \times 730 = 2.92 \cong 3 \text{ V}$$

Since the input voltage variation associated with the input current is of the order of 0.1 V (see Fig. 9.43a), there also is an appreciable voltage gain.

SUMMARY

◆ Individual charged particles in electric and magnetic fields obey Newton's laws. For electrons (of primary interest here),

$$\mathbf{f} = -e(\mathbf{\varepsilon} + \mathbf{u} \times \mathbf{B})$$

◆ In any electric field, KE gained = PE lost = $W_{ab} = eV_{ab}$. For an electron starting from rest (and $V < 4$ kV),

$$u = \sqrt{2(e/m)V} = 5.93 \times 10^5 \sqrt{V} \text{ m/sec}$$

In a uniform electric field $\varepsilon_x = +\varepsilon$, $f_x = -e\varepsilon$, and

$$a_x = -\frac{e\varepsilon}{m} \qquad u_x = -\frac{e\varepsilon}{m}t + U_0 \qquad x = -\frac{e\varepsilon}{2m}t^2 + U_0 t + X_0$$

◆ In any magnetic field, $\mathbf{f}$ is normal to $\mathbf{u}$ and no work is done. In a uniform magnetic field, the path is circular $(r = mU_0/eB)$.

◆ A cathode-ray tube consists of an electron gun producing a focused beam, a magnetic or electric deflection system, and a fluorescent screen for visual display.

◆ Electron emission from a solid requires the addition of energy equal to the work function; this energy can be obtained in various ways. The probability of an electron possessing energy eV_T varies as $e^{-eV_T/kT}$.

◆ In a vacuum diode, current is limited by the space charge and

$$I_b \cong K V_b^{3/2}$$

In a gas diode, cumulative ionization occurs, positive space charge is produced, and voltage drop is small.

In a phototube, electron emission is proportional to illumination.

◆ In a metal, electrons of mobility μ and drift velocity u constitute a current density $J = neu = ne\mu\varepsilon = \sigma\varepsilon$.

◆ In a semiconductor, thermally generated electrons and holes constitute a drift current density $J = (n\mu_n + p\mu_p)e\varepsilon = \sigma\varepsilon$. A hole is considered to be a positively charged particle.

◆ Low density doping with pentavalent (trivalent) elements produces n-type (p-type) semiconductor of greatly increased, temperature-dependent conductivity.

◆ For equilibrium, generation rate equals recombination rate and

$$np = n_i^2$$

In neutral n-type material, $n_n \cong N_d$ and $p_n \cong n_i^2/N_d$.
In neutral p-type material, $p_p \cong N_a$ and $n_p \cong n_i^2/N_a$.

◆ The diffusion current density due to nonuniform concentrations of randomly moving electrons and holes is

$$J = J_n + J_p = eD_n \frac{dn}{dl} - eD_p \frac{dp}{dl}$$

◆ A p-n junction diode is a single crystal with an abrupt change from p- to n-type material at the junction.
Diffusion of majority carriers across the junction uncovers bound charge, creates a potential hill, and encourages opposite drift of minority carriers.
Forward biasing reduces the potential hill, encourages diffusion.
Reverse biasing increases the potential hill, discourages diffusion.

$$I = I_s(e^{eV/kT} - 1)$$

Normal reverse current is very small and nearly constant.
At breakdown, reverse current is large and independent of voltage.

◆ Vacuum tubes and transistors possess basic amplifier characteristics.

◆ In a triode, a small grid voltage modulates the space charge, controls the plate current, and develops an amplified load voltage.
Tetrodes and pentodes provide improved external characteristics.

◆ A transistor consists of two p-n junctions in close proximity; normally, emitter junction is forward biased, collector reverse.
In common-base operation, a small emitter junction-voltage variation modulates the injected current, controls the collector current, and develops an amplified load voltage.

$$I_C = -\alpha I_E + I_{CO} \qquad \text{where } \alpha \cong 1$$

In common-emitter operation, a small base current controls the relatively larger collector current to achieve current amplification.

$$I_C = \beta I_B + I_{CEO} \qquad \text{where } \beta = \frac{\alpha}{1 - \alpha}$$

◆ Graphical analysis of highly nonlinear tubes and transistors is based on load-line construction.
Variations in input quantities about a properly selected quiescent point result in corresponding output variations.

REVIEW QUESTIONS

1. What quantities are analogous in the equations of motion of a mass in a gravitational field and motion of an electron in an electric field?
2. Define the following terms: electron-volt, electron gun, vector cross-product, work function, space-charge limited, and virtual cathode.
3. Justify the statement that "no work is done on a charged particle by a magnetic field."
4. Explain magnetic focusing of an electron beam.
5. Describe the motion of an electron starting from rest in a region of parallel electric and magnetic fields.
6. Sketch the pattern expected on a C-R tube screen when deflection voltages are $v_x = V \sin \omega t$ and $v_y = V \cos 2\omega t$.
7. What is the effect on a TV picture of varying the voltage on the control anode (Fig. 9.7)? On the accelerating anode?
8. Sketch a magnetic deflection system for a C-R tube.
9. Explain qualitatively the process of thermionic emission.
10. Explain the effect of space charge on diode current.
11. What happens in a diode operating normally if the cathode heating power is slowly reduced?
12. If $v(x) = V_m x^n$, is d^2v/dx^2 proportional to V_m?
13. Why is the voltage drop across a gas diode lower than across a similar vacuum diode for the same current?
14. Does the color of the light affect the curves of Fig. 9.15?
15. Explain why drift velocity in a solid is proportional to voltage, whereas in a vacuum u is proportional to $\sqrt{V}$.
16. How does resistance vary with temperature for a conductor? For a semiconductor? Why?
17. How does the speed of transmission of a "dot" along a telegraph wire compare with the drift velocity?
18. Define the following terms: mobility, conduction band, covalent band, electron-hole generation, recombination, doping, and intrinsic.
19. Describe the formation of a hole and its role in conduction.
20. In a semiconductor, what is the effect of doping with donor atoms on electron density? On hole density?
21. Is a semiconductor negatively charged when doped with donor atoms?
22. Why does the factor eV/kT appear in thermionic emission, electron-hole generation, and p-n junction current flow?
23. How do you expect the term n_i^2 to vary with temperature?
24. Is the approximation of Eq. 9-40 justified if $N_d = 100n_i$?
25. What are the two charge carriers and the two conduction mechanisms encountered in semiconductors?
26. Cite two nonelectrical examples of diffusion.
27. Define the following terms: junction, uncovered charge, majority carriers, transition region, injection, and potential hill.
28. Describe the forward, reverse, and breakdown characteristics of a junction diode.
29. Describe with sketches the operation of an np diode.

30. How is contact potential utilized in a thermocouple?

31. Sketch curves near the origin to distinguish between the v-i characteristics of ideal, thermionic, and semiconductor diodes.

32. Why does reverse saturation current vary with temperature?

33. Describe the behavior of a Zener diode.

34. Sketch, from memory, the v-i characteristics of an ideal voltage amplifier; superimpose the characteristics of a triode.

35. Explain the effect of the grid on the electric field at the cathode.

36. What is the power amplification of a negative grid triode?

37. Describe how voltage amplification is achieved by a triode.

38. Compared to a triode, what is the advantage of a tetrode? Of a pentode?

39. Explain the function of control, screen, and suppressor grids.

40. List the relative advantages of pentodes and transistors.

41. Explain with sketches the operation of a *pnp* transistor.

42. Why must the base be narrow for transistor action?

43. Describe how amplification is achieved by a transistor.

44. Sketch, from memory, the characteristics of an ideal current amplifier; superimpose the characteristics of a common-emitter transistor.

45. Explain common-base transistor characteristics in terms of diode characteristics.

46. Explain the role of the load-line in graphical analysis of amplifiers.

47. In an amplifier, what is the function of V_{bb}, V_{cc}, R_L?

48. Define the following terms: quiescent point, grid swing, signal current, voltage gain, and linear amplification.

EXERCISES

1. Compare the force on an electron in an electric field of $\mathcal{E} = 1$ V/m with that in the earth's gravitational field. Is it justifiable to neglect gravitational forces in practical problems?

2. An electron is accelerated from rest by a potential of 100 V applied across a 10-cm distance in a vacuum. Calculate the final velocity and the time required for transit. Repeat for a hydrogen ion. Express the energy gained by each particle in electron-volts.

3. For the electron of Exercise 2, derive expressions for velocity as a function of time and as a function of distance.

4. An electron with velocity U_0 passes through the hole shown in Fig. 9.48a, enters a retarding field, goes half-way to target T, and then falls back to membrane M. What is its velocity when it strikes M?

5. In Fig. 9.48, an electron is shot through a hole in the membrane M. The velocity of the electron as it passes through the hole is $U_0 = 10^6$ m/sec. The electric potential between the membrane and the target plate T can take on any one of the three distributions a, b, or c as shown in the graph.

  (a) Find the velocity u_a of the electron when it strikes the target under the condition of potential distribution a.

  (b) Find u_b for the potential distribution b.

  (c) What happens if potential distribution c exists?

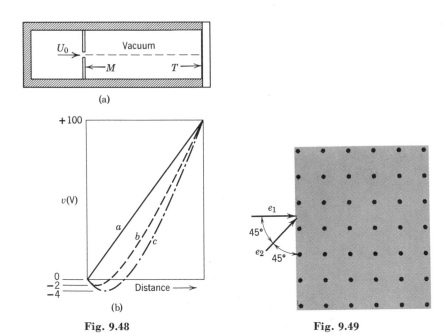

Fig. 9.48   Fig. 9.49

6. Two electrons, e_1 traveling at velocity u and e_2 traveling at velocity $2u$, enter an intense magnetic field directed out of the paper (Fig. 9.49). Sketch the paths of the electrons.

7. Compare the force on an electron moving with a velocity of 10^6 m/sec normal to the earth's magnetic field (5×10^{-5}T) with that due to the earth's gravitational field.

8. Given a vertical field $B = 2$T. An electron is moving with a speed of 1000 m/sec in direction N 53° W but inclined 60° with the horizontal. Draw a labeled sketch and determine the magnitude and direction of the force on the electron.

9. From Eq. 9-12 derive an expression for the force f on a conductor of length l carrying a current I in a direction at angle θ with respect to magnetic flux density B.

10. The accelerating potential of an electron gun is 3 kV. The beam is to be focussed magnetically onto a fluorescent screen 30 cm away. Determine the necessary magnetic field.

11. A C-R tube operates with an accelerating potential of 4 kV. The vertical deflecting plates are 3 cm long and 1 cm apart; length L in Fig. 9.8 is 25 cm.
   (a) Determine the deflection sensitivity.
   (b) What is the maximum allowable deflection voltage?
   (c) For a brighter picture, the acceleration potential is increased to 6 kV. What is the new deflection sensitivity?

12. How long is an electron in the deflecting region of the C-R tube of Exercise 11? If the deflecting voltage should not change more than 10% while deflection is taking place, approximately what frequency limit is placed on this deflection system?

13. In a cyclotron (see any physics book) hydrogen ions are accelerated by an electric field, curved around by a magnetic field, and accelerated again. If B is limited to 1.6T, what is the maximum ion velocity developed in a 60-inch diameter cyclotron?

14. For copper, the work function is 4.1 eV and the melting point is 1356°K. The corresponding values for tungsten are 4.52 eV and 3643°K. Compare the factor $e^{-W_W/kT}$ for these metals at 70% of the melting point and decide which is more likely to be used as a cathode.

15. Repeat Exercise 14 for copper and thorium with a work function of 3.40 eV and a melting point of 2120°K.

16. Calculate the escape velocity (mph) of a missile fired vertically from the earth and the escape velocity (mph) of an electron from a surface for which the barrier energy is 4 eV.

17. In a parallel-plane diode, electrons are emitted *copiously* with energies from zero to 5 eV. The plate potential with respect to the cathode is 40 V. Sketch, approximately to scale, the potential distribution and the electric field between cathode and anode (1 cm apart).

18. A vacuum diode can be considered as parallel-plane electrodes separated 2 cm with a potential difference of 100 V.

(a) If an electron leaves the cathode with initial velocity 10^6 m/sec, with what velocity does it strike the plate?

(b) What energy (in eV) is released when the electron strikes the plate? Where does this energy go?

(c) If the diode current is 50 mA, what power must the plate dissipate?

19. A vacuum diode can be considered to be a pair of parallel-plane electrodes separated 0.5 cm. The velocity distribution across the interelectrode space is given in Fig. 9.50.

(a) What is the typical emission energy in electron volts?

(b) Assuming the cathode is at zero potential, what is the anode potential?

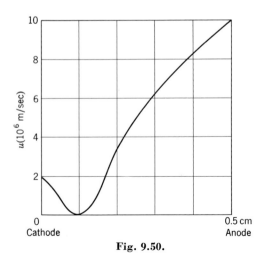

Fig. 9.50.

(c) Where is the virtual cathode with respect to the actual cathode?

(d) Sketch the potential distribution (clearly labeled) across the space.

(e) Sketch the distribution of charge density.

20. How is the transit time of an electron in a given diode affected by doubling the plate voltage? By doubling the electrode spacing?

21. A diode has the characteristic of the $v_c = 0$ curve in Fig. 9.45. Predict the current which will flow if the diode is connected in series with a 10-kΩ resistance and a 120-V battery.

22. In a certain practical diode, $I_b = 20$ mA when $V_b = 100$ V.

(a) Derive an approximate expression for $I_b = f(V_b)$.

(b) Predict the reading on a d-c milliammeter connected in series with the diode, a resistance of 5 kΩ, and a voltage $v = 100 \sin \omega t$ V.

23. A diode has the characteristic of the $v_C = 0$ curve in Fig. 9.45. Predict the reading on a d-c milliammeter connected in series with the diode, a resistance of 10 kΩ, and a voltage $v = 100 \sin \omega t$ V.

24. Ordinary house wiring is No. 12 copper wire (diam. = 0.081 in.) rated at 20 A. Predict the electron drift velocity at rated current.

25. Aluminum of atomic weight 27 and density 2.70 g/cm^3 has three valence electrons. Stating any assumptions, predict the electron drift velocity in No. 12 wire (diam. = 0.081 in.) carrying a current of 20 A.

26. A round rod of intrinsic silicon at room temperature is 5 cm long and 0.1 cm in diameter. Predict the current for a voltage of 2 V.

27. A small block of intrinsic germanium is 0.1 mm thick with square ends 1 mm on a side. What voltage is required across the ends for a current of 2 mA at room temperature?

28. The block of Exercise 27 is doped by adding 1 atom of indium per 10^7 atoms of germanium.

(a) How many atoms per hole-electron pair are there in intrinsic germanium?

(b) Is the doped material n-type or p-type? Why?

(c) In the doped material, what is the density of majority and minority carriers? Can one be neglected?

(d) What voltage is required for a current of 2 mA?

(e) By what factor has doping increased the conductivity?

29. Repeat Exercise 28, assuming that 1 in every 10^8 atoms of germanium is replaced by an atom of arsenic.

30. It is desired to increase the conductivity of silicon by a factor of 1000 by doping with phosphorous.

(a) What is the intrinsic conductivity of silicon at room temperature?

(b) Stating any necessary assumptions, what doping concentration is required?

31. A germanium rod 20 mm long and 1 mm square in cross section is to be modified so that a current of 1 A will develop a voltage of 0.1 V.

(a) What doping concentration of boron must be introduced to obtain the desired properties? State any assumptions.

(b) What is the new concentration of minority carriers?

32. Given that resistance $R = \rho l/A$, derive an expression for resistivity ρ in terms of carrier density, mobility and charge.

33. A semiconductor diode consists of a left-hand portion doped with antimony and a right-hand portion doped with boron.

(a) Sketch the diode, indicating the junction. Below, draw sketches of charge density, electric field, and potential distribution across the unbiased diode.

(b) Draw labeled arrows indicating directions of drift and diffusion of electrons, holes, and net currents.

(c) For forward bias, indicate the necessary polarity.

34. Draw a "rectifier" circuit and describe, with sketches, how an np junction diode can be used to rectify alternating currents.

35. A pn junction diode is biased so that the left (p) terminal is negative with respect to the right (n) terminal. In which direction is there a net motion of holes across the junction? Explain your reasoning in 2 or 3 short statements.

36. In a germanium pn junction diode, the density of holes drops from 10^{18} to $0.5 \times 10^{18}/m^3$ in $2\mu m$. Estimate the diffusion current density due to holes across the junction at room temperature.

37. In a reverse-biased junction, when all the available charge carriers are being drawn across the junction, increasing the reverse junction voltage does not increase the reverse current.

(a) At what voltage will the reverse current in a pn junction at room temperature reach 95% of its saturation value?

(b) If the reverse saturation current is 10 μA, calculate the current for a *forward* bias voltage of the magnitude determined in Part 1.

38. Plot the junction v-i characteristics ($-0.25 < v < +0.25$ V) for a pn diode with a reverse saturation current of 20 μA. Use an expanded scale for negative currents and assume room temperature.

39. The diode of Exercise 38 is connected in series with a 50-Ω resistor and a 3-V battery. Stating any necessary assumption, predict the current.

40. The semiconductor body of a certain junction diode has 2 Ω of resistance. With 2 V of reverse bias applied, the current is 10 μA. Predict the forward bias necessary for a current of 100 mA.

41. A diode with a reverse saturation current of 20 μA has an internal (body) resistance of 1 Ω and a Zener breakdown at 5 V. Sketch the diode v-i characteristics for $-10 < i < +10$ mA.

42. Using data from the plate characteristics of the 6J5 in Fig. A1, plot the *transfer* characteristics i_b versus v_c for $v_b = 100$, 200, and 300 V.

43. Repeat Exercise 42 for the 6SJ7 pentode in Fig. A4.

44. Assume that the v-i characteristics of the 6J5 in Fig. A1 follow the relation $i_b = K(\mu v_c + v_b)^n$ where $\mu = 20$. Estimate n by plotting the curve for $v_c = -6$ V on log-log paper.

45. Repeat Exercise 44 and estimate n by plotting data for $v_b = 200$ V on log-log paper.

46. Consider the 6SJ7 pentode of Fig. A4 as an approximation to the idealized transducer of Fig. 9.31. A load resistance of 50 kΩ is connected in the plate circuit and an average plate current of 4 mA is maintained. Estimate the voltage amplification possibilities of this transducer.

47. For a pnp transistor,

(a) Sketch the charge distribution when unbiased.

(b) Sketch the potential distribution when unbiased.

(c) Sketch the potential distribution when properly biased.

48. In Fig. 9.37a, voltage V_{EB} is disconnected and V_{CB} can be positive or negative.

(a) Sketch a curve of I_C versus V_{CB}, noting the given polarities.

(b) Connect V_{EB}, adjust for $I_E = -1$ mA, and repeat (a).

49. Repeat Exercise 48, asuming the transistor is *pnp*.

50. Consider the transistor of Fig. 9.43b as an approximation to the idealized current amplifier of Fig. 9.29. If an average collector current of 10 mA is maintained, estimate the current amplification possibilities of this device.

51. A two-port is defined by the following equations:

$$\begin{cases} v_E = 0.2 + 20i_E \\ i_C = -0.9i_E + 0.0001 \end{cases}$$

A 10-kΩ resistance is connected across the output (C) terminals, and a voltage $v = 0.3 + 0.1 \sin \omega t$ V is applied to the input (E) terminals. Determine the sinusoidal (signal) component of the output voltage and the voltage amplification.

52. A 6J5 triode (Fig. A1) is used in the circuit of Fig. 9.44a with $V_{cc} = 8$ V (polarity as shown), $V_{bb} = 400$ V, and $R_L = 25$ kΩ.

(a) Find i_b (graphically) for $v_i = 0, +2,$ and -2 V.

(b) If v_i is a sinusoid varying between $+2$ and -2 V, what is the corresponding incremental variation in i_b?

(c) What is the corresponding incremental variation in v_L?

(d) Is the circuit performing amplification? To what degree?

53. A 6AU6-A pentode (Fig. A3) is used as an elementary amplifier. A power source capable of supplying 300 V at 10 mA is available.

(a) Draw a load line for a load resistance of 20 kΩ.

(b) Select a value of V_{CC} to provide quiescent operation near the midpoint of the possible grid swing.

(c) Check the current at the quiescent operating point with the current rating of the power source.

(d) Determine, graphically, the a-c component of the plate current for a grid signal $v_i = 1 \sin \omega t$ V.

(e) Calculate the voltage gain for this amplifier.

(f) Sketch, to scale, the a-c component of plate current for a grid signal $v_i = 2 \sin \omega t$ V. Is it sinusoidal?

54. A 2N502 transistor (Fig. A7) is used in a circuit similar to that of Fig. 9.46a with $V_{BB} = 6$ V, $R_1 = 100$ kΩ, $R_L = 2$ kΩ, and $V_{CC} = 20$ V.

(a) Draw the load line and determine the quiescent point.

(b) Find i_C (graphically) for $i_i = 0, +30,$ and -30 μA.

(c) If i_i is a sinusoid varying between $+30$ and -30 μA, what is the corresponding variation in i_C?

(d) What is the approximate current gain of this amplifier?

55. A 2N502 transistor (Fig. A7) is to be used as an elementary current amplifier with $R_1 = 50$ kΩ and $R_L = 5$ kΩ.

(a) Draw a wiring diagram, carefully labeling polarities.

(b) For a quiescent operating point at $I_B = 30$ μA and $V_{CE} = 10$ V, specify approximate values of V_{BB} and V_{CC}.

(c) For a signal input current $i_i = 15 \sin \omega t$ μA, approximately what is the signal component of collector current? What is the current gain?

(d) For the current of (c), what is the signal voltage across R_L?

PROBLEMS

1. In deriving Eq. 9-11 we assumed that mass is a constant. Einstein demonstrated that $w = mc^2$ and $m/m_o = (1 - v^2/c^2)^{-\frac{1}{2}}$ where m_o is the rest mass and c is the velocity of light. Letting $u_o = (2eV/m_o)^{\frac{1}{2}}$, derive an equation for u, the true velocity of an electron at high speed in terms of u_o. Determine the percentage of error in Eq. 9-11 for $v = 20$ kV, a typical value in a television picture tube.

2. A magnetic field of flux density B is directed along the negative z axis and an electric field of intensity $\mathcal{E}$ is directed along the negative x axis. An electron starts at rest at the origin. Applying Newton's law, determine the components of the force on the electron, obtain a differential equation in terms of u_x and solve the differential equation for u_x in terms of two undetermined constants. (The evaluation of these constants and the determination of u_y are rather time-consuming. The final step would be to determine the equation of the cycloidal path followed by the electron.)

3. A C-R tube using magnetic deflection looks like Fig. 9.8, except that a uniform field of flux density B (out of the paper) exists over the length l. Prove that for small angular deflections (where $Y/L = \tan \alpha \cong \sin \alpha \cong \alpha$) the screen deflection is $Y = lLBe/mU_z$. Express the deflection in terms of accelerating potential V_a and compare with Eq. 9-22 for electric deflection.

4. Under space-charge limited conditions, the potential distribution in a parallel-plane diode is $v/V_b = (x/d)^{\frac{4}{3}}$, where d is the electrode spacing. Show that an electron leaving the cathode with zero velocity under space-charge conditions takes 50% longer to get to the plate than in the absence of space charge.

5. Derive Ohm's law for a metallic conductor of length l and area A, considering the effect on the conduction electrons of an applied voltage V. Define resistance R in terms of the dimensions of the conductor.

6. The incremental resistance of a nonlinear device is defined by $r = dv/di$. Derive a general expression for r for a semiconductor diode and approximate expressions for r with forward and reverse bias greater than 0.1 V.

7. A semiconductor specimen of unknown type is in a magnetic field B as shown in Fig. 9.51. When a current I is introduced, it is observed that the upper surface exhibits a positive potential with respect to the lower (the Hall effect). Is this p-type or n-type semiconductor?

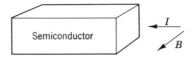

Fig. 9.51   Hall effect.

8. An elementary current amplifier is to supply an a-c output voltage of 5 V (rms) across a load resistance of 4 kΩ. Using a 2N502 transistor (Fig. A7), "design" the amplifier by specifying the components. Estimate the necessary input signal current.

♦ **DIODES**

♦ **VACUUM TRIODES**

♦ **TRANSISTORS**

CHAPTER **10**

Linear Models of Electronic Devices

Using ideal models of practical circuit elements, we developed powerful tools for the analysis of linear networks under a great variety of circumstances. Electronic devices, however, are inherently nonlinear. For example, in a space-charge controlled vacuum tube, the anode current varies as the three-halves power of the electrode voltages, and in a semiconductor the current across a junction varies exponentially with the junction voltage. It is possible to analyze the performance of such devices graphically as in Chapter 9, but this is laborious and the results lack generality. Fortunately, under certain conditions electronic devices can be represented by linear circuit models to which the powerful methods of linear analysis can be applied, and we now consider how this can be done.

The linear electrical model of a device is frequently called a *circuit model* because it is composed of ideal circuit elements. In addition to the basic elements previously employed, we shall make use of a *controlled source*, a voltage or current source in which the output is dependent on another variable in the system. With this single addition it is possible to devise relatively simple circuit models to represent complicated physical devices under specified conditions. The models are derived from the characteristic curves of the real devices and, when properly devised, can be used to predict accurately the behavior of vacuum tubes and semiconductor devices in such practical applications as rectification and amplification.

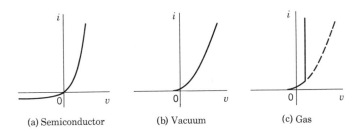

(a) Semiconductor   (b) Vacuum   (c) Gas

Fig. 10.1   Diode characteristics.

DIODES

The diode is a two-terminal, nonlinear device which presents a relatively low resistance to current flow in one direction and a relatively high resistance in the other.   In a semiconductor diode (Fig. 10.1a), under conditions of forward bias the diffusion of majority carriers is facilitated and an appreciable current will flow with a junction voltage of a few tenths of a volt; with reverse bias, there is only the current due to the motion of thermally generated minority carriers and this is very small.

In a vacuum diode with zero applied voltage, there is a small current due to the few electrons emerging from the cathode with initial velocities high enough to overcome the space charge (Fig. 10.1b).   With a small negative voltage, the current is zero; for positive voltages the current increases rapidly in the space-charge limited region.   In a gas diode, when the voltage reaches the ionizing potential of the gas there is a rapid increase in current with no further increase in voltage, and the characteristics are as in Fig. 10.1c.

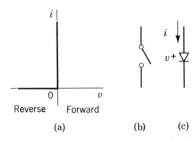

Reverse | Forward

(a)   (b)   (c)

Fig. 10.2   Ideal diode characteristic and circuit symbols.

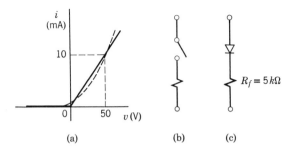

Fig. 10.3 Vacuum diode; approximate curve and circuit models.

Diode Circuit Models

The important diode characteristic is the discrimination between forward and reverse voltages. The ideal diode presents no resistance to current flow in the forward direction and an infinite resistance to current flow in the reverse direction. A selective switch, which is closed for forward voltages and open for reverse voltages, is equivalent to the ideal diode since it has the same current-voltage characteristic. Such a switch is represented in circuit diagrams by the symbol shown in Fig. 10.2c; the triangle points the direction of forward current flow.

The vacuum diode approaches the ideal in the reverse direction, but presents a finite resistance in the forward direction. Its behavior can be approximated by a circuit model based on the linearized characteristic curve of Fig. 10.3. For reverse voltages, the switch is open; for forward voltages, the switch is closed and the device presents a resistance R_f to current flow. In the case shown, the forward resistance is an average value estimated from the slope of the linearized curve. Here

$$R_f = \frac{V}{I} = \frac{50 \text{ V}}{0.01 \text{ A}} = 5000 \ \Omega$$

EXAMPLE 1

The diode of Fig. 10.3 is connected in the circuit of Fig. 10.4a. Predict the current in the load resistor $R_L = 5$ kΩ if $v = 100 \sin \omega t$ V.

SOLUTION. The circuit model to be analyzed is shown in Fig. 10.4b with a selective switch, or in Fig. 10.4c with an ideal diode. The two circuits are identical in interpretation. For $0 < \omega t < \pi$, v is positive, corresponding to forward bias, and

$$i_L = \frac{v}{R_f + R_L} = \frac{100 \sin \omega t}{(5 + 5) \times 10^3} = 10 \sin \omega t \text{ mA}$$

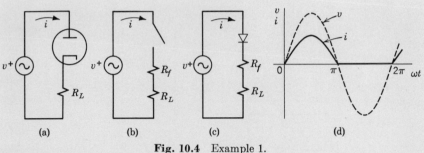

(a)   (b)   (c)   (d)

Fig. 10.4   Example 1.

For $\pi < \omega t < 2\pi$, v is negative, corresponding to negative bias and no current flows.   The answer is

$$\begin{cases} i_L = 10 \sin \omega t \text{ mA} & \text{for } 0 < \omega t < \pi \\ i_L = 0 & \text{for } \pi < \omega t < 2\pi \end{cases}$$

as plotted in Fig. 10.4d.

The characteristic curve for a gas diode can be linearized as in Fig. 10.5.   For values of forward voltage greater than the ionization potential, the resistance presented is small and in many cases can be neglected.   In the case shown, the voltage intercept is about 10 V and the forward resistance is estimated to be

$$R_f = \frac{\Delta V}{\Delta I} = \frac{12 - 10 \text{ V}}{0.01 - 0 \text{ A}} = 200 \text{ } \Omega$$

The circuit model includes a voltage source to indicate that the ideal diode is not forward biased until the voltage across the actual diode exceeds 10 V.

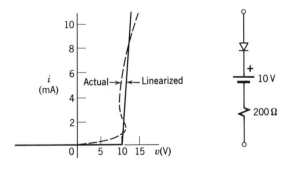

Fig. 10.5   Gas diode characteristic and circuit model.

EXAMPLE 2

If the gas diode of Fig. 10.5 is connected in the circuit of Fig. 10.4a, predict the maximum current in R_L.

SOLUTION. The maximum current will flow when $\omega t = \pi/2$ and $v = 100$ V. Then

$$i_L = \frac{v - 10}{R_f + R_L} = \frac{100 - 10}{200 + 5000} \cong 17 \text{ mA}$$

In a semiconductor diode in which the reverse saturation current is appreciable, this fact must be incorporated into the model. If the current-voltage characteristic is linearized as in Fig. 10.6, an approximate circuit model can be derived as shown. In the reverse direction, the effective resistance is R_r which is of the order of a megohm in a well designed rectifier diode. Since R_r is very high, in the forward direction the resistance is essentially R_f which may be only 5 or 10 Ω. In many practical rectifier applications, only the forward resistance need be considered and the model of Fig. 10.3c is satisfactory.†

Dynamic Resistance

The circuit models derived so far are based on piecewise linearization of the characteristic curves and are useful for predicting the behavior of diodes under static or d-c conditions or where relatively large swings in voltage occur, as in Example 1. A different approach is necessary if we

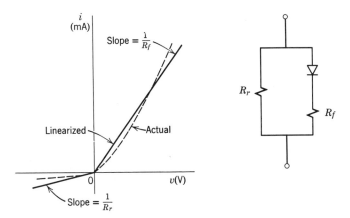

Fig. 10.6 Semiconductor diode characteristic and circuit model.

---

† For example, the manufacturers' ratings for the GE 1N3545 subminiature silicon rectifier indicate conservative values as follows: 1 V drop at 400 mA in the forward direction and only 75 μA reverse current under rated conditions.

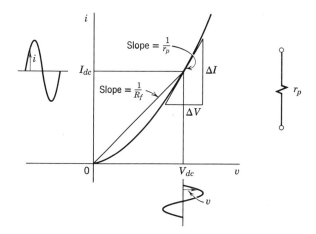

Fig. 10.7 Dynamic resistance and small-signal circuit model.

are interested in the response to small variations or "signals" superimposed upon d-c values. As shown in Fig. 10.7, a small signal voltage v superimposed on a steady voltage V_{dc} produces a corresponding signal current i. The current-voltage relation for small signals is defined by the slope of the curve at the operating point specified by V_{dc}. The *dynamic resistance* is defined as

$$r_p = \frac{dV}{dI} \cong \frac{\Delta V}{\Delta I} \quad \text{in ohms} \quad (10\text{-}1)$$

In general, the dynamic resistance r_p will differ appreciably from the static forward resistance $R_f = V/I$.

EXAMPLE 3

A voltage $v = 100 + 10\sqrt{2} \cos 300t$ V is applied to the circuit shown in Fig. 10.8. The characteristics of the diode are $R_f = 600\ \Omega$ and $r_p = 400\ \Omega$. Predict the voltage across the inductance.

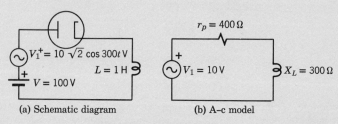

(a) Schematic diagram   (b) A–c model

Fig. 10.8 Example 3.

SOLUTION. For an ideal inductor, only a changing current produces a voltage; therefore, only the alternating component of current is significant. The a-c model is as shown. In terms of effective values,

$$V_L = \frac{V_1 X_L}{\sqrt{r_p{}^2 + X_L{}^2}} = \frac{10(300)}{\sqrt{400^2 + 300^2}} = 6 \text{ V}$$

VACUUM TRIODES

Two-Port Electronic Devices

A diode is a two-terminal device or one-port, and its circuit model also has a single pair of terminals. Triodes and transistors are two-ports and can be represented by the circuit in Fig. 10.9. In Chapter 8 equations were derived for replacing any linear passive two-port network by a T or π combination of one-port impedances. In deriving the circuit model of a triode or transistor, important differences result from the fact that these are active, nonlinear devices, not the passive, linear networks treated previously. However, the same basic approach can be used. Of the four variables, v_1, i_1, v_2, and i_2, only two are independent, and the general behavior can be defined by a pair of equations such as

$$\begin{cases} v_1 = f(i_1, i_2) \\ v_2 = f(i_1, i_2) \end{cases} \quad \text{or} \quad \begin{cases} i_1 = f(v_1, v_2) \\ i_2 = f(v_1, v_2) \end{cases} \tag{10-2}$$

For linear networks, the first pair of equations would define a set of impedances as parameters† and the second pair would define a set of

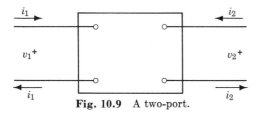

Fig. 10.9 A two-port.

---

† This is more easily seen if Eq. 10-2a is rewritten:

$$\begin{cases} V_1 = Z_{11}I_1 + Z_{12}I_2 \\ V_2 = Z_{21}I_1 + Z_{22}I_2 \end{cases} \quad \text{for the linear sinusoidal case.}$$

admittances as parameters.   Another acceptable formulation is

$$\begin{cases} i_1 = f(v_1, i_2) \\ v_2 = f(v_1, i_2) \end{cases} \tag{10-3}$$

For linear networks, the first equation of this pair would define an admittance and a current factor, and the second equation would define a voltage factor and an impedance.   This mixture is called a set of *hybrid parameters*, and it is a particularly convenient set to use for electronic devices.

Triode Parameters

The static plate characteristics for a typical triode are shown in Fig. 10.10; these curves are obtained by plotting steady currents observed for various combinations of steady grid and plate voltages.   The static characteristics also apply when the quantities vary with time if the frequency is not too high (see Fig. 11.19a).   For normal operation in the negative grid region, electrons are repelled by the negatively charged grid and no grid current flows.   For the triode, using conventional notation, Eqs. 10-3 become

$$\begin{cases} i_c = 0 \\ v_b = f(v_c, i_b) \end{cases} \tag{10-4}$$

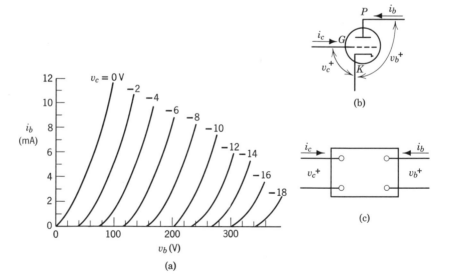

Fig. 10.10 The triode.   (a) Typical characteristics.   (b) Conventional notation. (c) Two-port representation.

where v_b and i_b are the plate voltage and current, and v_c and i_c are the grid voltage and current. Since $i_c = 0$ at all times, only the second equation is significant.

Because of the nonlinearity of this relation,† no simple model can be formulated to predict total voltage v_b. In a great many problems, however, we are interested only in the "small-signal" behavior of electronic devices; therefore, let us consider only small, "differential" changes in the variables. Taking the total differential of the plate voltage, we can write

$$dv_b = \frac{\partial v_b}{\partial v_c} dv_c + \frac{\partial v_b}{\partial i_b} di_b \tag{10-5}$$

Equation 10-5 says that a change in grid voltage dv_c and a change in plate current di_b both contribute to a change in plate voltage dv_b. The effectiveness of the partial contributions is dependent upon the coefficients $\partial v_b/\partial v_c$ and $\partial v_b/\partial i_b$.

If grid voltage is held constant, $dv_c = 0$, and the partial derivative with respect to plate current is equal to the total derivative or

$$\frac{\partial v_b}{\partial i_b} = \frac{dv_b}{di_b}\bigg|_{v_c = k} = r_p \tag{10-6}$$

where r_p is the *dynamic plate resistance* in ohms and is just equal to the reciprocal of the slope of a line of constant v_c. The dynamic plate resistance r_p is a vacuum tube *parameter* which is relatively constant over the normal operating range where the lines of constant v_c are approximately straight and nearly parallel.

A second tube parameter can be defined by holding the plate current constant so that $di_b = 0$ and

$$\frac{\partial v_b}{\partial v_c} = \frac{dv_b}{dv_c}\bigg|_{i_b = k} = -\mu \tag{10-7}$$

where μ is the *amplification factor*, a dimensionless quantity which measures the relative effectiveness of changes in grid and plate voltages in influencing the plate current. Since $\partial v_b/\partial v_c$ is always a negative quantity, the minus sign is used in the definition so that μ is always a positive number.

---

† Equation 9-29, derived from space-charge considerations, indicates that theoretically, $i_b = K(\mu v_c + v_b)^{3/2}$. While actual characteristic curves only approximate this relation, they show that the form of the equation is valid.

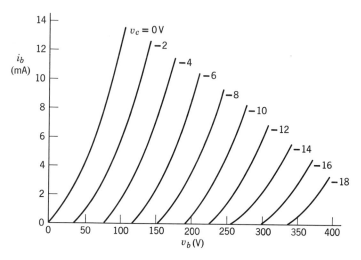

Fig. 10.11   Triode characteristics.

A third tube parameter whose usefulness will soon be evident is the partial derivative of plate current with respect to grid voltage. By keeping plate voltage constant,

$$\frac{\partial i_b}{\partial v_c} = \frac{d i_b}{d v_c}\bigg|_{v_b = k} = g_m \tag{10-8}$$

where g_m is the *transconductance* in mhos, so called because it is the ratio of a change in current at the output port to the corresponding change in voltage at the input port.

Evaluation of Tube Parameters

Tube parameters are usually specified by the manufacturer for typical operating conditions, or they may be calculated directly from the characteristic curves. The calculations are performed conveniently using the following approximate formulas:

$$r_p \cong \frac{\Delta v_b}{\Delta i_b}\bigg|_{v_c = k} \qquad \mu \cong -\frac{\Delta v_b}{\Delta v_c}\bigg|_{i_b = k} \qquad g_m \cong \frac{\Delta i_b}{\Delta v_c}\bigg|_{v_b = k} \tag{10-9}$$

EXAMPLE 4

Calculate the parameters r_p, μ, and g_m for the triode whose characteristics are given in Fig. 10.11, assuming small variations about the point defined by $v_b = 150$ V, $i_b = 7$ mA, and $v_c = -4$ V.

SOLUTION. Taking equal increments in both directions from the assumed operating point and reading the corresponding values, we have

$$r_p \cong \frac{\Delta v_b}{\Delta i_b}\bigg|_{v_c = -4V} = \frac{160 - 140}{(8.5 - 5.5) \times 10^{-3}} = \frac{20}{3 \times 10^{-3}} = 6.7 \text{ k}\Omega$$

$$\mu \cong -\frac{\Delta v_b}{\Delta v_c}\bigg|_{i_b = 7mA} = -\frac{190 - 110}{-6 - (-2)} = -\frac{80}{-4} = 20$$

$$g_m \cong \frac{\Delta i_b}{\Delta v_c}\bigg|_{v_b = 150V} = \frac{(10 - 4) \times 10^{-3}}{-3 - (-5)} = \frac{6 \times 10^{-3}}{2} = 3 \text{ m}\mho$$

Note that in Example 4 the numerical results approximately satisfy the equation

$$\mu = g_m r_p \tag{10-10}$$

It can be shown (see Exercise 17) that this is a general relation. It is useful when values for calculating one parameter are difficult to read from the characteristic curves and also as a quick check on calculations.

Small-Signal Circuit Model

The operation of the elementary triode amplifier of Fig. 10.12 is displayed on the graph of plate characteristics. The value of grid bias V_{cc} has been selected to permit variations of grid voltage without driving the grid positive and without moving into the excessively nonlinear region. The plate supply V_{bb}, determined by economic factors or other design criteria, and the load resistance R_L define the load line. The intersec-

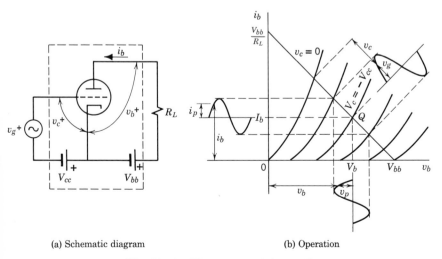

(a) Schematic diagram   (b) Operation

Fig. 10.12 Elementary triode amplifier.

tion of the load line and the curve $v_c = -V_{cc}$ determines the quiescent point Q. For no input signal, $v_g = 0$ and the steady or d-c values are V_c, V_b, and I_b.†

The input signal v_g is a small variation in grid voltage which produces corresponding variations in plate voltage (v_p) and plate current (i_p). As indicated in Fig. 10.12, the relations are:

$$v_c = V_c + v_g \qquad v_b = V_b + v_p \qquad i_b = I_b + i_p \qquad (10\text{-}11)$$

For a sinusoidal input signal, the plate current and voltage variations are practically sinusoidal; for $v_g = \sqrt{2}\, V_g \sin \omega t$, $i_p = \sqrt{2}\, I_p \sin \omega t$, and $v_p = -\sqrt{2}\, V_p \sin \omega t$. The d-c values fix the quiescent point and determine the values of the tube parameters; the a-c values correspond to the signals, which are of primary interest. We wish to devise a small-signal model which will hold only for a-c values and which will enable us to predict the performance of the tube in an a-c application such as this elementary amplifier.

For differential changes, Eq. 10-5 states that

$$dv_b = \frac{\partial v_b}{\partial v_c}\, dv_c + \frac{\partial v_b}{\partial i_b}\, di_b$$

When tube parameters are used, this becomes

$$dv_b = -\mu\, dv_c + r_p\, di_b \qquad (10\text{-}12a)$$

Replacing the differential quantities by increments, this becomes

$$\Delta v_b = -\mu \Delta v_c + r_p \Delta i_b \qquad (10\text{-}12b)$$

For small signals, the increments correspond to effective values of sinusoidal quantities or to the corresponding phasors and Eq. 10-12b becomes

$$V_p = -\mu V_g + r_p I_p \qquad (10\text{-}12c)$$

---

† The customary vacuum-tube nomenclature is:

Instantaneous values of time-varying quantities are represented by lower-case letters (v, i, p).

Steady values (maximum, average, d-c, or rms) are represented by capital letters (V, I, P).

Signal component values are indicated by subscripts p (plate circuit) and g (grid circuit).

Total instantaneous values or d-c values are indicated by subscripts b (plate circuit) and c (grid circuit).

Supply voltage magnitudes are indicated by repeated subscripts (V_{bb} and V_{cc}).

A similar but slightly different nomenclature is used with transistors.

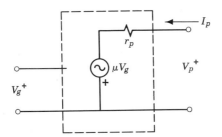

Fig. 10.13 Triode model with controlled voltage source.

This relation must be satisfied by the a-c circuit if it is to be a functional model.

Equation 10-12c says that the plate signal voltage consists of two parts. The first is a voltage directly proportional to the input signal voltage and can be represented by a controlled voltage source $-\mu V_g$. The second is a voltage directly proportional to plate signal current and can be represented by the voltage drop produced by current I_p flowing through a resistance r_p. The sum of these two voltages indicates that the two elements are in series and the circuit of Fig. 10.13 is the logical result. The portion of Fig. 10.13 inside the dashed line is a functional model, for small-signal performance at moderate frequencies, of the corresponding portion of the schematic diagram of Fig. 10.12.

An alternative form of the circuit model is obtained by starting from equations of the form of Eq. 10-2. For the triode, the second pair becomes

$$\begin{cases} i_c = 0 \\ i_b = f(v_c, v_b) \end{cases} \qquad (10\text{-}13)$$

For differential changes in the variables, we can write

$$di_b = \frac{\partial i_b}{\partial v_c}\,dv_c + \frac{\partial i_b}{\partial v_b}\,dv_b \qquad (10\text{-}14a)$$

Replacing the differential quantities by increments and using the tube parameters, this becomes

$$\Delta i_b = g_m \Delta v_c + \frac{1}{r_p}\,\Delta v_b \qquad (10\text{-}14b)$$

For small signals, the increments are identified as effective values of sinusoidal quantities and Eq. 10-14b becomes

$$I_p = g_m V_g + \frac{1}{r_p} V_p \qquad (10\text{-}15)$$

Equation 10-15 says that the plate signal current consists of two parts. In the corresponding parallel circuit, one branch contains a controlled current source $g_m V_g$ directly proportional to the input signal voltage and the other branch carries a current produced by the application of a voltage V_p across a resistance r_p. The circuit of Fig. 10.14 is the logical result.

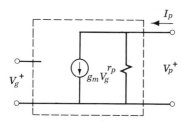

Fig. 10.14 Triode model with controlled current source.

EXAMPLE 5

The triode of Fig. 10.11 is used as an amplifier in the circuit of Fig. 10.15a. Derive a general relation for the signal voltage *gain* (ratio of output to input voltages) in terms of the tube parameters and the load resistance and predict the gain of this amplifier with a load resistance of 10 kΩ.

SOLUTION. Since we are interested only in the signals, the portion of the schematic diagram within the dashed line is replaced by the linear model as shown in Fig. 10.15b.

The output voltage is developed by the current from the controlled source flowing through the parallel combination of r_p and R_L. Therefore,

$$V_o = -g_m V_g \frac{r_p R_L}{r_p + R_L}$$

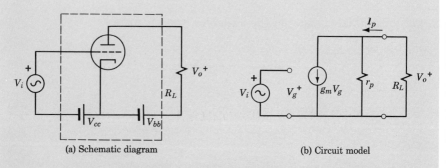

(a) Schematic diagram   (b) Circuit model

Fig. 10.15 Example 5.

and the gain is

$$\frac{V_o}{V_i} = \frac{V_o}{V_g} = -\frac{g_m r_p R_L}{r_p + R_L} \qquad (10\text{-}16)$$

Assuming that V_{cc} and V_{bb} have been chosen in accordance with the manufacturers' specifications to put the quiescent point in the normal operating range, the values of tube parameters calculated in Example 4 apply here also. The specific voltage gain is

$$\frac{V_o}{V_i} = -\frac{3 \times 10^{-3} \times 6.7 \times 10^3 \times 10 \times 10^3}{6.7 \times 10^3 + 10 \times 10^3} = -12$$

One general conclusion which can be drawn from Eq. 10-16 is that the gain of an amplifier increases as R_L increases and approaches $-g_m r_p$ as a limit. Note, however, that as R_L increases, a larger value of V_{bb} is necessary. A second general conclusion is that, since the gain is negative, the output voltage is 180° out of phase with the input voltage. Associated with a positive swing in grid signal voltage is a negative swing in plate signal voltage.

To simplify the discussion, the emphasis in this section is on triodes. However, the small-signal equations (Eqs. 10-12c and 10-15) and the linear circuit models (particularly Fig. 10.14) hold equally well for tetrodes and pentodes. The range of parameter values available in vacuum tubes is indicated in Table 10-1. (For pentodes, values of μ are not well defined.)

TABLE 10-1 Some Vacuum-Tube Parameters

	Type	$r_p(\text{k}\Omega)$	$g_m(\text{m}\mho)$	μ
6J5	Medium-μ triode	6.7	3	20
12AX7	High-μ twin triode	80	1.25	100
2A3	Power triode	0.8	5.25	4.2
6SJ7	Sharp-cutoff pentode	1000	1.6	. . . . .
6AU6	High-gain pentode	1000	5.2	. . . . .
6AQ5	Beam power pentode	50	4.1	. . . . .

TRANSISTORS

In the elementary transistor amplifier shown in Fig. 10.16, the input is a signal voltage v_s superimposed on the emitter-base bias voltage V_{EE}.

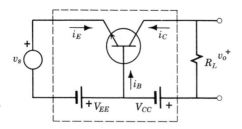

Fig. 10.16 Elementary transistor amplifier.

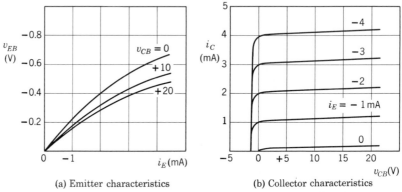

(a) Emitter characteristics   (b) Collector characteristics

Fig. 10.17   Typical transistor characteristics (common base).

The signal voltage modulates the barrier height at the emitter-base junction and causes a signal current i_e to flow. The resulting variation in collector current $i_c \cong -\alpha i_e$ develops a voltage across the load resistor R_L which may be an amplified version of the input voltage. In this configuration, the base is common to both input and output circuits.

Transistor Circuit Models

The quantitative behavior of an amplifier can be determined graphically from characteristic curves such as those in Fig. 10.17, but this is not a good approach with transistors for two reasons. First, the work is laborious and the results lack generality, as was true for vacuum tubes. Second, individual transistors of a given type vary widely in their characteristics and the curves provided by the manufacturers are only general indications of how that type behaves on the average. By proper circuit design, individual variations can be compensated for and accurate performance predictions can be made on the basis of convenient models.

As in the case of vacuum tubes, we assume small signals which are evidenced by small variations in circuit voltages and currents superimposed on steady or d-c values. With this limitation, we are justified in assuming linear relations among signals in devices which are highly nonlinear in their gross behavior. On this basis, the complicated physical device inside the dotted portion of Fig. 10.16 is to be replaced, insofar as small signals are concerned, by a linear circuit model.

The T-Circuit Model

The general relations for the transistor, a two-port, can be expressed in terms of voltages or currents as the independent variables. Again we have the choice of whether to deal with impedances, admittances, or a hybrid combination in defining parameters. If we choose to work with impedances, the general relations for a common-base transistor are

$$
\begin{cases}
v_{EB} = f_1(i_E, i_C) \\
v_{CB} = f_2(i_E, i_C)
\end{cases}
\tag{10-17}
$$

In contrast to the negative-grid triode, the input current in a transistor is appreciable, and it is to be expected that the linear model will be more complicated.

By taking the total differential, Eqs. 10-17 become

$$
\begin{cases}
dv_{EB} = \dfrac{\partial v_{EB}}{\partial i_E} di_E + \dfrac{\partial v_{EB}}{\partial i_C} di_C \\
\\
dv_{CB} = \dfrac{\partial v_{CB}}{\partial i_E} di_E + \dfrac{\partial v_{CB}}{\partial i_C} di_C
\end{cases}
\tag{10-18}
$$

Taking two steps in one, we note that differentials can be approximated by small increments and we recognize increments as equivalent to small signals. Then Eqs. 10-18 can be written

$$
\begin{cases}
v_{eb} = \dfrac{\partial v_{EB}}{\partial i_E} i_e + \dfrac{\partial v_{EB}}{\partial i_C} i_c = z_{11} i_e + z_{12} i_c \\
\\
v_{cb} = \dfrac{\partial v_{CB}}{\partial i_E} i_e + \dfrac{\partial v_{CB}}{\partial i_C} i_c = z_{21} i_e + z_{22} i_c
\end{cases}
\tag{10-19}
$$

where the parameters of the form $\partial v / \partial i$ are recognized as impedances.

The first equation of Eq. 10-19 says that the emitter-base voltage v_{eb} is the sum of two components. This indicates a series combination of two elements, the first of which is an impedance drop $z_{11} i_e$. The second element is a voltage in the emitter circuit directly proportional to the current in the collector circuit; this is properly represented by a controlled voltage source $z_{12} i_c$. When the same reasoning is applied to the equation for the collector-base voltage and the results combined, the small-signal circuit model of Fig. 10.18a is the logical result.

As anticipated, the linear model of a transistor is more complicated than that of a triode. A possible simplification is to eliminate one controlled source by an algebraic substitution. If the circuit of Fig. 10.18b is equivalent to that of Fig. 10.18a, the same relations between terminal quantities must apply. For the one-source circuit, these relations are

$$
\begin{cases}
v_e = (r_e + r_b) i_e + r_b i_c \\
v_c = r_b i_e + a i_e r_c + r_b i_c + r_c i_c
\end{cases}
\tag{10-20}
$$

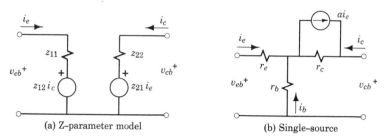

(a) Z–parameter model   (b) Single–source

Fig. 10.18   Small-signal circuit models for transistors.

Comparing Eqs. 10-19 and 10-20, the conditions for equivalence are

$$z_{11} = r_e + r_b \qquad z_{21} = r_b + ar_c$$

$$z_{12} = r_b \qquad z_{22} = r_b + r_c \qquad (10\text{-}21)$$

Note that in this active device, $z_{12} \neq z_{21}$. It can be shown† that the factor a is approximately equal to α, the forward current gain in the common-base configuration, within the limits of accuracy of most calculations.

Each element of the T-circuit model is, in a rough way, physically related to a component of the actual transistor. (At moderate frequencies, up to a megacycle or so, the impedances are pure resistances; at higher frequencies the circuit must be appropriately modified.) The input resistance r_e is related to the dynamic resistance of the forward-biased emitter-base junction and is a function of the emitter current.‡ The resistance r_b includes an ohmic resistance, due to the long, thin section of semiconductor through which base current must flow, and is usually several hundred to 1000 ohms. The resistance r_c is related to the dynamic resistance of the reverse-biased collector-base junction and is usually one to several megohms. Values for α range from 0.90 to 0.999, with typical values in the region of 0.98.

EXAMPLE 6

A transistor has the following parameters: $r_e = 25$ Ω, $r_b = 1$ kΩ, $r_c = 1$ MΩ, and $\alpha = 0.98$.

(a) For a signal input $i_s = 10$ μA predict the output signal voltage across a load resistance $R_L = 10$ kΩ (see Fig. 10.19a).

---

† See p. 127, Alley and Attwood: *Electronic Engineering*, John Wiley and Sons, 1962.
‡ Emitter resistance is given approximately by the equation $r_e \cong kT/ei_E$; at room temperature, $r_e \cong 25/i_E$ Ω where i_E is in mA (see Problem 9-6).

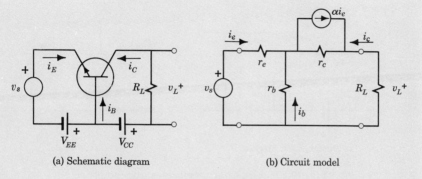

(a) Schematic diagram   (b) Circuit model

Fig. 10.19   Example 6.

(b) What signal voltage v_s is required under these conditions, and what is the voltage gain?

SOLUTION.   (a) For these calculations, the transistor is replaced by the small-signal linear model of Fig. 10.19b where $i_e = i_s$. Summing voltages around the output loop,

$$\Sigma v = 0 = (i_e + i_c)r_b + (\alpha i_e + i_c)r_c + i_c R_L$$

Solving,

$$i_c = -\frac{r_b + \alpha r_c}{r_b + r_c + R_L} \quad i_e = -\frac{(1 + 980) \times 10^3}{(1 + 1000 + 10) \times 10^3} \times 10 \times 10^{-6} = -9.7 \ \mu A$$

Therefore,

$$v_L = -i_c R_L = 9.7 \times 10^{-6} \times 10 \times 10^3 = 97 \text{ mV}$$

(b) Summing voltages around the input loop,

$$\Sigma v = 0 = v_s - i_e r_e - (i_e + i_c)r_b$$

Solving,

$$v_s = i_e r_e + (i_e + i_c)r_b = 10 \times 10^{-6} \times 25 + (10 - 9.7) \times 10^{-6} \times 10^3 = 0.55 \text{ mV}$$

The voltage gain is

$$\frac{v_L}{v_s} = \frac{97}{0.55} = 176$$

Common-Emitter Configuration

One advantage of a model is that it may provide new insight into the behavior of the actual device.   Insofar as small signals are concerned, the linear model of Fig. 10.19b can replace the actual physical transistor with its d-c supplies connected as shown.   If the transistor is reconnected

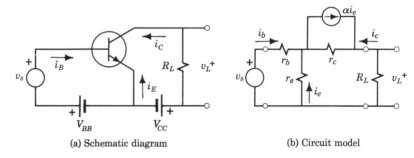

(a) Schematic diagram   (b) Circuit model

Fig. 10.20   Elementary common-emitter amplifier.

as shown in Fig. 10.20, the base-emitter terminals become the input port
and the collector-emitter terminals become the output port to represent
this *common-emitter* configuration.   The model is merely rearranged, but
the device performance is dramatically changed by this rearrangement
as indicated by the following example.

EXAMPLE 7

The transistor of Example 6 is reconnected as a common-emitter amplifier
with the same load resistance.   For the same output voltage, predict the signal
input current now required.

SOLUTION.   As indicated in Fig. 10.20,

$$i_s = i_b \quad \text{and} \quad i_e = -i_b - i_c$$

Summing the voltages around the output loop,

$$\Sigma v = 0 = (i_b + i_c)r_e + \alpha(-i_b - i_c)r_c + i_c r_c + i_c R_L$$

Solving,

$$i_b = -\frac{r_e + (1 - \alpha)r_c + R_L}{r_e - \alpha r_c} i_c$$

Substituting the given values,

$$i_s = i_b = -\frac{(0.025 + 20 + 10) \times 10^3}{(0.025 - 980) \times 10^3}(-9.7 \times 10^{-6}) \cong -0.3 \ \mu A$$

In comparison to the signal current of 10 μA required in the common-base amplifier, only 0.3 μA is required in the common-emitter configuration.   There is an
effective current gain of $10/(-0.3) = -33$.   The negative sign indicates a phase
reversal similar to that which occurs in a triode amplifier.

The possibility of a current gain as well as a voltage gain is an important advantage of the common-emitter amplifier.   Because this configuration is used so extensively, we are justified in deriving a special model.

While the model of Fig. 10.21a can be used, it is not convenient because the controlled source is not a function of the input current; also, the character of the current gain is obscured in this model. A better form is that of Fig. 10.21b where β and r_d are to be determined.

If these two circuits are to be equivalent, the potential of terminal c with respect to node n must be identical in both cases. For the left-hand circuit,

$$v_{cn} = (i_c + \alpha i_e)r_c = i_c r_c - \alpha i_b r_c - \alpha i_c r_c$$

Multiplying the i_b term by $(1 - \alpha)/(1 - \alpha)$,

$$v_{cn} = i_c(1 - \alpha)r_c - \frac{\alpha}{1 - \alpha}(1 - \alpha)r_c i_b \qquad (10\text{-}22)$$

For the right-hand circuit,

$$v_{cn} = i_c r_d - \beta r_d i_b \qquad (10\text{-}23)$$

Comparing Eqs. 10-22 and 10-23, it is seen that

$$r_d = (1 - \alpha)r_c \quad \text{and} \quad \beta = \frac{\alpha}{1 - \alpha} \qquad (10\text{-}24)$$

Now the character of the current gain is more clear. The effect of a variation in base current (a signal input to the base) appears in the collector circuit as a controlled source whose magnitude is $\alpha/(1 - \alpha)$ times as great. For a typical transistor with $\alpha = 0.98$, $\beta = 0.98/0.02 = 49$. Under certain conditions the common-base arrangement is superior, but where current amplification as well as voltage amplification is important, the common-emitter amplifier possesses obvious advantages. Under other circumstances (discussed in Chapter 11), the *common-collector* configuration is advantageous.

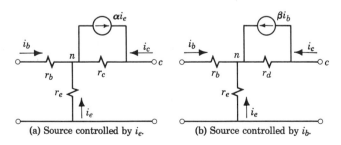

(a) Source controlled by i_e.   (b) Source controlled by i_b.

Fig. 10.21 Common-emitter T-circuit models.

The h-Parameter Model

For any configuration and any small-signal application, a linear model can be used to represent the transistor and predict its performance. Hybrid parameters are most commonly used and are most frequently supplied by manufacturers. The chief advantages of h-parameters are the ease with which they can be determined in the laboratory and the facility with which they can be handled in circuit calculations.

Choosing input current i_I and output voltage v_O as the independent variables and rewriting Eqs. 10-3 in conventional transistor notation,

$$\begin{cases} v_I = f_1(i_I, v_O) \\ i_O = f_2(i_I, v_O) \end{cases} \tag{10-25}$$

For the common-emitter configuration, for example, v_I is the base-emitter voltage and i_O is the collector current. Taking the total differential, these become

$$\begin{cases} dv_I = \dfrac{\partial v_I}{\partial i_I}\, di_I + \dfrac{\partial v_I}{\partial v_O}\, dv_O \\[2ex] di_O = \dfrac{\partial i_O}{\partial i_I}\, di_I + \dfrac{\partial i_O}{\partial v_O}\, dv_O \end{cases} \tag{10-26}$$

Again we note that differentials can be approximated by small increments and we identify increments as small signals. Then Eqs. 10-26 can be written as

$$\begin{cases} v_i = \dfrac{\partial v_I}{\partial i_I}\, i_i + \dfrac{\partial v_I}{\partial v_O}\, v_o = h_i i_i + h_r v_o \\[2ex] i_o = \dfrac{\partial i_O}{\partial i_I}\, i_i + \dfrac{\partial i_O}{\partial v_O}\, v_o = h_f i_i + h_o v_o \end{cases} \tag{10-27}$$

where h_i = input impedance with output short-circuited (ohms),

h_f = forward transfer current ratio with output short-circuited,

h_r = reverse transfer voltage ratio with input open-circuited,

h_o = output admittance with input open-circuited (mhos).

The first of Eqs. 10-27 says that the input voltage is the sum of two components. This indicates a series combination of an impedance drop $h_i i_i$ and a controlled voltage source $h_r v_o$ directly proportional to the output voltage. The second equation indicates a parallel combination of a controlled current source

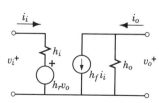

Fig. 10.22 General h-parameter circuit model.

$h_f i_i$ and an admittance current $h_o v_o$. The h-parameter model of Fig. 10.22 follows from this line of reasoning.

EXAMPLE 8

The transistor of Examples 6 and 7 has the following hybrid parameters: $h_{ie} = 2250\ \Omega$, $h_{re} = 12.5 \times 10^{-4}$, $h_{fe} = 49$, and $h_{oe} = 50\ \mu\mho$. For a common-emitter amplifier with $R_L = 10\ k\Omega$, predict the input signal current and voltage required for an output of 97 mV (the previously calculated value).

SOLUTION. In the output loop of the circuit of Fig. 10.23,

$$v_L = - \frac{h_{fe} i_b}{h_{oe} + 1/R_L}$$

Solving,

$$i_b = - \frac{(h_{oe} + 1/R_L)v_L}{h_{fe}} = - \frac{(50 + 100) \times 10^{-6} \times 0.097}{49} = -0.3\ \mu A$$

For the input loop,

$$v_s = h_{ie} i_b + h_{re} v_L = 2250 \times (-0.3 \times 10^{-6}) + 12.5 \times 10^{-4} \times 0.097$$

$$\cong (-0.67 + 0.12) \times 10^{-3} = -0.55\ mV$$

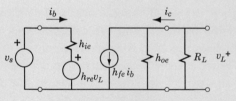

Fig. 10.23   Example 8.

Determination of *h* Parameters

The general model is applicable to any transistor configuration. In a specific case, the parameters are identified by a second subscript b, e, or c, depending on whether the base, emitter, or collector is the common element. These are small-signal values implying small a-c variations about operating points defined by d-c values of voltage and current. Under these conditions, a short-circuited output means there is no a-c output voltage and only a d-c voltage exists. For example, h_{ib} is the a-c or dynamic input impedance for the common-base configuration with the collector-base voltage held constant.

TABLE 10-2   Typical Transistor Characteristics

	2N525	2N1613		2N699B	
			Min.	Typ.	Max.
$h_{ie}(\text{k}\Omega)$	1.4	2.2		2.8	
$h_{re}(\times 10^{-4})$	3.37	3.6		3.5	
h_{fe}	44	55	35	70	100
$h_{oe}(\mu\mho)$	27	12.5		11	
$h_{ib}(\Omega)$	31	27	20	27	30
$h_{rb}(\times 10^{-4})$	5	0.7		0.5	1.25
h_{fb}	−0.978	−0.98		−0.987	
$h_{ob}(\mu\mho)$	0.60	0.16	0.1	0.12	0.5
α	0.978				
$r_c(\text{M}\Omega)$	1.67				
$r_e(\Omega)$	12.5				
$r_b(\Omega)$	840				

Just as for the triode, such a parameter could be defined as

$$h_{ib} = \frac{dv_{EB}}{di_E}\bigg|_{v_{CB}=k}$$

and determined from the slope of the line of constant v_{CB} on the input characteristics (Fig. 10.16). In the same way, the other parameters could be determined from the families of static characteristic curves. In actual practice, however, the parameters are determined experimentally by measuring the a-c voltages or currents which result from a-c signals introduced at the appropriate locations. For example, to determine h_{fe}, a small a-c voltage is applied between base and emitter and the resulting a-c currents in the base lead and the collector lead are measured (the collector circuit must be effectively short-circuited to ac). Then h_{fe} is the ratio of collector current to base current and is just equal to β. Similar measurements permit the determination of the other small-signal parameters.

Since transistor parameters vary widely with operating point, measurements are made under standard conditions. Unless otherwise stated, values are for a frequency of 270 cps† at room temperature (25°C) with an emitter current of 1 mA and a collector-base voltage of 5 V. Transistor manufacturers publish typical, minimum, and maximum values of the parameters along with average static characteristics. Typical values are shown in Table 10-2. An engineer designing a transistor amplifier, for example, must arrange the circuit so that the performance of the amplifier is within specifications despite expected variations in transistor parameters. (See Chapter 19.)

---

† A frequency of 1 kc is also quite common.

SUMMARY

◆ The small-signal performance of complicated and highly nonlinear electronic devices can be predicted using relatively simple linear models.

◆ The important characteristic of a diode is the discrimination between forward and reverse voltages.

The ideal diode presents zero resistance in the forward direction and infinite resistance in the reverse direction; it can be represented by a selective switch.

Actual diodes depart from the ideal to some extent. Depending on the required precision, various circuit models can be derived by piecewise linearization of the characteristic curves.

◆ For steady conditions, an average resistance $R_f = V/I$ can be calculated from the slope of the linearized characteristic. In some semiconductor applications, the reverse resistance R_r must also be considered.

◆ For small signals superimposed on steady values, the significant parameter is the dynamic resistance $r_p = dV/dI$, the reciprocal of the slope of the I-V characteristic at the operating point.

◆ For small signals in the normal operating region, two-port devices such as triodes and transistors can also be represented by circuit models.

◆ Depending on the choice of independent variables, the models consist of impedances, admittances, or a combination of the two, along with controlled sources.

A controlled source is an energy or signal source in which the output is dependent upon another variable in the system.

◆ The procedure in deriving the small-signal circuit model of a nonlinear two-port is:

1. Write the governing equation in terms of the chosen variables.

2. Take the total differential to obtain the corresponding equations for small variations.

3. Note that differentials can be approximated by small increments, recognize such increments as equivalent to small signals, and write the corresponding equations for small signals.

4. Interpret the small-signal equations in terms of an electrical circuit with appropriate parameters, including passive elements and controlled sources.

◆ The properly derived model can replace the actual device insofar as small-signal operation at moderate frequencies is concerned; the precision of the results depends on the precision with which the parameters are known.

◆ For a triode, the two forms of the small-signal equation and the corresponding circuit models are:

$$I_p = g_m V_g + \frac{1}{r_p} V_p \qquad V_p = -\mu V_g + r_p I_p$$

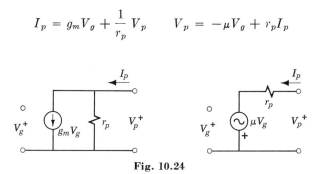

Fig. 10.24

◆ Values of the parameters are supplied by manufacturers or can be calculated from the static characteristic curves.

◆ For a transistor, in contrast to the negative-grid triode, the input current is appreciable and the linear model is slightly more complicated. Using hybrid parameters for the common-emitter configuration, the small-signal equations and the corresponding circuit model are:

$$V_{be} = h_{ie} I_b + h_{re} V_{ce}$$

$$I_c = h_{fe} I_b + h_{oe} V_{ce}$$

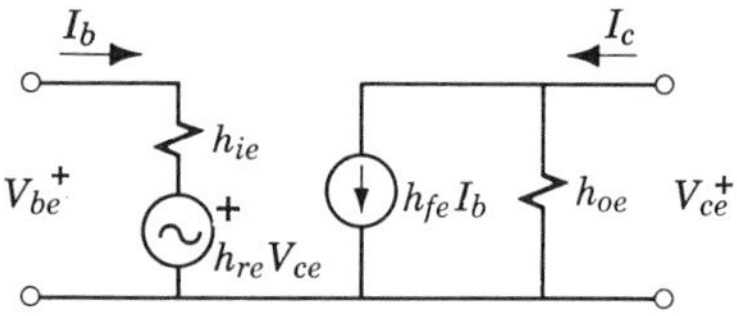

Fig. 10.25

Because individual transistors vary widely from the norm, it is customary to use parameter value ranges published by the manufacturer, minimizing the effects of variations by proper circuit design.

◆ While the common-cathode (triode) and common-emitter (transistor) configurations are used most widely, other configurations are possible, and under certain conditions (to be described in the next chapter) are preferable.

REVIEW QUESTIONS

1. Why do we wish to replace actual devices with fictitious models?
2. Why do we insist on *linear* models?
3. Cite an example from aeronautical, chemical, civil, industrial, and mechanical engineering of a process or a device which is customarily analyzed in terms of a mathematical or physical model.
4. Explain what is meant by a "controlled source" and give an example.
5. In what respects does a vacuum diode differ from an ideal diode? A gas diode? A semiconductor diode?
6. Explain what is meant by a "linearized characteristic curve."
7. Explain, on a physical basis, the shape of the I-V curve of a gas diode.
8. Explain the differences between V/I, $\Delta V/\Delta I$, dV/dI, and $\partial V/\partial I$.
9. Explain the difference between static resistance and dynamic resistance.
10. Represent a water turbine as a three-port and identify the input or output quantity at each port.
11. Represent an automobile with driver as a three-port and identify the input or output quantity at each port.
12. Explain, with a circuit diagram, how static characteristic curves for a triode can be obtained in the laboratory.
13. Why is the a-c model of a triode normally simpler than an equally precise model of a transistor?
14. In analytic geometry, what does $z = f(x, y)$ represent in general? Could $i_b = f(v_c, v_b)$ be similarly represented? What is the graphical interpretation of $\partial z/\partial y$?
15. Sketch a set of triode characteristics and define, graphically, the three parameters.
16. What are the criteria for selecting the quiescent point in an amplifier?
17. Does the circuit of Fig. 10.12 contain any information not in Eq. 10-12? Why use the circuit?
18. Could a triode be operated with the plate-cathode terminals as the input port and the grid-cathode terminals as the output port? What potential distribution would be necessary to obtain an output current?
19. What is meant by the statement: "The results of a graphical analysis of performance from characteristic curves lack generality"?
20. Why are no d-c supplies such as batteries shown in the linear models? What is the a-c impedance of a battery?
21. Draw the schematic diagram of a transistor in the common-collector configuration with the output taken across a resistance in the emitter load.
22. If the common-emitter and common-cathode configurations are analogous, what is analogous to the plate? To the grid?
23. Explain how a current gain is obtained in a transistor amplifier.
24. Define the h-parameters graphically in terms of common-base characteristic curves. Why are h-parameters not calculated this way?

EXERCISES

1. An element of a circuit consists of a resistance R carrying a current i under a voltage v. Draw a labeled circuit in which the resistance is replaced by (a) a controlled voltage source and (b) a controlled current source.

2. An element of a circuit consists of an inductance L carrying an exponential current i under a voltage v. Draw a labeled circuit in which the inductance is replaced by (a) a controlled voltage source and (b) a controlled current source.

3. An element of a circuit consists of a capacitance C carrying an exponential current i under a voltage v. Draw a labeled circuit in which the capacitance is replaced by (a) a controlled voltage source and (b) a controlled current source.

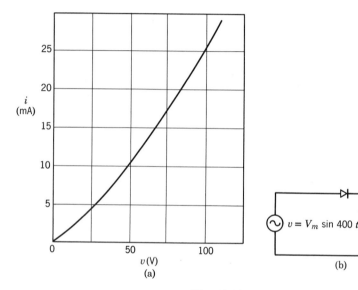

Fig. 10.26

4. A diode having the characteristics of Fig. 10.26a is to be used in the circuit of Fig. 10.26b.

(a) Represent the diode (in the region $0 < v < 50$ V by a circuit model consisting of an ideal diode and an average value of forward resistance.

(b) For $V_m = 100$ V and $R_L = 5$ kΩ, calculate the average current delivered to R_L.

(c) Sketch one cycle of the applied voltage and show the current i and the voltage across the diode v_d as functions of time.

5. Replace the diode of Fig. 10.26a with a circuit model which will hold, approximately, for voltages near 100 V.

6. Replace the diode of Fig. 10.27 with a circuit model which will hold, approximately, for currents near 2 A.

7. A diode is represented by a selective switch and resistances $R_f = 100$ Ω and $R_r = 1000$ Ω. Sketch the I-V characteristic for this representation in the voltage range from -20 to $+20$ V.

8. The diode of Exercise 7 is connected in series with a load resistance $R_L = 1000$ Ω. A square voltage wave of maximum value ± 20 V is applied to the

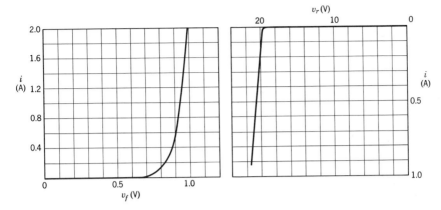

Fig. 10.27 Silicon diode characteristics. **Fig. 10.28** Zener diode characteristics.

series combination. Sketch the applied voltage and current as functions of time and calculate the average load current.

9. Devise a circuit model to represent, approximately, the Zener diode of Fig. 10.28.

10. The characteristic of a vacuum diode is given by the equation $i_b = K v_b^{3/2}$. Find the dynamic resistance at an operating point defined by $i_b = 10$ mA and $v_b = 100$ V.

11. The junction characteristic of a semiconductor diode is given by the equation $I = I_s(e^{40V} - 1)$. Derive an expression for the dynamic resistance as a function of current and evaluate r_p for $I = 1$ mA.

12. The diode of Fig. 10.26a is used in the circuit of Fig. 10.29 where $v = 10 \sin 2000t$ V and $R_L = 1000$ Ω.

(a) If $V = 100$ V, replace the diode with an appropriate model and predict the a-c voltage across R_L.

(b) Repeat for $V = 25$ V and compare the result to that of part (a).

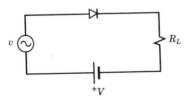

Fig. 10.29

13. Starting from the second pair of Eqs. 10-2, and assuming a linear two-port network, derive a circuit model with admittance parameters (Y_{11}, etc.).

14. Starting from the second pair of Eqs. 10-2, and assuming a nonlinear two-port device, derive a small-signal circuit model with admittance parameters (y_{11}, etc.).

15. Determine the triode parameters μ, r_p, and g_m for the tube of Fig. A2.

(a) At an operating point defined by $v_c = -1$ V and $v_b = 200$ V.

(b) At an operating point defined by $v_c = -3$ V and $v_b = 300$ V.

16. Determine the parameters μ, r_p, and g_m for the pentode of Fig. A3.

(a) At an operating point defined by $v_c = -1.5$ V and $v_b = 140$ V.

(b) At an operating point defined by $v_c = -2.5$ V and $v_b = 240$ V.

17. Working from general relations in terms of increments, prove that $\mu = g_m r_p$. Use this relation to check the results of Exercise 15.

18. Using the circuit of Fig. 10.13, derive a general expression for voltage gain with a load resistance R_L. What is the limiting value of voltage gain as R_L is increased?

19. The characteristics of a triode are given by $i_b = 10^{-5}(20v_c + v_b)^{3/2}$ A. Devise a small-signal linear circuit model for a quiescent point of $v_c = -5$ V and $v_b = +200$ V.

20. The characteristics of a two-port electron tube (a pentode) are given by $i_1 = 0$ and $i_2 = (v_1 + 0.001\, v_2 + 10.8)^{3/2}$ mA.

Devise a small-signal circuit model for this device at an operating point defined by $v_1 = -2$ V and $v_2 = +200$ V.

21. Determine the voltage gain of the pentode of Exercise 20 used as an amplifier with $R_L = 20$ kΩ.

22. The characteristics of a semiconductor two-port are given by

$$v_E = 0.025 \ln (1 + i_E/1\ \mu\text{A}) \quad \text{and} \quad i_C = -0.98 i_E + 10^{-7}(e^{40v_C} - 1)$$

Devise a small-signal model for this device at an operating point defined by $i_E = 2$ mA and $v_C = -10$ V.

23. For a certain triode, $\mu = 50$ and $g_m = 2$ m$\mho$.

(a) If the plate voltage is held constant and the grid voltage is made less negative by 1 V, what change in plate current will occur?

(b) If the grid voltage is held at the new value, what change in plate voltage will be required to bring the plate current back to its original value?

24. A 12AT7 triode ($\mu = 55$, $r_p = 5.5$ kΩ, $g_m = 10$ m$\mho$) is used as an elementary amplifier. Specify the load resistance R_L for a voltage gain of 40.

25. An elementary amplifier with a voltage gain of 60 is needed. Select an appropriate triode from those listed in Table 10-1 and specify the value of load resistance R_L.

26. A 6J5 triode is used as an elementary amplifier. The load consists of the parallel combination of a 10-kΩ resistor and a 0.01-μF capacitor. For an input signal $v = 0.1\sqrt{2} \sin 10{,}000t$ V, predict the magnitude and phase of the output voltage across the load. (See Table 10-1.)

27. A triode is connected to a load which is nearly a pure inductance L. Derive a general expression for voltage gain as a function of the frequency ω of the input signal.

28. A transistor has the following parameters:

$$r_e = 20\ \Omega, \ r_b = 1\ \text{k}\Omega, \ r_c = 2\ \text{M}\Omega, \text{ and } \alpha = 0.95.$$

It is connected as a common-base amplifier with $R_L = 2$ kΩ and a constant-voltage input V_s.

(a) What signal input current is required for an output voltage of 0.2 V rms?

(b) What is the voltage gain?

29. Calculate β and r_d for the transistor of Exercise 28 and repeat parts (a) and (b) for a common-emitter amplifier.

30. A 2N525 transistor is used as an elementary common-base amplifier with a load resistance $R_L = 5$ kΩ.

(a) Using the T-circuit model, what signal voltage V_s is required to produce an output voltage of 0.2 V rms?

(b) Repeat part (a), assuming that the signal source has an internal resistance of 1 kΩ in series with V_s.

31. Repeat Exercise 30, using the common-emitter configuration.

32. Derive a general expression for the voltage gain in Fig. 10.19b, assuming negligible internal impedance of the source.

33. Repeat Exercise 32, assuming the signal source has an internal resistance R_s in series with V_s.

34. A common-emitter amplifier uses a 2N1613 transistor connected to a 4-kΩ load resistance. The available signal current is 20 μA.

(a) Draw and label an appropriate h-parameter linear model.

(b) Determine the output current and output voltage.

35. A 2N699B *npn* transistor is used as a common-emitter amplifier supplied by a signal source with an internal resistance $R_s = 700$ Ω. The desired signal output across the 5-kΩ load resistor is 1 V rms.

(a) Draw and label the schematic diagram and an appropriate small-signal model, using h-parameters.

(b) Neglecting h_{re}, determine the input signal current required for the desired output. Is neglecting h_{re} reasonable here? Calculate the current gain.

(c) Calculate the voltage gain of the amplifier and the required value of signal source voltage V_s.

36. If the T-circuit of Fig. 10.21b and the h-parameter model of Fig. 10.23 are equivalent, the input impedances of the two circuits must be the same under all conditions, for example, with the output shorted ($R_L = 0$). Using this hint, derive an expression for h_{ie} in terms of β, r_b, r_e and r_d.

37. Use the hint of Exercise 36 to derive an expression for h_{oe}.

38. Draw a schematic diagram of a transistor in the common-collector configuration and represent it by an a-c model using hybrid parameters.

(a) Evaluate h_{oc} in terms of h_{oe}.

(b) Evaluate h_{rc} in terms of h_{re}.

PROBLEMS

1. A strain gauge is a resistive element with a known relation between a change in length and the corresponding change in resistance. Fine wire (in the form of a grid on a paper backing) is cemented directly to the member being strained and the change in resistance is measured on a bridge or observed on an oscilloscope. The resistance of a given strain gauge is initially 1000 Ω; for small changes in length, the resistance changes 2% for a 1% change in length.

(a) Devise an approximate d-c circuit model for the strain gauge (specifying values of the circuit elements) such that output current I is a function of the strain ϵ and the applied voltage V.

(b) Devise an a-c circuit model for $V = 20$ V and determine the variation in strain ϵ corresponding to an output current $i = 0.1 \sin 500t$ mA.

2. A d-c generator can be considered as a three-port with a mechanical input (speed), an electrical input (field current I_f) and an electrical output (V, I). If speed is held constant, the characteristics of a certain generator are as shown in Fig. 10.30. Devise and draw a small-signal linear model, specifying the parameters for operation at $I_f = 0.8$ A and $R_L = 2.5\ \Omega$. For a small variation in I_f, predict the corresponding variation in output current I and express the result as a current gain.

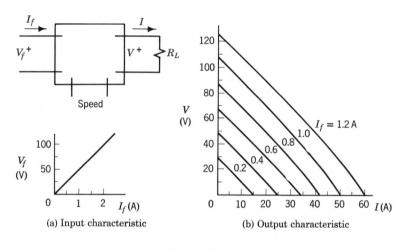

(a) Input characteristic   (b) Output characteristic

Fig. 10.30

3. A standard two-wire 110-V a-c cord is connected to the left-hand box (Fig. 10.31) on the top of which there are two single-pole, single-throw switches. Two wires lead to the second box on which there are two standard light bulbs. Using your knowledge of diodes, devise a circuit so that switch A will control light A and switch B will control light B, independently.

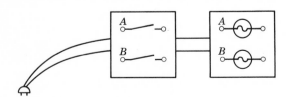

Fig. 10.31

4. An elementary transistor amplifier is to be used as a pre-amplifier for a "hi-fi" set. The output of the phonograph pickup (low internal impedance) is only 8 mV, but 1 V is required as the input to the power amplifier which drives the loudspeaker. "Design" the pre-amplifier by specifying a suitable transistor and the appropriate load resistor.

5. The circuit of Fig. 10.32 permits operating a transistor from a single battery. While it appears complicated at first glance, it can be reduced to a simpler circuit for a-c analysis. Draw an appropriate model for the transistor alone and then add elements representing the remainder of the circuit. For a-c signals of moderate frequency, neglect the reactance of the capacitors C_1 and C_2 and draw the resulting simplified circuit.

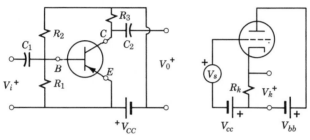

Fig. 10.32   **Fig. 10.33**

6. In a particular triode application (Fig. 10.33) the usual load resistance is omitted and a cathode resistance R_k is inserted. V_{cc} and V_{bb} are adjusted to bring operation to an appropriate quiescent point. Replace the triode with a small-signal linear model and derive a general expression for V_k in terms of V_s and the tube parameters.

CHAPTER **11**

Electronic Amplifiers

The two major applications of electronic devices are in amplifying and in switching. Using the characteristics of two-port devices described in Chapter 9 and the linear models derived in Chapter 10, we are now ready to study the analysis and design of practical electronic amplifiers. The use of tubes and transistors in switching and other nonlinear applications is discussed in Chapters 12 and 13.

The design of electronic amplifiers to meet critical performance, weight, and cost specifications requires a great deal of knowledge and judgment. Electrical engineers will gain this detailed knowledge in subsequent courses and the judgment from practical experience. Other engineers will be more concerned with the use of existing amplifiers; if they do any design (in connection with instrumentation, for example), it will be under circumstances where optimum performance is not essential.

Our purpose here is to discuss the factors which influence amplifier performance, illustrate the basic analysis techniques, and present methods for designing simple amplifiers and predicting their performance. Our approach is first to look at the practical considerations in amplifier operation and devise circuits for maintaining the proper operating conditions, then to analyze the performance of one type of power amplifier and one type of small-signal amplifier, and finally to describe briefly some other important types of amplifiers.

PRACTICAL AMPLIFIERS

Amplifier Classification

There are many ways of describing amplifiers. A *single-stage* amplifier consists of one amplifying element and the associated circuitry; in general, several such elements are combined in a *multistage* amplifier. In a sound reproduction system, the first stages are *small-signal* voltage (or current) amplifiers designed to amplify the output of a phonograph pickup, a few millivolts, up to a signal of several volts. The final stage is a *large-signal* or *power* amplifier which supplies sufficient power, several watts, to drive the loudspeaker.

Such amplifiers are called *audio* amplifiers if they amplify signals from, say, 30 to 15,000 cps. In measuring structural vibrations, temperature variations, or the electrical currents generated within the human body, very low-frequency signals are encountered; to handle signals from zero frequency to a few cycles per second, *direct-coupled* amplifiers are used. In contrast, the *video* amplifier in a television receiver must amplify picture signals with components from 30 to 4,000,000 cps.

A video amplifier is a *wide-band* amplifier which amplifies equally all frequencies over a broad frequency range. A typical *radio-frequency* amplifier for the FM broadcast band (around 100 Mc) is *tuned* to select and amplify the signal from one station and reject all others. In this chapter we are interested in simple untuned small-signal and power amplifiers.

Amplification and Distortion

The terms amplification and gain are used almost interchangeably. For sinusoidal signals or for a particular sinusoidal component of a periodic signal the voltage gain is

$$\mathbf{A}_v = \frac{\mathbf{V}_{out}}{\mathbf{V}_{in}} = A e^{j\theta}$$

where $\mathbf{A}_v$ is the complex ratio of two phasors. In a *linear amplifier* A and θ are independent of signal amplitude and frequency, and the output signal is a replica of the input signal.†

If there is *distortion* in the amplifier, the output is not a replica of the input. In Fig. 11.1, output is not proportional to input and there is *nonlinear* or *amplitude* distortion. In other words, A is not a simple constant. As a result of amplitude distortion, there are frequency com-

---

† If $\theta = k\omega$, a time lag is introduced, but there is no phase distortion.

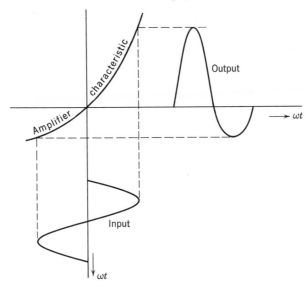

Fig. 11.1   Amplitude distortion.

ponents in the output which are not present in the input.   Fourier analysis of the output would reveal the presence of a "second harmonic," a component of twice the frequency of the "fundamental" input signal. Amplitude distortion usually occurs when excessively large signals are applied to nonlinear elements such as tubes or transistors.

At the other extreme is distortion due to *noise*, random signals unrelated to the input.   If the input signal is too small, the output consists primarily of noise and is not a replica of the input   The "snow" which appears on a television screen when only a weak signal is available is a visual representation of noise.   One source of noise is the random thermal motion of electrons in the amplifier circuit elements.   The *shot effect* of individual electrons arriving at the plate of a vacuum tube is another source of noise.   Noise is of greatest importance in input stages where signal levels are small; any noise introduced there is amplified by all subsequent stages.   The *dynamic range* of any amplifier is bounded at one end by the level at which signals are obscured by noise and at the other by the level at which amplitude distortion becomes excessive.

In Fig. 11.2, the *frequency response curve* of an audio ꞏmplifier indicates that there is *frequency distortion;* all frequencies (within a finite band) are not amplified equally.   In other words, A is a function of frequency.   A signal consisting of a fundamental at 1 kc, a tenth harmonic at 10 kc, and a hundredth harmonic at 100 kc would have a different

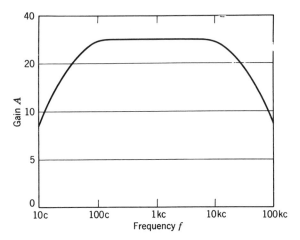

Fig. 11.2   Frequency distortion.

waveform after amplification.   No amplifier is completely free from frequency distortion.

If θ is a function of frequency, the relative amplitudes of the signal components may be unchanged but the relative phase positions are shifted.   As shown in Fig. 11.3, such *phase distortion* changes the shape

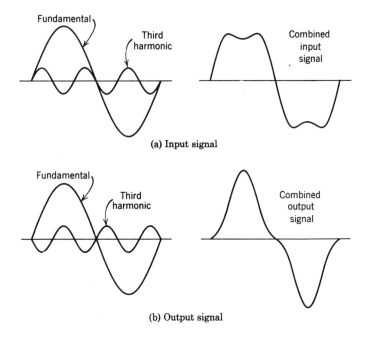

(a) Input signal

(b) Output signal

Fig. 11.3   Phase distortion.

of the output wave. The eye is sensitive to such distortion but the ear is not; a human ordinarily cannot distinguish between the two signals. On the other hand, the ear is quite sensitive to amplitude or frequency distortion.

Phase and frequency distortion are due to circuit elements such as capacitive and inductive reactances which are frequency dependent. Some tube and transistor parameters also are frequency dependent. In the design of untuned or wide-band amplifiers special steps are taken to reduce the variation in gain with frequency.

Practical Considerations

For small signals at moderate frequencies the voltage or current gain is calculated by using the linear a-c models of Chapter 10. But using these models presumes that the tube or transistor is maintained at the proper operating point and that many practical requirements have been met. Some of the practical considerations in amplifier design are illustrated in the simplified two-stage audio amplifier of Fig. 11.4.

Biasing. Tubes and transistors are maintained at the proper operating point by d-c power supplies and biasing networks. In portable units, batteries are used; in other units, the readily available 60-cps current is rectified and filtered to provide the necessary direct current. In Fig. 11.4, the battery V_{CC} supplies the collector voltages to transistors TR1 and TR2 and, through resistors R_B and R_D, the base biasing currents. When several different bias voltages are required, they are obtained from a voltage divider or by series *dropping* resistors.

Coupling. The voltage generated in the phonograph pickup is coupled to TR1 by a combination of R_{VC} and C_C. Variable resistor R_{VC} provides volume control by voltage-divider action. Transistor TR1 is coupled to the second stage by means of load resistor R_L and coupling

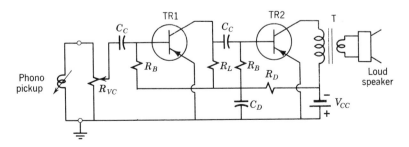

Fig. 11.4 Simplified two-stage phonograph amplifier.

capacitor C_C. Such an R-C coupling circuit develops a useful signal output across R_L and transfers it to the input of the next stage, but d-c voltages and currents are blocked by C_C.

The loudspeaker is coupled to TR2 by transformer T. Transformer coupling is more expensive than R-C coupling, but it is more efficient and it permits impedance matching for improved power transfer. The combination of R_D and C_D is a *decoupling filter* to prevent feedback of amplified signals to the low-level input stage. Such feedback is likely to occur when the common battery supplying several stages begins to age and develops an appreciable internal resistance.

Load Impedance. If possible, the load impedance of an untuned amplifier is made purely resistive to minimize the variation in gain with frequency. In tuned amplifiers, the load impedance is usually a parallel resonant circuit. For voltage amplifiers, large values of R_L are desirable; but large R_L requires large supply voltages, so the selected value is a compromise.

Input and Output Impedance. When several amplifier stages are connected in *cascade*, the output characteristics of one stage are influenced by the input characteristics of the next. For a-c signals, the load resistance of TR1 is effectively shunted by the biasing resistance R_B and also by the input resistance of TR2. The effective load resistance used in calculating the gain of the first stage is a combination of all three. Ideally the input impedance of an amplifier stage should be high to minimize "loading" of the preceding stage, and the output impedance should be low for efficient power transfer.

Unintentional Elements. Figure 11.4 is a wiring diagram and shows components, not circuit elements. Even a short, straight conductor can store a small amount of energy in the form of a magnetic field or an electric field (between the conductor and ground or a metal chassis). The magnetic field effect is important only at extremely high frequencies and is neglected here; the electric field effect can be represented by a wiring capacitance C_W.

In the same way we represent the energy storage due to a difference in potential between the electrodes of a vacuum tube by *interelectrode capacitances*. At a transistor junction there is a charge separation and a potential difference across the depletion region; a change in junction potential causes a change in charge distribution ($q = Cv$) and this effect is represented by a *junction capacitance* C_j.

Transistors exhibit another charge storage effect. Under equilibrium conditions, the base must be electrically neutral. The charge from majority carriers (holes in a *p-n-p* transistor) diffusing from the emitter into the base is neutralized by carriers (electrons in *p-n-p*) from the base connection. A sudden change in emitter-base potential causes a transfer of charge into or out of the base; this effect is represented by a *diffusion capacitance* C_d. The circuit model used for analyzing amplifier performance must include these unintentional elements and, therefore, it is quite different from the wiring diagram of Fig. 11.4.

BIASING

The *v-i* characteristics of individual transistors vary widely and they are sensitive to temperature change; as a result, biasing transistor amplifiers for optimum performance requires special care. In contrast, biasing vacuum-tube amplifiers is fairly simple because tube characteristics are predictable and stable.

Triode Biasing

While the amplifier of Fig. 11.5a will work satisfactorily, the modified version in Fig. 11.5b has three advantages. First, the input capacitor C_1 removes any d-c component from the input signal which might affect the operating point. Second, input and output voltages have a common terminal, the so-called "ground" which is usually the metal chassis on which components are mounted. Third, only a single d-c supply is required.

The plate current $i_b = I_b + i_p$ flows through the parallel combination of C_k and R_k. If *by-pass capacitor* C_k is chosen large enough, the react-

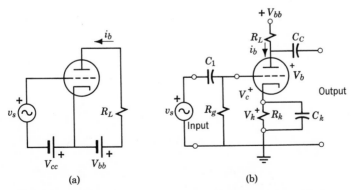

Fig. 11.5 Triode amplifier with (a) battery bias and (b) cathode resistor bias.

ance $1/\omega C_k$ to I_p (the a-c component of plate current) is very small, and practically no a-c voltage appears between cathode and ground (see Example 1). All the d-c component flows through R_k and a d-c voltage

$$V_k = I_b R_k \tag{11-1}$$

is developed. If grid current is zero (as in a negative-grid triode), there is no voltage drop across R_g and the potential of the grid with respect to the cathode is

$$V_c = -V_k = -I_b R_k \tag{11-2}$$

If the quiescent point is specified, I_b and V_c are known and R_k can be calculated from Eq. 11-2.

If, instead, V_{bb}, R_L, and R_k are known, the load line can be drawn and the quiescent point obtained graphically. The equation of the load line with cathode-resistor bias is

$$v_b = V_{bb} - (R_L + R_k)i_b \tag{11-3}$$

Equation 11-2 can be plotted by choosing a few values of V_c and determining the corresponding I_b; the intersection of this *grid-bias line* with the load line locates the quiescent point.

The *grid-return* resistance R_g is necessary for proper operation of the amplifier. The negative grid attracts any positive gas ions in the imperfect vacuum. A return path for these charges is provided by R_g and the grid is held at ground potential as assumed in deriving Eq. 11-2. With R_g of the order of a megohm, there is little loading of the input signal.

EXAMPLE 1

The elementary amplifier of Example 9 in Chapter 9 is to be operated with cathode-resistor bias. Specify the value of R_k and the new value of V_{bb}, and check the effectiveness of $C_k = 30$ μF at 50 cps. (See Figs. 9.44a and 9.45.)

SOLUTION. The Q point corresponds to $V_c = -4$ V, $V_b = 150$ V, and $I_b = 7$ mA. Therefore, by Eq. 11.2,

$$R_k = -\frac{V_c}{I_b} = \frac{4}{0.007} \cong 570 \ \Omega$$

The plate battery now also supplies the cathode bias. Therefore,

$$V'_{bb} = V_{bb} - V_c = 290 - (-4) = 294 \text{ V}$$

Alternatively, V'_{bb} can be calculated by summing the voltages around the plate loop (Fig. 11.5b). When this is done,

$$V'_{bb} = V_b + I_b(R_L + R_k) = 150 + 0.007(20,570) = 294 \text{ V}$$

To check the effectiveness of C_k, note that for $I_p = 1$ mA,

$$V_s = V_g = \frac{V_p}{A_v} = \frac{R_L I_p}{A_v} = \frac{20}{15} = 1.33 \text{ V}$$

Under this condition the a-c voltage developed across C_k is only

$$V = \frac{I_p}{\omega C_k} = \frac{0.001}{2\pi 50 \times 30 \times 10^{-6}} \cong 0.1 \text{ V}$$

which is small compared to V_g. At all frequencies higher than 50 cps, the voltage is even less.

Pentode Biasing

The biasing arrangement for a pentode is only slightly more complicated than for a triode. In Fig. 11.6, the suppressor grid is tied directly to the cathode to provide the desired electric field adjacent to the positive plate. The screen grid is supplied from V_{bb} through resistor R_{g2} and by-passed by capacitor C_{g2}. If the desired screen voltage and current are known from manufacturer's data, the necessary resistance can be calculated from

$$V_{g2} = V_{bb} - R_{g2} I_{g2} - V_k \tag{11-4}$$

The control grid bias V_c is provided by cathode resistor R_k, by-passed by C_k. The cathode current includes the screen grid current (which may be 30 to 50% as large as the plate current) and the applicable equation is

$$V_c = -(I_b + I_{g2}) R_k \tag{11-5}$$

Once the screen and suppressor grids are properly biased, the performance of a pentode amplifier is determined from the v-i characteristics and the load line or from the small-signal linear model.

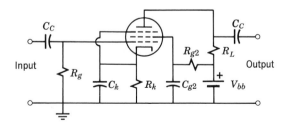

Fig. 11.6 Pentode amplifier.

Transistor Biasing

In normal operation of a transistor the emitter-base junction is forward-biased and the collector-base junction is reverse-biased. In the common-emitter configuration these bias voltages have the same polarity, so a single battery can supply both through an appropriate circuit.   Let us look at the general problem, discover why the simplest approach is unsatisfactory, and then analyze one common method of providing a satisfactory solution.

The objective is to *establish* the proper operating point and to *maintain* it despite variations in ambient temperature and variations among individual transistors of the same type.   Furthermore, this objective is to be achieved without adversely affecting the desired performance of the circuit.   The biasing problem is difficult because of:

(a) The complicated interrelations among transistor variables,

(b) The wide variations in I_{CO} and β ($= h_{fe}$) expected among mass-produced transistors, and

(c) The inherent sensitivity of semiconductors to temperature.

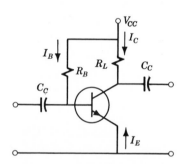

Fig. 11.7   Fixed-current bias.

Fixed-Current Bias.   One possibility is to provide the desired d-c base current from V_{CC} as in Fig. 11.7.   For a forward-biased emitter the junction voltage is a fraction of a volt and may be neglected in comparison to V_{CC}. On this basis, the quiescent base current is $I_B \cong V_{CC}/R_B$ and the operating point would be determined if the collector characteristics were known precisely.

But the characteristics are not known precisely.   For steady or d-c values, Eq. 9-54 becomes

$$I_C = \frac{\alpha}{1 - \alpha}\, I_B + \frac{I_{CO}}{1 - \alpha} = \beta I_B + (1 + \beta)I_{CO} \qquad (11\text{-}6)$$

For a fixed value of I_B, collector current I_C will vary widely with the small changes in I_{CO} and in α (or large changes in β) expected when transistors are interchanged.   Also, I_C will vary widely with temperature changes because β increases with temperature and I_{CO} will approximately double for a 10°C increase in temperature.   To illustrate, if $\acute{\alpha} = 0.98$, $\beta = 49$, and I_C will increase 50 times as fast as I_{CO}.

Thermal Runaway

The power loss in a transistor is primarily at the collector junction since the voltage there is high compared to the low voltage at the forward-biased emitter junction. If the collector current I_C increases, the power developed tends to raise the junction temperature. This causes an increase in I_{CO} and β and a further increase in I_C which tends to raise the temperature higher. In a transistor operating at high temperature (because of high ambient temperature or high developed power) a regenerative heating cycle may occur which will result in *thermal runaway* and, possibly, destruction of the transistor.

For equilibrium, the power developed in the transistor is equal to the power dissipated to the surroundings. The power dissipated by conduction is proportional to the difference between junction and ambient temperatures. Therefore,

$$P_{\text{developed}} = P_{\text{dissipated}} = Q_\tau = \frac{\tau_J - \tau_A}{R_\tau} \qquad (11\text{-}7)$$

For a constant ambient temperature τ_A, the increase in dissipation ability due to an increase in junction temperature is $\Delta Q_\tau = \Delta \tau_J / R_\tau$. Equilibrium will be upset and thermal runaway may occur when the increase in power to be dissipated is greater than the increase in dissipation ability, or when $\Delta P > \Delta \tau_J / R_\tau$. One way to avoid the cumulative effect is to cool the collector junction; power transistors utilize the heat dissipating capacity of the metal chassis on which they are mounted. Another way is to use an effective biasing circuit.

Self Bias. The ingenious self-biasing circuit of Fig. 11.8 decreases the effect of changes in α or temperature on the quiescent operating point. Its operation is based on the fact that the critical variable to be stabilized is the collector current rather than the base current. The combination of R_1 and R_2 constitutes a voltage divider to bring the base to the proper potential to forward bias the emitter junction. If I_C tends to increase, perhaps because of an increase in I_{CO} due to a rise in temperature, the current $I_C + I_B$ in R_E increases, raising the potential of the emitter with respect to ground. This, in turn, reduces the forward bias on the emitter junction, reduces the emitter current and, therefore, limits the increase in I_C. In other words, any increase in collector current modifies the bias in such a way as to oppose an increase in I_C.

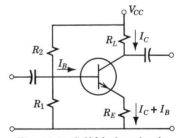

Fig. 11.8 Self-biasing circuit.

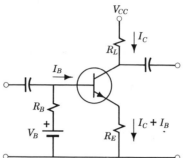

Fig. 11.9 Thévenin equivalent of self-biasing circuit.

Quantitative analysis of the circuit is simplified if the voltage divider is replaced by its Thévenin equivalent (Fig. 11.9) where

$$V_B = \frac{R_1}{R_1 + R_2} V_{CC} \quad \text{and} \quad R_B = \frac{R_1 R_2}{R_1 + R_2} \qquad (11\text{-}8)$$

If the small voltage across the emitter junction is neglected and the ohmic resistances of emitter and base are neglected or absorbed in R_E and R_B, Kirchhoff's voltage law around the base circuit yields

$$V_B - I_B R_B - (I_C + I_B) R_E = 0 \qquad (11\text{-}9)$$

From Eq. 11-6,

$$I_B = \frac{I_C - (1 + \beta) I_{CO}}{\beta} \qquad (11\text{-}10)$$

Substituting in Eq. 11-9 and solving

$$I_C = \frac{\beta V_B + (1 + \beta)(R_B + R_E) I_{CO}}{R_B + R_E + \beta R_E} \qquad (11\text{-}11)$$

Neglecting the variation in β (which may be quite important),

$$\frac{\Delta I_C}{\Delta I_{CO}} \cong \frac{dI_C}{dI_{CO}} = (1 + \beta) \frac{1}{1 + \beta \dfrac{R_E}{R_B + R_E}} \cong (1 + \beta) \frac{1}{1 + \beta \dfrac{R_E}{R_B}} \qquad (11\text{-}12)$$

If $\beta = 49$ as in the previous illustration and if $R_E = 0.1 R_B$ (a reasonable value), the *stability factor* is

$$S = \frac{\Delta I_C}{\Delta I_{CO}} \cong (1 + 49) \frac{1}{1 + 49(0.1)} \cong \frac{50}{6}$$

or the increase in I_C for a given change in I_{CO} is only one-sixth as large as it was with fixed-current bias. It turns out that the variation in I_C due to a given variation in β has been reduced similarly.†

EXAMPLE 2

A germanium transistor with a nominal β of 49 and $I_{CO} = 4$ μA is used in the circuit of Fig. 11.8 with $R_1 = 10$ kΩ, $R_2 = 100$ kΩ, $R_E = 1$ kΩ, and $R_L = 5$ kΩ. If I_C is to be in the range from 1 to 2 mA, what is the allowable temperature range?

SOLUTION.

$$R_B = \frac{R_1 R_2}{R_1 + R_2} = \frac{10 \times 100}{10 + 100} = 9.1 \text{ k}\Omega$$

By Eq. 11-12,

$$S = \frac{\Delta I_C}{\Delta I_{CO}} = (1 + \beta)\frac{1}{1 + \beta(R_E/R_B)} = 50\frac{1}{1 + 49(1/9.1)} = 7.8$$

For a change of 1 mA in I_C,

$$\Delta I_{CO} = \frac{1}{7.8} \text{ mA} = 128 \text{ } \mu\text{A}$$

and the maximum allowable value of I_{CO} is

$$I'_{CO} = I_{CO} + \Delta I_{CO} = 4 + 128 = 132 \text{ } \mu\text{A}$$

Assuming that the reverse saturation current doubles every 10°C,

$$I'_{CO} = I_{CO}(2)^{\Delta \tau/10}$$

or

$$\Delta \tau = 10 \log_2 \frac{I'_{CO}}{I_{CO}} = 10 \log_2 \frac{132}{4} \cong 10 \times 5 = 50° \text{ C}$$

Assuming that temperature is constant and $V_{CC} = 12$ V, it can be shown (can you do it?) that a variation in β from 20 to 180 produces a variation in I_C of less than 0.4 mA.

Bias Design, Approximate Method

In practice, the ratio R_E/R_B is limited. R_B must not be too small because it appears directly across the input and tends to load the input signal source. Also, R_E must not be too large because part of the d-c supply voltage V_{CC} appears across R_E. As R_E is increased, less voltage is available for developing an output signal across R_L, and the collector circuit efficiency is reduced. To prevent an undesirable a-c voltage variation across R_E, it is customarily by-passed by an appropriate capacitor which serves the same function as C_k in the cathode-bias circuit of a vacuum tube.

---

† See p. 168 of C. L. Searle, et al., *Elementary Circuit Properties of Transistors*, John Wiley and Sons, New York, 1964.

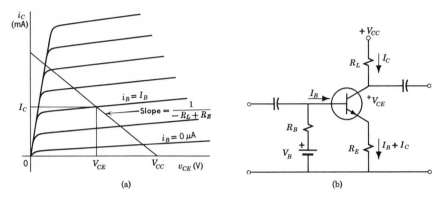

Fig. 11.10   Approximate bias design.

The designer must select values of R_1, R_2, and R_E to provide optimum performance; but the criteria are different in every situation and skill and experience are essential to an optimum design. If large temperature changes are not expected and if less than optimum performance is acceptable, the following procedure† is satisfactory:

1. Select an appropriate nominal operating point (I_C, I_B, and V_{CE}) from the manufacturer's data (see Fig. 11.10a).

2. Arbitrarily assume that $V_E = I_E R_E \cong I_C R_E \cong 3$ V and solve for

$$R_E \cong \frac{3}{I_C} \tag{11-13}$$

3. Select V_{CC} and R_L.

(a) If V_{CC} is specified, $R_L \cong \dfrac{(V_{CC} - V_{CE} - 3)}{I_C}$ (11-14)

(b) If R_L is specified, $V_{CC} \cong 3 + V_{CE} + I_C R_L$ (11-15)

4. Arbitrarily select R_B equal to 10 or 15 times R_E.   (11-16)
   (This gives a stability factor S of around 7 to 14.)

5. Calculate $V_B = I_B R_B + V_{BE} + (I_B + I_C)R_E$ (11-17)
   (Lacking other information, assume $I_B \cong I_C/\beta$ and $V_{BE} \cong 0.2$ V for germanium or 0.7 V for silicon.)

6. Calculate R_2 and R_1 (see Eqs. 11-8) from

$$R_2 = R_B \frac{V_{CC}}{V_B} \quad \text{and} \quad R_1 = \frac{R_B R_2}{R_2 - R_B} \tag{11-18}$$

---

† C. L. Searle, et al.: *op. cit.* p. 167.

The exact sequence in which these steps are taken can be modified to fit a given situation.

AUDIO POWER AMPLIFIERS

To drive a loudspeaker or a recording instrument requires an appreciable amount of power. In analyzing or designing a *power amplifier*, large signals and the accompanying nonlinearity must be considered and the small-signal linear models of Chapter 10 are inadequate. Tubes and transistors capable of delivering high power output are expensive and, therefore, careful attention to efficient amplifier design is justified.

The basic design problem is to provide the desired power output with a stable circuit which uses the amplifying tube or transistor efficiently and safely. Because of the similarity of their characteristics, pentodes† and transistors can be discussed concurrently. Let us first consider the permissible operating regions, see how operating point and load resistance are selected, derive expressions for power and efficiency, and then analyze a common type of audio-frequency amplifier that uses a power transistor.

Permissible Operating Region

An electronic amplifier must operate without introducing excessive distortion and without exceeding the voltage, current, and power limitations of the device. The permissible operating region can be indicated on the output characteristics of the device as in Fig. 11.11. Lines A represent the maximum allowable power dissipation for the devices; these are hyperbolas defined by $V_{CE}I_C = P_C$ or $V_bI_b = P_b$, where P_C and P_b are established by the manufacturer. Operation above this line may damage the device. Line B in Fig. 11.11a reflects the fact that at high collector voltages the avalanche effect causes a rapid increase in collector current and the curves become nonlinear. There is no such abrupt limit on pentode plate voltage.

For either transistor or pentode there are regions of excessive nonlinearity which should be avoided. Lines C bound the region in which collector or plate current is approaching zero and a further decrease in signal value (i_B or v_c) does not produce a corresponding decrease in output current. Lines D bound the region in which a further increase in signal does not produce a corresponding increase in output current. Line

---

† While triodes are satisfactory as low-distortion power amplifiers, pentodes are more efficient and for the same output power require less input voltage than triodes.

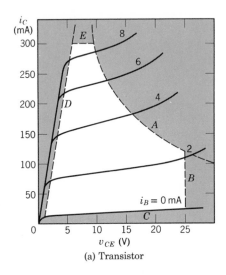

(a) Transistor

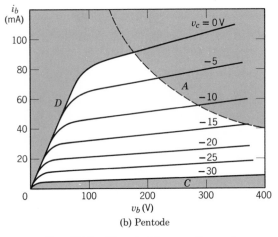

(b) Pentode

Fig. 11.11   Permissible operating regions.

E indicates an arbitrary limit within which the transistor manufacturer guarantees his specifications rather than a maximum allowable current. The upper limit for pentode current is the boundary of the negative grid region.

Operating Point and Load Line

The purpose of the biasing arrangement is to locate and maintain operation in the permissible region.   Within this limitation we wish to obtain maximum power output.   In general, the load line should lie below the maximum dissipation curve, and its slope (determined by the load resist-

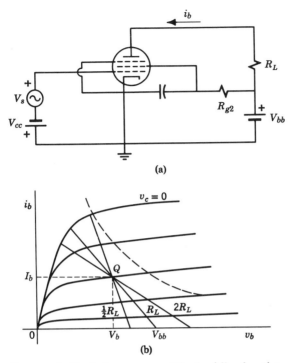

(a)

(b)

Fig. 11.12   Pentode power amplifier load-line location.

ance R_L) should reflect a compromise between large signals and low distortion.

The factors influencing the choice of load resistance are illustrated for the pentode in Fig. 11.12. The operating point shown allows a large swing in grid voltage without leaving the permissible operating region. Load resistance R_L results in a large plate current swing and large plate voltage swing. If a value of $\frac{1}{2}R_L$ is used, the plate current swing is slightly larger, but the voltage swing is much smaller. If a value of $2R_L$ is used, the plate voltage swing is increased but the current swing is decreased and the high-current end of the swing is in a region of increasing distortion. The load line for R_L (through the *knee* of the $v_c = 0$ curve) appears to be optimum; this choice can be checked by calculating power output and distortion for several values of R_L.

Transformer Coupling

As shown in Fig. 11.12, the supply battery voltage V_{bb} must exceed the average plate voltage V_b by the average voltage drop across the load resistor $I_b R_L$. The necessary supply voltage can be reduced and two

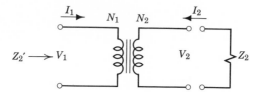

Fig. 11.13 An ideal transformer.

other benefits obtained by using a *transformer* to couple the output signal to the load.

A transformer (discussed in detail in Chapter 16) consists of two coils wound on a common magnetic core. A changing flux in the core induces voltages in the windings proportional to the number of turns. In an ideal transformer (closely approximated by a real transformer),

$$\frac{V_2}{V_1} = \frac{N_2}{N_1} \tag{11-19}$$

The current ratio can be predicted by noting that in an ideal transformer there is no power loss, and the power in must equal the power out. Therefore, a *step-down* in current must accompany a *step-up* in voltage or

$$\frac{I_2}{I_1} = \frac{V_1}{V_2} = \frac{N_1}{N_2} \tag{11-20}$$

If an impedance Z_2 is connected to the *secondary*, the impedance seen at the *primary* is, by Eqs. 11-19 and 11-20,

$$Z_2' = \frac{V_1}{I_1} = \frac{(N_1/N_2)V_2}{(N_2/N_1)I_2} = \left(\frac{N_1}{N_2}\right)^2 \frac{V_2}{I_2} = \left(\frac{N_1}{N_2}\right)^2 Z_2 \tag{11-21}$$

On the basis of this brief discussion, we can see three important advantages of the transformer as a coupling device in audio power amplifiers (see Fig. 11.14):

1. Only a changing flux induces voltage and, therefore, direct currents are not "transformed." The transformer passes on the a-c signal, but d-c supply currents are kept out of the load. Some devices would be damaged or their characteristics would be adversely affected by direct currents.

2. The resistance of the primary winding is low and, therefore, the d-c voltage drop across it is low. With transformer coupling, the supply voltage V_{bb} is approximately equal to V_b instead of $V_b + I_b R_L$.

3. The transformer transforms impedance and permits impedance matching for improved power transfer. By proper choice of the turns ratio, the low resistance of a loudspeaker can be made to appear to a tube or transistor as a much higher value.

To gain these benefits, the output of an audio power amplifier is usually coupled to the load by a transformer. The performance of a well-designed transformer approaches the ideal over the major part of the audible range, but the output falls off at very low and very high frequencies (see Fig. 16.19).

Power and Efficiency

The calculation of power and efficiency can be illustrated for the case of the simplified transformer-coupled transistor amplifier of Fig. 11.14. The choice of a load line for a transistor amplifier is based on considerations similar to those for the pentode. Once R_L' is selected, the turns ratio N_1/N_2 is selected to match the actual load resistance R_L.

Assuming a sinusoidal signal current in a resistive load, the amplitude of the sinusoid is just one-half the difference between the maximum and minimum values of current, and the rms value is

$$I_c = \frac{1}{2\sqrt{2}} (I_{max} - I_{min}) \tag{11-22}$$

The output power is

$$P_o = I_c^2 R_L' = V_c I_c = \frac{V_c^2}{R_L'} \tag{11-23}$$

where V_c is the rms value of the signal voltage across R_L'.

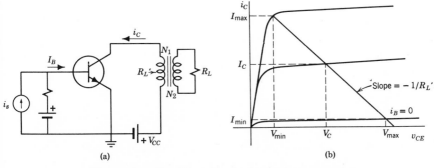

Fig. 11.14 Simplified circuit of transformer-coupled power amplifier.

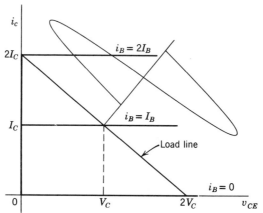

Fig. 11.15   Idealized current amplifier.

The average power supplied by the collector battery (R_E is to be small and is neglected for the moment) is

$$P_{CC} = V_{CC}I_C \cong V_C I_C \qquad (11\text{-}24)$$

with transformer coupling.   For sinusoidal signals, the average power dissipated in the transistor is

$$P_d = \frac{1}{2\pi} \int_0^{2\pi} v_{CE}i_C \, d(\omega t)$$

$$= \frac{1}{2\pi} \int_0^{2\pi} (V_C - \sqrt{2}\, V_c \cos \omega t)(I_C + \sqrt{2}\, I_c \cos \omega t) \, d(\omega t)$$

$$= V_C I_C - V_c I_c \qquad (11\text{-}25)$$

This interesting result indicates that the power dissipated is the difference between a constant input and a variable output.   The losses are low when the output is high, and the maximum power must be dissipated in the quiescent condition with no signal applied.

The efficiency of the output circuit (the collector circuit of a transistor or the plate circuit of a vacuum tube) is output over input or

$$\text{Efficiency} = \frac{P_o}{P_i} = \frac{V_c I_c}{V_C I_C} \qquad (11\text{-}26)$$

The theoretical limit for efficiency in this type of amplifier can be determined by considering the idealized current amplifier whose characteristics are shown in Fig. 11.15.   A signal of amplitude equal to I_B produces a total current swing from $2I_C$ to zero and a total voltage swing from $2V_C$ to zero. The ideal efficiency is

$$\frac{P_o}{P_i} = \frac{(V_C/\sqrt{2})(I_C/\sqrt{2})}{V_C I_C} \times 100 = 50\% \qquad (11\text{-}27)$$

At maximum signal input, the actual efficiency of transistor amplifiers is around 45%, pentode amplifiers 35%, and triode amplifiers 25%. (How is maximum efficiency related to the shape of the actual characteristic curves for these three devices?) The corresponding *average* efficiencies with variable signal inputs are usually much lower.

EXAMPLE 3

The audio amplifier of Fig. 11.16 employs the silicon power transistor whose characteristics are shown. The manufacturer specifies a maximum collector current of 1 A, maximum collector-emitter voltage of 50 V, and maximum power dissipation (with case held at 25°C) of 5 W. At the anticipated operating temperature, $\beta \cong 50$ and $I_{CO} = 250\ \mu A$; a stability factor of $S \cong 10$ should be satisfactory. The amplifier is to be designed for maximum power output to a load of 5 Ω; approximate results are satisfactory.

SOLUTION. The first step is to determine the operating point. The maximum dissipation line $i_C v_{CE} = 5$ W is sketched in as shown. The line for maximum power output will be tangent to the hyperbola and there is a range of slopes with nearly equal output powers. The high-voltage region is slightly more linear than the high-current region, so the full allowable voltage is used and the current is limited by dissipation. At $V_C = 50/2 = 25$ V and $I_C = 0.2$ A,

$$P_{CC} = V_C I_C = 25 \times 0.2 = 5 \text{ W}$$

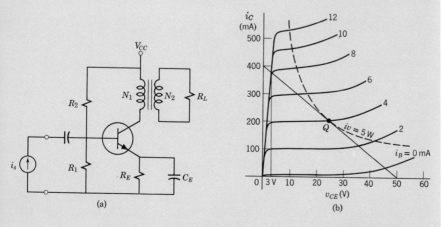

(a)

(b)

Fig. 11.16 Transistor power amplifier design.

and the corresponding load resistance is $2V_C/2I_C$ or

$$R_L' = \frac{V_C}{I_C} = \frac{25}{0.2} = 125 \ \Omega$$

To design the bias circuit by the approximate method, we assume a voltage $V_E = 3$ V and solve for the emitter resistance. By Eq. 11-13,

$$R_E \cong \frac{V_E}{I_C} = \frac{3}{0.2} = 15 \ \Omega$$

Then the necessary supply voltage is

$$V_{CC} = V_C + 3 = 25 + 3 = 28 \text{ V}$$

For a stability factor of approximately 10, we try $R_B = 12R_E$ and check. By Eq. 11-12,

$$S = \frac{\Delta I_C}{\Delta I_{CO}} = (1 + \beta) \frac{1}{1 + \beta(R_E/R_B)} = 51 \frac{1}{1 + 50(\frac{1}{12})} = 9.9 \cong 10$$

and we conclude that a value of $R_B = 12 \times 15 = 180 \cong 200 \ \Omega$ is satisfactory. Next, we read $I_B = 4$ mA, assume $V_{BE} = 0.6$ V for silicon, and by Eq. 11-17,

$$V_B = I_B R_B + V_{BE} + (I_B + I_C)R_E$$

$$= 0.004 \times 200 + 0.6 + (0.204)15 = 0.8 + 0.6 + 3.06 \cong 4.5 \text{ V}$$

To complete the bias design, by Eqs. 11-18,

$$R_2 = R_B \frac{V_{CC}}{V_B} = 200 \frac{28}{4.5} = 1250 \ \Omega$$

$$R_1 = \frac{R_B R_2}{R_2 - R_B} = \frac{200 \times 1250}{1250 - 200} \cong 240 \ \Omega$$

To determine the amplifier performance, we note that the load line intersects the $i_B = 8$ mA line at $V_{min} \cong 3$ V, and therefore the maximum undistorted voltage swing is $V_C - V_{min} = 25 - 3 = 22 \text{ V} = \sqrt{2} \ V_c$. The power output is

$$P_o = \frac{V_c^2}{R_L'} = \frac{(22/\sqrt{2})^2}{125} = 1.94 \text{ W}$$

Neglecting R_E, the collector circuit efficiency is

$$\frac{P_o}{P_{CC}} = \frac{1.94}{5} \times 100 \cong 39\%$$

If the emitter resistance loss is included, $V_{CC} = 28$ V and, assuming $I_E \cong I_C$, the efficiency is reduced to

$$\frac{P_o}{V_{CC}I_C} = \frac{1.94}{28 \times 0.2} \times 100 \cong 35\%$$

The desired transformer should match the 5-Ω load to the 125-Ω load line and a commercial unit would be so labeled. The turns ratio should be (by Eq. 11-21)

$$\frac{N_1}{N_2} = \sqrt{R_L'/R_L} = \sqrt{125/5} = 5$$

FREQUENCY RESPONSE OF SMALL-SIGNAL AMPLIFIERS

In a "small-signal" amplifier, the input signals are small in comparison to the d-c bias and the resulting output swings are small in comparison to the quiescent operating values of voltage and current. Under small-signal operation, bias is not critical and amplitude distortion is easily avoided. While graphical analysis is possible, the linear models developed in Chapter 10 are much more convenient to use.

We have already used the linear models to predict the performance of single-stage amplifiers at moderate frequencies. Now we are going to consider the effect of cascading several stages and investigate the gain of untuned amplifiers as a function of frequency. Pentodes and transistors with RC coupling (Fig. 11.6) are commonly employed for small-signal amplification in the frequency range from a few cycles per second to several megacycles and, therefore, they are emphasized in this discussion. While tubes and transistors operate on entirely different physical bases, their external behavior is quite similar and the same approach is used in predicting their frequency responses.

Frequency-Response Curve

The voltage gain of one stage of an RC-coupled amplifier is shown in Fig. 11.17. The gain is relatively constant over the *midfrequency range*, but falls off at lower frequencies and at higher frequencies. In ordinary amplifiers, the frequency response curve is symmetric if frequency is plotted on a logarithmic scale as shown. The *bandwidth* is defined by lower and upper *cutoff frequencies* or *half-power frequencies* f_1 and f_2, just

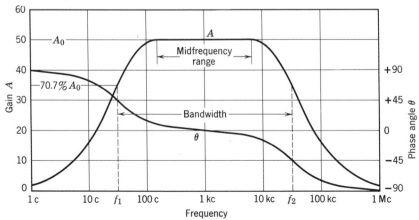

Fig. 11.17 Frequency response of RC-coupled single-stage amplifier.

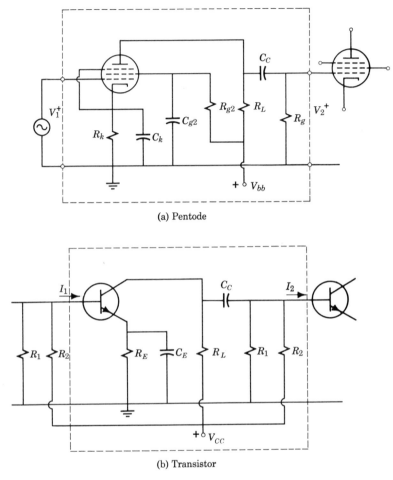

(a) Pentode

(b) Transistor

Fig. 11.18   Typical resistance-capacitance coupled amplifiers.

as in the frequency response of a resonant circuit.   At the half-power frequencies, the response is 70.7% of the midfrequency gain, or $A_1 = A_2 = A_0/\sqrt{2}$, and the phase angle $\theta = \pm 45°$.

The effect of circuit changes on frequency response can be determined experimentally.   If R_L in Fig. 11.18 is increased, the entire gain curve is raised.   (Would you have predicted this?)   If C_k is disconnected, the entire gain curve is lowered.   (Why?)   If C_C is doubled, the low-frequency response is improved.   (Is this to be expected?)   If a small capacitance is connected in parallel with R_L, the high-frequency response is adversely affected.   (Why?)   Our objective in this section is to develop methods for predicting quantitatively the effect of circuit parameters and device parameters on frequency response and the associated phase shift.

Small-Signal Amplifier Models

The expected input signals consist of sinusoids of various amplitudes and frequencies. Knowing the components of the input and the response of the amplifier, we can easily predict the output. Our approach is to replace the actual amplifier circuit by a linear model which responds in the same way to a-c signals. The tube or transistor is replaced by its linear model (see Figs. 10.24 and 10.25). It is presumed that the electronic device is operating at an appropriate point and the d-c bias voltages and currents are of no concern. We assume that bias resistors such as R_k and R_E are properly by-passed so they do not appear in the a-c model. Batteries are essentially short circuits to a-c signals, so they are omitted. On the other hand, unintentional elements such as interelectrode capacitances and wiring capacitances, which do not appear in the wiring diagram, must be shown in the amplifier model.

Application of this approach to one stage of the vacuum-tube amplifier of Fig. 11.18a results in the linear circuit model shown in Fig. 11.19a. C_{pk} is the plate-cathode interelectrode capacitance and C_w is the distributed wiring capacitance. Note that the input characteristics of the next tube affect the performance of this stage. Capacitance C_g represents the effective input capacitance; for a pentode this is primarily C_{gk} since C_{gp} is very small because of the shielding effect of the screen grid.

A similar approach to one stage of the transistor amplifier of Fig. 11.18b results in the model shown in Fig. 11.19b. It is assumed that h_{re} is negligibly small and $1/h_{oe}$ is shown as an output resistance (instead of h_{oe} as a

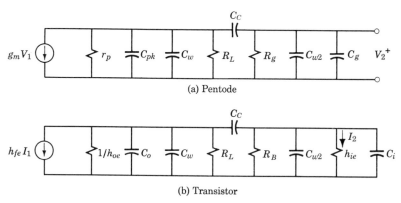

(a) Pentode

(b) Transistor

Fig. 11.19 Linear circuit models of RC-coupled amplifiers.

conductance). C_o is an effective output capacitance. Note that one stage of current amplification includes the input of the following transistor. R_B is the parallel equivalent of R_1 and R_2. C_i is an effective input capacitance representing the combination of junction capacitances and diffusion capacitance.

The determination of the values of individual elements in Fig. 11.19 is quite difficult; the specific values depend upon such factors as quiescent voltage and current, operating temperature, gain of the following stage, and configuration of the physical circuit. The important thing from our viewpoint here is that an actual amplifier can be replaced, insofar as small signals are concerned, by a linear circuit model which can be analyzed by methods we have already mastered. Fortunately, the models for tube and transistor are similar in form and the same analysis can be used for both.

The linear models of Fig. 11.19 hold fairly well for frequencies from a few cycles per second to several megacycles. It would be possible to perform a general analysis on the circuits as they stand, but it is much more convenient, and more instructive, to consider some simplifying approximations. We recall that for series and parallel combinations of resistance R and capacitance C,

$$Z_{\text{ser}} = \sqrt{R^2 + (1/\omega C)^2} = R\sqrt{1 + (1/\omega CR)^2}$$

$$Y_{\text{par}} = \sqrt{(1/R)^2 + (\omega C)^2} = \frac{1}{R}\sqrt{1 + (\omega CR)^2} = \frac{1}{Z_{\text{par}}} \quad (11\text{-}28)$$

If $\omega CR \geq 10$, $Z_{\text{ser}} \cong R$ within 0.5%; if $\omega CR \leq 1/10$, $Y_{\text{par}} \cong 1/R$ within 0.5% and $Z_{\text{par}} \cong R$. The fact that gain is independent of frequency over the midfrequency range (Fig. 11.17) indicates that there is a range of frequencies over which the capacitive effects are negligible. This is the case in practical amplifiers (see Exercise 18), and it leads to another important conclusion. Since ωC increases with frequency, series capacitances become important only at frequencies lower than the midfrequencies and parallel capacitances become important only at frequencies higher than the midfrequencies. This means that the frequency response of an RC amplifier can be divided into three regions. In the midfrequency range, the capacitances can be neglected. In the low-frequency range, the series capacitance C_C must be considered. In the high-frequency range, the parallel capacitances must be considered.

Midfrequency Gain

For frequencies around $\omega = 10^4$ rad/sec ($f = 1590$ cps), the linear circuit models of Fig. 11.19 can be replaced by the purely resistive circuits

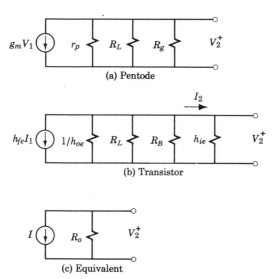

(a) Pentode

(b) Transistor

(c) Equivalent

Fig. 11.20 Midfrequency linear circuit model.

of Fig. 11.20a and b. In each case the parallel resistance can be combined into an equivalent resistance R_o and the output voltage is simply $\mathbf{V}_2 = -\mathbf{I}R_o$.

Pentode. For the pentode, $I = g_m V_1$, R_o is the parallel equivalent of r_p, R_L, and R_g, and the output voltage is

$$\mathbf{V}_2 = -\mathbf{I}R_o = -g_m \mathbf{V}_1 R_o$$

The *midfrequency voltage gain* is

$$\mathbf{A}_{vo} = \frac{\mathbf{V}_2}{\mathbf{V}_1} = -g_m R_o = -\mu \frac{R_o}{r_p} \tag{11-29}$$

since $g_m = \mu/r_p$. Note that R_o is determined in part by r_p and is always less than r_p. Therefore, A_{vo} (a real number) is always less than μ.

Transistor. For the common-emitter transistor, $I = h_{fe} I_1$, R_o is the parallel equivalent of $1/h_{oe}$, R_L, R_B, and h_{ie}, and the output voltage is

$$\mathbf{V}_2 = -h_{fe} \mathbf{I}_1 R_o$$

Since $\mathbf{I}_2 = \mathbf{V}_2/h_{ie}$, the *midfrequency current gain* is

$$\mathbf{A}_{io} = \frac{\mathbf{I}_2}{\mathbf{I}_1} = -h_{fe} \frac{R_o}{h_{ie}} \tag{11-30}$$

Note that R_o is determined in part by h_{ie} and is always less than h_{ie}. Therefore A_{io} is always less than h_{fe}.

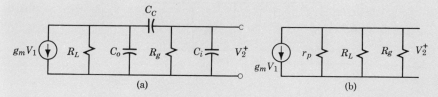

Fig. 11.21   Example 4.

EXAMPLE 4

A pentode with $g_m = 2100$ $\mu\mho$ and $r_p = 1$ MΩ is used in an R-C coupled amplifier with $R_L = 25$ kΩ and $C_C = 0.05$ μF.   The combined output capacitance (interelectrode and wiring) is estimated to be 100 pF.   The combined input capacitance (wiring and interelectrode) is estimated to be 100 pF.   If $R_g = 1$ MΩ, predict the voltage gain at 2000 cps.

SOLUTION.   The circuit model is shown in Fig. 11.21a with r_p neglected in comparison to R_L as a first approximation.   At

$$\omega = 2\pi f = 2\pi \times 2000 = 4000\pi \text{ rad/sec},$$

$$\frac{1}{\omega C_o} = \frac{1}{\omega C_i} = \frac{1}{4000\pi \times 10^{-10}} \cong 800 \text{ k}\Omega$$

$$\frac{1}{\omega C_C} = \frac{1}{4000\pi \times 5 \times 10^{-8}} \cong 1.6\text{k}\Omega$$

By inspection, C_C is effectively in series with R_g and the reactance of C_C is negligibly small compared to the resistance of R_g.   With C_C omitted, the reactances of C_o and C_i are effectively in parallel with the very much smaller R_L and they can be neglected (Fig. 11.21b).   In other words, 2000 cps is in the "mid-frequency" range of this amplifier,

$$\frac{1}{R_o} = \frac{1}{r_p} + \frac{1}{R_L} + \frac{1}{R_g} = \left(\frac{1}{1} + \frac{40}{1} + \frac{1}{1}\right) \times 10^{-6} = 42 \times 10^{-6} \mho$$

and, by Eq. 11-29,

$$A_o = -g_m R_o = -2100 \times 10^{-6} \times \frac{1}{42 \times 10^{-6}} = -50$$

Low-Frequency Response

Below the mid-frequencies, the susceptances of the parallel capacitances are negligibly small, but the reactance of the coupling capacitance C_C becomes increasingly important.   If R_l is the equivalent of the parallel resistances to the *left* of C_C (in Fig. 11.19) and R_r the equivalent of the parallel resistances to the *right* of C_C, the low-frequency circuit for tube or transistor becomes as shown in Fig. 11.22a.   By Thévenin's theorem, the

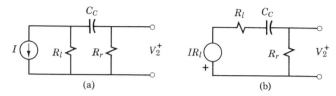

Fig. 11.22 Low-frequency linear circuit model.

parallel combination of source I and resistance R_l can be transformed into the more convenient form of Fig. 11.22b.

Pentode. If R_o is the equivalent of R_l and R_r in parallel (as before) and R_1 the equivalent of R_l and R_r in series, the output voltage for the pentode is

$$\mathbf{V}_2 = -\frac{IR_lR_r}{(R_l + R_r) + 1/j\omega C_C} = -g_m\mathbf{V}_1 R_o \frac{1}{1 - j(1/\omega C_C R_1)}$$

The *low-frequency voltage gain* is

$$\mathbf{A}_{vl} = A_{vo}\frac{1}{1 - j(1/\omega C_C R_1)} \tag{11-31}$$

In words, the low-frequency gain is related to the midfrequency gain by a complex factor dependent upon frequency and an RC product. As frequency is decreased, an increasing fraction of the developed voltage IR_l appears across C_C and the voltage available at the output is reduced.

Transistor. Using the same definitions of R_o and R_1, we can express the output voltage for the transistor as

$$\mathbf{V}_2 = -\frac{h_{fe}\mathbf{I}_1 R_l R_r}{(R_l + R_r) + 1/j\omega C_C} = -h_{fe}\mathbf{I}_1 R_o \frac{1}{1 - j(1/\omega C_C R_1)}$$

Since $\mathbf{I}_2 = \mathbf{V}_2/h_{ie}$, the *low-frequency current gain* is

$$\mathbf{A}_{il} = A_{io}\frac{1}{1 - j(1/\omega C_C R_1)} \tag{11-32}$$

Comparing Eqs. 11-31 and 11-32, we see that transistor current gain and pentode voltage gain at low frequencies are related to the corresponding midfrequency gains by the same complex factor. In general, we can write

$$\frac{\mathbf{A}_l}{A_o} = \frac{\mathbf{A}_{vl}}{A_{vo}} = \frac{\mathbf{A}_{il}}{A_{io}} = \frac{1}{1 - j(1/\omega C_C R_1)} \tag{11-33}$$

where $\mathbf{A}_l/A_o$ is the *relative gain* at low frequencies.

By definition the lower half-power or cutoff frequency is the frequency at which the relative gain is 70.7 %. This occurs at the frequency

$$\omega_1 = 2\pi f_1 = \frac{1}{C_C R_1} \tag{11-34}$$

since for $\omega = \omega_1$, $1/\omega C_C R_1 = 1$ and

$$\frac{A_1}{A_o} = \frac{1}{1 - j1} = 0.707 \underline{/+45^\circ} \tag{11-35}$$

Note that the cutoff frequency is just a convenient measure of the low-frequency response of the amplifier and does not imply that no amplification occurs below this frequency. A more general expression can be written in terms of dimensionless ratios. When the expression for ω_1 is substituted, Eq. 11-33 becomes

$$\frac{A_l}{A_o} = \frac{1}{1 - j(\omega_1/\omega)} = \frac{1}{1 - j(f_1/f)} \tag{11-36}$$

indicating that every elementary RC-coupled amplifier has the same characteristic low-frequency response. It would be nice if we could obtain a similar expression which adequately describes the high-frequency response of RC-coupled amplifiers.

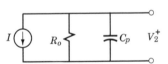

Fig. 11.23 High-frequency linear circuit model.

High-Frequency Response

Above the mid-frequencies, the reactance of C_C is negligibly small, but the susceptances of the parallel capacitances become increasingly important. With C_C considered as a short circuit, all the elements are in parallel and the high-frequency approximation of the circuit model of Fig. 11.19 becomes the simple circuit of Fig. 11.23.

Pentode. For the pentode the output voltage developed across the parallel combination of R_o and C_p is

$$V_2 = -I \frac{R_o(1/j\omega C_p)}{R_o + 1/j\omega C_p} = -g_m V_1 \frac{R_o}{R_o(j\omega C_p) + 1}$$

In terms of the midfrequency gain A_o, the *high-frequency* voltage gain is

$$A_{vh} = A_{vo} \frac{1}{1 + j\omega C_p R_o} \tag{11-37}$$

The high-frequency gain is also related to A_o by a complex factor dependent on frequency and an RC product. As frequency increases, an increasing fraction of the developed current I flows through the shunting capacitance C_p and the output voltage is reduced.

The relative gain at high frequencies is

$$\frac{\mathbf{A}_h}{A_o} = \frac{1}{1 + j\omega C_p R_o} \tag{11-38}$$

By definition the upper cutoff frequency ω_2 is the frequency at which the relative gain is 70.7%. Therefore,

$$\omega_2 = 2\pi f_2 = \frac{1}{C_p R_o} \tag{11-39}$$

since for $\omega = \omega_2$, $\omega C_p R_o = 1$ and

$$\frac{\mathbf{A}_2}{A_o} = \frac{1}{1 + j1} = 0.707 \underline{/-45°} \tag{11-40}$$

When the expression for ω_2 is substituted, Eq. 11-38 becomes

$$\frac{\mathbf{A}_h}{A_o} = \frac{1}{1 + j(\omega/\omega_2)} = \frac{1}{1 + j(f/f_2)} \tag{11-41}$$

Transistor. The analysis of the high-frequency response of transistor amplifiers is complicated by the fact that h_{fe} is itself frequency dependent. The *lumped* circuit model of Fig. 11.19b is only an approximation of an effect which is, in fact, *distributed* throughout a finite region in the transistor. Finite times are required for signals in the form of changes in charge density to be propagated across the base. At low and medium frequencies, the collector current variation i_c is proportional to the emitter current variation i_e. At higher frequencies, $\alpha = -i_c/i_e$ begins to decrease in magnitude and a phase lag appears. It is customary to define an *alpha cutoff* frequency f_α at which α is equal to 70.7% of its low-frequency value.

Since $\beta = h_{fe}$ is a function of alpha, there is also a *beta cutoff* frequency f_β, and in the common-emitter configuration the significant relation between current phasors is

$$\frac{\mathbf{I}_c}{\mathbf{I}_b} = \frac{\beta}{1 + j(\omega/\omega_\beta)} = \frac{\beta}{1 + j(f/f_\beta)} \tag{11-42}$$

For alloy-junction transistors used in audio amplifiers, this effect may become important at 10 to 20 kilocycles. For special high-frequency mesa and planar transistors, the effect may be unimportant up to several megacycles. The physical parameters which govern the high-frequency characteristics of solid-state devices are of great importance to transistor designers. From our standpoint as amplifier users, however, the important fact is that the high-frequency gain characteristics of transistor amplifiers also can be described by Eq. 11-41.

EXAMPLE 5

One stage of an amplifier (Fig. 11.24a) consists of a transistor ($h_{fe} = 60$, $h_{oe} = 1.5 \times 10^{-5}$ ℧, $h_{ie} = 2$ kΩ, $h_{re} \cong 0$, $f_\beta = 2$ Mc) biased with $R_B = 5$ kΩ and $R_E = 500$ Ω. The total effective parallel capacitance for the transistor and circuit is estimated to be 800 pF.

(a) Specify the approximate value of R_L to put the upper cutoff frequency f_2 at 200 kc.

(b) Predict the midfrequency current gain with the R_L specified.

(c) Specify the approximate values of C_C and C_E to put the lower cutoff frequency f_1 at 100 cps.

SOLUTION. (a) Since the beta cutoff is well above the upper frequency specified, we assume that the circuit model of Fig. 11.24b is applicable. C_p is estimated at 800 pF and, therefore, by Eq. 11-39,

$$R_o = \frac{1}{2\pi f_2 C_p} = \frac{1}{2\pi \times 200 \times 10^3 \times 8 \times 10^{-10}} = 995 \ \Omega \cong 1 \ \text{k}\Omega$$

But

$$\frac{1}{R_o} = 10^{-3} \ \text{℧} = \frac{1}{R_L} + h_{oe} + \frac{1}{R_B} + \frac{1}{h_{ie}} = \frac{1}{R_L} + (0.15 + 2 + 5) \times 10^{-4} \ \text{℧}$$

and solution of this equation yields

$$R_L \cong 3.5 \ \text{k}\Omega$$

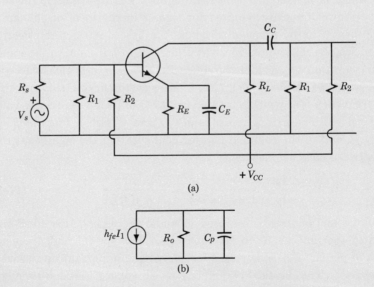

(a)

(b)

Fig. 11.24   Transistor RC amplifier and high-frequency model.

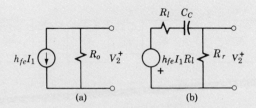

Fig. 11.25 Midfrequency and low-frequency models.

(b) The midfrequency current gain is, by Eq. 11-30,

$$A_o = -h_{fe} \frac{R_o}{h_{ie}} = -60 \frac{10^3}{2 \times 10^3} = -30$$

(c) In the low-frequency model of Fig. 11.25b,

$$R_l = \frac{R_L/h_o}{R_L + 1/h_o} = \frac{3.5 \times 1/0.015}{3.5 + 1/0.015} = 3.32 \text{ k}\Omega$$

$$R_r = \frac{R_B h_{ie}}{R_B + h_{ie}} = \frac{5 \times 2}{5 + 2} = 1.43 \text{ k}\Omega$$

and

$$R_1 = R_l + R_r = 3.32 + 1.43 = 4.75 \text{ k}\Omega$$

Hence, by Eq. 11-34,

$$C_C = \frac{1}{2\pi f_1 R_1} = \frac{1}{2\pi \times 100 \times 4.75 \times 10^3} = 0.33 \ \mu\text{F}$$

This calculation is based on the assumption that R_E is adequately by-passed by C_E. An accurate analysis of the effect of C_E is not justified here; an approximate formula† indicates that $1/\omega_1 C_E$ should be less than $R_s/(1 + h_{fe})$ where R_s is the impedance of the source for this stage. If R_s is around 2000 Ω, this indicates that C_E should be greater than

$$C_E = \frac{1 + h_{fe}}{2\pi f_1 R_s} = \frac{61}{2\pi \times 100 \times 2000} \cong 50 \ \mu\text{F}$$

Tiny capacitors rated at 50 μF and 6 V are frequently used for C_E in audio amplifiers.

MULTISTAGE UNTUNED AMPLIFIERS

To amplify the signal from a strain gage or a microphone to a power level which is adequate to drive a recorder or a loudspeaker usually

---

† General Electric Transistor Manual, p. 113, 1962.

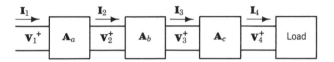

Fig. 11.26   Block diagram of amplifiers in cascade.

requires several stages of amplification.   If the final power amplifier is a vacuum tube, appreciable voltage is required to provide the necessary grid swing, and several stages of voltage amplification may be necessary. If the final amplifier is a transistor, appreciable driving current is needed and several stages of current amplification may be required.

Cascading

The stages are usually connected in cascade; the output of one stage is connected to the input of the next.   By defining a single stage to include the input characteristics of the next amplifying element, as we have, the combined effect of cascaded stages is easy to predict.   In Fig. 11.26, the individual stages are represented by rectangular blocks labelled with the individual voltage gains.   The overall voltage gain is

$$A = \frac{\mathbf{V}_4}{\mathbf{V}_1} = \frac{\mathbf{V}_2}{\mathbf{V}_1}\frac{\mathbf{V}_3}{\mathbf{V}_2}\frac{\mathbf{V}_4}{\mathbf{V}_3} = \mathbf{A}_a\mathbf{A}_b\mathbf{A}_c \tag{11-43}$$

or

$$A\ \underline{/\theta} = A_aA_bA_c\ \underline{/\theta_a + \theta_b + \theta_c} \tag{11-44}$$

In words, the overall voltage gain is the product of the gain amplitudes and the sum of the phase shifts; both A and θ are functions of frequency. A similar statement would describe the overall current gain.†

Gain in Decibels

The calculation of overall gain in multistage amplifiers or control systems is simplified by using a logarithmic unit.   By definition, the power gain in bels (named in honor of Alexander Graham Bell) is the logarithm to the base 10 of the power ratio.   A more convenient unit is the *decibel*

---

† It should be pointed out that in precise calculations the interaction between output and input makes it necessary to consider all stages simultaneously.   The load on stage c influences the input impedance to c which in turn determines the output impedance of stage b, etc.   By neglecting h_{re}, for example, we have avoided this difficulty but sacrificed precision.

where

$$\text{Gain in db} = \text{db} = 10 \log \frac{P_2}{P_1} \tag{11-45}$$

Since for a given resistance, power is proportional to the square of the voltage,

$$\text{Gain in db} = 10 \log \frac{V_2{}^2}{V_1{}^2} = 20 \log \frac{V_2}{V_1} \tag{11-46}$$

In general, the input and output resistances of an amplifier are not equal. However, the decibel is such a convenient measure that it is used as a unit of voltage (or current) gain, regardless of the associated resistances.

EXAMPLE 6

Express in db the relative gain of a transistor amplifier at the lower cutoff frequency.

SOLUTION. At f_1 the output voltage is 0.707 of the midfrequency value. Therefore,

$$\text{Relative gain in db} = 20 \log \frac{V_1}{V_0} = 20 \log 0.707 \cong -3 \text{ db}$$

Alternatively, this is a half-power frequency. Therefore,

$$\text{Relative gain in db} = 10 \log \frac{P_1}{P_0} = 10 \log 0.5 \cong -3 \text{ db}$$

The gain is said to be "down 3 db" at the cutoff frequencies.

One advantage of the decibel unit is that when response is plotted in db the overall response curves of a multistage amplifier can be obtained by adding the individual response curves. In Fig. 11.27, the response

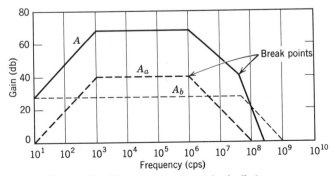

Fig. 11.27 Frequency-response in decibels.

curves for two stages a and b are plotted in db. Equations 11-36 and 11-41 indicate that for $f \ll f_1$ relative gain is proportional to frequency, and for $f \gg f_2$ relative gain is inversely proportional to frequency. On log-log scales, these relations are straight lines and the response of an RC-coupled amplifier can be approximated by curve A_a. (Actually, the gain is down 3 db at the *break points*.) A second amplifier with better low-frequency response is approximated by curve A_b. The overall gain of the combination is the sum of the two curves, and the straight-line approximation is easily drawn.

Gain-Bandwidth Product

The bandwidth of an amplifier is defined as $B = \omega_2 - \omega_1 \cong \omega_2$ since ω_1 is usually so small compared to ω_2. To increase bandwidth for a given parallel capacitance C_p, Eq. 11-39 indicates that the equivalent output resistance R_o must be reduced. But reducing R_o reduces the midfrequency gain (Eq. 11-29). For a pentode, the product of gain magnitude and bandwidth is

$$A_o\omega_2 = g_m R_o \frac{1}{R_o C_p} = \frac{g_m}{C_p} \tag{11-47}$$

Since C_p is primarily interelectrode capacitance and g_m is a tube parameter, the gain-bandwidth product is a constant for a specific tube. For a 6AU6 with $g_m = 5200 \ \mu\mho$ and $C_p \cong 11 \ \text{pF}, g_m/C_p \cong 480 \times 10^6 \ \text{rad/sec} \cong$ 75 Mc. With this tube a gain of 30 permits a 2.5-Mc bandwidth; if a bandwidth of 5 Mc is required, the maximum gain possible is 15.

A transistor has a similar *figure of merit*, but it is usually expressed in a different way. If the high-frequency response is limited by the beta cutoff, the bandwidth is approximately f_β and the maximum possible gain is β, so the gain-bandwidth product is

$$A_o f_2 \leq \beta f_\beta \cong \alpha f_\alpha = f_T \tag{11-48}$$

The quantity f_T is usually specified by the manufacturer and typically ranges from 50 kc for alloy-junction power transistors to 1000 Mc for high-frequency transistors.

EXAMPLE 7

The specifications for a certain germanium grown transistor indicate a minimum h_{fe} of 40 and a typical f_T of 8 Mc. Is this transistor suitable as a radio-frequency amplifier at 1 Mc?

SOLUTION. By Eq. 11-48,

$$f_\beta = \frac{f_T}{\beta} = \frac{f_T}{h_{fe}} = \frac{8 \text{ Mc}}{40} = 0.2 \text{ Mc}$$

While some current gain is possible at 1 Mc, the beta cutoff is only 0.2 Mc and another transistor should be selected.

OTHER TYPES OF AMPLIFIERS

The emphasis in this chapter is on untuned linear amplifiers. Some special forms of these amplifiers and some different types of amplifiers deserve mention.

Push-Pull Amplifiers

Much of the distortion introduced in large-signal amplifiers can be eliminated by using two tubes or transistors in the *push-pull* circuit of Fig. 11.28. The input transformer T_1 receives a sinusoidal voltage from a low-level source. The signals applied to the two grids are 180° out of phase, and the resulting plate currents are 180° out of phase. The output transformer T_2 delivers to the load a current which is proportional to the difference of the two plate currents. If the dynamic characteristics of the two tubes are identical, the even-harmonic distortion components just cancel and the only distortion is that due to odd harmonics. Also the performance of transformer T_2 (a critical component) is improved because the d-c components of i_{b1} and i_{b2} just cancel and magnetic core saturation and the accompanying nonlinearity are avoided.

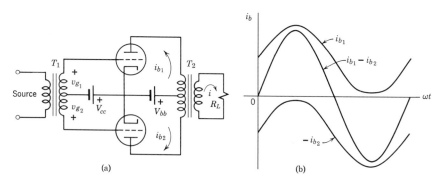

Fig. 11.28 Basic push-pull amplifier circuit.

Tuned Amplifiers

The gain of a tube or transistor amplifier depends on the load imped-ance. If a high-Q parallel resonant circuit is used for the load (Fig. 11.29), a very high resistance is presented at the resonant frequency and, therefore, the voltage gain is high. The frequency response curve has the same shape as that of the resonant circuit. A narrow band of fre-quencies near resonance is amplified well, but signals removed from the resonant frequency are discriminated against.

The high selectivity of the load impedance eliminates nonlinear dis-tortion; any harmonics in the input signal or in the collector current itself develop little voltage across the load impedance. As long as the col-lector current has a component at the resonant frequency, the output is nearly sinusoidal. High efficiency, without distortion, is achieved by operating the transistor in a nonlinear region.

Class B and C Operation

If corresponding values of v_c and i_b are obtained from the load line of Fig. 11.12b and plotted as in Fig. 11.30, the transfer characteristic is

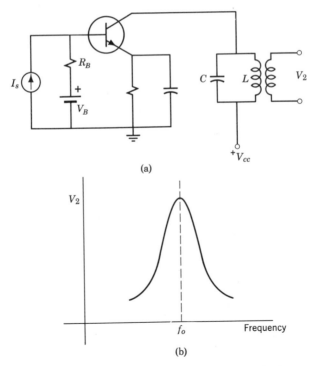

(a)

(b)

Fig. 11.29 Transistor tuned amplifier and frequency response.

obtained. For distortion-free operation of untuned amplifiers the operating point is placed in the center of the linear part of the transfer characteristic and output current flows throughout the input-signal cycle. This is called *class A* operation and results in low distortion and also low efficiency because of the high value of I_b with respect to the output signal current.

If the amplifier is biased to cutoff, output current flows only during the positive half-cycle and the output is badly distorted. The resulting *class B* operation is useful in a push-pull circuit. The second tube supplies the other half-cycle of output current and the even harmonic distortion is cancelled. The average value of plate current is much lower and, therefore, the d-c power input is less and the efficiency is higher.

If the amplifier is biased beyond cutoff, output current flows during only a small part of the cycle. With *class C* operation, the output is highly distorted, but with a tuned load impedance this presents no prob-

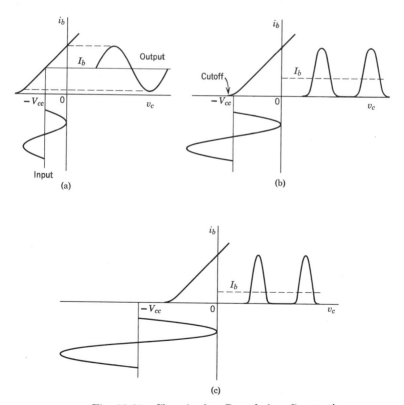

Fig. 11.30 Class A, class B, and class C operation.

lem.   The tuned circuit selects the fundamental component of the signal and rejects all others.   A sinusoidal output is obtained and the efficiency is high because the average plate current is relatively low.

SUMMARY

♦   An amplifier is a device for raising the level of a signal voltage, current, or power.   For sinusoidal signals, the voltage gain is

$$A = \frac{V_{out}}{V_{in}} = Ae^{j\theta}$$

If A and θ are constant (or if $\theta = k\omega$), and if $V_{out} = AV_{in}$, the amplification is linear and there is no distortion.

♦   In practical amplifiers, power supplies and biasing networks must maintain operation at the proper point, coupling circuits must transfer signals from one stage to the next without excessive discrimination, load impedances must provide desired output without requiring excessive supply voltages, and the effect of unintentional elements must be taken into account.

♦   For a vacuum tube, self-adjusting bias is provided by cathode current flowing through a cathode resistor effectively by-passed.

♦   For a transistor, the biasing circuit must maintain the operating point despite variations in temperature and device parameters; a combination of emitter resistor (effectively by-passed) and voltage divider works satisfactorily.
    The factor $S = \Delta I_C/\Delta I_{CO}$ is a useful measure of stability.
    For noncritical design, an approximate bias procedure is available.

♦   The permissible operating region of a tube or transistor is defined by maximum allowable current, voltage, power, and distortion.
    For large-signal class A operation, the midpoint of a properly located load line is the optimum quiescent point.
    Transformer coupling reduces the required supply voltage, isolates the signal output, and permits impedance matching.

♦   In an idealized transformer-coupled, class A current amplifier:
    Input power (d-c) $= P_i = V_{CC}I_C = V_CI_C$

    Output power (max) $= P_o = V_cI_c = \frac{1}{2}V_CI_C$

    Efficiency (max) $= \dfrac{P_o}{P_i} = \dfrac{V_cI_c}{V_CI_C} = 50\%$

◆ Linear models are used to predict the performance of amplifiers in which signals are much smaller than bias values.

◆ For one stage of R-C coupled voltage (or current) amplification,
Midfrequency gain is $\qquad A_o = -g_m R_o \qquad$ (or $-h_{fe} R_o / h_{ie}$)

Low-frequency response is $\mathbf{A}_l = A_o \dfrac{1}{1 - j(\omega_1/\omega)}$

High-frequency response is $\mathbf{A}_h = A_o \dfrac{1}{1 + j(\omega/\omega_2)}$

Bandwidth is $\qquad B = \omega_2 - \omega_1 = \dfrac{1}{C_p R_o} - \dfrac{1}{C_C R_1}$

◆ The frequency-response curves of all RC-coupled amplifiers are similar in shape. In transistor amplifiers the high-frequency response may be governed by the reduction in β ($= h_{fe}$).

◆ For two stages of amplification in cascade, the overall gain is

$$A \underline{/\theta} = A_1 A_2 \underline{/\theta_1 + \theta_2}$$

Gain in db $= 10 \log (P_2/P_1)$ or $20 \log (V_2/V_1)$.

◆ The gain-bandwidth product is a measure of amplifier capability.
Pentode: $A_o \omega_2 \le g_m/C_p \qquad$ Transistor: $A_o \omega_2 \le \beta f_\beta \cong \alpha f_\alpha = f_T$

◆ The push-pull amplifier reduces distortion for a given output and improves the operation of output transformers.

◆ The tuned amplifier uses a resonant load circuit to obtain high selectivity and low distortion.

◆ Class B and C amplifiers operate efficiently because output current is cut off during ineffective parts of the signal cycle.

REVIEW QUESTIONS

1. Distinguish between tuned and wide-band amplifiers and give an application of each (other than those in the text).
2. Distinguish between frequency, phase, and amplitude distortion. Explain the effect of each in a hi-fi system.
3. What determines the dynamic range of an amplifier?
4. What is the purpose of biasing in a tube? In a transistor?
5. What are the relative merits of RC and transformer coupling?
6. Explain the practical considerations involved in the selection of values for: R_g, R_L, R_k, C_k, R_{g2}, and C_C.
7. What are the advantages of cathode resistor bias over battery bias?
8. Why is fixed-current transistor bias unsatisfactory?
9. Explain thermal runaway.

10. Explain the function of each circuit element in Fig. 11.31.

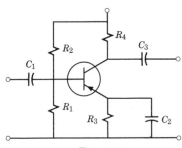
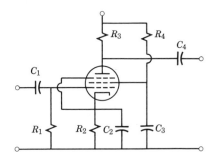

Fig. 11.31   Fig. 11.32

11. Explain the function of each circuit element in Fig. 11.32.
12. Define the stability factor and explain its use.
13. What are the practical limits on R_1 and R_3 in Fig. 11.31?
14. How are the quiescent point and load line related to the permissible operating region?
15. Sketch a set of transistor characteristics and indicate regions of high amplitude distortion.
16. Explain the statement: "A power transistor runs cool when the power output is high."
17. Why is the maximum efficiency expected from a class A triode amplifier less than that from a pentode?
18. What determines whether a signal is "small" or "large"?
19. Why are pentodes preferred over triodes for wide-band amplifiers?
20. Distinguish between mid-frequency range and bandwidth.
21. In Fig. 11.18, explain the effects of eliminating C_k and halving C_C.
22. Draw a wiring diagram of one-stage of an RC-coupled triode amplifier and draw a linear circuit model which is valid for frequencies from 20 cps to 200 kc.
23. For the circuit model of the preceding question, state reasonable assumptions and derive circuit models valid for low, medium, and high frequencies.
24. Define in words and in symbols the cutoff frequencies.
25. What limits the low-frequency response of a pentode? Of a transistor?
26. What limits the high-frequency response of a pentode? Of a transistor?
27. Why is emphasis placed on voltage gain of a pentode amplifier and current gain of a transistor amplifier?
28. Compare pentode and transistor amplifiers on the following characteristics: input impedance, voltage gain, current gain, and maximum efficiency.
29. What is meant by "cascading"? Where is it used?
30. What are the advantages of the decibel as a unit?
31. Define the "gain-bandwidth product." Why is it useful?
32. Explain how push-pull amplifiers work. Where are they used?
33. How are "tuned amplifiers" tuned? Where are they used?
34. Explain why class B operation is more efficient than class A.

EXERCISES

1. One triode unit of a 12AX7 (Fig. A.2) is to be operated in the circuit of Fig. 11.5b. For $V_{bb} = 400$ V, $V_{cc} = 1.5$ V, and $R_L = 200$ kΩ, specify R_k.

2. One triode unit of a 12AX7 is operated in the circuit of Fig. 11.5b with $V_{bb} = 300$ V, $R_L = 100$ kΩ, and $R_k = 1$ kΩ. Locate the quiescent point.

3. If the signal voltage across R_k in Exercise 2 is to be less than 0.1 V for a signal current of 1 mA at 60 cps, specify C_k.

4. A 6AU6-A pentode (Fig. A.3) is to be operated in the circuit of Fig. 11.6 with $V_{bb} = 400$ V, $V_{c2} = 150$ V, $V_{c1} = -2$ V, and $R_L = 25$ kΩ. Specify R_k and R_{g2}.

5. A 6AU6-A pentode (Fig. A.3) is to be operated in the circuit of Fig. 11.6 with $V_{bb} = 400$ V, $V_{c2} = 150$ V, $R_L = 50$ kΩ, and $R_k = 700$ Ω. Locate the operating point and specify R_{g2}.

6. A certain germanium transistor with $I_{CO} = 6$ μA and β ranging from 100 to 300 is operated in the circuit of Fig. 11.7 with $I_B = 100$ μA.

   (a) Calculate the range of values of I_C expected.

   (b) If $\beta = 200$ and if I_{CO} quadruples as a result of temperature increase, calculate the change in I_C expected.

7. A certain silicon transistor with $I_{CO} = 1$ μA and β ranging from 20 to 50 is operated in the circuit of Fig. 11.7 with $I_B = 30$ μA.

   (a) Calculate the range of values of I_C expected.

   (b) If $\beta = 30$ and if I_{CO} quadruples as a result of temperature increase, predict the change in I_C.

8. The transistor of Exercise 6 is operated in the self-biasing circuit of Fig. 11.9 with $V_B = 6$ V, $R_B = 10$ kΩ, and $R_E = 500$ Ω. Predict the variation in I_C expected under the conditions of parts (a) and (b) of Exercise 6.

9. The transistor of Exercise 7 is operated in the self-biasing circuit of Fig. 11.9 with $V_B = 4$ V, $R_B = 30$ kΩ, and $R_E = 3$ kΩ. Predict the variation in I_C expected under the conditions of parts (a) and (b) of Exercise 7.

10. A 6AQ5-A pentode (Fig. A.5) is to be operated at a quiescent point defined by $V_c = -15$ V and $V_b = 250$ V ($V_{c2} = 250$ V). For the circuit of Fig. 11.12a and a load resistance of 5 kΩ, estimate the power input, the maximum power output, and the efficiency.

11. Repeat Exercise 10, using transformer coupling to the load. If the load is 50 Ω, specify the transformer turns ratio.

12. The transistor of Fig. 11.16 is to be operated with $V_{CE} = 20$ V and power dissipation limited to 3 W (maximum $V_{CE} = 50$ V).

   (a) Determine the nominal I_B and a suitable R_L' for maximum power output.

   (b) Calculate power in, maximum power out, and efficiency.

13. The permissible operating region of a power transistor is defined by $P_d = 5$ W, $I_C(\text{max}) = 1$ A, $V_{CE}(\text{max}) = 100$ V and $V_{CE}(\text{min}) = 2$ V.

   (a) Sketch the transistor characteristics.

   (b) Select quiescent points for $R_L' = 250$ Ω, 500 Ω, and 1000 Ω.

   (c) Recommend one of the values of R_L', explaining your reasoning.

14. The permissible operating region of a transistor is defined by $P_d = 2$ W, $I_C(\text{max}) = 1$ A, $V_{CE}(\text{max}) = 60$ V, and $V_{CE}(\text{min}) = 2$ V.

   (a) Sketch the transistor characteristics and select a quiescent point.

   (b) Select an R_L' for nearly maximum power output.

(c) Calculate power in, maximum power out, and efficiency.

(d) Assuming $\beta = 50$, what input signal current is required?

15. For a sinusoidal input signal of 15 V amplitude, plot to scale the output voltage of the amplifier of Exercise 10. Superimpose a sinusoid of the same peak-to-peak value and identify the character of any distortion present.

16. A 6L6-GC beam power pentode (Fig. A.6) is operated as a transformer-coupled amplifier with a quiescent point at $V_{c1} = -14$ V, $V_{c2} = 250$ V, and $V_b = 250$ V.

(a) For a load resistance of 2500 Ω, calculate the power in.

(b) Assuming Eq. 11.22 applies here also, estimate maximum power out and efficiency.

17. One stage of an R-C coupled amplifier uses a pentode for which $r_p = 1$ MΩ, $g_m = 2$ m℧, and $C_{pk} = 10$ pF. Total wiring capacitance is estimated at 20 pF, R_L is 10 kΩ, and $C_C = 0.1$ μF. For the following stage $C_g = 20$ pF and the maximum allowable R_g is 1 MΩ.

(a) Draw and label a linear circuit model valid for a wide range of frequencies.

(b) Draw and label simplified circuit models valid for low, medium, and high frequencies.

(c) Calculate the midfrequency gain and the upper and lower cutoff frequencies. Define "midfrequency" for this amplifier.

(d) Plot three key points on the frequency-response curve (voltage gain versus frequency) and sketch in the complete curve. (For a logarithmic plot on ordinary graph paper let unit distance correspond to a factor of 10 in frequency.)

18. A silicon transistor ($h_{oe} = 11$ μ℧, $h_{ie} = 2.8$ kΩ, $h_{fe} = 70$, and $h_{re} = 3.5 \times 10^{-4}$) is used in the circuit of Fig. 11.18b with $R_L = 10$ kΩ, $C_C = 5$ μF, $R_E = 2$ kΩ, $C_E = 50$ μF, $R_1 = 10$ kΩ, and $R_2 = 100$ kΩ. It is estimated that $C_o + C_w = 50$ pF and $C_{w2} + C_i = 100$ pF. List the assumptions made in deriving the circuit of Fig. 11.20c and check their validity at $f = 5000$ cps.

19. Predict the frequency response of the one-stage amplifier of Exercise 18 and draw the frequency response curve showing current gain and phase angle as functions of frequency on a logarithmic scale. Plot just enough points to permit drawing the curve.

20. On the same graph with the results of Exercise 19, draw the curves for an amplifier using two such stages.

21. A pentode with input capacitance $= 50$ pF, output capacitance $= 5$ pF, $g_m = 3$ m℧, and $r_p = 100$ kΩ, is used as an RC-coupled amplifier. If $R_L = 20$ kΩ, $C_C = 0.05$ μF, $R_g = 1$ MΩ, and total wiring capacitance is estimated to be 20 pF, predict the frequency response. Sketch the frequency-response curve for the amplifier indicating the midfrequency range and the upper and lower cutoff frequencies.

22. A pentode with $g_m = 5$ m℧ and $r_p = 200$ kΩ is used in an RC-coupled amplifier with $R_g = 1$ MΩ and total C_p estimated to be 100 pF. The voltage gain per stage is to be 50 and the response is to be satisfactory down to 20 cps. Define "satisfactory" and specify the load resistance and the coupling capacitance.

23. A transistor with h-parameters equal to those given in Exercise 18 has a beta cutoff frequency of 50 kc. Determine the frequency response of a one-stage amplifier using this transistor in the circuit of Exercise 18.

24. A single-stage pentode R-C coupled amplifier used in a mechanical engineering experiment must have a gain at 1 cps equal to 90% of its mid-frequency gain.

(a) What lower cutoff frequency is required?

(b) If $g_m = 2$ m℧, $r_p = 100$ kΩ, $R_L = 100$ kΩ, and if the input resistance to the following stage is 1 MΩ, what value of C_C is required?

(c) The upper cutoff frequency of the completed amplifier is measured to be 80 kc; what is the effective parallel capacitance?

(d) If the gain is halved by reducing R_L, is the required value of C_C reduced proportionately?

25. A single-stage transistor amplifier has a midfrequency current gain of 30 and a lower cutoff frequency of 50 cps. Predict the corresponding values for an amplifier consisting of three such stages in cascade.

26. A pentode amplifier stage is characterized by $g_m = 2$ m℧, $r_p = 100$ kΩ, $R_g = 1$ MΩ, and $C_p = 100$ pF. How many stages are required to provide a gain of 1000 with an upper 70.7% frequency of at least 100 kc?

27. The input to a single-stage of transistor amplification is 2 mV (rms) across an input resistance of 2 kΩ. The output is 5 V(rms) across a load resistance of 5 kΩ.

(a) Express the power gain in decibels.

(b) Express the voltage gain and current gain in decibels.

28. The power loss in one kilometer of coaxial telephone cable is 2 db.

(a) What is the power loss in two-kilometers of telephone cable?

(b) What is the total power loss from San Francisco to New York?

(c) What power input is required at San Francisco to deliver 1 μW at New York? Would amplifiers be desirable?

29. A telephone system using cable with a power loss of 2 db/km requires a minimum signal of 1 μW.

(a) If amplifiers are located 40 km apart, what amplifier output power is required?

(b) Assuming 20% overall amplifier efficiency, what total input power is required for San Francisco-to-New York transmission?

(c) Compare the result of part (b) to the answer for part (c) of Exercise 28.

30. An amplifier consists of the following stages:

Stage 1, mid-frequency power gain = 5 db, $f_1 = 0$ cps, $f_2 = 2$ Mc.
Stage 2, mid-frequency power gain = 25 db, $f_1 = 10$ cps, $f_2 = 1$ Mc.
Stage 3, mid-frequency power gain = 20 db, $f_1 = 100$ cps, $f_2 = 100$ kc.

(a) Plot the individual and overall response curves.

(b) If the mid-frequency output is to be 2 W, what input power is required?

31. The gain-bandwidth product for a 6SJ7 pentode is 150×10^6 rad/sec and $g_m = 2000$ μ℧.

(a) What is the effective parallel capacitance for this tube?

(b) What mid-frequency gain is possible for an $f_2 = 2.5$ Mc?

(c) What R_o is necessary for an $f_2 = 2.5$ Mc?

32. A transistor with a nominal $\beta = 30$ has a gain-bandwidth product $f_T = 12$ Mc. Describe, quantitatively, the high-frequency characteristics of this transistor. What is the current gain in db at 12 Mc?

33. Each stage of a transistor amplifier is to provide a current gain of approximately 80 with $f_2 \cong 2$ Mc; the load resistance of each stage is essentially the input resistance (h_{ie}) of the next stage.   In selecting the transistor, what values of h_{fe} and f_T are required?

PROBLEMS

1. An inexperienced designer uses the biasing circuit of Fig. 11.7. For a germanium transistor with nominal $I_{CO} = 10\ \mu A$ and $\alpha = 0.98$ at 25°C, he calculates I_C for $I_B = 50\ \mu A$. If α is actually 0.99 and the junction temperature is around 55°C, predict (approximately) the value of I_C. Using the self-biasing circuit of Fig. 11.9 with $V_B = 3.6$ V, $R_B = 9$ kΩ, and $R_E = 1$ kΩ, calculate I_C for the nominal and actual conditions. Draw a conclusion regarding the effectiveness of this biasing method.

2. A germanium transistor with $\beta = 40$ and $I_{CO} = 2\ \mu A$ is to be operated as a single-stage audio amplifier supplied by a source consisting of $V_s = 10$ mV in series with $R_s = 1$ kΩ. The specified operating point is $I_C = 1$ mA and $V_{CE} = 5$ V ($V_{CC} = 12$ V) and a stability factor of around 8 is to be provided. Draw an appropriate wiring diagram and, *stating* all assumptions, design the bias network.

3. A 6AQ5-A pentode is to be operated as a transformer-coupled audio amplifier. The available power supply provides 250 V and the input signal voltage is 10 V(rms). *Stating* all assumptions, design an appropriate circuit (draw the wiring diagram, specify quiescent point, specify R_L', R_{g2}, R_k) and predict the power output to a 16-Ω loudspeaker.

4. The permissible operating region of a power transistor is defined by $P_d = 2$ W, $I_C(max) = 1$ A, $V_{CE}(max) = 60$ V, and $V_{CE}(min) = 2$ V at $I_C = 100$ ma. This transistor is to be operated as a transformer-coupled audio amplifier delivering 0.5 W to a 10-Ω loudspeaker. *Stating* all assumptions, design an appropriate circuit (draw the wiring diagram and specify quiescent point, bias resistances, supply voltage, and transformer turns ratio), and calculate the input power and the efficiency.

5. Demonstrate that the maximum theoretical efficiency for a class A amplifier with a resistive load in the collector or plate circuit (not transformer coupled) is 25%.

6. Derive an approximate expression for midfrequency *voltage* gain of one stage of common-emitter RC-coupled amplification, stating reasonable assumptions.

7. A pentode operating at $V_{c1} = -1.5$ V, $V_{c2} = 100$ V, $I_{c2} = 1.3$ mA, $V_b = 200$ V, and $I_b = 3.5$ mA has the following characteristics: $g_m = 5.2$ m℧, $r_p = 1.5$ MΩ, and $c_p = 11$ pF. *Stating* all assumptions, design a one-stage amplifier (specify circuit values and supply voltages) to provide a mid-frequency gain of 100 with satisfactory response from 20 cps to as high as possible.

8. A *pnp* transistor operating at $I_C = 1$ mA, $I_B = 20\ \mu A$, and $V_{CE} = 5$ V has the following characteristics: $h_{ie} = 3$ kΩ, $h_{fe} = 60$, $h_{oe} = 10\ \mu℧$, $h_{re} \cong 0$, $f_T = 1$ Mc. *Stating* all assumptions, design a one-stage audio amplifier (specify circuit values and supply voltage) to provide a mid-frequency output of 0.6 V from a phonograph pickup represented by an open-circuit voltage of 8 mV and resistance of 1 kΩ.

♦ **RECTIFIERS**
♦ **FILTERS**
♦ **MODULATORS**
♦ **DEMODULATORS**

CHAPTER **12**

Nonlinear Electronic Devices

In an amplifier we desire the output signal to be an enhanced replica of the input and, therefore, the transfer characteristic should be linear. Because tubes and transistors are inherently nonlinear, in amplifiers we use bias to establish a suitable operating point and then restrict the signal amplitude to the linear region.

For other purposes we desire to exploit the nonlinear characteristics of electronic devices. To convert an alternating current into a direct current, we wish the output to be quite different from the input. To achieve precise control of a key variable, we establish a condition in which a small change in the controlled variable produces a disproportionate change in a corrective factor. To superimpose intelligence on an easily radiated high-frequency sinewave, we arrange to distort the sinewave in a controlled way. In each of these situations nonlinearity is a virtue.

Our objective here is to learn to predict the performance of nonlinear electronic devices and, in simple cases, to design devices to meet specifications. Our approach is to study a few of the more common applications of nonlinearity and to outline principles and approaches which are useful generally. The devices selected for discussion include rectifiers, filters, regulators, modulators, and detectors.

RECTIFIERS

The nonlinear characteristic of a diode is used to convert alternating current into unidirectional, but pulsating, current in the process called *rectification*. The pulsations are removed in a frequency-selective circuit called a *filter*.

Half-Wave Rectifier

The characteristics of three common types of diodes used in rectification are shown in Fig. 12.1a. Ideally, a diode should conduct current freely in the forward direction and prevent current flow in the reverse direction (Fig. 12.1b). Practical diodes only approach the ideal; semiconductor diodes, for example, present a small but appreciable resistance in the forward direction and permit a finite current to flow in the reverse direction. The circuit model of Fig. 12.1c is based on a piecewise linearization of the semiconductor characteristic. For most calculations the reverse current flow is negligibly small; in some cases the forward resistance also can be neglected.

A practical rectifier circuit is shown in Fig. 12.2a. A transformer supplied from 110-V, 60-cps house current provides the desired output voltage which is applied to a series combination of diode (a vacuum diode is shown) and load resistance R_L. For approximate analysis, the actual diode is represented by an ideal diode and a forward resistance R_f; the internal resistance of the transformer is neglected or absorbed into R_f.

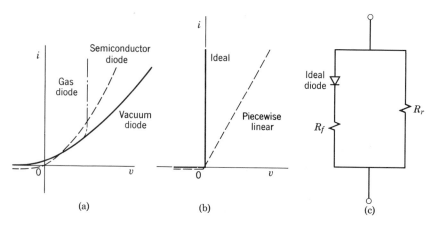

Fig. 12.1   Diode characteristics and circuit models.

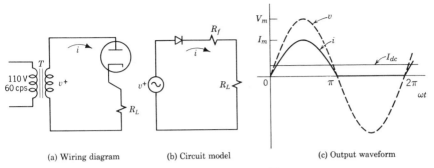

(a) Wiring diagram   (b) Circuit model   (c) Output waveform

Fig. 12.2 Half-wave rectifier.

For $v = V_m \sin \omega t$, the resulting current is

$$
\begin{cases}
i = \dfrac{v}{R_{\text{total}}} = \dfrac{V_m \sin \omega t}{R_f + R_L} & 0 \leq \omega t \leq \pi \\
i = 0 & \pi \leq \omega t \leq 2\pi
\end{cases}
\tag{12-1}
$$

as shown in Fig. 12.2c.

The purpose of rectification is to obtain a unidirectional current. The d-c component of the load current is the average value or

$$
I_{\text{dc}} = \frac{1}{2\pi} \int_0^{2\pi} i \, d(\omega t) = \frac{1}{2\pi} \int_0^{\pi} \frac{V_m \sin \omega t}{R_f + R_L} \, d(\omega t) + 0
$$

$$
= \frac{1}{2\pi} \frac{V_m}{R_f + R_L} \Big[-\cos \omega t \Big]_0^{\pi} = \frac{V_m}{\pi(R_f + R_L)} = \frac{I_m}{\pi}
\tag{12-2}
$$

The current through the load resistance consists of half-sinewaves, and the d-c component is approximately 30 % of the maximum value.

Full-Wave Rectifier

The bridge rectifier circuit of Fig. 12.3 provides a greater d-c value from the same transformer voltage. When the transformer voltage $v = v_{ad}$ is positive, the current flow is along path *abcd* as shown and a half-sinewave of current results. When the applied voltage reverses, the voltage $v_{da} = -v_{ad}$ is positive and the current flow is along path *dbca*. The current through the load resistance is always in the same direction, and the d-c component is twice as large as in the half-wave rectifier or

$$
I_{\text{dc}} = \frac{2}{\pi} \frac{V_m}{R_f + R_L} = \frac{2I_m}{\pi}
\tag{12-3}
$$

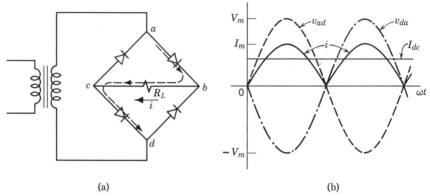

(a)   (b)

Fig. 12.3   Full-wave bridge rectifier.

The bridge circuit is disadvantageous because four diodes are required
and two diodes and their power-dissipating resistances are always in
series with the load.   The full-wave rectifier circuit of Fig. 12.4 uses a
more expensive transformer to produce the same result with only two
diodes and with higher operating efficiency.   The second output winding
on the transformer provides a voltage v_2 which is 180° out of phase with v_1;
such a *center-tapped* winding serves as a *phase inverter*.   While v_1 is positive, current i_1 is supplied through diode 1; while v_1 is negative, no current flows through diode 1 but v_2 is positive and, therefore, current i_2 is
supplied through diode 2.   The current through the load resistance is
$i_1 + i_2$ and $I_{\mathrm{dc}} = 2I_m/\pi$ as before.

In addition to the forward resistance R_f and reverse resistance R_r (or
reverse current I_{CO}), the important design parameters of a diode are the

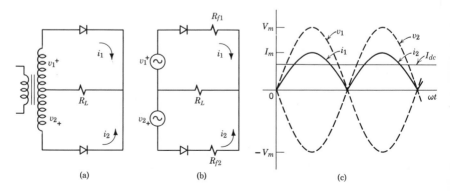

(a)   (b)   (c)

Fig. 12.4   Full-wave rectifier with phase inverter.

maximum forward current and the peak inverse voltage. For example, diffused-junction silicon rectifiers are available in ratings up to 600 A of rectified forward current. The peak inverse voltage (PIV) is the maximum reverse bias which can be applied without breakdown and it may be critical in high-voltage power supplies. Silicon rectifiers are available in PIV ratings up to 1000 V; for higher voltage applications, rectifiers can be connected in series if provision is made to insure equal voltage division between units.

Ripple Factor

The desired result of rectification is direct current, but the output currents of the rectifier circuits described obviously contain large alternating components along with the d-c component. As a measure of the effectiveness of rectification we define the *ripple factor r* where

$$r = \frac{I_{ac}}{I_{dc}} = \frac{V_{ac}}{V_{dc}} = \frac{\text{rms value of a-c components}}{\text{d-c component}} \tag{12-4}$$

Since the power dissipated in the load resistance defines the rms value of current, and since the total power is the sum of the power dissipated by the direct and alternating components (see Exercise 4),

$$I_{rms}^2 R_L = I_{dc}^2 R_L + I_{ac}^2 R_L \tag{12-5}$$

Therefore, $I_{ac}^2 = I_{rms}^2 - I_{dc}^2$ and

$$r = \frac{\sqrt{I_{rms}^2 - I_{dc}^2}}{I_{dc}} = \sqrt{\left(\frac{I_{rms}}{I_{dc}}\right)^2 - 1} \tag{12-6}$$

If the ripple factor is low, the circuit is performing the conversion from alternating current to direct current effectively.[†]

EXAMPLE 1

Determine and compare the ripple factors of the half-wave and full-wave rectifier circuits.

SOLUTION. For the half-wave rectifier of Fig. 12.2,

$$I_{rms} = \sqrt{\frac{1}{2\pi} \int_0^{2\pi} i^2 \, d(\omega t)} = \sqrt{\frac{1}{2\pi} \int_0^{\pi} (I_m \sin \omega t)^2 \, d(\omega t)} = I_m \sqrt{\frac{\pi/2}{2\pi}} = \frac{I_m}{2} \tag{12-7}$$

---

† For a more complete discussion of rectifiers and filters, see Jacob Millman, *Vacuum-Tube and Semiconductor Electronics*, McGraw-Hill Book Co., New York, 1958.

Therefore (by Eqs. 12-2 and 12-7),

$$\frac{I_{\rm rms}}{I_{\rm dc}} = \frac{I_m/2}{I_m/\pi} = \frac{\pi}{2} = 1.57$$

and

$$r = \sqrt{(1.57)^2 - 1} = 1.21 \text{ or } 121\%$$

For the full-wave rectifier of Fig. 12.4, $I_{\rm rms} = I_m/\sqrt{2}$ and $I_{\rm dc} = 2I_m/\pi$. Therefore,

$$\frac{I_{\rm rms}}{I_{\rm dc}} = \frac{I_m/\sqrt{2}}{2I_m/\pi} = \frac{\pi}{2\sqrt{2}} = 1.11$$

and

$$r = \sqrt{(1.11)^2 - 1} = 0.48 \text{ or } 48\%$$

FILTERS

Although using full-wave instead of half-wave rectification reduces the a-c component from 121% to 48% of the d-c component, the output is still unsatisfactory for most electronic purposes.

Capacitor Filter

The ripple factor can be greatly reduced by *a filter* consisting of a capacitor shunted across the load resistor. The capacitor can be thought of as a low-impedance path taken by the a-c components of the rectified wave, or it can be thought of as a "tank" which stores charge during the period when the diode is conducting and releases charge to the load during the nonconducting period.

If the diode resistance is small and if the steady state has been reached, the operation is as shown in Fig. 12.5. At time $t = 0$, the source volt-

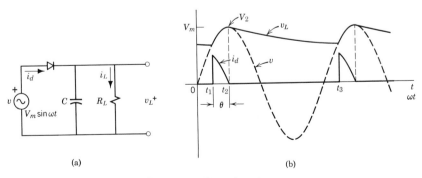

(a)   (b)

Fig. 12.5 Capacitor filter.

age v is zero but the load voltage $v_L = v_C$ is appreciable because the previously charged capacitor is discharging through the load. At $t = t_1$, the increasing supply voltage slightly exceeds v_L and the diode conducts. The diode current i_d rises abruptly to satisfy the relation $i_C = C\,dv/dt$ and then decreases to zero; the diode switches off when v drops below v_L. During the charging period, $t_1 < t < t_2$,

$$v_L = V_m \sin \omega t \tag{12-8}$$

During the discharging period, $t_2 < t < t_3$,

$$v_L = V_2\, e^{-(t-t_2)/RC} \tag{12-9}$$

as expected from the natural response of the RC circuit. At time t_3, the supply voltage again exceeds the load voltage and the cycle repeats.

The load current i_L is directly proportional to load voltage v_L. Because i_L never goes to zero, the average value or d-c component is relatively large as compared to the half-wave rectifier alone and the a-c component is correspondingly lower. The ripple factor is greatly reduced by the use of the capacitor.

Capacitor Filter—Approximate Analysis

Design charts are available in handbooks published by rectifier manufacturers† which relate R_L, C, r, and V_L/V_m. The following approximate analysis, which gives satisfactory results for most purposes, illustrates the roles played by the various circuit parameters. We assume that:

1. The time constant $R_L C$ is large enough so that the charging interval $t_2 - t_1$ is small compared to time T for one cycle.
2. The diode current, a portion of a cosine wave, can be approximated by a triangular pulse.
3. The sinusoidal and exponential segments of the v_L curve can be approximated by straight lines.
4. Diode switching time t_2 occurs at the peak of the supply voltage wave so that $V_2 = V_m$.

On the basis of these assumptions, the behavior is described by Fig. 12.6.

For a given load and capacitor, we are interested in determining the necessary supply voltage, the diode rating, and the resulting voltage

---

† Page 135, *Zener Diode and Rectifier Handbook*, Motorola Inc., 1961, Phoenix, Arizona.

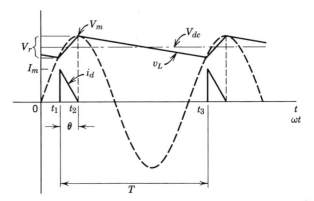

Fig. 12.6 Capacitor filter—approximate analysis.

variation. If the charging interval is negligibly small, the load current
is supplied by the capacitor and the charge transferred is

$$Q = I_{dc}T \cong C\Delta V_C = CV_r \qquad (12\text{-}10)$$

Solving, the ripple voltage is

$$V_r \cong \frac{I_{dc}T}{C} = \frac{I_{dc}}{fC} \qquad (12\text{-}11)$$

where f is the frequency, usually 60 cps. The necessary supply voltage is

$$V_m = V_{dc} + \frac{V_r}{2} = V_{dc} + \frac{I_{dc}}{2fC} \qquad (12\text{-}12)$$

The charging interval for the capacitor corresponds to the *conduction
angle* for the diode which is

$$\theta = \cos^{-1} \frac{V_m - V_r}{V_m} \qquad (12\text{-}13)$$

and the conduction time is

$$t_2 - t_1 = \frac{\theta}{2\pi} T \qquad (12\text{-}14)$$

The charge carried through the load is equal to the charge conducted by
the diode during the triangular pulse, therefore

$$I_{dc}T \cong \tfrac{1}{2}I_m(t_2 - t_1) = \tfrac{1}{2}I_m \frac{\theta}{2\pi} T$$

or

$$I_m \cong I_{dc}\frac{4\pi}{\theta} = I_{dc}\frac{720°}{\theta°} \qquad (12\text{-}15)$$

The ripple voltage consists of a triangular wave of maximum value $V_r/2$ and rms value $V_r/2\sqrt{3}$ (see Exercise 7.1c). The ripple factor is

$$r = \frac{V_{ac}}{V_{dc}} = \frac{V_r}{2\sqrt{3}\,V_{dc}} = \frac{I_{dc}/V_{dc}}{2\sqrt{3}\,fC} = \frac{1}{2\sqrt{3}\,fCR_L} \qquad (12\text{-}16)$$

These relations apply to a half-wave rectifier; similar equations can be derived for a full-wave rectifier. By using these approximate relations, the performance of an existing filter can be determined or a filter can be designed to meet specifications.

EXAMPLE 2

A load ($R_L = 4000\ \Omega$) is to be supplied with 200 V at 50 mA with a ripple factor of less than 2%. Design a rectifier-filter combination to meet these specifications.

SOLUTION. Assuming a 60-cps supply and the half-wave rectifier with capacitor filter of Fig. 12.5a, the design is as follows:

From Eq. 12-16,

$$C = \frac{1}{2\sqrt{3}\,rfR_L} = \frac{1}{2\sqrt{3} \times 0.02 \times 60 \times 4000} = 60\ \mu\text{F}$$

By Eq. 12-16,

$$V_r = 2\sqrt{3}\,V_{dc}r = 2\sqrt{3} \times 200 \times 0.02 = 13.9\ \text{V}$$

By Eq. 12-12,

$$V_m = V_{dc} + \frac{V_r}{2} = 200 + \frac{13.9}{2} \cong 207\ \text{V}$$

By Eq. 12-13,

$$\theta = \cos^{-1}\frac{V_m - V_r}{V_m} = \cos^{-1}\frac{193}{207} = 21.5°$$

By Eq. 12-15,

$$I_m = I_{dc}\frac{720°}{\theta°} = 0.050 \times \frac{720}{21.5} = 1.68\ \text{A}$$

The peak inverse voltage occurs when the supply voltage reaches its negative maximum and the voltage across the diode is $V_m + v_L \cong 2V_m = 414\ \text{V}$. A diode rated at $I_m = 1.75\ \text{A}$ and PIV = 500 V would be satisfactory.

L-Section Filters

Instead of a capacitor in parallel with the load resistance, an inductor or "choke" coil in series with the load can be used to reduce the ripple factor (Fig. 12.7). An inductance offers relatively high impedance to the a-c components of current while passing the d-c components without opposition. But inductors in the sizes required for low ripple are rela-

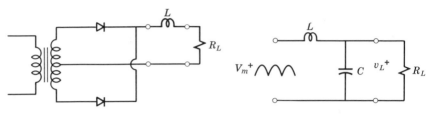

Fig. 12.7   Series inductor filter.   **Fig. 12.8**   L-section filter.

tively expensive.   For a given investment, the combination of inductance and capacitance shown in Fig. 12.8 gives better results.   Such a two-port is called an L-*section* because of its geometry.

If the inductance L is greater than a certain critical value† L_c where

$$L_c \cong \frac{R_L}{6\pi f} \cong \frac{R_L}{1000} \qquad (12\text{-}17)$$

for 60-cps operation, the flywheel effect of the inductance keeps the current flowing continuously (instead of in short pulses) and the output voltage changes only slightly with changes in R_L.   The analysis of the filtering action under this condition is a straightforward application of a-c circuit theory.

As represented in Fig. 12.8, the output of a full-wave rectifier consists of a series of half-sinewaves.   The Fourier series representation of such a periodic wave is

$$v = \frac{2}{\pi} V_m(1 - \tfrac{2}{3} \cos 2\omega t - \tfrac{2}{15} \cos 4\omega t - \tfrac{2}{35} \cos 6\omega t - \cdots) \qquad (12\text{-}18)$$

The first term, a constant, represents the d-c component of relative magnitude 1.   The second term is a second harmonic of relative magnitude $\tfrac{2}{3}$ and frequency 2ω.   The succeeding terms in this infinite series are smaller and, furthermore, they are easier to filter out (Why?).   Our analysis is concerned with the second harmonic term because if that is filtered out effectively, all the higher harmonics are removed even more effectively (see Exercise 8).

A common problem is to determine the ripple factor in the voltage across R_L for given values of L and C.   These values are not critical and it is convenient to make simplifying assumptions which reduce the work

---

† See Millman, op. cit.

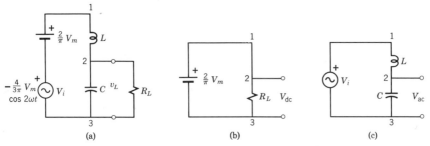

Fig. 12.9 L-section filter analysis by superposition.

involved. In the circuit of Fig. 12.9 let us assume that:

1. The input voltage to the filter is $v = (2/\pi)V_m - (4/3\pi)V_m \cos 2\omega t$.

2. The resistance of inductor L is negligibly small and, therefore, the full d-c component of voltage appears across R_L.

3. The admittance $2\omega C$ is large compared to $1/R_L$ (as it must be for good filtering) and $Z_{RC} = Z_{23} \cong 1/2\omega C$.

4. The reactance of the inductor $2\omega L$ is large compared to Z_{RC} (as it must be for good filtering), and $Z_{13} \cong 2\omega L$.

Since the filter is linear, the principle of superposition is applicable and the circuit of Fig. 12.9a can be replaced by an equivalent combination of two circuits. By inspection of the voltage divider in Fig. 12.9c (R_L has been neglected),

$$\frac{V_{ac}}{V_i} = \frac{Z_{23}}{Z_{13}} = \frac{1/2\omega C}{2\omega L - 1/2\omega C} \cong \frac{1}{4\omega^2 LC} \tag{12-19}$$

or

$$V_{ac} = \frac{1}{4\omega^2 LC} V_i = \frac{1}{4\omega^2 LC} \frac{4V_m}{3\pi \sqrt{2}}$$

This is the only significant ripple component, so the ripple factor is

$$r = \frac{V_{ac}}{V_{dc}} = \frac{4V_m}{4\omega^2 LC(3\pi \sqrt{2})} \cdot \frac{\pi}{2V_m} = \frac{\sqrt{2}}{12\omega^2 LC} = \frac{0.47}{4\omega^2 LC} \tag{12-20}$$

EXAMPLE 3

The load of Example 2 is to be supplied from a full-wave rectifier with an L-section filter consisting of $L = 10$ H and $C = 10$ μF. Determine the ripple factor.

SOLUTION. By Eq. 12-17, $L_c = 4000/1000 = 4$ H. Therefore $L > L_c$ and the a-c analysis is applicable.

Assuming 60-cps operation, for the second harmonic,

$$X_L = 2\omega L = 2(2\pi\ 60)10 = 7540\ \Omega$$

$$X_C = \frac{1}{2\omega C} = \frac{1}{2(2\pi\ 60)10^{-5}} = 133\ \Omega$$

and assumptions 3 and 4 appear to be justified.
The rms value of the second harmonic input component is, by Eq. 12-18,

$$\frac{2}{3\sqrt{2}}\,V_{dc} \cong 94\ \text{V}$$

The filter reduces this to (Eq. 12-19):

$$V_{ac} \cong \frac{1/2\omega C}{2\omega L}\,V_i = \frac{133}{7540}\,94 = 1.66\ \text{V}$$

The ripple factor is

$$r = \frac{V_{ac}}{V_{dc}} = \frac{1.66}{200} \cong 0.008 \cong 0.8\%$$

The same result is obtained directly from Eq. 12-20.

To reduce the ripple factor further, a second L-section can be added before the load resistor. For two identical sections, the denominator of Eq. 12-20 becomes $(4\omega^2 LC)^2$.

Zener Diode Voltage Regulator

Filters are designed to minimize the rapid variations in load voltage due to cyclical variations in rectifier output voltage. There are other reasons for load voltage variation. If the amplitude of the supply voltage (V_m) fluctuates, as it does in practice, the d-c voltage will fluctuate. If the load current changes due to a change in R_L, the d-c voltage will change due to the IR drop in the transformer, rectifier, and inductor (if any). A filter cannot prevent these types of variation and if the load voltage is critical, a *voltage regulator* must be employed. Gas tubes and Zener diodes are suitable for voltage regulation.

A simple Zener diode voltage regulator (Fig. 12.10a) consists of a series voltage dropping resistance R_S and a Zener diode in parallel with the load resistance R_L. Voltage V_1 is the d-c output of a rectifier-filter. The function of the regulator is to keep V_L nearly constant with changes in V_1 or I_L. The operation is based on the fact that, in the Zener breakdown region, small changes in diode voltage are accompanied by large changes in diode current (see Fig. 9.23). The large currents flowing through R_S produce voltages which compensate for changes in V_1 or I_L. In the operating region, the circuit model of the Zener diode consists of

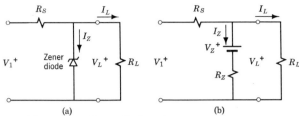

(a)   (b)

Fig. 12.10 Zener diode voltage regulator.

a series combination of a constant voltage source and a small resistance. The following example illustrates the operation.

EXAMPLE 4

A load draws a current varying from 10 to 100 mA at a nominal voltage of 100 V. A regulator consists of $R_S = 200\ \Omega$ and a Zener diode represented by $V_Z = 100$ V and $R_Z = 20\ \Omega$ (Fig. 12.10b).

(a) For $I_L = 50$ mA, determine the variation in V_1 corresponding to a 1% variation in V_L.

(b) For V_1 constant, determine the variation in V_L corresponding to a variation in I_L from 50 to 10 mA.

SOLUTION. To place the diode well into the Zener breakdown region, a minimum current $I_Z(\text{min}) = 0.1 I_L(\text{max}) = 0.1 \times 100 = 10$ mA is used.

(a) $V_L = V_Z + I_Z R_Z = 100 + 0.01(20) = 100.2$ V

and

$$V_1 = V_L + (I_L + I_Z)R_S = 100.2 + (0.05 + 0.01)200 = 112.2 \text{ V}$$

If V_L increases by 1% or 1 V, $V_L' = 101.2$ V,

$$I_Z' = \frac{V_L' - V_Z}{R_Z} = \frac{101.2 - 100}{20} = 0.06 \text{ A}$$

and

$$V_1' = V_L' + (I_L + I_Z')R_S = 101.2 + (0.05 + 0.06)200 = 123.2 \text{ V}$$

A change in V_1 of 11 V produces a change in V_L of only 1 V.

(b) For $V_L = 100.2$ V and $I_L = 0.05$ A, $V_1 = 112.2$ V. Applying Kirchhoff's voltage law to the left-hand loop,

$$V_1 - (I_Z' + I_L')R_S - V_Z - I_Z'R_Z = 0$$

Solving with $I_L' = 10$ mA,

$$I_Z' = \frac{V_1 - V_Z - I_L'R_S}{R_S + R_Z} = \frac{112.2 - 100 - (0.01)20}{200 + 20} = 0.046 \text{ A}$$

Then

$$V_L' = V_Z + I_Z'R_Z = 100 + 0.046(20) \cong 100.9 \text{ V}$$

A 40 mA change in I_L produces a change in V_L of only 0.7 V.

MODULATORS AND DEMODULATORS

We know that in the universe there are millions of stars like our sun with planets which may be capable of supporting life as we know it. There is a very small but finite probability that intelligent beings in another solar system are attempting to communicate with us. What would they say? One suggestion is that the message might consist of prime numbers since these are not ordinarily found in nature and would indicate the existence of reasoning beings. How would they send such a message? An electromagnetic wave such as light or a radio wave can be propagated through free space and could serve as a *carrier;* the intelligence could be superimposed on the carrier in the process called *modulation.*

Modulation

Modulation is another example of the versatility of electronic devices. The same diode which converts alternating current to direct current in a rectifier can be used as a *modulator* to superimpose information on a carrier and also as a *demodulator* to recover the original information after transmission, millions of miles in the case of the Mariner satellite that took pictures of Mars. A related application is the *harmonic generator* in which the higher harmonics labeled distortion in an amplifier become the desired output. When the output is to be different from the input, we utilize the nonlinear characteristics of the device.

In a typical communications or control system, the information is transmitted as a modulated carrier. The information may be an audible sound, an animated picture, a temperature reading, a valve setting, or a meteorite count. The important property of the carrier is the ease with which it is transmitted. The modulation process consists of modifying some characteristic of the carrier in accordance with the information. If the carrier is an electrical signal described by

$$a = A \sin (\omega t + \phi) \qquad (12\text{-}21)$$

there are three characteristics available for modulation. In *amplitude modulation* (AM), the amplitude A is varied; in *frequency modulation* (FM), the frequency ω is controlled. Variation of phase angle ϕ results in *phase modulation.*

Amplitude Modulation

The emphasis here is on amplitude modulation in which the amplitude of the carrier signal is directly proportional to the amplitude of the

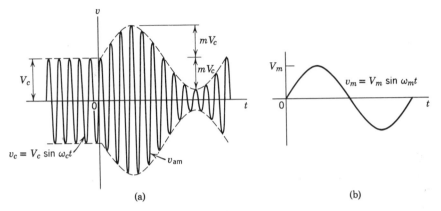

Fig. 12.11   Sinusoidal carrier amplitude-modulated by sinusoidal signal.

modulating signal.   In AM radio broadcasting, for example, the carrier frequency might be 910 kc and the modulating frequency might be 264 cps corresponding to middle C on the piano.   In Fig. 12.11, the unmodulated carrier is described by

$$v_c = V_c \sin \omega_c t \qquad (12\text{-}22)$$

At time $t = 0$, the carrier amplitude is modulated by a signal described by

$$v_m = V_m \sin \omega_m t \qquad (12\text{-}23)$$

The *degree of modulation* is defined by

$$m = \frac{V_m}{V_c} \qquad (12\text{-}24)$$

and is equal to approximately 80% in the illustration.

The equation of the amplitude-modulated wave is

$$v_{am} = (1 + m \sin \omega_m t) V_c \sin \omega_c t \qquad (12\text{-}25)$$

$$= V_c \sin \omega_c t + m V_c \sin \omega_m t \sin \omega_c t$$

$$= V_c \sin \omega_c t - \frac{m V_c}{2} \cos (\omega_c + \omega_m)t + \frac{m V_c}{2} \cos (\omega_c - \omega_m)t\dagger \qquad (12\text{-}26)$$

This equation reveals that the amplitude-modulated wave consists of three sinusoidal components of constant amplitude.   The carrier and the

---

† Since $\sin a \sin b = -\frac{1}{2} \cos (a + b) + \frac{1}{2} \cos (a - b)$.

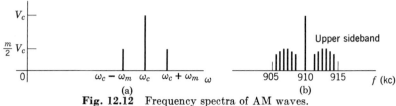

Fig. 12.12   Frequency spectra of AM waves.

upper and lower *side frequencies* are shown in the frequency spectrum of Fig. 12.12a.   In general the modulating signal is a complicated wave containing several components and the result is a carrier plus upper and lower *sidebands*.   If the 910 kc carrier of an AM station is modulated by frequencies from 100 to 4500 cps, the frequency spectrum is as shown in Fig. 12.12b.   The station is assigned a *channel* 10 kc wide to accommodate side frequencies from 0 to 5000 cps.   The amplifiers in radio transmitters and receivers are designed to amplify well over a 10-kc bandwidth and to discriminate against frequencies outside this range.   Channels for FM broadcast are 200 kc wide and permit a wider frequency response for higher fidelity.   For satisfactory television transmission sidebands approximately 6 Mc wide are required.

A Nonlinear Modulator

The combination of two signals to produce an AM wave requires a nonlinear element.   Practical devices for this purpose have many forms to meet special requirements.   One common modulating system consists of a class C radio-frequency amplifier (operating in the nonlinear portion of the transfer characteristic) in which the output voltage is nearly proportional to the d-c supply voltage.   Varying the supply voltage in accordance with the modulating signal produces an amplitude-modulated output signal.   (Would varying the supply voltage on a class A amplifier produce the same result?)

To illustrate the modulating effect of nonlinearity, consider the electronic device whose characteristic is shown in Fig. 12.13.   A diode, a triode, a transistor, or even a coil with an iron core could provide such a characteristic.   The nonlinear device is connected in series with a small resistance R and the *sum* of two sinusoidal voltages is applied.   Using the analytical technique of Chapter 8, we can approximate a portion of the characteristic by the first three terms of a power series (Eq. 8-36) and write

$$i = a_0 + a_1 v + a_2 v^2 \qquad (12\text{-}27)$$

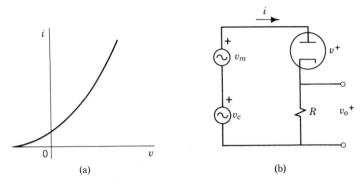

Fig. 12.13 Nonlinear device as a modulator.

If R is small compared to the resistance of the device,

$$v = v_m + v_c = V_m \sin \omega_m t + V_c \sin \omega_c t$$

Then

$$i = a_0 + a_1 V_m \sin \omega_m t + a_1 V_c \sin \omega_c t$$
$$+ a_2 V_m^2 \sin^2 \omega_m t + a_2 V_c^2 \sin^2 \omega_c t + 2a_2 V_m V_c \sin \omega_m t \sin \omega_c t$$

Substituting for $\sin^2 \omega t$ and $\sin \omega_m t \sin \omega_c t$ and rearranging terms,

$$i = a_0 + \frac{a_2 V_m^2}{2} + \frac{a_2 V_c^2}{2} + a_1 V_m \sin \omega_m t + a_1 V_c \sin \omega_c t$$
$$- \frac{a_2 V_m^2}{2} \cos 2\omega_m t - \frac{a_2 V_c^2}{2} \cos 2\omega_c t$$
$$- a_2 V_m V_c \cos (\omega_c + \omega_m)t + a_2 V_m V_c \cos (\omega_c - \omega_m)t \qquad (12\text{-}28)$$

The output voltage v_o is directly proportional to current i and contains the same nine components: The first three terms constitute a steady or d-c component dependent on the amplitude of the input signals as expected in a nonlinear device. The next two terms are "amplified" versions of the input signals resulting from the linear term of Eq. 12-27. Then there are two terms representing second-harmonic distortion components generated by the nonlinearity. The last two terms correspond to the sum and difference frequencies desired in the amplitude-modulated wave. If ω_m is small compared to ω_c, the fifth, eighth, and ninth terms are relatively close together in the frequency spectrum (Fig. 12.12) and may be amplified by a tuned amplifier which discriminates against all the other components. Every AM radio receiver incorporates such a tuned amplifier. The tuning is accomplished by a variable capacitor adjusted as the dial is turned.

EXAMPLE 5

A carrier signal $v_c = 100 \sin 10^7 t$ V is to be modulated by a signal $v_m = 100 \sin 10^4 t$ V, using a device with a characteristic defined by $i = v + 0.003v^2$ mA. The resulting current is filtered by a circuit which passes all frequencies from 2 to 15 krad/sec and rejects all others. Describe the output signal.

SOLUTION. Comparing the device characteristic to Eq. 12-27, $a_0 = 0$, $a_1 = 1$, and $a_2 = 0.003$. Only the fifth, eighth and ninth components in Eq. 12-28 have frequencies within the passband of the filter.

The magnitudes of the carrier and side-frequency components are:

$$a_1 V_c = 100 \text{ mA} \quad \text{and} \quad a_2 V_m V_c = 30 \text{ mA}$$

Therefore, the output signal is

$$i = 100 \sin 10^7 t - 30 \cos 1.001 \times 10^7 t + 30 \cos 0.999 \times 10^7 t \text{ mA}$$

Comparing the second component with the corresponding component in Eq. 12-26,

$$\frac{m I_c}{2} = \frac{m}{2} \times 100 = 30 \quad \text{or} \quad m = \frac{60}{100}$$

and the degree of modulation is 60%.

Pulse Modulation

The process of transmitting a measured quantity to a remote location for display, recording, or use is called *data transmission* or *telemetry*. The transmission may be by radio-frequency carrier through space or by high-frequency carrier on a telephone line or cable. Common applications include chemical process control, power station operation, and in-flight missile testing. A single wave can be divided into many channels and each channel can carry information from a different sensing device. At the receiving end frequency-selective circuits are used to sort out the information from the various channels.

The information may be carried in the form of continuous modulation signals or in the form of pulses. The familiar International Morse Code in which the carrier is turned on and off to form dots and dashes is one form of amplitude modulation. The *pulse-modulated* wave in Fig. 12.14a represents the letter "a"; this is called pulse duration modulation (PDM). In pulse amplitude modulation (PAM) the information is carried in the height of the pulses. Pulse position modulation (PPM) uses short pulses at varying intervals to convey the information; the PPM signal in Fig. 12.14d can be derived by differentiating and rectifying the PDM signal directly above. In pulse code modulation (PCM), the position of the pulses carries information in a binary code. Pulse modulation systems are described in Chapter 21.

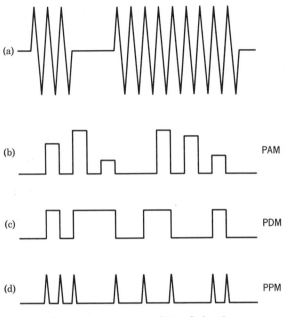

(a)

(b)   PAM

(c)   PDM

(d)   PPM

Fig. 12.14   Pulse modulated signals.

Square-Law Demodulator

Recovery of the original audio-frequency modulating signal from the sum of three radio-frequency signals in Example 5 requires another wave-distorting process called *demodulation* or *detection*. The same nonlinear device used for modulation will also serve for detection. In detection the important factor is the second-degree term in Eq. 12-27. Letting

$$i = a_2 v^2 \qquad (12\text{-}29)$$

and substituting v from Eq. 12-26,

$$i = a_2 V_c{}^2 \sin^2 \omega_c t + a_2 \left(\frac{mV_c}{2}\right)^2 \cos^2(\omega_c + \omega_m)t + a_2 \left(\frac{mV_c}{2}\right)^2 \cos^2(\omega_c - \omega_m)t$$

$$- a_2 mV_c{}^2 \sin \omega_c t \cos (\omega_c + \omega_m)t + a_2 mV_c{}^2 \sin \omega_c t \cos (\omega_c - \omega_m)t$$

$$- 2a_2 \left(\frac{mV_c}{2}\right)^2 \cos (\omega_c + \omega_m)t \cos (\omega_c - \omega_m)t \qquad (12\text{-}30)$$

The identification of these six terms with sinusoidal components is possible with the aid of the trigonometric identities. In particular we recall that the product of two sinusoids of different frequencies yields sum and difference frequency components and, therefore,

$$\sin \omega_c t \cos (\omega_c + \omega_m)t = \tfrac{1}{2} \sin (2\omega_c + \omega_m)t + \tfrac{1}{2} \sin \omega_m t \qquad (12\text{-}31)$$

If ω_m is small compared to ω_c, a frequency spectrum of Eq. 12-30 shows that the ω_m component indicated in Eq. 12-31 is easily separated from all other components and a replica of the original modulating signal is obtained.

The Diode Detector

The most commonly used demodulator is the same diode rectifier and filter capacitor shown in Fig. 12.5 and repeated in Fig. 12.15. In an elementary radio receiver, the r-f signals intercepted by the antenna flow to the ground through the primary of a transformer. The secondary of the transformer is tuned to develop a relatively large voltage at the frequency of the desired station. This amplitude-modulated a-c voltage is rectified by the diode and the voltage on the capacitor tends to follow the peaks of the half sinewaves. The d-c component and the modulating audio-frequency component of the output flow through the earphone receivers, but the inductance of the earphone winding filters out the radio-frequency component. It is emphasized again that in a diode serving as a demodulator, the key property is its nonlinearity.

A Communication System

If part of the output of an amplifier is fed back into the input in just the right way (discussed in Chapter 19), it is possible to obtain self-

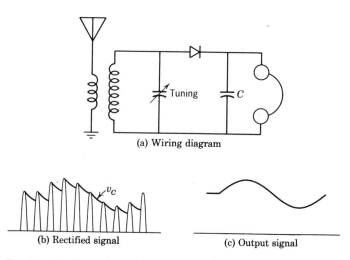

(a) Wiring diagram

(b) Rectified signal   (c) Output signal

Fig. 12.15   Elementary radio receiver using diode detector.

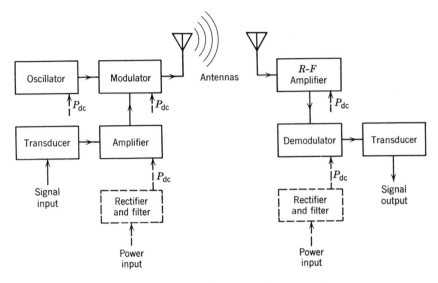

Fig. 12.16 Elements of a communication system.

sustained oscillations. Such an amplifier is called an *oscillator* or a *signal generator*. With the addition of the oscillator to our repertory of electronic devices we have all the essential elements of a telemetry or communication system (Fig. 12.16).

In a radio broadcasting system the signal input is an audible variation in air pressure or a mechanical vibration of a phonograph needle. The transducer, a microphone or pickup, converts the acoustic vibration into an electrical signal which, when amplified, is available for modulating. The radio-frequency carrier signal is generated in the oscillator and combined with the audio-frequency signal in the modulator. Usually the modulator stage also performs amplification so that a high-level amplitude-modulated signal is fed into the transmitting antenna. Energy is radiated from the antenna in the form of an electromagnetic wave, part of which is intercepted by the receiving antenna. The selected carrier and sidebands are amplified and fed into the demodulator. The detector output, usually amplified further, is converted by the transducer (a loudspeaker) into a replica of the original input signal. The power required may be obtained from 60-cps a-c lines, converted into d-c power by rectifier-filter combinations, and supplied to each stage of the communication system.

SUMMARY

◆ A nonlinear device is able to rectify, modulate, or demodulate.

◆ A rectifier converts alternating current into unidirectional current. In half-wave rectification with a resistive load,

$$I_{dc} = \frac{1}{2\pi} \int_0^\pi \frac{V_m \sin \omega t}{R_f + R_L} \, d(\omega t) = \frac{1}{\pi} \frac{V_m}{R_f + R_L} = \frac{I_m}{\pi}$$

A bridge circuit, or center-tapped transformer, permits full-wave rectification.

In full-wave rectification with a resistive load, $I_{dc} = 2I_m/\pi$.

◆ The effectiveness of rectification is measured by the ripple factor

$$r = \frac{V_{ac}}{V_{dc}} = \frac{I_{ac}}{I_{dc}} = \sqrt{\left(\frac{I_{rms}}{I_{dc}}\right)^2 - 1}$$

◆ A filter reduces the ripple by absorbing voltage variations or opposing current variations or both.

A capacitor filter stores charge on voltage peaks and delivers charge during voltage valleys; an approximate analysis shows that

$$r \cong \frac{1}{2\sqrt{3}\, fCR_L} \qquad \text{(with half-wave rectification)}$$

In L-section filters, the inductor opposes current changes and the capacitor absorbs voltage peaks; a-c circuit analysis shows that

$$r \cong \frac{0.47}{4\omega^2 LC} \qquad \text{(with full-wave rectification)}$$

◆ A voltage regulator minimizes changes in d-c load voltage.

In Zener or gas diodes small voltage changes cause large current changes which produce voltage drops to compensate for variations in V_{in} or I_{out}.

◆ A modulator superimposes information on a carrier by modifying the carrier amplitude, frequency, or phase.

An AM wave consisting of carrier and sidebands is described by

$$v_{am} = V_c \sin \omega_c t - \frac{mV_c}{2} \cos (\omega_c + \omega_m)t + \frac{mV_c}{2} \cos (\omega_c - \omega_m)t$$

Information can be carried by pulse amplitude, duration, or position.

◆ A demodulator recovers the original signal from the modulated wave. A diode detector behaves like a rectifier with a capacitor filter.

REVIEW QUESTIONS

1. Draw the transfer characteristic for a triode with load resistance and label the linear and nonlinear regions.
2. Apply sinusoidal inputs to the linear and nonlinear regions (Question 1), and sketch and describe the outputs.
3. Given a *real* semiconductor in a half-wave rectifier circuit, sketch the voltage waveform across a load resistor. Repeat for an *ideal* diode.
4. Explain the operation of a full-wave bridge rectifier.
5. Explain the operation of a capacitor filter after a full-wave rectifier.
6. During capacitor discharge, why doesn't some of the current flow through the diode?
7. What is the effect on the ripple factor of the circuit in Fig. 12.5 of doubling R_L? Of halving C? Of doubling V_m?
8. How does the maximum allowable diode current limit the value of C?
9. Does Eq. 12-18 apply if L is too small? Why?
10. Sketch and explain the operation of a voltage regulator using the gas diode of Fig. 9.14.
11. Sketch and label the spectrum of frequencies transmitted by your favorite AM station during a typical music program.
12. Explain how a nonlinear device produces amplitude modulation and demodulation.
13. How many telephone conversations (two-way) can be carried on a telephone cable which transmits frequencies up to 8 Mc? How many television programs?
14. Why is a high frequency needed for a radio broadcast carrier?

EXERCISES

1. A semiconductor diode with $R_f = 1$ kΩ and $R_r = 10$ kΩ is connected in series with $R_L = 1$ kΩ. A square voltage wave with peak values of ± 100 V is applied to the series combination.
   (a) Sketch the square voltage waveform and the waveform of i_L.
   (b) Calculate the d-c current in R_L and the rms voltage across R_L.
2. A voltage $v = 200 \sin \omega t$ V is applied across a series combination of $R_L = 400$ Ω and a diode with a forward resistance $R_f = 100$ Ω.
   (a) Sketch, on the same graph, labelled curves showing v, i, and v_d (the voltage across the diode).
   (b) A d'Arsonval type d-c ammeter and an electrodynamometer type a-c ammeter are connected in series with R_L. Predict the readings on these instruments.
   (c) D-c voltmeters are connected across R_L and across the diode. Predict the readings on these instruments. Does $I_{dc}R = V_{dc}$?
3. Rectification efficiency is defined as the ratio of d-c power delivered to the load to a-c power delivered to the rectifier circuit (rectifier and load).
   (a) Calculate the rectification efficiency of the single-phase rectifier circuit in Exercise 1 for a square-wave input, assuming $R_r = \infty$.

(b) Repeat for a full-wave rectifier using two identical rectifiers and a center-tapped transformer.

(c) Repeat for a full-wave bridge rectifier using four identical diodes.

4. Derive Eq. 12.5 given that $i = I_{dc} + i_{ac}$ where I_{dc} is the average value and i_{ac} is the varying component of a periodic wave.

5. A 60-cps half-wave rectifier with a capacitor filter ($C = 20 \ \mu F$) supplies 10 mA of direct current to a load resistance of 20 kΩ. Estimate the transformer secondary voltage (rms), the ripple factor, the conduction angle, and the peak diode current.

6. Repeat Exercise 5 with $C = 40 \ \mu F$.

7. A 60-cps half-wave rectifier circuit with a capacitor filter is to be designed to supply 300 V at 30 mA with less than 3% ripple factor.

(a) Draw a clearly labeled wiring diagram and a graph showing supply voltage, load voltage, and diode current as functions of time.

(b) Approximately what transformer secondary voltage (rms) is required?

(c) Using the approximate analysis, estimate the capacitance required.

(d) Estimate the peak diode current.

(e) On the graph of part (a), indicate the peak inverse voltage and estimate its value.

8. The output of a 60-cps full-wave rectifier is applied to the filter shown in Fig. 12.8. The filter reactances at 60 cps (Note!) are $X_L = 1050 \ \Omega$ and $X_C = 200 \ \Omega$. The d-c voltage across $R_L = 10 \ k\Omega$ is 300 V.

(a) Determine the a-c ripple voltage (rms) in the output.

(b) Determine the rms value of the next higher harmonic in the output.

9. The specifications of Exercise 7 are to be met by a full-wave rectifier and an L-section filter with $C = 8 \ \mu F$. Assuming that the rectifier output voltage is represented by the first two terms of the Fourier series,

(a) Calculate the required transformer secondary voltage (rms), stating any necessary assumptions.

(b) Specify the required value of inductance L.

(c) Determine the factor by which the filter has reduced the magnitude of the a-c voltage component.

(d) Predict, without detailed calculation, the a-c voltage across R_L if two L-sections in cascade are used.

10. A full-wave rectifier uses a transformer supplying 300 V (maximum value across each half of the secondary) at 60 cps to diodes of negligible resistance, an L-section filter, and a load resistance of 5 kΩ. The filter inductor has an inductance of 10 H and a resistance of 250 Ω.

(a) Write an approximate expression for the rectifier output voltage.

(b) Estimate the d-c voltage output.

(c) Specify the filter capacitor for a ripple factor of 0.01.

11. A very effective filter consists of a shunt capacitor ($C_1 = 8 \ \mu F$) followed by an L-section ($L = 20 \ H$ and $C_2 = 8 \ \mu F$) to form a "π-section." With a full-wave rectifier the principal ripple component across the first capacitor is estimated to be $v = 0.05 V_{dc} \sin 2\omega t$.

(a) Draw a labeled wiring diagram of the complete rectifier and filter.

(b) Estimate the ripple factor in the output. (Assume input at 60 cps.)

12. A d-c voltage source consists of $V_s = 22$ V and $R_s = 20 \ \Omega$, as shown in Fig. 12.17a.

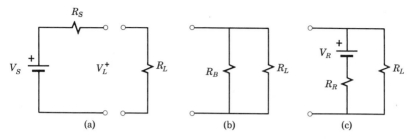

Fig. 12.17

(a) Calculate the percent variation in load voltage V_L as R_L varies from 200 to 400 Ω.

(b) Repeat for Fig. 12.17b with "bleeder" resistance $R_B = 200$ Ω.

(c) Repeat for Fig. 12.17c with $V_R = 20$ V and $R_R = 4$ Ω.

(d) Summarize the voltage regulation properties of circuits (b) and (c).

(e) What passive electronic device could replace the regulator of circuit (c)?

13. A Zener diode with $V_Z = 30$ V and $R_Z = 10$ Ω is used in the circuit of Fig. 12.10a with $R_S = 20$ Ω. The maximum allowable current $I_Z = 300$ mA.

(a) For $V_L = 33$ V and $I_L = 100$ mA, calculate R_L and V_1.

(b) If R_L stays constant and V_1 drops by 10%, predict the percent change in V_L.

(c) If V_1 stays constant at the value calculated in part (a) and I_L increases to 200 mA, predict the new V_L.

14. If R_L in Exercise 13(a) stays constant and V_1 drops to 29 V, predict the new values of V_L and I_Z (Careful!).

15. Station KFAX ("110 on your dial") is broadcasting a signal consisting of middle C with 60% modulation.

(a) Write the equation of the amplitude-modulated wave as a function of time and identify the components.

(b) For the signal in part (a), what fraction of the total power radiated is in the intelligence-bearing sidebands?

(c) The Federal Communications Commission limits the amount of "over-modulation" (i.e., greater than 100%). Why is such a limitation desirable? Why would a radio engineer wish to operate under conditions where over-modulation occurs occasionally?

16. A 1200-kc carrier has its amplitude varied sinusoidally from zero to $2V_c$ at a rate of 2000 times per second. Sketch the resulting modulated wave and list the frequencies of the components appearing in the transmitted wave.

17. (a) List in order of increasing frequency and show on a frequency spectrum all the components occurring when two voltages $v_1 = 2 \sin \omega t$ and $v_2 = 5 \sin 10 \, \omega t$ are multiplied together.

(b) If the product of v_1 and v_2 is applied to a device for which $i = v + 0.1v^2$, repeat part (a) for the components in the output current.

18. Channel 4, a typical TV channel, extends from 66 to 72 Mc. A ruby laser operates in the red region with a wavelength of 7000 Å. If the useful band-width of a laser beam is equal to 0.2% of its carrier frequency, how many TV channels could be carried on a single laser beam?

19. A signal $v = A \sin 50{,}000t + B \sin 51{,}000t$ is applied to the input of a device whose output is defined by $i = av + bv^2$.

(a) List the frequencies of the components appearing in the output.

(b) Show the components on a frequency spectrum.

(c) Under what conditions does this represent demodulation?

20. Show the components of Eq. 12-28 on a frequency spectrum. Which are important in amplitude modulation?

21. Identify the sinusoidal components represented by the terms of Eq. 12-30 and show them on a frequency spectrum. Which are important in demodulation?

22. Draw a clearly labeled block diagram of a telemetry system for recording on the ground the blood pressure of an astronaut during a manned missile flight.

PROBLEMS

1. In the circuit of Fig. 12.5, $V_m = 400$ V, $C = 10$ μF, $R_L = 4$ kΩ, and the diode resistance is negligible.

(a) Plot to a large scale the variation in load voltage v_L.

(b) Calculate precisely the d-c voltage across the load and the maximum value of diode current.

(c) Compare the answers to part (b) with results obtained by the approximate analysis and draw conclusions regarding the validity of the approximate method in this extreme example.

2. While constructing the filter described in Example 3, a technician suggests replacing the inductor L with a much cheaper resistor with the same "impedance." What is the ripple factor if this is done? Is this a practical solution? (See data in Example 2.) Under what circumstances might this be a practical solution?

3. Redesign the filter of Example 2 with a full-wave rectifier. Compare the results with those for a half-wave rectifier.

4. A load of resistance $R_L = 250$ Ω requires a d-c voltage of 50 ± 0.5 V. A Zener diode for which $V_Z = 49$ V and $R_Z = 5$ Ω is available. Design a voltage regulator which will keep the load voltage within the prescribed limits even though the supply voltage varies ± 5V.

5. A device having the characteristic $i = av^2$ is proposed as a modulator in place of the diode in Fig. 12.13. Will this device provide amplitude modulation?

6. The output of a radio transmitter consists of a 4-Mc carrier with 50% modulation at 2 kc. What fraction of the total power transmitted is in the intelligence-bearing sidebands? It is suggested that efficiency of point-to-point transmission could be improved if the carrier and lower sideband are "suppressed" and only the upper sideband is transmitted. The carrier (of known frequency) would be added at the *receiver*. Will this "work"? Justify your answer and comment on the bandwidth required and the efficiency gained.

◆ **WAVESHAPING**
◆ **LOGIC CIRCUITS**
◆ **LOGIC OPERATIONS**

CHAPTER **13**

Waveshaping and Logic Circuits

The original Telstar satellite was a 170-pound, million-dollar communications package containing 1464 diodes, 1024 transistors, and 1 vacuum tube. A veritable space laboratory, it included complete receiving and transmitting facilities, elaborate control equipment, and complicated experimental apparatus. In addition to amplification, the semiconductor devices performed a great variety of functions.

A major virtue of electronic circuits is the ease, speed, and precision with which voltage and current waveforms can be controlled. Rectifying and filtering transform inexpensive sinusoidal currents into more useful direct currents; modulating and demodulating permit the use of easily transmitted high-frequency waves to carry low-frequency information. Other useful circuit functions include differentiating, integrating, clipping, and clamping.

The "sound" transmitted by a television carrier modulated by an audio-frequency wave is in the form of *continuous* signals; the signal amplitude or frequency can take any value within a wide range of values. In contrast, the information which triggers the scanning of the picture tube is in the form of *discrete* or *digital* signals; the signal is present or absent. One purpose of waveshaping circuits is to produce digital signals in the form of precisely timed pulses.

The processing of information in digital form requires special circuits, and the efficient design of digital circuits requires a special numbering system and even a special form of algebra. The circuits must provide for storing instructions and data, receiving new data, making decisions, and communicating the results. For example, an automatic airline reservation system must receive and store information from the airline regarding the number of seats available on each flight, respond to inquiries from travel agents, subtract the number of seats requested from the number available or add the number of seats cancelled, handle 50 or so requests per minute, and keep no one waiting more than a minute.

Information processing is an important component of all branches of engineering. The astronautical engineer may be designing a programmed guidance system. The chemical engineer may require an automatic process control system. The civil engineer may be concerned with traffic flow data. The petroleum engineer may wish to have a continuous record of soil properties during drilling. The mechanical engineer may need a continuous analysis of gas turbine operation. The industrial engineer may be developing an automatic inventory control system. In addition, nearly every scientist engaged in experimental work can benefit from the new data processing techniques.

In this chapter, only a brief look at this important field can be provided. The design of practical circuits for optimum performance is left to advanced courses for students with special interests. The emphasis here is on understanding the principles of waveshaping and appreciating the possibilities in logic operations.

WAVESHAPING

Some of the basic waveshaping functions are illustrated by a radar pulse-train generator. The word *radar* stands for *r*adio *d*etection *a*nd *r*anging. A very short burst of high-intensity radiation is transmitted in a given direction; a return echo indicates the presence, distance, direction, and speed of a reflecting object. The operation of a radar system requires a precisely formed series of timing pulses. Typically, these may be of 5 μsec duration with a repetition rate of 500 pulses per sec. Starting with a 500-cps sinusoidal generator, the pulse train could be developed as shown in Fig. 13.1. Can you visualize some relatively simple electronic circuits which would perform the indicated functions?

Differentiating

There are special amplifiers for precise differentiation and integration (described in Chapter 20), but within limits the simple circuit of Fig. 13.2 provides an output which is the derivative of the input. For the special

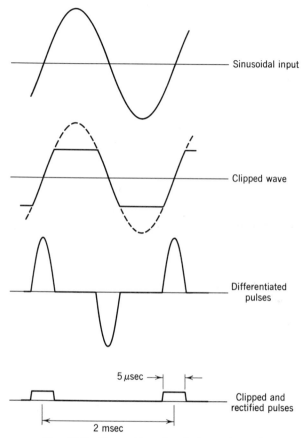

Sinusoidal input

Clipped wave

Differentiated
pulses

5 μsec →| |←

Clipped and
rectified pulses

2 msec

Fig. 13.1   Generation of a timing pulse train.

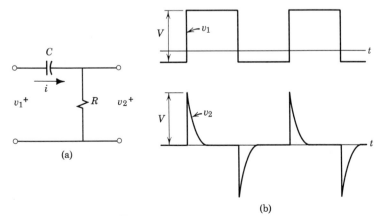

v_1

V

t

v_2

V

t

C

i

$v_1{}^+$ R $v_2{}^+$

(a)

(b)

Fig. 13.2   Differentiating circuit.

case of a rectangular input voltage wave (Fig. 13.2b), the output voltage is proportional to the RC charging current in response to a step input voltage. In this case a linear circuit transforms a rectangular wave into a series of short pulses if the time constant $\tau = RC$ is small compared to the period of the input wave.

The general operation of this circuit is revealed if we make some simplifying assumptions. Applying Kirchhoff's voltage law to the left-hand loop,

$$v_1 = v_C + v_R \cong v_C \qquad (13\text{-}1)$$

if v_R is small compared to v_C. Then

$$i = C\frac{dv_C}{dt} \cong C\frac{dv_1}{dt}$$

and

$$v_2 = v_R = Ri \cong RC\frac{dv_1}{dt} \qquad (13\text{-}2)$$

The output is approximately proportional to the derivative of the input. Can you visualize another combination of linear elements which would perform differentiation?

Integrating

From our previous experience with circuits we expect that if differentiating is possible, integrating is also. In Fig. 13.3b, a square wave of voltage has been applied long enough for a cyclic operation to be established. The time constant RC is a little greater than the half-period of

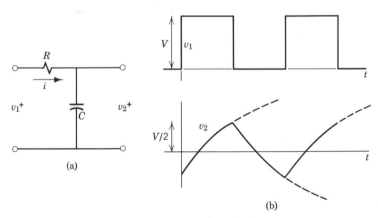

Fig. 13.3 Integrating circuit.

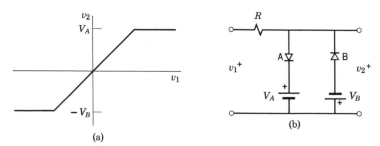

Fig. 13.4 Clipping characteristic and circuit.

the square wave. The capacitor C charges and discharges on alternate half-cycles, and the output voltage is as shown.

If the time constant RC is large compared to the period T of the square waves, only the straight portion of the exponential appears and the output is the *saw-tooth* wave in which voltage is directly proportional to time. In general,

$$v_1 = v_R + v_C \cong v_R = iR \tag{13-3}$$

if v_C is small compared to v_R(i.e. $RC > T$). Then

$$v_2 = \frac{1}{C} \int i \, dt \cong \frac{1}{RC} \int v_1 \, dt \tag{13-4}$$

and the output is approximately proportional to the integral of the input. If necessary, the magnitude of the signal can be restored by linear amplification.

Clipping

A *clipping* circuit provides an output voltage v_2 equal to (or proportional to) the input voltage v_1 up to a certain value V; above V the wave is clipped off. If both positive and negative peaks are to be clipped, the desired transfer characteristic is as shown in Fig. 13.4a. The switching action of diodes is used to provide clipping in Fig. 13.4b. The bias is set so that diode A conducts whenever $v_1 > V_A$ and diode B conducts whenever $v_1 < -V_B$. When $-V_B < v_1 < V_A$, neither diode conducts and voltage v_1 appears across the output terminals. When either diode is conducting, the difference between v_1 and v_2 appears as a voltage drop across R.

EXAMPLE 1

A sinewave $v_1 = 20 \sin \omega t$ V is applied to the circuit of Fig. 13.5a. Predict the output voltage v_2

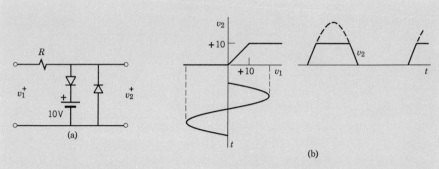

Fig. 13.5   Clipping and rectifying circuit.

SOLUTION. In this circuit the first diode and the 10-V battery provide clipping for voltages greater than $+10$ V. With $V_B = 0$, the second diode provides clipping of all negative voltages or rectification. The circuit characteristic and resulting output are as shown in Fig. 13.5b.

Graphical Determination of Diode Characteristic

Diodes, resistors and batteries can be connected in a variety of series and parallel combinations. In some cases, the transfer characteristic can be determined by inspection as in the clipping circuits just described. In other cases, the graphical methods for analysis of nonlinear circuits employed in Chapter 8 are useful.

The basic principle is that the characteristic of the combination is the composite of the characteristics of the individual components. For components in series, the composite is obtained by adding component voltages. For components in parallel, the composite is obtained by adding component currents.

In Fig. 13.6a, a battery of voltage V_B is in series with a real diode

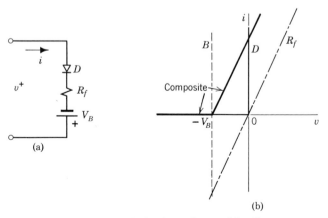

Fig. 13.6 $v\text{-}i$ characteristic of a series combination.

represented by an ideal diode D with forward resistance R_f. The v-i characteristics of the individual components are shown in Fig. 13.6b. Since the components are in series, for any value of current the total voltage is the sum of the component voltages. For $i = 0$, for example, $v_D = 0$, $v_R = 0$, and $v_B = -V_B$; the total voltage $= -V_B$. For all negative currents $v_D = \infty$; for positive currents, $v = -V_B + R_f i$. The composite characteristic is obtained readily by a graphical addition of voltage characteristics.

EXAMPLE 2

Determine the voltage transfer characteristic of the circuit in Example 1 by graphical addition.

SOLUTION. The procedure is first to determine v_2 and v_1 as functions of i and then to determine the v_2 versus v_1 characteristic.

The characteristic of diode B is drawn in Fig. 13.7b, and then the series combination of diode A and the 10-V battery. Since $i = i_a + i_b$, the v_2 versus i characteristic is obtained by adding the current curves; the result is shown in Fig. 13.7c. The v_R versus i characteristic is drawn and then $v_1 = v_2 + v_R$ is obtained by adding voltage curves. For $0 \le v \le 10$, $v_1 = v_2$ as shown on the transfer characteristic of Fig. 13.7d. For $v_1 < 0$ and $> +10$, v_2 is held constant at these values by the diodes.

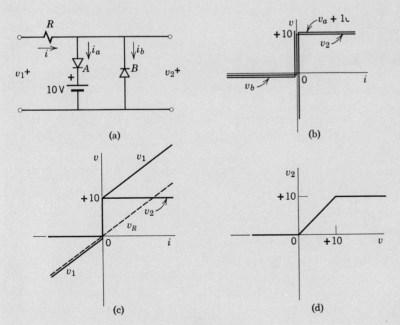

Fig. 13.7

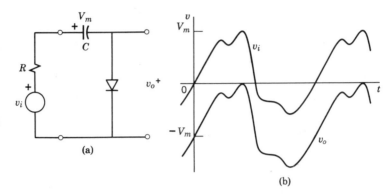

Fig. 13.8   A diode clamping circuit.

Clamping

To provide satisfactory pictures in television receivers, it is necessary that the peak values of certain variable signal voltages be held or *clamped* at predetermined levels.   In passing through R-C coupled amplifiers, the reference level is lost and a *clamper* or *d-c restorer* is used.

In the circuit of Fig. 13.8a, if R is low the capacitor tends to charge up to the peak value of the input wave, just as in the half-wave rectifier with capacitor.   When the polarity of v_i reverses, the capacitor voltage remains at V_m because the diode prevents current flow in the opposite direction.   Neglecting the small voltage across R, the output voltage across the diode is

$$v_o = v_i - V_m \qquad (13\text{-}5)$$

The signal waveform is unaffected, but a d-c value just equal to the peak value of the signal has been introduced.   The positive peak is said to be clamped at zero.

If the amplitude of the input signal changes, the d-c voltage across C also changes (after a few cycles) and the output voltage again just touches the axis.   If the diode is reversed, the negative peaks are clamped at zero.   If a battery is inserted in series with the diode, the reference level of the output may be maintained at voltage V_B.

Clamping and rectifying are related waveshaping functions performed by the same combination of diode and capacitor.   In the rectifier the variable component is rejected and the d-c value is transmitted; in the clamper the variable component is transmitted and the d-c component is restored.

LOGIC CIRCUITS

Digital computers, automatic dialing systems, process controls, and instrumentation systems have the ability to take action in response to input stimuli and in accordance with instructions. For example, in the high reliability systems employed in manned space vehicles a common provision is the so-called "vote-taking" procedure in which action is taken if and only if two of three parallel devices recommend action.

In performing such functions, an information processing system follows a certain *logic;* the basic logic operations involved are described as AND, OR, NOT AND (NAND), and NOT OR (NOR). Electronic circuits can perform such operations dependably, at great speed, and with little power consumption. Our purpose here is to describe the basic logic circuits, indicate how diodes can be used to perform the logic operations, and then show how transistors can perform the operations more effectively.

Gates

A *gate* is a device which allows a signal to pass only under prescribed conditions. If the gate is open, the signal (usually in the form of a pulse) is passed on; if the gate is closed, there is no signal output. First we consider gates employing magnetically operated switches called *relays*. If the switches are normally open, they close when input signals in the form of currents are applied to the relay coils.

In Fig. 13.9, the lamp is turned on if switch A AND switch B are closed; it is therefore called an AND circuit or AND gate. In Fig. 13.10, the lamp is turned on if switch A OR switch B is closed OR if both are closed; it is, therefore, called an OR circuit. In general, there may be several inputs and the output may be fed to several other logic elements. In Fig. 13.11, there are three inputs and there is an output (the lamp is lighted) only if switches A AND B AND C are closed.

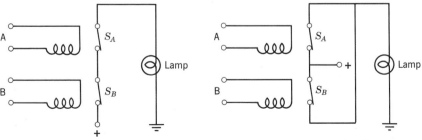

Fig. 13.9 AND circuit.   **Fig. 13.10** OR circuit.

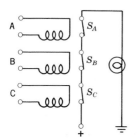

Fig. 13.11 Three-input
AND circuit.

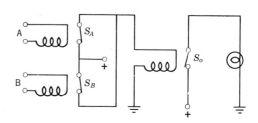

Fig. 13.12 NOR circuit.

The output may be *inverted*. For example, in the circuit of Fig. 13.12, if switch A OR B is closed, the output switch S_o (normally closed) is opened and the lamp is NOT lighted; for input at A OR B, there is NOT an output. This is called an INVERTED OR circuit, or a NOT OR circuit, or a NOR circuit. Another possibility is an EXCLUSIVE OR circuit in which there is an output if switch A OR B is closed, but NOT if switches A AND B are closed. (Can you conceive such an arrangement?)

The Binary Number System

In the decimal system a quantity is represented by the *value* and the *position* of a digit. The number 503.14 means

$$500 \quad + 0 \quad\quad + 3 \quad\quad +\tfrac{1}{10} \quad\quad + \tfrac{4}{100}$$

or

$$5 \times 10^2 + 0 \times 10^1 + 3 \times 10^0 + 1 \times 10^{-1} + 4 \times 10^{-2}$$

In other words, 10 is the *base* and each position to the left or right of the decimal point corresponds to a *power* of 10. Perhaps it is unfortunate that we do not have 12 fingers, because in certain ways 12 would be a better base. In fact, such a base-twelve or *duodecimal* system was used by the Babylonians, and we still use 12 in subdividing the foot, the year, and the clock face.

In representing data by ON-OFF switch position, there are only two possibilities and the corresponding numbers are "1" and "0." In such a *binary* system the base is 2 and the total number of fingers on both hands is written 1010 since

$$1 \times 2^3 + 0 \times 2^2 + 1 \times 2^1 + 0 \times 2^0 = 8 + 0 + 2 + 0 = 10$$

In electronic logic circuits the numbers "1" and "0" usually correspond to two easily distinguished voltage levels. For example, "1" may correspond to a voltage of approximately $+10$ V and "0" to a voltage near zero. The circuit designer is free to choose these levels.

Diode Logic Circuits

An ideal diode, which can be closely approximated by a semiconductor diode, is a "synchronous switch" because whenever the diode is forward-biased, it allows current to pass freely (the switch is ON), and when reverse-biased, no current flows (the switch is OFF). This switching action can be very rapid and trouble-free because there are no moving parts, inertia effects, contact bounce, or coil inductance.

The operation of diodes in performing logic functions is illustrated in the following examples. In Fig. 13.13, the input signals are in the form of positive pulses equal to or greater than 10 V. If there is input to A AND B AND C, there is no current flow through R, no voltage drop across R, and a positive voltage appears at the output. (This is a "single-line" diagram and all voltages are with respect to ground, which may or may not be shown.) If any one of the inputs is zero, current flows through that forward-biased diode, the output voltage drops to zero, and there is no output. Note that the same function could be performed by using resistors in place of the diodes. The advantage of the diodes is that they isolate the inputs from each other; a large positive pulse at terminal A has no effect on inputs B and C.

In Fig. 13.14 the output of the diode OR circuit appears across R. A positive input at A OR B OR C produces a positive voltage across R and raises the potential of point P. But this output is inevitably less than the input and after several cascaded operations the signal would decrease

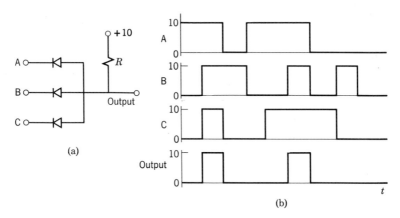

Fig. 13.13 Diode AND circuit and typical response.

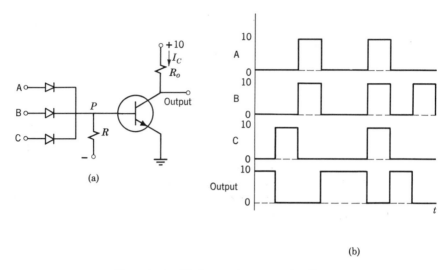

(a)

(b)

Fig. 13.14   Diode-transistor NOR circuit.

below a dependable level.   To avoid this, a transistor is used as an amplifier.   With no input, the emitter-base junction is reverse biased, little or
no collector current flows and the output voltage is +10 V.   With an
input at A OR B OR C, the emitter-base junction is forward-biased and
I_C causes a voltage drop across R_o, dropping the output to nearly zero
(V_{CE} is usually a few tenths of a volt).   Note that the output is inverted
and this is a NOT OR (NOR) circuit.

Transistors as Switches

The number of electronic elements in a logic circuit can be reduced by
taking advantage of the switching capabilities of transistors.   For amplification, the transistor is operated in the *linear* or *normal* region with the
emitter-base junction forward-biased and the collector-base junction
reverse-biased.   If both junctions are reverse-biased, practically no
collector current flows and the transistor is said to be operating in the
cutoff region.   In the basic switching circuit of Fig. 13.16, if the input
voltage is zero, V_{OB} reverse-biases the base-emitter junction and operation is at point 1 in Fig. 13.15.   The collector current is practically zero
($I_C \cong I_{CO}$) and the *switch* whose contacts are the collector and emitter
terminals is "open."   The cutoff current is exaggerated in Fig. 13.15; a
typical value of collector current of less than 0.1 mA with an applied voltage of 8 V corresponds to a d-c *cutoff resistance* of around 100,000 Ω.

A positive voltage pulse applied to the input terminal forward-biases
the emitter-base junction, causes an appreciable base current, and moves

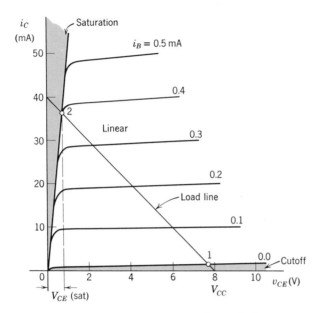

Fig. 13.15 Transistor operating regions.

operation to point 2 (Fig. 13.15). An increase in base current above 0.4 mA produces no further effect on collector current and the transistor is said to be operating in the *saturation region*. The minimum voltage drop across the "switch" is called *collector saturation* voltage $V_{CE(\text{sat})}$ and is typically a few tenths of a volt. Note that if V_{CE} is less than V_{BE}, the collector-base junction is also forward-biased. As indicated in Fig. 13.15, a collector current of around 40 mA at a saturation voltage of 0.4 V corresponds to a *saturation resistance* of around 10 Ω. When the transistor switch is "closed," the collector current is determined primarily by the load resistance and $I_C \cong V_{CC}/R_L$.

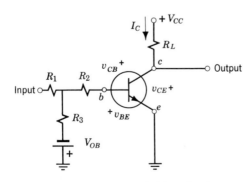

Fig. 13.16 Transistor switching circuit.

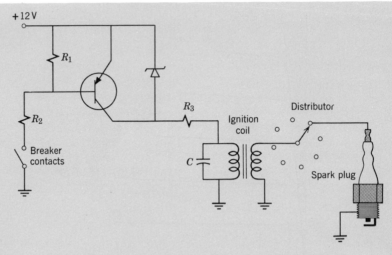

Fig. 13.17 An elementary transistorized ignition system.

EXAMPLE 3

Devise a solid-state automobile ignition system in which breaker contact burning is minimized and output voltage does not fall off at high engine speed.

SOLUTION. Burning of the breaker contacts in conventional systems occurs because the full primary current of the ignition coil, 4 or 5 A, must be interrupted. Output voltage falls off at high speed because of insufficient time for full primary current build up. Both of these difficulties can be eliminated by using a transistor as a switch.

As shown in Fig. 13.17, the transistor is normally in cutoff. Closing the breaker contacts provides forward bias through the voltage divider R_1 and R_2; the breaker current is a few tenths of an ampere and burning is minimized. With the transistor in saturation, ballast resistor R_3 permits a maximum collector current of 7 to 12 A (instead of the conventional 4 or 5 A) and the coil requirements are less stringent. The switching time of transistors is small compared to the interval between firings even at high engine speed, and output voltage ($= M \, di_1/dt$) is relatively constant. The Zener diode protects the transistor against the high voltage induced in the primary when the primary current is interrupted.

Transistor Logic Circuits

Transistor switches can be connected in series or parallel to provide AND or OR gates similar to those achieved with diodes. In Fig. 13.18, the transistor switches are held OFF by the negative bias voltages; positive pulses applied to terminals A AND B close the series switches and drop the

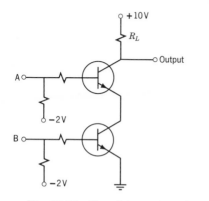

Fig. 13.18 Transistor NAND gate.

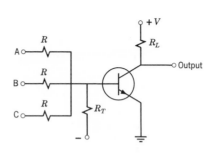

Fig. 13.19 Basic NOR gate.

output potential from $+10$ to 0 V. Because of the inversion, the function performed is NOT AND or NAND.

The ability of the transistor to restore a signal to its original level permits accomplishing logic functions with fewer electronic elements. For many purposes the circuit of Fig. 13.14 can be replaced by that in Fig. 13.19. In the latter circuit, a positive input at terminal A OR B OR C causes sufficient base current to put the transistor in saturation. The inexpensive resistors provide the OR gating since the bias current requirement is not stringent. The transistor amplifies and inverts and the function is NOT OR or NOR. (R_T is large compared to R and provides temperature stability by insuring that the transistor is held OFF if I_{CO} should increase with temperature.) Most logic operations can be realized by combinations of NOR gates; along with a suitable memory unit, the NOR gate is the basic building block of many logic systems.

EXAMPLE 4

Two basic NOR units are combined into the logic system shown in Fig. 13.20.

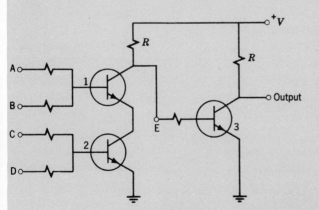

Partial Truth Table

A	B	C	D	E	Output
0	0	0	0	1	0
1	0	0	0	1	0
0	0	1	0	1	0
1	0	1	0	0	1

Fig. 13.20 Series transistor AND gate.

(a) What function is performed by the third transistor? (b) Draw up a "truth table," showing the output for each of the unique input combinations.

SOLUTION. (a) A positive voltage at E (represented by "1") closes switch 3 and drops the output to zero, therefore the third transistor is an inverter.

(b) Transistors 1 and 2 are NOR units connected in series. If there is a positive input at A OR B AND if there is a positive input at C OR D, there is a negative signal at E. This is inverted to provide a positive output as shown in the last line of the partial "truth table." (Can you complete the truth table?)

The Bistable Multivibrator

Along with the *decision* elements just described, we need a *memory* element to store instructions and results. A binary storage device must have two distinct states, and it must remain in one state until instructed to change. It must change rapidly from one state to the other, and the state value (0 or 1) must be clearly evident. The *bistable multivibrator* or *flip-flop*, a simple device which meets these requirements inexpensively and reliably, is used in all types of digital data processing systems.

The operation of the flip-flop is based on the switching and amplifying properties of a transistor. In the switch in Fig. 13.21a, the voltage divider R_a-R_b reverse-biases the base-emitter junction and the transistor is in cutoff or the switch is open; because of inversion, a positive voltage appears at the output terminal. If a positive pulse is applied to the input, the base-emitter junction is forward-biased, the switch is closed, and the output voltage drops to zero (nearly). The voltage change at the output may be much higher than the input switching voltage.

To follow the operation of the flip-flop, assume that T_2 is conducting

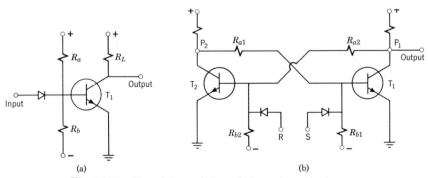

(a)   (b)

Fig. 13.21   Transistor switch and elementary flip-flop.

(closed) and T_1 is cut off (open). With T_2 conducting, the potential of point P_2 is zero and, in combination with the negative voltage applied to R_{b1}, this insures that T_1 is cut off. With T_1 cut off, the potential of point P_1 is large and positive and this supplies the bias which insures that T_2 is conducting. In other words, this is a stable state which we may designate as the 0 state of this binary storage element.

A positive pulse applied to terminal R has no effect since T_2 is already conducting. However, a positive pulse at S (the *set* terminal) causes T_1 to begin conducting, the potential of P_1 drops, the forward bias on T_2 is reduced, the potential of P_2 rises, the forward bias on T_1 increases, the potential of P_1 drops further, T_1 goes into saturation, and T_2 is cut off. The output voltage is zero and this indicates another stable state which we may designate as the 1 state. In a well-designed flip-flop, this change in state takes place in a fraction of a microsecond, and we see that this simple device satisfies all the requirements of a binary storage element.

If a flip-flop in the 1 state receives a positive pulse at R (the *reset* terminal), transition proceeds in the opposite direction (since the device is symmetric) and the device is reset to the 0 state. In the practical flip-flop of Fig. 13.22, additional circuit elements are included. The coupling

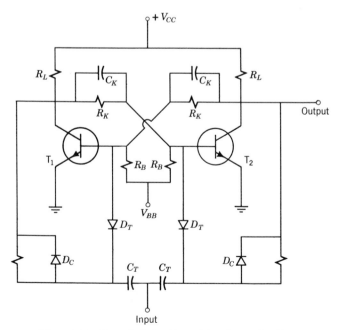

Fig. 13.22 Practical flip-flop with trigger circuit.

capacitors C_K speed up the switching by providing "overdrive" to the transistor being turned on.   The trigger circuit consisting of D_C, C_T, and D_T "steers" the negative input pulse to whichever transistor is ON (say T_2).   This turns OFF T_2 and turns ON T_1.   The process is reversed at the next input pulse and the flip-flop has become a binary counter.

EXAMPLE 5

Devise a combination of flip-flops so that every fourth input pulse is indicated at the output.

In	A_1	A_2	B_1	B_2	Out
	0	1	0	1	
1	1	0	0	1	0
2	0	1	1	0	0
3	1	0	1	0	0
4	0	1	0	1	1

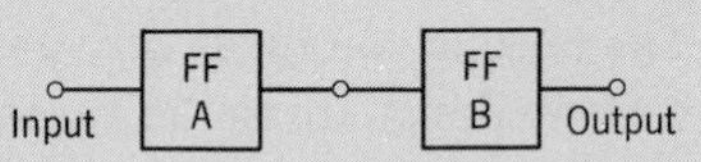

Fig. 13.23   Example 5: A scale-of-four counter.

SOLUTION.   Two practical flip-flops in cascade (Fig. 13.23) produce the desired result.   All input pulses are assumed to be negative.   Initially transistors A_1 and B_1 are OFF (the 0 state) and transistors A_2 and B_2 are ON (the 1 state). A change in state of transistor A_2 from 0 to 1 produces a negative output pulse which will trigger B_1.   A similar change in state of transistor B_2 produces an indicated output (perhaps on a neon lamp).   The second input pulse switches B_1 ON (the 1 state), and the fourth input pulse switches B_2 ON and registers as the first count of four.   This scale-of-four counter can be extended to a scale-of-sixteen counter; using feedback, the latter can be converted to reset itself after 10 input pulses and it becomes a decimal counter (see Problem 4).

LOGIC OPERATIONS

By using decision elements and memory elements, systems can be devised to carry out extremely complicated operations in accordance with instructions.   From the unlimited number of possible illustrations, two have been chosen for discussion here.   In these illustrations AND, OR, and NOT elements are shown; in practical computers the versatile NOR element would be used.

The Half-Adder

In a digital computer subtraction, multiplication, and division are modified forms of addition.   The numbers to be added are arranged so that digits in the same position are aligned; the sum of these digits is then

A	B	Sum	Carry
0	0	0	0
0	1	1	0
1	0	1	0
1	1	0	1

(a)

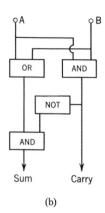

(b)

Fig. 13.24   The half-adder.

obtained, possibly with a carry.   The truth table for the addition of two binary numbers A and B is as shown in Fig. 13.24a.

Looking at the truth table, we can write: "The Sum is (A or B) AND NOT (A AND B).   The Carry is (A AND B)."   This statement can be translated into the logic diagram shown in Fig. 13.24b.   Pulses at A and B (from flip-flops) combine to form a Sum and a Carry.   The circuit is called a *half-adder* because there is no provision to introduce carries.   A complete addition system includes a half-adder followed by sufficient full-adders for the required number of places.   Another formulation of the relation displayed in the truth table is: "The Sum is NOT [(A AND B) or NOT (A OR B)].   The Carry is NOT (NOT A OR NOT B)."   This statement can be translated into a logic system using five identical NOR units. Can you do it?

The Vote-Taker

To improve reliability, it is desired that action be taken if at least two of three parallel sensing devices recommend it.   For example, a critical switch may be thrown only if two of three independent checking systems indicate that all safety precautions have been taken.   If 1 stands for YES and 0 for NO, the truth table is shown in Fig. 13.25a.   In case (4), C votes YES but A and B vote NO, so no action is taken.   In case (5), C votes NO, but A and B vote *yes*, so action is taken.

Over a century ago George Boole, the English mathematician, developed a set of laws applicable to logical relations.   Boolean algebra is useful in expressing the relation displayed in the truth table in mathematical form and in pointing the way to the simplest realization of a complicated logic operation.   Without Boolean algebra we must feel our

Case	A	B	C	Out
(1)	0	0	0	0
(2)	1	0	0	0
(3)	0	1	0	0
(4)	0	0	1	0
(5)	1	1	0	1
(6)	0	1	1	1
(7)	1	0	1	1
(8)	1	1	1	1

(a)

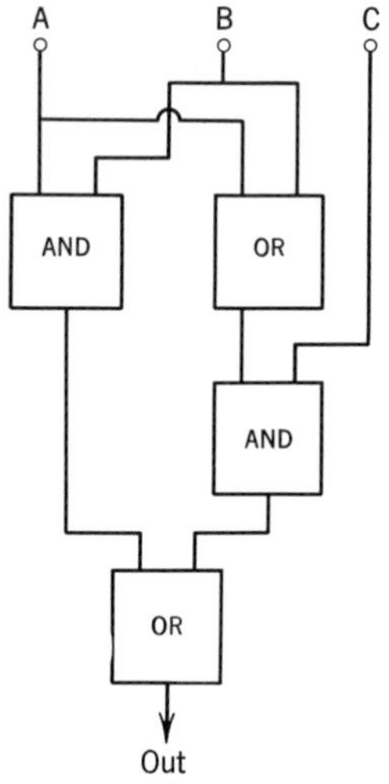

Fig. 13.25   The vote taker.   (b)

way along by trial and error.   Looking at the truth table, we can write: "Action is to be taken if A AND B AND NOT C, OR B AND C AND NOT A, OR A AND C AND NOT B, OR A AND B AND C so indicate."   An equivalent but simpler statement is: "Action is to be taken if A AND B, OR C AND (A OR B) so indicate," where (A OR B) includes the possibility of (A AND B). The second statement can be derived from the first by using Boolean algebra.   The logic designer then translates the operational relation into the logic diagram shown in Fig. 13.25b.

SUMMARY

◆ Waveforms can be shaped easily, rapidly, and precisely.
  An RC circuit can perform differentiation or integration.
  A diode-resistor-battery circuit can perform clipping.
  A peak-charging capacitor can clamp signals to desired levels.
  The characteristics of diode-resistor-battery combinations can be determined graphically by adding currents or voltages.

◆ Logic circuits employ discrete instead of continuous signals.
  A gate passes a signal only under prescribed conditions.
  Basic logic operations employ AND, OR, NAND, and NOR gates.
  Binary data systems are based on ON-OFF switch positions.

◆ Diode logic circuits are simple, but allow signal deterioration.

◆   Transistor logic circuits are more expensive, but perform better. A change in base bias can switch a transistor from cutoff (open) to saturation (closed) almost instantaneously.

◆   The flip-flop is an inexpensive binary storage device.

◆   NOR elements and flip-flops are the basic units of computers.

REVIEW QUESTIONS

1. Explain in words the operation of a differentiator and an integrator.
2. Sketch differentiating and integrating circuits without capacitors.
3. Explain the operation of a diode clipper.
4. A circuit which clips tops and bottoms is sometimes called a "slicer." Sketch a slicer circuit and explain its operation.
5. Sketch a clamping circuit and explain its operation.
6. Distinguish between AND, OR, and NOR functions.
7. Why is the binary system useful in electronic data processing?
8. Draw a diode OR circuit and explain its operation.
9. Can a diode circuit perform inversion? Explain.
10. Explain how a transistor can be used as a controlled switch.
11. What are the advantages of transistors as logic elements?
12. What is a flip-flop? What is its function in a computer?
13. In what respect is an ordinary wall switch like a flip-flop?
14. How many flip-flops are required for a scale-of-sixteen counter?
15. What is a "truth table"? How is it used?
16. Describe a flip-flop in terms of two NOR units.

EXERCISES

1. Stating the necessary simplifying assumptions, demonstrate that the circuit of Fig. 13.26 is an integrator.

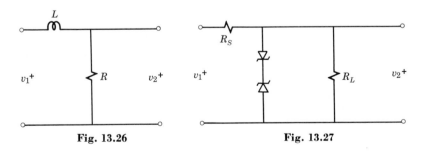

Fig. 13.26   **Fig. 13.27**

2. Two Zener diodes are connected as shown in Fig. 13.27. For $v_1 = V_m \sin \omega t$, where V_m is large compared to the Zener breakdown voltage, plot $v_2(t)$. What function is performed by this circuit?

3. A 2N699B transistor in the common-emitter configuration is biased for quiescent operation at $I_B = 1$ mA with $V_{CC} = 20$ V and $R_L = 200$ Ω. The input signal is $i_b = 20 \sin \omega t$ mA. Sketch the input signal and collector current waveform on the same time axis. What function is performed by this device?

4. A 6J5 triode is operated with $V_{bb} = 200$ V, $V_{cc} = 6$ V, and $R_L = 20$ kΩ. A series combination of $v_1 = 100 \sin \omega t$ V and $R_1 = 1$ MΩ is connected to the input.

   (a) Draw a labeled wiring diagram.

   (b) If the input resistance of the grid-cathode "diode" is approximately 1000 Ω for positive grid voltages, estimate the actual grid voltage when $v_1 = 100$ V.

   (c) Sketch v_1 and the a-c component of the plate voltage on the same time axis. What function is performed by this circuit?

5. In Fig. 13.28, $V_a = 3$ V, $V_b = 6$ V, and $R = 1$ kΩ.

   (a) Sketch the transfer characteristic v_2 versus v_1.

   (b) For $v_1 = 20 \sin \omega t$ V, sketch v_2 on the same time axis.

   (c) For $v_1 = \pm 20$ V, what is the current i?

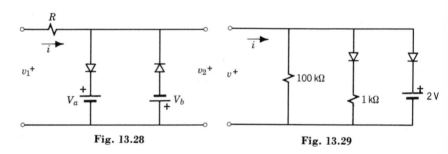

Fig. 13.28   Fig. 13.29

6. Sketch the $v - i$ characteristic of each branch of the circuit of Fig. 13.29 and, by graphical addition, the overall characteristic.

7. Repeat Exercise 6 for the circuit of Fig. 13.30.

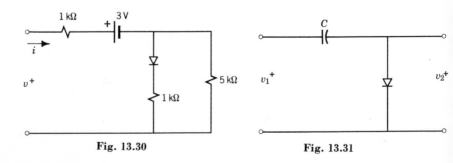

Fig. 13.30   Fig. 13.31

8. For the diode in Fig. 13.31, $R_f = 10\ \Omega$ and $R_r = 10\ \text{k}\Omega$; $C = 1\ \mu\text{F}$. A square voltage wave with peak values of ± 10 V and a period of 2 msec is applied at $t = 0$.

(a) If the capacitor is initially uncharged, determine v_2 during the first millisecond.

(b) What is the voltage on C after 1 msec?

(c) Determine v_2 during the second millisecond.

(d) Sketch v_1 and v_2 for two complete cycles.

(e) What function is performed by this circuit?

9. In Fig. 13.31, $v_1 = 10 \sin 100t$ V for 1 sec and then changes to $v_1' = 20 \sin 100t$ V. Sketch v_2 for time near $t = 1$ sec. (Assume C large.)

10. (a) Write the following decimals in binary: 1, 4, 10, 21, 31.

(b) Write the following binaries in decimal: 00101, 01101, 10101, 11000.

11. (a) Write the following decimals in binary: 2, 5, 12, 20, 40.

(b) Write the following binaries in decimal: 00011, 00110, 01010, 10011.

12. Considering only positive pulses, construct a truth table for the circuit of Fig. 13.32. Identify the circuit.

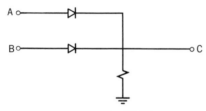

Fig. 13.32

13. Considering only positive pulses, construct a truth table for the circuit of Fig. 13.33. Identify the circuit.

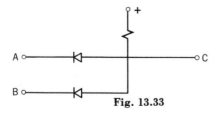

Fig. 13.33

14. If a short voltage pulse appears across R in Fig. 13.34, what voltage appears at terminal C? Considering only short positive pulses, construct a truth table for this device and identify it.

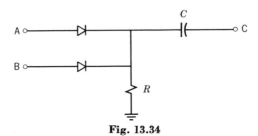

Fig. 13.34

15. Considering short negative pulses only, construct a truth table for the circuit of Fig. 13.35. Identify the circuit.

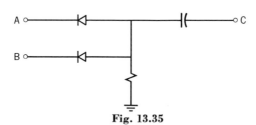

Fig. 13.35

16. Assuming $I_{CO} = 1\,\mu A$ and $V_{CE(\text{sat})} = 0.5$ V for a 2N699B operating with $V_{CC} = 20$ V and $R_L = 400\ \Omega$, estimate the saturation and cutoff resistances for switching operation.

17. Identify the logic circuit in Fig. 13.36.

(a) What are the functions of R and C?

(b) Draw up a truth table for this circuit.

(c) What advantages does this circuit possess over the corresponding diode circuit?

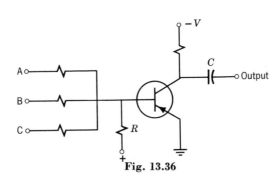

Fig. 13.36

18. Repeat Exercise 17 for Fig. 13.37.

19. In Fig. 13.37, $R = 200$ kΩ, $R_1 = 20$ kΩ, $R_2 = 5$ kΩ, C is omitted, and the inputs consist of negative pulses of amplitude 10 V. For these transistors, cutoff resistance $R_{CO} = 100$ kΩ and saturation resistance $R_{sat} = 50$ Ω.

(a) Analyze the situation and determine the voltage distribution when all inputs are zero and when all inputs are -10 V.

(b) Draw up a "voltage truth table," showing actual output voltages expected for various combinations of input pulses.

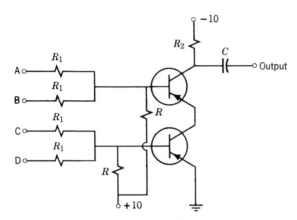

Fig. 13.37

20. Draw up a truth table for a two-input "Exclusive OR" logic unit. Using relays, devise an "Exclusive OR" circuit.

21. The flip-flop in Fig. 13.22 is triggered by negative pulses applied to the Input. A neon bulb is placed between output of transistor T_2 and ground.

(a) Does the bulb glow when T_2 is ON (closed) or OFF?

(b) If T_1 is ON and a negative pulse is applied to the Input, what happens to the bulb?

(c) If another input pulse is applied, what happens to the bulb?

22. The Output of the flip-flop in Exercise 21 is differentiated and rectified (so only negative pulses remain) and fed into another identical flip-flop (T_3 and T_4) with a neon bulb N_2 across R_L of T_4.

(a) If T_1 and T_3 are initially OFF, what pattern of lights is seen?

(b) Construct a table showing the initial pattern of lights and the pattern after each of four pulse inputs to the first flip-flop.

(c) How many flip-flops are required to count up to sixteen?

PROBLEMS

1. A simple square-wave generator is needed at home to provide an output of ± 10 V. A 60-W light bulb and a range of Zener diodes are available. Devise a suitable circuit.

2. A highway traffic counter consists of a road tube, a pressure-activated set of contacts, and a magnetic relay type counter. The high current required for fast counts on four-lane highways produces rapid contact burning and excessive maintenance costs. Devise a circuit to overcome this difficulty. Use a standard 12-V storage battery.

3. To permit the use of very low supply voltages, a NOR unit is to use two *pnp* transistors and a load resistor only. Draw a suitable circuit diagram using no other components. Show required polarities.

4. Four flip-flops (like Fig. 13.22) are connected in cascade to form a scale-of-sixteen counter. Symbolically represent each switching element by a square (two per stage) and show the input and the output for each stage. Show the path taken by pulses in the counter. Using feedback links to reintroduce counts into earlier stages, show how the circuit can be converted to a decimal counter, i.e., a counter with one output pulse for every ten input pulses.

PART III

ELECTROMAGNETIC DEVICES

CHAPTER 14

Energy Conversion Phenomena

In one sense civilization is the process whereby Man strives to become master of his environment. His success in overcoming the natural limitations of the physical world is directly related to his ability to control small and large amounts of energy. As one example, the capabilities of his senses have been greatly extended by precisely controlled devices which enable him at one extreme to communicate over vast distances and at the other to look into the nucleus of an atom. In Part II of this book we were concerned primarily with electronic devices for controlling and processing information; consideration of the associated energy was secondary.

The civilization process has also been dependent upon Man's ability to work far beyond the limitations of his own muscles. Long ago Man learned to harness animals to supply power, and then he succeeded in converting the power of the winds and rivers to his purposes. Only recently has he learned to use the energy stored in fuels to develop mechanical power and, even more recently, electrical power. Part III is concerned primarily with devices for converting energy to and from electrical form. For practical reasons, the emphasis is on devices which employ magnetic fields in electrical-mechanical energy conversion. First, however, we take a general look at energy sources, conversion methods, and some interesting new devices which hold great promise for the future.

Energy Supply

Our interest in energy conversion methods is heightened by the population explosion and the aspiration revolution.   Currently about 95% of our energy comes from fossil fuels (coal, natural gas, and petroleum) with the remainder from hydro and nuclear plants.   Estimates of the world resources of fossil fuels vary widely, but it appears that at our *present* rate of consumption the supply might last a thousand years or so.   The time of resource exhaustion seems comfortingly remote until we consider the changes taking place in population and standards of living.

The world population is now about 3 billion and doubling every 37 years.   The per capita use of energy in the United States has doubled in the last 10 years.   But if the world's peoples are to enjoy the standard of living which we accept as a matter of course, their energy consumption must increase many fold.   Taking into account the unprecedented demands of an expanding population, the exhaustion of our supply of fossil fuels appears to be only a few decades away.   New sources and more efficient conversion methods must be found, and solution of the problems associated with these new developments will require the concerted efforts of many engineers.

Energy Sources

The important present and future sources of energy include solar radiation, chemical reaction, and nuclear reaction.

Solar.   Each day there comes to the Earth from the Sun in the form of direct solar radiation an amount of energy equivalent to many years of consumption at our present rate.   Summer radiation intensity is of the order of 1 kilowatt on each square meter, and if efficient conversion methods were available, a small fraction of the Earth's surface could supply our current needs.   Some use is made of direct radiation in powering remote installations and space laboratories, but at present the indirect effects of solar radiation are more significant.

Some of the radiation causes evaporation of sea water which returns to the Earth as rain; a hydroelectric plant in the mountains receives its energy from the Sun indirectly.   Another part of the radiation causes the growth of plants and animals which are consumed by man as fuel for his muscles.   The fossil fuels represent the cumulative effect of millions of years of irradiation of living organisms and their subsequent transformation into coal and petroleum.

Chemical.   The basic idea of chemistry is that elements such as hydrogen, carbon, and oxygen can combine to form compounds, such as methane or carbon dioxide or water, which have properties entirely different from those of their constituents. Chemical binding is fundamentally an electrical phenomenon. In *ionic binding* one or more electrons are transferred from one atom to another, and the resulting charged ions are drawn together by the force of electrical attraction. For example, common salt consists of Na^+ ions surrounded by Cl^- ions. In *covalent binding* each atom contributes an electron to form a shared pair, and there is an increased density of negative charge in the region between the positively charged nuclei. For example, carbon forms four covalent bonds in most of its compounds.

In chemical reactions energy is either absorbed or evolved. In charging a storage battery, the rearrangement of the reacting compounds requires an energy input equal to the increased chemical energy. In the combustion of gasoline the new compounds possess less chemical energy and the difference is available as heat. Most of the world's power comes from the combustion of fossil fuels.

Nuclear. When a molecule of hydrogen or carbon is burned, the energy released is a few electron-volts. In contrast, the energy released in nuclear *fission* is many million electron-volts per atom. In terms of energy released per unit mass, uranium fission "fuel" is nearly 3 million times as effective as coal; in terms of energy per unit cost, uranium fuel is about 400 times as effective. The total energy stored in fissionable material in the earth's crust appears to be of the same order of magnitude as the supply of fossil fuel. The number of nuclear power plants has increased rapidly, and it is predicted that by the year 2000 nearly half of the world's power production will be from nuclear reactors.

When heavy nuclei split in the process of fission, about 0.1% of the original mass is converted into energy. In the *fusion* of two deuterons (isotopes of hydrogen) to form a helium atom, about 0.6% of the original mass is converted into energy. Since an appreciable fraction (0.015%) of all hydrogen is in the form of deuterium, ordinary sea water represents an unlimited supply of energy if fusion reactions can be initiated and controlled. To overcome the electrostatic repulsion between two deuterons requires energies corresponding to temperatures of millions of degrees. Such *thermonuclear* reactions can be initiated by the explosion of an A-bomb (nuclear fission) and sustained by the energy released by fusion; the result is an H-bomb which may yield energies equivalent to many millions of tons of TNT. If useful power is to be obtained from fusion, ways must be found to confine and control the thermonuclear reactions.

Energy and Entropy

In a general consideration of energy conversion there are two fundamental principles which were originally formulated in connection with
thermodynamics. The *first law* of thermodynamics states that energy
can be converted from one form to another, but it can be neither created nor destroyed. In applying this so-called "law of conservation of
energy," matter is included as a form of energy. One application is the
heat balance, a detailed expression of the fact that all the energy inputs
to a system must equal the sum of all the energy outputs plus any increase
in energy storage. We shall make use of this approach in analyzing the
performance of electromechanical devices.

The *second law* of thermodynamics says that no device, actual or ideal,
can both continuously and completely convert heat into work; some of
the heat is unavailable and must be rejected. For example, no engine
could extract heat from sea water and convert it to work with no effect
other than the cooling of the water. This so-called "law of degradation
of energy" stipulates what transformations of energy are possible, whereas
the first law governs the energy relations in a possible transformation.
The unavailability of energy is measured by a property called *entropy*
which has some of the characteristics of probability; a uniform distribution of energy corresponds to a high entropy. We say that the energy
of the universe remains constant, while the entropy tends toward a maximum. One of the primary activities of the engineer is directing the
inevitable degradation of energy so that in the process some useful result
is obtained.

An important characteristic of energy is whether it has an *ordered* or
disordered form. The energy of an electric current in an inductor or the
energy of a rotating flywheel is said to be ordered. In contrast, the
random thermal energy of electrons or atoms in a solid is said to be disordered. Energy conversion from an ordered form to a disordered form,
as in i^2R heating or friction braking, can be achieved with 100% efficiency.
The efficiency of energy conversion between ordered forms, as in an electric generator, can approach 100%. However, the efficiency of conversion from disordered to ordered form, as in a steam turbine (thermal to
mechanical), is limited by the requirement that some energy be rejected;
the maximum conceivable efficiency of such a conversion is $(T_1 - T_2)/T_1$
where T_1 is the highest temperature (°K) in the cycle and T_2 is the lowest
naturally available temperature. This concept of a limiting efficiency
for heat engines was presented in 1824 by the then young French engineer
Sadi Carnot.

Electrical Energy Generation

One reason for the usefulness of electrical energy is that it is highly ordered and therefore it can be converted efficiently into other forms. On the other hand, it cannot be stored conveniently, so it is usually generated as it is needed. The great variety of energy conversion possibilities is displayed in Fig. 14.1.

The great bulk of electrical energy is still generated in the process used by Edison in his first central station in 1882. Fossil fuel is burned to obtain heat to convert water into steam to drive mechanical engines to force electrical conductors through a magnetic field to generate voltage and current. An atomic power plant differs only in that the heat is obtained from nuclear reaction. In a hydroelectric plant the electrical generator is driven by a water turbine instead of a steam turbine. The virtue of magnetic-field generators is that high permeability materials permit extremely high energy densities and therefore high output from a machine of given volume. The low overall efficiency of the thermal-mechanical-electrical generating system (typically less than 40%) has been tolerated in the past because of the abundance of low-cost fuel.

Since chemical energy is more ordered than thermal energy, higher conversion efficiencies are to be expected in generators employing chemical reaction. In a *voltaic cell*, two dissimilar electrodes are separated by an electrolyte in which conduction takes place by the motion of positive and negative ions. The chemical reactions at the electrode-electrolyte surfaces provide the energy for continuous current production. In a *primary* cell, such as the ordinary dry cell or mercury battery, the energy conversion is accompanied by irreversible changes in cell composition and the cell has a limited life. In a *secondary* cell, such as the lead-acid storage battery, the chemical reactions are reversible. During discharge, lead sulphate and water are formed; the water dilutes the sulfuric acid electrolyte and the specific gravity of the electrolyte is an indication of the state of charge. The battery is charged by sending a current from an external source through the electrolyte in the opposite direction. The reactions are reversed, lead and lead dioxide are formed at the negative and positive plates, respectively, and the battery is restored to its original condition.

Fuel Cells

A device which continuously converts the chemical energy in a fuel directly into electrical energy is very attractive. By avoiding the intermediate thermal energy stage, the cost and complexity of thermal-

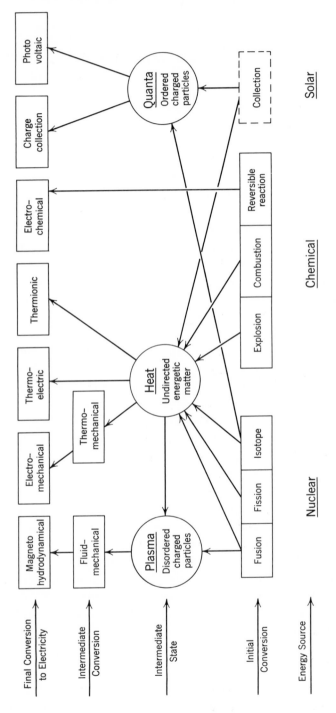

Fig. 14.1 Energy conversion to electrical form. (Courtesy General Electric Company)

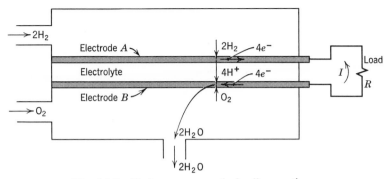

Fig. 14.2 Hydrogen-oxygen fuel cell operation.

to-mechanical-to-electrical conversion apparatus is eliminated and the Carnot efficiency limitation is removed. The *fuel cell* is such a device; already it has been used to supply power in space vehicles and it shows great promise for the future.

The operation of a hydrogen–oxygen fuel cell of the type used in the Gemini spacecraft is illustrated in Fig. 14.2. The cell consists of two chambers and two porous electrodes separated by an electrolyte. Hydrogen supplied to the upper chamber diffuses through electrode A and, in the presence of a catalyst, reacts with the electrolyte to form positive ions and free electrons. The ions migrate through the electrolyte to electrode B where they combine with oxygen and the electrons, which have passed through the external load circuit, to form water. The reaction at electrode A is

$$2H_2 \rightarrow 4H^+ + 4e^-$$

and that at electrode B is

$$4H^+ + 4e^- + O_2 \rightarrow 2H_2O$$

The important point is that the electrons are forced to do useful work before the reaction is completed. In a properly designed cell, most of the energy which would appear as heat in a combustion reaction is available as electrical energy.

A "hydrox" fuel battery gives several times as much energy as the same weight of storage battery, and the pint of drinking water produced with each kilowatt-hour is a useful by-product. Theoretical efficiencies of over 90% are indicated for some types of fuel cells and efficiencies over 80% have been obtained in the laboratory. Fuel cells which burn ordinary hydrocarbon fuels in air are already available. Inexpensive hydrocarbon fuel batteries operating at 80% efficiency could double the

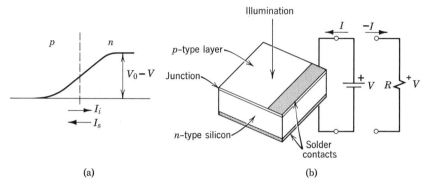

Fig. 14.3   Solar cell principle and construction.

energy potential of our fossil fuel resources.   High efficiency at partial load and quiet operation without exhaust are additional advantages.

Solar Cells

Knowing the tremendous energy available in the form of solar radiation, we can appreciate the possibilities of a device which converts light energy directly into electrical energy.   The semiconductor *solar cell* operates with fair efficiency, has an unlimited life, and has a high power capacity per unit weight.   Already it is an important source of power for long-term satellites, and continued improvement in operating characteristics will make it competitive in other applications.

The operation can be explained in terms of our knowledge of *p-n* junction diodes.   As a result of the diffusion of majority carriers near the junction (see Figs. 9.24 and 9.25) a potential barrier is created.   Under conditions of forward bias (Fig. 14.3a), the potential barrier is slightly reduced, the number of majority carriers with sufficient energy to climb the potential "hill" is increased, and a net forward current flows.   If now the junction region is irradiated with photons possessing sufficient energy, electron-hole pairs are created and the density of minority carriers is greatly increased.   (On a percentage basis, the increase in majority carriers is much smaller.)   Practically all the minority carriers drift across the junction and contribute a component I_p to the diode current. Equation 9-48 becomes

$$I = I_s \, e^{eV/kT} - I_s - I_p \qquad (14\text{-}1)$$

since I_p is in the same direction as the I_s due to thermally generated carriers.   For high light intensity and low bias voltage the net current

$$I = I_s(e^{eV/kT} - 1) - I_p \qquad (14\text{-}2)$$

is negative and the solar cell is *charging* the bias battery. Such a *p-n* junction diode is a source of electrical energy. Alternatively, the solar cell may supply a load R where $V = (-I)R$.

A practical solar cell is constructed so that the junction is exposed to the light. As shown in Fig. 14.3b, a very thin layer of *p*-type material is created by diffusion of acceptor atoms into a heavily doped *n*-type silicon wafer. Electrical contact is provided by a thin translucent nickel plating (not shown) and a solder contact over the bottom and along one edge of the top. Because the current and voltage output of a single cell are small, cells are usually connected in series and parallel to form solar batteries. Overall efficiencies are in the range from 10 to 15% and satellite units provide 10 to 15 watts per pound. These favorable operating characteristics, the plentiful supply of the chief ingredient silicon, and the ease of mass production of the units all point to increased use of solar cells for energy conversion.

Thermoelectric Converters

The fuel cell is based on an old idea; it has become important recently because of advances in basic science which resulted in higher efficiencies. The solar cell is a modern development based on new insights into semiconductor phenomena. The *thermoelectric* converter represents a new application of an old idea. In 1821, Seebeck noted that heat applied to a junction of dissimilar metals could produce a small current in a closed circuit. The efficiency of conversion was so low, however, that his *thermocouples* were applied only for measurement purposes. Advances in solid-state theory and technology have led to higher efficiencies and the design of practical energy converters.

The operation of a semiconductor converter is similar to that of a solar cell in that energy is added to generate electron-hole pairs near a *p-n* junction; the directional characteristic of the junction produces a separation of charge and a net current flow which is available to do work. As shown in Fig. 14.4a, the hot junction is maintained at temperature T_1 by an input of thermal energy. Holes generated near the junction drift across the junction into the *p* region, and electrons drift into the *n* region. At the cold junction, the effect is less and therefore there is a net flow of current consisting of electrons in the *n* material and holes in *p* material.

Note that if minority carriers drift across a *p-n* junction, they must gain energy and this energy is provided by the heat source. If minority carriers are *forced* through junction 1 in the direction shown in Fig. 14.4a, junction 1 is *cooled*. This is the *Peltier effect* and permits the use of a *p-n* junction as a heater or a cooler, depending on the direction of current

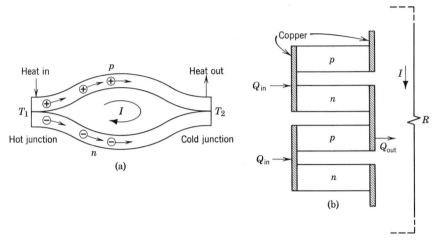

Fig. 14.4   Semiconductor thermoelectric converters.

flow.   In this case, electrical energy is used to provide a *heat pump* effect.
Figure 14.4b shows a more practical form of converter arrangement.
Because good thermoelectric materials are usually poor thermal conductors, the active elements are kept short and the heat input is by way
of a good thermal and electrical conductor such as copper.   The net
thermoelectric effect is unaffected.   Since the output is only about
100 μV per °K, many junctions are connected in series; in terms of heat
flow, the elements are in parallel.

A great advantage of the thermoelectric converter is that any form of
thermal energy can be used.   However, since the input energy is disordered, the efficiency of this device can only approach the Carnot ideal
$(T_1 - T_2)/T_1$.   Materials have been developed which provide conversion efficiencies as high as 13%, but practical units operate at considerably
lower efficiencies.   Sacrificing efficiency for simplicity, Russian engineers
have developed a kerosene-burning unit which supplies the few watts of
power needed for a radio receiver in a remote location.

Thermionic Converters

Just as the semiconductor diode led to the modern thermoelectric
converter, the vacuum diode is the basis for another new device for the
direct conversion of heat to electrical energy.   In the *thermionic* converter, heat supplied to the cathode (emitter) provides the electrons with
more than enough energy to overcome the cathode work function.   The
electrons escape with sufficient energy to move to the anode (collector)
against a potential difference which includes an output voltage across a

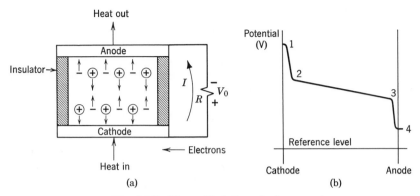

Fig. 14.5 Vapor-filled thermionic converter.

load. In a practical converter, the retarding effect of the space charge must be kept low and the anode temperature must be kept low to prevent anode emission.

The space-charge effect can be reduced by making the cathode-anode spacing very small; this is difficult to do in large units. Another possibility is to neutralize the negative space charge with slow-moving positive ions. Filling the space with cesium vapor greatly reduces the space charge and also improves the effective work functions of the cathode and anode surfaces. The operation of a vapor-filled thermionic converter is shown diagrammatically in Fig. 14.5a.† The heat supplied to the cathode produces a great quantity of electrons with energies corresponding to the potential at point 1 in Fig. 14.5b. Just outside the emitter surface negative space charge is high and an appreciable part of the escape energy is lost. A much smaller potential drop (from V_2 to V_3) occurs across the balance of the neutralized cathode-anode space. A free electron just outside the anode gives up energy corresponding to $V_3 - V_4$ upon entering the anode lattice structure. (Where does this energy go?) The energy available for useful work in an external load corresponds to potential V_4.

The thermionic converter is a high-temperature, low-voltage, high-current device. Cathodes operate efficiently at temperatures around 2000°K and this matches the delivery temperature of energy from a solar furnace or a nuclear reactor. Efficiencies are limited by the second law of thermodynamics but are expected soon to be near 20%. Since the

---

† See V. C. Wilson, "Thermionic Power Generation," p. 75, *IEEE Spectrum*, May 1964.

unit is light and rugged, it may be desirable for compact portable power plants. Another promising application is as the first stage in a nuclear power plant; the heat rejected at the anode could be used by a conventional steam turbine and the overall plant efficiency would be increased.

Magnetohydrodynamic Converters

Creation involves the recognition of new relations among known facts. Consider the following facts: A voltage can be induced in a conductor moving in a magnetic field; thermal energy can be converted to kinetic energy in the form of a high-velocity stream of gas; gases can be made conducting by ionization or by seeding with ionized vapor. Looking at these facts in the light of knowledge gained in studying the behavior of gas tubes, the propagation of shock waves, and air ionization during missile reentry, engineers conceived a generator-engine based on the new science of *magnetohydrodynamics* (MHD). In the next decade devices employing this concept may be propelling vehicles in the outer reaches of the solar system or producing huge quantities of electrical energy here on Earth.

While the design of practical MHD generators is challenging some of the best engineers and scientists, the principle of operation is simple. As shown in Fig. 14.6, ionized gas or *plasma* leaves the nozzle at high velocity and enters a transverse magnetic field. The charged particles experience a force $\mathbf{f} = q\mathbf{u} \times \mathbf{B}$ which drives positive ions upward and negative ions or electrons downward. If a conducting path is provided, an electrical current flows from the upper electrode through an external load to the lower electrode. The electrical energy is gained at the expense of mechanical energy abstracted from the moving gas just as in a turbine. The energy conversion process is reversible; if electrical energy is supplied to force an electric current in the opposite direction, the average velocity of the plasma is increased and the device is operating as an engine.

The operating characteristics of an MHD generator provide a guide to its potential applications. It works well at high temperatures (around $3000°\text{K}$) and this indicates the possibility of high overall efficiency (up to 55%) in a power plant. The output increases directly as the volume increases, whereas the losses increase more slowly; MHD would be more competitive in large units (several hundred megawatts). The demands on channel and electrode materials are severe under continuous operation; however, a solid-propellant rocket motor and a simple MHD converter could supply large amounts of electrical power in short bursts. In spite of the unsolved problems in obtaining high conductivity plasmas, high

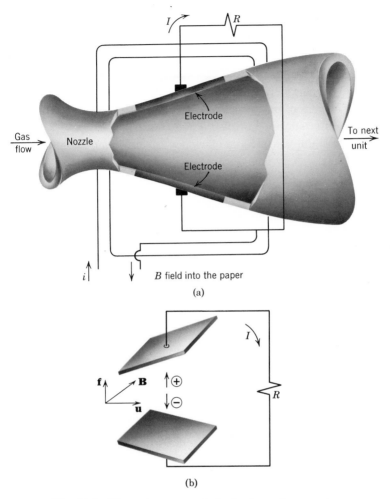

Fig. 14.6 Elementary magneto-hydrodynamic generator.

combustion and heat transfer rates, and durable materials, MHD power generation appears to have an important future.

SUMMARY

◆ The future course of civilization depends on Man's ability to improve the efficiency with which existing energy resources are used and to develop new sources of energy.

◆ Known supplies of fossil fuels are inadequate to meet future needs resulting from the population explosion and the aspiration revolution.

◆ Chemical reaction, solar radiation, and nuclear reaction are the important sources of energy for the near and distant future.

◆ The second law of thermodynamics indicates what energy transformations are possible; the first law governs the energy relations in a possible energy transformation.
The efficiency of energy conversion depends on whether the energy quantities are ordered or disordered (random).
The maximum conceivable efficiency of conversion from thermal to mechanical energy is given by the Carnot relation.

◆ While the great bulk of electrical energy is now generated by traditional thermal-mechanical-electrical devices, fuel and solar cells, and thermoelectric, thermionic, and magnetohydrodynamic converters show great promise for the future.   Each of the last four of these is closely related to a previously studied electronic device.

PROBLEMS

The following problems are similar to practical engineering assignments in that the information available is inadequate for precise calculations. Simplifying assumptions must be made; your instructor may indicate appropriate values or handbooks can be consulted. Be sure to state all assumptions made and to indicate clearly the line of reasoning followed.

1. Compare a 20-gallon gasoline tank and a storage battery occupying the same volume on each of the following criteria: total energy content, mechanical energy available for automotive propulsion, energy cost per mile at in-town speeds.
2. In a large power plant the steam input to the turbine is at 1000°F and the condenser-cooling water from a lake is at 50°F. The overall plant efficiency is 40%. If improved engineering would permit using steam at 1100°F, what overall efficiency would be expected?
3. A fuel cell weighing 25 lb has a continuous capacity of 200 W; a 6-lb plug-in fuel cartridge provides 15 hr of full-load operation. Also available are rechargeable batteries with a specific capacity of 40 W-h/lb. Compare the weights of fuel cells and batteries to be transported to a remote location for 10 hr of operation at 200 W and for 10 days of operation.
4. Estimate the fraction of the total area of your city to be covered by solar cells if the total electrical load were to be supplied by solar radiation.
5. If the steam turbine of Problem 2 is preceded by a thermionic converter with a cathode at 3000°F and anode at 2000°F, what improvements in overall efficiency might be expected?

◆ MAGNETIC FIELDS
◆ MAGNETIC CIRCUITS

CHAPTER 15

Magnetic Fields and Circuits

It was pointed out in Chapter 14 that while there are some exciting new developments in energy conversion, at present practically all electrical power is generated by devices employing magnetic fields. It is also true that most electrical energy is consumed in devices employing magnetic fields in the conversion of electrical to mechanical energy. Most electro-mechanical devices could more properly be called *electromagnetomechanical* devices because magnetic fields provide the essential coupling in the energy-conversion process. The predominance of magnetic coupling is due to the high energy densities obtainable with commonly available magnetic materials; high energy density results in high power capacity per unit volume of machine.

We have already worked with magnetic fields in two different situations. We defined inductance as a measure of the ability of a circuit component to store energy in a magnetic field (Chapter 2) and employed the resulting *v-i* characteristic in analyzing circuits exhibiting this property. Also, we defined magnetic flux density in terms of the force on a moving charge and used this concept in studying the motion of electrons in a uniform magnetic field (Chapter 9). In the next three chapters we are going to study the operating principles of some important energy conversion devices in order to learn to predict their performance. We need a quantitative understanding of magnetic fields and the magnetic circuits employed to establish them.

MAGNETIC FIELDS

The behavior of an electric circuit can be completely described in terms of the voltage and current at various points along the path constituting the circuit. In contrast it is characteristic of fields that they are distributed throughout a region and must be defined in terms of two or three dimensions. What is a magnetic field? About all we can say is that it is a region of space with some very useful properties. Does it really exist? From our standpoint it is a convenient concept for describing and predicting the behavior of devices which do exist.

Magnetic Flux and Flux Density

Magnetic fields are created by electric charge in motion and, in turn, the strength of magnetic fields is measured by the force exerted on a moving charge. In vector notation, the defining equation (Eq. 2-6) is

$$f = qu \times B \qquad (15\text{-}1)$$

A *magnetic flux density* B of one tesla "exists" when a charge q of 1 coulomb moving normal to the field with a velocity u of 1 meter per second experiences a force f of 1 newton. If u is at an angle θ with respect to B (see Fig. 9.3), the direction of f is normal to the plane containing u and B and the magnitude of f is $quB \sin \theta$.

The summation obtained by integrating flux density over an area† is *magnetic flux* ϕ in webers defined by

$$\phi = \int B \cdot dA \qquad (15\text{-}2)$$

---

† The vector dA has a magnitude dA and a direction *normal* to area dA.

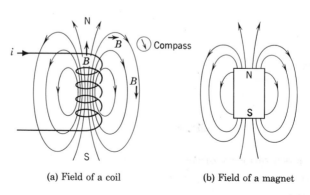

(a) Field of a coil   (b) Field of a magnet

Fig. 15.1 Two-dimensional representation of magnetic fields.

In describing a magnetic field, we represent magnetic flux by *lines of magnetic force* or just *lines*. The lines are drawn tangent to the flux density vector at any point in the field (Fig. 15.1). The lines are close together where the flux density is high. An important fact is that the amount of magnetic flux leaving any closed surface is just equal to the amount entering; in other words, magnetic flux lines are continuous. This fact can be expressed mathematically by the equation

$$\oint \mathbf{B} \cdot d\mathbf{A} = 0 \qquad (15\text{-}3)$$

where the symbol $\oint$ indicates integration over a closed surface. In Fig. 15.1b the lines close within the magnet.

Fields Due to Currents

In establishing magnetic fields, we are interested in arranging the motion of charge to achieve a maximum effect. Copper conductors wound in compact coils provide an effective arrangement in many situations. To determine the magnetic effect of charges moving in conductors in various configurations, we first consider the effect of a current i flowing in a short element of conductor ds (Fig. 15.2). If all the charge dq in the element moves a distance ds in time dt, the velocity u is ds/dt or $ds = u\, dt$. Then

$$i\, ds = \frac{dq}{dt}(u\, dt) = dq\, u \qquad (15\text{-}4)$$

and current i in element ds is equivalent to charge dq at velocity u.

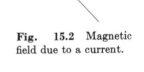

Fig. 15.2 Magnetic field due to a current.

Experiments (first performed by the ingenious French physicist André Ampère in 1820) indicate that the contribution of current i in element ds to the magnetic flux density dB at point P is proportional to the current i and the cosine of angle α and inversely proportional to the square of the distance r. In MKS units,

$$dB = \mu\, \frac{i\, ds \cos \alpha}{4\pi r^2} \qquad (15\text{-}5)$$

The factor μ is a property of the material surrounding the conductor and is called the *permeability* in webers/ampere-meter or the equivalent henrys/meter. The direction of the $d\mathbf{B}$ vector is tangent to the circle with its center on the extension of ds and passing through the point P as shown. A convenient rule is that *if the conductor is grasped in the right hand with the thumb extending in the direction of i, the fingers curl in the direction of B.*

Magnetic Field Intensity

The permeability of free space is $\mu_o = 4\pi \times 10^{-7}$ H/m; the ratio of the permeability of any substance to that of free space is called the *relative permeability* μ_r, a dimensionless number. The relative permeability for most materials is near unity; the permeabilities of air and copper, for example, are practically the same as that of free space. The relative permeabilities of the *ferromagnetic* materials (iron, cobalt, nickel, and their alloys) may be in the hundreds or thousands. In other words, the magnetic flux density produced by a given current in a coil wound on a ferromagnetic core may be several thousand times as great as the flux density produced in air by the same current and coil.

To eliminate the effect of the medium, it is convenient to define the *magnetic field intensity H* where

$$H = \frac{B}{\mu} \qquad (15\text{-}6)$$

in A/m. The magnetic field intensity is a measure of the *tendency* of a moving charge to produce flux density; the actual value of B produced depends on the permeability of the medium.

Ferromagnetism

The spin of an orbital electron constitutes charge in motion, and therefore magnetic effects occur on an atomic level. In the atoms of most materials these electron spins are cancelled out by other electron spins, so there is no net effect. In ferromagnetic materials, however, there are unbalanced electron spins and also a tendency for neighboring atoms to align themselves, so that their magnetic effects all add up.[†] In a specimen of unmagnetized ferromagnetic material, there are small *domains* in which all the atoms are aligned. Each domain (on the order of a thousandth of an inch in extent) is a region of intense magnetization. However, the domains are randomly oriented (Fig. 15.3) and the specimen exhibits no net external magnetic field.

If an external field is applied, there is a tendency for the tiny magnets to align with the applied magnetic field or *polarize* just as a compass

---

† See J. M. Ham and G. R. Slemon, *Scientific Basis of Electrical Engineering*, John Wiley and Sons, 1961, New York.

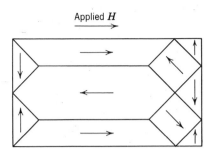

Applied H

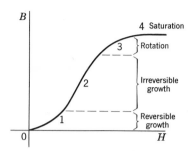

Fig. 15.3 Domains in an unmagnetized specimen.

Fig. 15.4 Magnetization curve for
iron.

needle tends to align itself with the Earth's field.   At low values of field
intensity H (region 1 in Fig. 15.4), domains nearly aligned with the applied
field grow at the expense of adjacent, less favorably aligned domains in an
elastic (reversible) process.   This results in an increase in flux density B
over that expected in free space.   As H is increased (region 2), the direction of magnetization of misaligned domains switches, in an irreversible
process, and this contributes to a rapid increase in B.   At higher values of
H (region 3), the directions of magnetization rotate until the contributions
of all domains are aligned with the applied field.   A further increase in
field intensity produces no further effect within the ferromagnetic material and the material is said to be *saturated* (region 4).   Commercial magnetic steels (usually called "iron") tend to saturate at flux densities of
1 to 2 teslas.   For very high values of H the slope of the B-H curve
approaches μ_o.

The flux density in a ferromagnetic material is the sum of the effects
due to the applied field intensity H and the *magnetic polarization M* produced within the material.   This relation can be expressed by the
equation

$$B = \mu_o(H + M) \tag{15-7}$$

This can be rewritten as

$$B = \mu_o \left(1 + \frac{M}{H} \right) H = \mu_o \mu_r H = \mu H \tag{15-8}$$

From Fig. 15.4 it is clear that M/H is not a constant and therefore μ_r, the
relative permeability, is not a constant.   Because μ_r is greatly affected
by rolling, stamping, and other material processing and because it
depends on the previous history of magnetization (see Fig. 16.4), μ_r
is seldom known precisely.   For many calculations an average, constant
value of μ_r can be assumed.

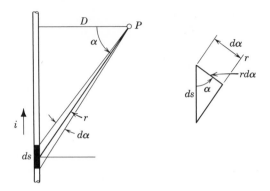

Fig. 15.5   Field around a long conductor.

Field Around a Long Straight Conductor

Equation 15-5 expresses the contribution dB at point P by a current i in element ds.   To determine the field around a conductor carrying current, we can obtain the total effect by integration.   For the infinitely long straight conductor of Fig. 15.5, $r = D/\cos \alpha$.   Then, considering differentials,

$$ds \cos \alpha = r \, d\alpha = \frac{D}{\cos \alpha} \, d\alpha$$

and

$$\frac{ds \cos \alpha}{r^2} = \frac{(D/\cos \alpha) \, d\alpha}{D^2/\cos^2 \alpha} = \frac{\cos \alpha \, d\alpha}{D}$$

Substituting in Eq. 15-5 and integrating,

$$B = \frac{\mu i}{4\pi} \int_{-\infty}^{+\infty} \frac{\cos \alpha}{r^2} \, ds = \frac{\mu i}{4\pi D} \int_{-\pi/2}^{+\pi/2} \cos \alpha \, d\alpha = \frac{\mu i}{4\pi D} \left[\sin \alpha \right]_{-\pi/2}^{\pi/2} = \frac{\mu i}{2\pi D}$$

$$(15\text{-}9)$$

EXAMPLE 1

A straight conductor 1 m long and 2 mm in diameter carries a current of 10 A. Determine and plot the magnitude of the magnetic flux density in the air around the conductor.

SOLUTION.   For distances up to 1 cm, this is a "long" conductor.   Taking the permeability of air as μ_o, at the surface of the conductor $D = 0.001$ m and

$$B = \frac{\mu i}{2\pi D} = \frac{4\pi \times 10^{-7} \times 10}{2\pi \times 0.001} = 2 \times 10^{-3} \text{ T}$$

The flux density B varies inversely as the distance D as shown in Fig. 15.6.

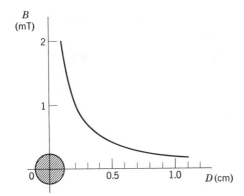

Fig. 15.6 Flux density around a long conductor.

An important principle can be demonstrated by considering the field intensity around a long straight conductor. From Eqs. 15-6 and 15-9,

$$H = \frac{B}{\mu} = \frac{i}{2\pi D} \qquad (15\text{-}10)$$

Along a circle of radius D the field intensity is constant and the line integral is

$$\oint \mathbf{H} \cdot d\mathbf{l} = \frac{i}{2\pi D} \cdot 2\pi D = i \qquad (15\text{-}11)$$

While the relation is derived here for a special case, it has a general interpretation. *The line integral of field intensity along any closed path is just equal to the current linked.* The quantity $\int \mathbf{H} \cdot d\mathbf{l}$ is called the *magnetomotive force* (mmf) because in magnetic circuits it plays a role analogous to the electromotive force in electric circuits. This principle, sometimes called the *mmf law*, is very useful in determining the fields due to currents in conductors of various configurations.

Field Produced by a Toroidal Coil

One conductor configuration for creating a strong magnetic field consists of many turns of wire wound on a cylindrical form; such a *solenoid* (Fig. 15.1a) may have an air core or, for greater flux density, an iron core. Another common form is the *toroid* of Fig. 15.7 in which the wire is wound on a doughnut-shaped core. Let us use the mmf law to investigate the field in the vicinity of the toroidal coil.

Since closed path a links no current, the mmf along this path is zero; since $\int dl$ is finite, net H must be zero. We conclude that there is no field

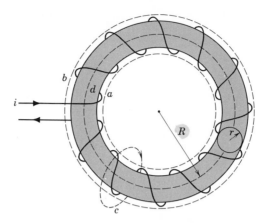

Fig. 15.7 A torodial coil.

intensity and no magnetic flux in the direction of path a. Following the same reasoning, what conclusion do you reach regarding path b?

Closed path c links current i once and, therefore, an mmf of i A exists. The net current flow is clockwise around the toroid. Applying the right-hand rule, the resulting H and $B = \mu_0 H$ are in the direction of the arrow. A small amount of magnetic flux goes through the hole and into the paper. The flux density at any point in the interior or exterior could be calculated by using Ampere's law (Eq. 15-5).

If there are N turns on the toroid, closed path d links the current i N times. We know that the magnetic field is due to charge in motion. Insofar as path d is concerned, there are N conducting paths in parallel, each carrying a current $i = q/t$. We conclude that the total effect is as if a current Ni were linked once. By Eq. 15-11 the magneto-motive force in ampere-turns† is

$$\oint \mathbf{H} \, dl = H(2\pi R) = Ni$$

and

$$HL = NI$$

$$B = \mu H = \frac{\mu}{2\pi R} Ni \tag{15-12}$$

If the toroid has a circular cross section with a radius r, the core area is πr^2. If r is small compared to R, the flux density can be assumed to be uniform at the value given by Eq. 15-12 where R is the mean radius.

---

† Since the number of turns is a dimensionless quantity, the *unit* of mmf is the *ampere*. However, we shall use "ampere-turns" (abbreviated A-t) to emphasize the significance of the number of turns in the usual case of a multiturn coil.

$$NI = \frac{BL}{\mu}$$

On the basis of this assumption,

$$\phi = BA = \frac{\mu}{2\pi R} Ni(\pi r^2) = \frac{\mu r^2}{2R} Ni \qquad (15\text{-}13)$$

EXAMPLE 2

A coil consists of 1000 turns wound on a toroidal core with $R = 6$ cm and $r = 1$ cm. To establish a total magnetic flux of 0.2 mWb in a nonmagnetic core, what current is required? Repeat for an iron core with a relative permeability of 2000.

SOLUTION. For a nonmagnetic core $\mu = \mu_o$. By Eq. 15-13,

$$i = \frac{2R\phi}{\mu r^2 N} = \frac{2 \times 6 \times 10^{-2} \times 2 \times 10^{-4}}{4\pi \times 10^{-7} \times 10^{-4} \times 10^3} \cong 190 \text{ A}$$

For an iron core, $\mu = \mu_o\mu_r = 2000 \, \mu_o$, and

$$i = \frac{190}{2000} = 0.095 \text{ A} = 95 \text{ mA}$$

The flux density is

$$B = \frac{\phi}{A} = \frac{2 \times 10^{-4}}{\pi \times 10^{-4}} \cong 0.64 \text{ T}$$

which is well below the saturation value for commercial "iron."

Letting $l = 2\pi R$ represent the length of the core and $\mathcal{F} = Ni$ the effective mmf, Eq. 15-13 can be rewritten as

$$\phi = \mu \frac{A}{l} \mathcal{F} \qquad (15\text{-}14)$$

Does the form of this equation look familiar? Is there an analogy between this equation and Eq. 9-32a? Do you see any possibility of considering a magnetic field as a "circuit"?

Summary of Magnetic Field Relations

Before leaving the subject of magnetic fields, let us list six important relations:

$$\mathbf{f} = q\mathbf{u} \times \mathbf{B} \qquad\qquad dB = \frac{\mu i \, ds \cos \alpha}{4\pi r^2}$$

$$\int \mathbf{B} \cdot d\mathbf{A} = \phi \qquad\qquad \oint \mathbf{B} \cdot d\mathbf{A} = 0$$

$$\mathbf{B} = \mu \mathbf{H} \qquad\qquad \oint \mathbf{H} \cdot d\mathbf{l} = Ni$$

Three of these relations are definitions. Can you identify them? The other three relations are based on experimental observations. Can you write out statements of the principles involved? While many electric terms, such as voltage, current, and watt, are familiar because they are used in everyday activities, this is not true of magnetic terms. You should not go beyond this point without being sure that you know the precise names and the units of each of the variables represented in these six relations.

MAGNETIC CIRCUITS

A magnetic field is usually a means to an end rather than an end in itself. We wish to establish regions of intense magnetic flux density because of the effect of such fields on moving charges. The action of the field can produce beam deflection in an oscilloscope, torque in a motor, or voltage in a generator. By an optimum arrangement of coil and ferromagnetic material the engineer provides the necessary magnetic field at the lowest cost or with a minimum weight.

The Magnetic Circuit Concept

Equation 9-32a indicates that in an electric circuit the current I is proportional to voltage V and the constant of proportionality is the conductance G; the conductance depends on the geometry of the conducting path and a property called conductivity. Equation 15-14 indicates that flux ϕ is proportional to magnetomotive force $\mathfrak{F}$ and the constant of proportionality depends on the geometry of the magnetic path and a property called permeability. The analogy is emphasized if we write the relations for Fig. 15.8 as follows:

$$\frac{V}{I} = R = \frac{1}{\sigma}\frac{l}{A} \qquad \frac{\mathfrak{F}}{\phi} = \mathfrak{R} = \frac{1}{\mu}\frac{l}{A} \qquad (15\text{-}15)$$

The ratio of mmf $\mathfrak{F}$ to flux ϕ is $\mathfrak{R}$, the *reluctance* in ampere-turns/weber.

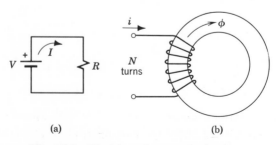

(a)   (b)

Fig. 15.8   Electric and magnetic circuits.

TABLE 15-1 Electric and Magnetic Circuit Analogies

Electric		*Magnetic*	
Current density	J	Magnetic flux density	B
Current	I	Magnetic flux	ϕ
Electric field intensity	$\mathcal{E}$	Magnetic field intensity	H
Voltage	V	Magnetomotive force	$\mathcal{F}$
Conductivity	σ	Permeability	μ
Resistance	R	Reluctance	$\mathcal{R}$

$$\mathcal{E}l = V = IR = \frac{J}{\sigma} l \qquad\qquad Hl = \mathcal{F} = \phi\mathcal{R} = \frac{B}{\mu} l$$

In many practical situations the flux density is uniform and a circuit approach, using a calculated reluctance, is possible.

EXAMPLE 3

Calculate the current required in Example 2 with the iron core by using a circuit approach.

SOLUTION. First the reluctance of the path is calculated. By Eq. 15.15,

$$\mathcal{R} = \frac{1}{\mu}\frac{l}{A} = \frac{1}{2000 \times 4\pi \times 10^{-7}}\frac{2\pi \times 0.06}{\pi(10^{-2})^2} = 4.75 \times 10^5 \text{ A-t/Wb}$$

Then

$$\mathcal{F} = Ni = \phi\mathcal{R} = 2 \times 10^{-4} \times 4.75 \times 10^5 = 95 \text{ A-t}$$

and the current required in a 1000-turn coil is

$$i = \frac{\mathcal{F}}{N} = \frac{95 \text{ A-t}}{1000\text{t}} = 0.095 \text{ A} = 95 \text{ mA}$$

It must be emphasized that nothing "flows" in a magnetic circuit. Another difference is that in ferromagnetic materials permeability varies widely with flux density, whereas in most conductors conductivity is independent of current density within the normal operating range. In spite of these differences, the magnetic circuit concept is very useful. The analogous quantities are shown in Table 15-1.

Magnetic Circuit Calculations

The circuit approach is particularly useful if the magnetic field is confined to paths of simple geometry and if the flux density is uniform within each component of the path. In the relay of Fig. 15.9a, the coil wound on a *core* 1 establishes a magnetic flux which is largely confined to a path consisting of a fixed iron *yoke* 2, a movable iron *armature* 3, and an *air gap* 4. Half of a four-pole generator is shown in Fig. 15.9b. Flux ϕ_1 follows

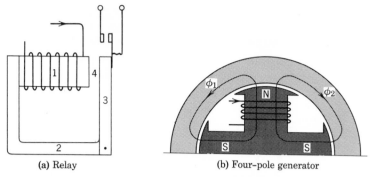

(a) Relay   (b) Four-pole generator

Fig. 15.9   Devices incorporating series and parallel magnetic circuits.

a path consisting of a pole structure N, an air gap, a yoke, another air gap, and a pole structure S.   There are four similar magnetic circuits.

Reasoning by analogy from electric circuits, we conclude that: For magnetic circuit elements in series,

$$\phi_1 = \phi_2 = \cdots = \phi_n \quad \text{and} \quad \mathfrak{F} = \mathfrak{F}_1 + \mathfrak{F}_2 + \cdots + \mathfrak{F}_n$$

For magnetic circuit elements in parallel,

$$\phi = \phi_1 + \phi_2 + \cdots + \varphi_n \quad \text{and} \quad \mathfrak{F}_1 = \mathfrak{F}_2 = \cdots = \mathfrak{F}_n$$

In magnetic circuits the "source" of mmf is usually a coil carrying a current.   (It could be a permanent magnet.)   The "applied" mmf is just equal to the sum of the mmf "drops" across the elements of a series magnetic circuit.   The mmf "drops" across parallel elements are equal; the total flux is the sum of the fluxes in parallel elements.

Series Magnetic Circuits

A common problem is to find the current required to establish a given flux distribution.   The procedure is as follows:

1. Analyze the magnetic circuit into a combination of elements in which the flux density is approximately uniform.

2. Determine the flux density $B = \phi/A$ in each element and the corresponding field intensity H.

3. Calculate the mmf drops $\mathfrak{F} = Hl$ in each element.

4. Calculate the total mmf and the required current.

The calculation of the mmf drop across an air gap is straightforward if it is assumed that the flux density is the same as that in the adjoining iron elements.   Actually, there is always some *fringing* of magnetic flux (Fig. 15.10a) and the flux density in the gap is lower than in the adjacent

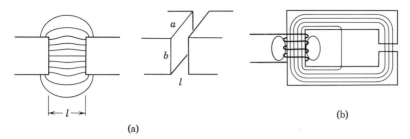

(a)

(b)

Fig. 15.10 Airgap fringing and leakage.

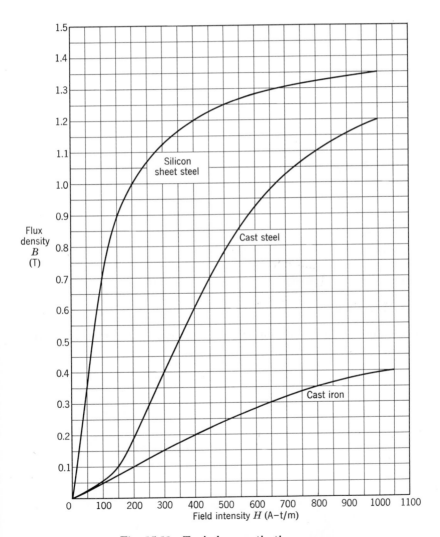

Fig. 15.11 Typical magnetization curves.

iron.   One approximate rule for accounting for fringing in short gaps is to increase each dimension (a and b) by the length of the gap.   However, neglecting fringing gives a conservatively high value for the mmf drop and simplifies the calculation.   Some flux produced by a coil may return through a short air path (Fig. 15.10b) and never reach the air gap.   This *leakage flux* is usually small if the permeability of the iron is high.   As a result of flux leakage, a higher mmf is required to establish a given flux in the air gap.

The mmf drop across an iron section can be calculated by assuming a value of relative permeability or by working from average data in the form of *magnetization curves*.   Curves similar to those in Fig. 15.11 are available from manufacturers of magnetic materials.   It must be emphasized that these are typical curves and results based on such data are not precise.   In fact, variations in values of magnetic properties of 3 to 5% are to be expected and there is no point in attempting more precise calculations.

EXAMPLE 4

Given the magnetic circuit shown in Fig. 15.12 with 500 turns wound on each leg, find the current required to establish a flux of 4 mWb across the 0.1-cm air gaps.

SOLUTION.   Following the procedure outlined, we consider the magnetic circuit to consist of two iron elements and two air gaps in series.   We assume that fringing is negligible and that the effective length of the cast steel element is $25 + 2.5 + 2.5 = 30$ cm (Fig. 15.12b); the increased flux density at the inner corner is partially offset by the decreased flux density at the outer corner.

Sheet steel: $B = \dfrac{\phi}{A} = \dfrac{4 \times 10^{-3} \text{ Wb}}{0.05 \times 0.08 \text{ m}^2} = 1 \text{ T}$

From Fig. 15.11, $H = 200$ A-t/m and $\mathfrak{F} = Hl = 200 \times 0.8 \cong 160$ A-t

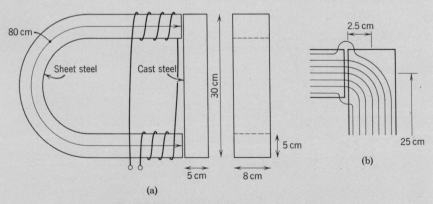

80 cm

Sheet steel   Cast steel

30 cm

5 cm

5 cm   8 cm

(a)

2.5 cm

25 cm

(b)

Fig. 15.12   Series magnetic circuit for Example 4.

Cast steel: $$B = \frac{\phi}{A} = \frac{4 \times 10^{-3} \text{ Wb}}{0.05 \times 0.08 \text{ m}^2} = 1 \text{ T}$$

From Fig. 15.11, $H = 670$ A-t/m and $\mathcal{F} = Hl = 670 \times 0.3 \cong 200$ A-t

Air gaps: $$\mathcal{F} = 2Hl = 2\frac{B}{\mu}l = \frac{2\phi l}{A\mu_o} = \frac{2 \times 4 \times 10^{-3} \times 1 \times 10^{-3}}{4 \times 10^{-3} \times 4\pi \times 10^{-7}} = 1590 \text{ A-t}$$

The total mmf required is $160 + 200 + 1590 = 1950$ A-t.

Since the mmfs of the two coils are in the same direction, the effective number of turns is 1000 and the current required is

$$i = \frac{\mathcal{F}}{N} = \frac{1950}{1000} = 1.95 \text{ A}$$

Note that in Example 4 the high permeability of the iron results in a small mmf drop even though the path length is great compared to the length of the air gap. Since the mmf drop across the air gap is the predominant factor, as a first approximation the other mmf drops can be neglected. As a second approximation, the iron elements can be taken into account using average values of permeability.

EXAMPLE 5

Repeat Example 4, using the first and second approximations described in the preceding paragraph.

SOLUTION. Assuming all the reluctance is in the air gap,

$$i = \frac{\mathcal{F}}{N} = \frac{1590}{1000} \cong 1.6 \text{ A}$$

For the second approximation we note from Fig. 15.11 that for $B \leq 1$ T,

Sheet steel: $$\mu_r = \frac{B}{\mu_o H} \cong \frac{1}{4\pi \times 10^{-7} \times 200} \cong 4000$$

Cast steel: $$\mu_r = \frac{B}{\mu_o H} \cong \frac{1}{4\pi \times 10^{-7} \times 700} \cong 1000$$

Then

$$\mathcal{R} = \mathcal{R}_a + \mathcal{R}_{ss} + \mathcal{R}_{cs} = \frac{1}{\mu_o A}\left(\frac{l_a}{\mu_a} + \frac{l_{ss}}{\mu_{ss}} + \frac{l_{cs}}{\mu_{cs}}\right)$$

$$= \frac{1}{4\pi \times 10^{-7} \times 4 \times 10^{-3}}\left(\frac{2 \times 10^{-3}}{1} + \frac{0.8}{4000} + \frac{0.3}{1000}\right) \cong 5 \times 10^5 \text{ A-t/Wb}$$

and

$$i = \frac{\mathcal{F}}{N} = \frac{\phi \mathcal{R}}{N} \cong \frac{4 \times 10^{-3} \times 5 \times 10^5}{1000} \cong 2 \text{ A}$$

We conclude that the method to be used in a given problem depends on the data available and the precision required.

Series Circuit With Given Mmf

In Example 4 the problem is to find the mmf required for a given flux distribution. Knowing the flux density in each element of the circuit, we can determine the corresponding field intensity and mmf. Finding the precise flux distribution resulting from a given mmf is a more difficult problem because of the nonlinearity of the magnetization curves. (The approximate methods used in Example 5 assume linearity and work equally well for both classes of problems.)

The methods of analysis outlined in Chapter 8 are applicable to nonlinear magnetic circuits. The method of piecewise linearization (see Fig. 8.27) is essentially the approach used in Example 5, where we assumed average values of relative permeability. If there is a single nonlinear element, a load line can be constructed as in Fig. 8.29. (If a magnetic circuit consists of an iron element, an air gap, and a multiturn coil, what are the analogs of V_T, R_T, and R_N?) An effective approach is first to obtain a rough approximation by assuming all the reluctance is in the air gap and then to proceed by "educated" trial and error.

EXAMPLE 6

A toroidal core of cast steel has a cross section of 10 cm^2 and an average length of 35 cm with a 1-mm air gap. It is wound with 200 turns of wire carrying a current of 3 A. Determine the total flux across the gap.

SOLUTION. As a first approximation, assume that all the mmf is across the air gap. Then

$$B = \mu H = \frac{\mu_o \mathfrak{F}}{l} = \frac{\mu_o N i}{l} = \frac{4\pi \times 10^{-7} \times 200 \times 3}{10^{-3}} = 0.75 \text{ T}$$

The actual value of B is less than this value because of the mmf drop in the cast steel. Assuming $B = 0.6$ T,

$$\mathfrak{F}_a = H_a l_a = \frac{B l_a}{\mu_o} = \frac{0.6 \times 10^{-3}}{4\pi \times 10^{-7}} \cong 480 \text{ A-t}$$

From Fig. 15.11,

$$H_{cs} \cong 400 \text{ A-t/m} \quad \text{and} \quad \mathfrak{F}_{cs} = H_{cs} l_{cs} \cong 400 \times 0.35 = 140 \text{ A-t}$$

The total mmf required is $480 + 140 = 620$ A-t. This is within 3% of the $3(200) = 600$ A-t available and, therefore, $B = 0.6$ T is an acceptable value. The total flux is

$$\phi = BA = 0.6 \times 10 \times 10^{-4} = 0.6 \text{ mWb}$$

Parallel Magnetic Circuits

The analysis of magnetic circuits containing parallel elements is based on analogy with the corresponding electric circuits. The same mmf (voltage) exists across elements in parallel and the total flux (current) is the sum of the fluxes in the parallel elements. The procedure is illustrated in the following numerical example.

EXAMPLE 7

A flux of 3.6×10^{-4} Wb is to be established in the center leg of the sheet steel core shown in Fig. 15.13 (all dimensions in cm). Find the necessary current in the 300-turn coil.

SOLUTION. Possible flux paths have been sketched in to indicate the general distribution of flux. Assuming that flux density between points a and b is approximately uniform, the flux density in the center leg is

$$B_1 = \frac{\phi_1}{A_1} = \frac{3.6 \times 10^{-4}}{0.02 \times 0.02} = 0.9 \text{ T}$$

From Fig. 15.11,

$$H_1 = 150 \text{ A-t/m} \quad \text{and} \quad \mathfrak{F}_{ab} = H_1 l_1 \cong 150 \times 0.06 = 9 \text{ A-t}$$

Then

$$H_2 = \frac{\mathfrak{F}_{ab}}{l_2} \cong \frac{9}{(6 + 6 + 6)10^{-2}} = \frac{9}{0.18} = 50 \text{ A-t/m}$$

From Fig. 15.11,

$$B_2 \cong 0.35 \text{ T} \quad \text{and} \quad \phi_2 = B_2 A_2 = 0.35 \times 4 \times 10^{-4} = 1.4 \times 10^{-4} \text{ Wb}$$

Then

$$\phi = \phi_1 + \phi_2 = (3.6 + 1.4)10^{-4} = 5 \times 10^{-4}$$

and

$$B = \frac{\phi}{A} = \frac{5 \times 10^{-4}}{4 \times 10^{-4}} = 1.25 \text{ T}$$

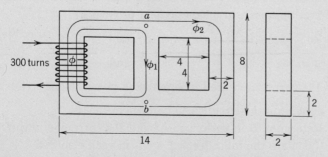

Fig. 15.13 Parallel magnetic circuit (Example 7).

From Fig. 15.11, $H = 500$ A-t/m and $\mathfrak{F} = Hl = 500 \times 0.18 = 90$ A-t.   The required current is

$$i = \frac{\mathfrak{F} + \mathfrak{F}_{ab}}{N} = \frac{90 + 9}{300} = 0.33 \text{ A}$$

SUMMARY

◆ Magnetic flux density **B** is defined in terms of the force exerted on a moving charge by the equation $\mathbf{f} = q\mathbf{u} \times \mathbf{B}$.
   The contribution of an element ds carrying a current i is

$$dB = \frac{\mu i \, ds \cos \alpha}{4\pi r^2} \text{ teslas}$$

◆ Magnetic flux ϕ is defined as a summation of flux density by
$$\phi = \int \mathbf{B} \cdot d\mathbf{A} \text{ webers}$$

   Magnetic flux lines are continuous or $\oint \mathbf{B} \cdot d\mathbf{A} = 0$.

◆ The permeability of free space is $\mu_o = 4\pi \times 10^{-7}$ henrys/meter.
   The relative permeability of a material is $\mu_r = \mu/\mu_o$.

◆ Magnetic field intensity **H** is defined by

$$\mathbf{H} = \frac{\mathbf{B}}{\mu} \text{ amperes/meter (or A-t/m)}$$

   The line integral of magnetic field intensity along any closed path is just equal to the current linked or
$$\oint \mathbf{H} \cdot d\mathbf{l} = i \text{ amperes (or A-t)}$$

◆ Ferromagnetism is due to the magnetic effects of unbalanced electron spins and the behavior of domains under the action of external magnetic fields.   The resulting magnetic polarization M is defined by

$$B = \mu_o(H + M) = \mu_o\mu_r H$$

◆ Analogies between magnetic and electric quantities provide the basis for a circuit approach to magnetic field problems.

   Series: $\phi_1 = \phi_2 = \cdots = \phi_n$ and $\mathfrak{F} = Ni = \Sigma Hl$

   Parallel: $\mathfrak{F}_1 = \mathfrak{F}_2 = \cdots = \mathfrak{F}_n$ and $\phi = \Sigma BA$

◆ To find the current required to establish a given magnetic flux:

   1. Subdivide the circuit into uniform elements.
   2. Determine B in each element and the corresponding H.
   3. Calculate the mmf drops $\mathfrak{F} = Hl$ in each element.
   4. Calculate the total mmf and the required current.

Magnetization curves provide B-H data for magnetic materials.

◆ To find magnetic flux for a given current, use graphical analysis, piecewise linearization, or trial and error. Magnetic calculations are never precise; in a practical device with an air gap the mmf drop in the iron may be negligible.

REVIEW QUESTIONS

1. What is a magnetic field? What are its properties?
2. How could you determine experimentally if a magnetic field is present?
3. What are lines of magnetic force? How are they useful?
4. What is the flux density at the center of a long, straight, copper conductor carrying current i? A similar iron conductor?
5. Why is iron magnetic and aluminum is not?
6. Why does relative permeability vary with flux density?
7. Sketch the flux distribution around a straight conductor.
8. Explain Eq. 15.11 for a permanent magnet.
9. Given an $i\,ds$ element, what factors determine dB at point P?
10. Sketch analogous magnetic and electric circuits and list four analogous terms. How are these circuits basically different?
11. List five magnetic field quantities with their symbols and units.
12. In magnetic circuits, what corresponds to Kirchhoff's laws?
13. Explain the statement: "Applied mmf equals the sum of the mmf drops."
14. Under what circumstances can all the mmf be assumed across the air gap?
15. Given the current in a coil wound on a magnetic core with air gap, outline the procedure for finding total flux.

EXERCISES

1. Consider a conducting element of length s carrying a current i consisting of carriers of charge q and velocity u. Taking into account area A, carrier density n, and total charge Q·demonstrate that $is = Qu$.
2. In Fig. 15.14, a current i in the short element produces a flux density B_1 at point 1. Determine the magnitude and the direction of the flux density vectors at points 2, 3, and 4.

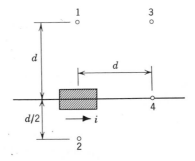

Fig. 15.14

3. Two long, straight conductors separated a distance d in air and carrying a current I constitute an electric circuit.

(a) Reproduce Fig. 15.15 and sketch the lines of magnetic flux (in the plane of the paper) in the vicinity of the two wires.

(b) Does the Theorem of Superposition apply to magnetic fields?

(c) Sketch a graph of the *magnitude* of field intensity as a function of position along the line joining the centers. Exclude the region within the wires.

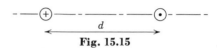

Fig. 15.15

4. Repeat Exercise 3 for two conductors carrying current in the *same* direction.

5. Starting from Ampère's law (Eq. 15-5), derive an expression for the flux density at the center of a single-turn circular coil of radius R. Repeat for a compact coil of N turns.

6. Starting from Ampère's law (Eq. 15-5), derive an expression for the flux density at the center of a square coil L meters on a side carrying a current I. Repeat for a compact coil of N turns.

7. Demonstrate that the units of H are amperes/meter.

8. A long straight conductor carrying a current I passes through the center of a thin toroidal ring of mean diameter 5 cm and relative permeability 2000. Predict the flux density in the ring.

9. Calculate the average value of relative permeability for flux densities up to $B = 0.3$ T for:

(a) Cast iron.

(b) Cast steel.

(c) Silicon sheet steel.

10. Calculate about 5 values and plot a graph of relative permeability versus flux density for silicon sheet steel.

11. A symmetric core of cast steel is similar to that in Fig. 15.16 but with no air gap. If $a = c = 10$ cm, $b = 60$ cm, and $d = 70$ cm, find the total magnetic

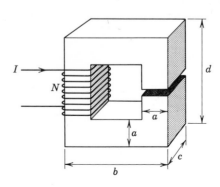

Fig. 15.16

flux produced by a current of 1.1 A in the 1000-turn coil.   Repeat for a core of silicon sheet steel.

12. A symmetric core similar to that in Fig. 15.16, but with no air gap, is to carry a total flux of 10 mWb.   Dimensions are $a = c = 10$ cm, $b = 60$ cm, and $d = 70$ cm.

(a) If the core is made up of silicon sheet steel, estimate the current required in a 100-turn coil.

(b) Repeat for a cast steel core.

(c) Repeat for a cast iron core.

13. The core of Fig. 15.16 is silicon sheet steel with $a = c = 5$ cm, and $b = d = 30$ cm; the air gap is 5 mm long.

(a) Estimate the current required in the 200-turn coil to establish a total magnetic flux of 2 mWb across the air gap.

(b) Estimate the error in percent which would result from neglecting the mmf drop in the iron.

14. The core of Fig. 15.16 is silicon sheet steel with $a = c = 5$ cm and $b = d = 30$ cm.   You are to estimate the total flux across the 5-mm air gap when the current is 15 A in the 400-turn coil.

(a) What assumption could be made to obtain an approximate value of B? Make such an assumption and calculate B.

(b) Is the actual value larger or smaller than this B?

(c) Assume a value of B and calculate the corresponding I.

(d) Compare this value of I with the given current.   If they agree within 5%, the problem is solved; if not, repeat parts (c) and (d).

15. The symmetric core of Fig. 15.17 is silicon sheet steel with $a = 5$ cm, $b = 10$ cm, $c = 40$ cm, and $d = 25$ cm. $N_1 = N_2 = 360$ turns.   Estimate the value of $I_1 = I_2$ to produce a total magnetic flux of 5 mWb across the 5-mm air gap.   (*Hint:* Can symmetry be used to simplify this problem?)

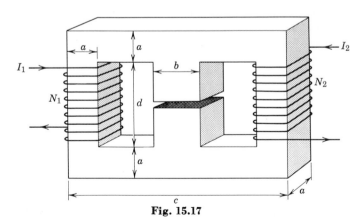

Fig. 15.17

16. A single 360-turn coil on the center leg of the core of Exercise 15 replaces the two coils on the outer legs.   Without detailed calculation, predict the required current I in terms of I_1.

17. The core of Fig. 15.17 is made of cast steel with $a = 10$ cm, $b = 20$ cm, $c = 80$ cm, and $d = 50$ cm. A single coil of 500 turns is wound on the center leg and carries a current of 3 A. Find the total magnetic flux across the 2 mm air gap. (*Hints:* Can symmetry be used to simplify this problem? Is the procedure of Exercise 14 applicable here?)

18. The core of Fig. 15.17 is made of cast steel with $a = 1$ cm, $b = 2$ cm, $c = 8$ cm, and $d = 5$ cm. $N_1 = N_2 = 50$ turns. $I_1 = 1$ A and $I_2 = -1$ A.

(a) Draw the analogous electric circuit.

(b) Sketch the flux distribution showing lines close together where flux density is high, etc.

(c) Estimate the flux density in the 2-mm air gap.

PROBLEMS

1. A long straight conductor of radius R carries a current I. Derive an expression for the field intensity *within* the conductor as a function of distance from the center.

2. A circular coil of radius R carrying a current I lies in the x-y plane with its center at the origin. Derive an expression for the flux density B as a function of distance along the z axis.

3. The core of Fig. 15.16 is silicon sheet steel with $a = c = 5$ cm and $b = d = 30$ cm. You are to estimate the total flux across the 5-mm air gap when the current is 15 A in the 400-turn coil.

(a) Plot a graph of ϕ versus $\mathfrak{F}$ for this core, using Fig. 15.11.

(b) Draw a "load line" representing the combination of coil mmf and air-gap reluctance.

(c) Determine the total flux across the air gap.

(d) Check by determining the current required to establish this flux.

4. A core of silicon sheet steel has the general shape of Fig. 15.16. Stating all assumptions, determine a ratio of effective length of iron l_i to effective length of air l_a to define the conditions under which the mmf drop in the iron can be neglected without introducing an error greater than 5 % in the flux calculations.

5. A core similar to that of Fig. 15.16, but without an air gap, is placed around the neck of a TV picture tube to obtain magnetic deflection. A coil identical to that shown is wound on the right-hand leg with current I in such a direction as to produce a *counterclockwise* mmf (i.e., opposing that created by the coil on the left-hand leg.) Sketch the resulting magnetic field and describe qualitatively the deflection obtained.

◆ A-C EXCITATION OF MAGNETIC CIRCUITS
◆ TRANSFORMER OPERATION
◆ LINEAR CIRCUIT MODELS
◆ TRANSFORMER PERFORMANCE

CHAPTER 16

Transformers

In 1831 Michael Faraday applied a voltage to one coil and observed a voltage across a second coil wound on the same iron core. Fifty-three years later at an exhibition in Turin, Italy, the English engineers Gaulard and Gibbs demonstrated an "electric system supplied by inductors," using "secondary generators" with open iron cores.† Three young Hungarian engineers, Déri, Bláthy, and Zipernowsky, who visited the Turin exhibition, recognized the disadvantages of the open core and started work on an improved version. Five weeks later they shipped their "Transformer No. 1," a 1400-W model with a closed core of iron wires. Seventy-five of their transformers were used to supply the 1067 Edison lamps which illuminated the 1885 Budapest exhibition. In one observer's words: "A new system of distribution has been inaugurated which . . . bids fair to mark an epoch . . . . It becomes possible to conduct the current from one central station to many consumers, even over very great distances." That prediction has come true and the transformer is a key energy-conversion device in modern power-distribution systems.

The transformer transfers electrical energy from one circuit to another by means of a magnetic field which links both circuits. There are three reasons for investigating its behavior at this point in our studies: The

---

† Halacsy-von Fuchs: "Transformer Invented 75 Years Ago," *Electrical Engineering*, June 1961.

transformer illustrates the use of magnetic circuits in energy conversion, it provides a good example of voltages induced by a changing magnetic field, and transformer action is the basis of operation of induction motors and other important electromechanical devices. First we consider magnetic circuits with sinusoidal flux variation, then we investigate the voltage and current relations in coils linking the same magnetic circuit. Next we treat the transformer as a two-port and derive a circuit model, and finally we use the model to predict transformer performance.

A-C EXCITATION OF MAGNETIC CIRCUITS

When a steady or d-c voltage exists across a coil linking a magnetic core, the current which flows is limited by the resistance of the winding. The voltage RI developed across the resistance is just equal to the applied voltage V and the device of Fig. 16.1a can be represented by the circuit model of Fig. 16.1b. The magnetic flux ϕ established in the core is determined by the magnetizing force H in ampere-turns/meter, the properties of the core as defined by a B-H curve, and the cross-sectional area A of the core.

In contrast, when an a-c voltage exists across the same coil, the current is limited by the impedance of the winding. The voltage drop due to resistance is usually small, and the voltage drop due to inductive reactance is approximately equal to the applied voltage. The magnetic flux in the core is just that required to produce an induced voltage approximately equal to the applied voltage. In the circuit model of Fig. 16.1c, this effect is represented by an inductance L. Originally we described inductance as a measure of energy stored in a magnetic field, but we defined it as a circuit quantity in terms of its v-i characteristic. Now we are in a position to consider inductance in terms of the magnetic field which it represents.

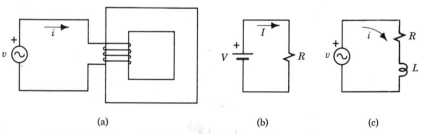

(a)   (b)   (c)

Fig. 16.1   Magnetic circuit excited by d-c and a-c voltages.

Induced Voltage and Inductance

On the basis of his experiments, Faraday concluded that the voltage induced in a multiturn coil linking a changing magnetic field is proportional to the number of turns N and to the time rate of change of flux ϕ or

$$v = N\frac{d\phi}{dt} = \frac{d\lambda}{dt} \tag{16-1}$$

where λ (lambda) is the number of *flux linkages* in weber-turns. If, in a 10-turn coil, 8 turns link a flux of 1 Wb and 2 turns link a flux of only 0.9 Wb, the total flux linkage is 8 × 1 plus 2 × 0.9 or 9.8 Wb-t. (Here again the number of turns is a dimensionless quantity, but we carry the term in the unit as a reminder of its physical significance.)

The polarity of the induced voltage can be determined by *Lenz's law* which says that the induced voltage is always in such a direction as to *tend to oppose* the change in flux linkage which produces it. Consider, for example, the case of a coil linked by a *decreasing* flux. If a closed path is provided, the current caused by the induced voltage will be in such a direction as to produce *additional* flux.

In general, the relation between flux and current is nonlinear; however, in many practical situations linearity can be assumed with negligible error. If the flux in a magnetic circuit varies sinusoidally so that

$$\phi = \Phi_m \sin \omega t$$

the induced voltage in an N-turn coil is

$$v = N\frac{d\phi}{dt} = N\omega\Phi_m \cos \omega t$$

The rms value of this sinusoidal voltage is

$$V = \frac{V_m}{\sqrt{2}} = \frac{N\omega\Phi_m}{\sqrt{2}} = \frac{2\pi}{\sqrt{2}} Nf\Phi_m = 4.44Nf\Phi_m \tag{16-2}$$

For a-c excitation, the resulting flux Φ_m depends on the frequency as well as the magnitude of the applied voltage. If the resistance drop is neglected, the current which flows is just that required to establish the flux specified by Eq. 16-2.

By the definition of inductance the voltage developed is

$$v = L\frac{di}{dt}$$

Combining this definition with Faraday's law,

$$L\frac{di}{dt} = N\frac{d\phi}{dt} = \frac{d\lambda}{dt}$$

or

$$L = N\frac{d\phi}{di} = \frac{d\lambda}{di} \qquad (16\text{-}3)$$

For a linear magnetic circuit, ϕ is proportional to i or

$$L = \frac{N\phi}{i} = \frac{\lambda}{i} \qquad (16\text{-}4)$$

and another interpretation of inductance is the number of flux linkages per unit of current.

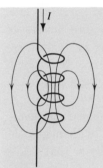

EXAMPLE 1

A current of 2 A in a coil produces a magnetic field described by the flux pattern shown in Fig. 16.2 where each line represents 1 mWb of flux. Determine the flux linkage created and the inductance of the coil.

SOLUTION. Since 2 coil turns link 4 mWb and the other 2 turns link only 2 mWb, the total flux linkage is

$$\lambda = 2 \times 4 \times 10^{-3} + 2 \times 2 \times 10^{-3} = 12 \text{ mWb-t}$$

By Eq. 16.4 the inductance is

Fig. 16.2 Ex-ample 1.

$$L = \frac{\lambda}{i} = \frac{12 \times 10^{-3}}{2} = 6 \times 10^{-3} \text{ H} = 6 \text{ mH}$$

In Example 1 we see the important factors in designing an inductance. If many turns are wound on a high-permeability core, the flux linkage per ampere is high and the inductance is correspondingly great.

Energy Storage in a Magnetic Field

Another interpretation of inductance is as a measure of the ability of a circuit component to store energy in a magnetic field (Eq. 2-14). This is an important concept because the magnetic field is frequently a coupling medium in transforming energy from one form to another. How can the stored energy be calculated?

In the toroidal core of Fig. 16.3a the mmf is $\mathfrak{F} = Ni = Hl$. Assuming that the core is "thin" ($r \ll R$), B and H are uniform across the area A and the total flux is $\phi = BA$. Starting with an unmagnetized core, we can store energy by building up a current and creating a magnetic field. The magnetic field energy stored comes from the electric circuit and the

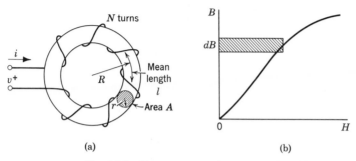

(a)   (b)

Fig. 16.3 Energy storage in a magnetic field.

electrical input is

$$W = \int_0^t vi \, dt = \int_0^t N \frac{d\phi}{dt} \cdot i \, dt = \int_0^\phi Ni \, d\phi \qquad (16\text{-}5)$$

But $Ni = \mathfrak{F} = Hl$ and $d\phi = A \, dB$, therefore

$$Ni \, d\phi = (Hl)(A \, dB) = (lA)H \, dB$$

where lA is the volume of the magnetic core. The energy stored per unit volume is

$$W_v = \frac{W}{lA} = \int_0^B H \, dB \qquad (16\text{-}6)$$

which can be interpreted as the area between the magnetization curve and the B axis (Fig. 16.3b). Assuming linear magnetic characteristics or a constant permeability, $B = \mu H$ and Eq. 16.6 can be integrated to yield

$$W_v = \int_0^B H \, dB = \int_0^B \frac{B}{\mu} \, dB = \frac{1}{2} \frac{B^2}{\mu} \qquad (16\text{-}7)$$

or

$$W_v = \int_0^B H \, dB = \int_0^H \mu H \, dH = \frac{1}{2} \mu H^2 \qquad (16\text{-}8)$$

Either of these expressions can be used to calculate the *energy density* in any part of a magnetic field.

EXAMPLE 2

An N-turn coil is wound on a thin toroidal core of relative permeability μ_r, cross section A, and length l_i with an air gap of length l_a. For a flux density B in the iron, compare the energy densities and the total energies in the iron and in the air.

SOLUTION. Assuming uniform flux distribution and neglecting fringing and leakage flux, the flux density in the air is the same as in the iron. By Eq. 16.7,

$$\frac{W_{va}}{W_{vi}} = \frac{B^2/\mu_o}{B^2/\mu_o\mu_r} = \mu_r \tag{16-9}$$

or the energy density in the air in a series magnetic circuit is μ_r times as great as that in the iron.
The ratio of the total energies is

$$\frac{W_a}{W_i} = \mu_r \frac{l_a A_a}{l_i A_a} = \mu_r \frac{l_a}{l_i} \tag{16-10}$$

The greater volume of the iron influences the distribution of total energy. However, note that if the relative permeability is 2000 and if the length of the air gap is 1% of the length of the iron, more than 95% of the energy stored is in the air. In many practical problems all the energy stored can be assumed to be in the air gap. (What essential function does the iron perform?)

Hysteresis

In magnetizing a ferromagnetic material by reorientation of the domains, most of the effects are irreversible (inelastic). When the external field is removed, the magnetic material does not return to its original state. If an iron specimen is saturated, point 1 in Fig. 16.4a, and then the field is removed ($H = 0$), the magnetic condition follows the line from 1 to 2. The ordinate at point 2 is called the *residual magnetism*. If a positive H is again applied, the condition follows the path 2 to 3. A negative magnetizing force (the *coercive force*) is required to bring the flux density to zero as at point 4. A large negative H produces saturation in the opposite direction (point 5). Reversing the magnetizing force causes the magnetic condition to follow the path 5 to 1. If the magnetizing force is due to an alternating current, the *hysteresis loop* is traced out once each cycle. (Look up the meaning of *hysteresis* in a dictionary.)

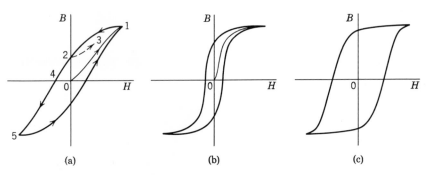

(a)   (b)   (c)

Fig. 16.4   Hysteresis loops.

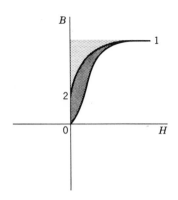

Fig. 16.5 Hysteresis loss.

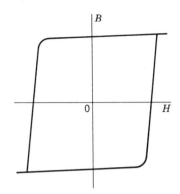

Fig. 16.6 Square hysteresis loop.

Just as a metal strip gets warm when it is repeatedly flexed, magnetic material gets warm when it is cyclically magnetized. In both cases, the energy which appears as an increase in temperature is due to inelastic action. The energy input to an initially unmagnetized sample (of unit volume) is the area between the curve 0-1 and the B axis; the energy returned is the area between the curve 1-2 and the B axis (Fig. 16.5). The difference in these areas is the energy converted to heat in an irreversible process. Following this line of reasoning for a complete cycle, we see that the area of the hysteresis loop is just equal to the energy lost per cycle. For silicon steel the loop is narrow (Fig. 16.4b) and the *hysteresis loss* is small; for a "permanent magnet" the coercive force is large and the loop is fat (Fig. 16.4c). The area of the loop increases nonlinearly with maximum flux density. An empirical formula developed by Steinmetz for commercial magnetic steels gives the hysteresis power loss in watts as

$$P_h = K_h f B_m{}^n \tag{16-11}$$

where the constant K_h and exponent n vary with the core material; n is often assumed to be 1.6.

In some magnetic materials the hysteresis loop is nearly rectangular (Fig. 16.6). In such *square-loop* materials the slope of the sides of the B-H curve is large and a small change in H can *switch* the core from nearly saturated in one direction to nearly saturated in the other. A tiny core and coil can serve as a magnetic flip-flop in switching circuits or as a storage element in a computer.

Eddy Currents

In early electric generators nearly three-fourths of the mechanical input appeared as heat in the magnetic circuit. A small part of this energy

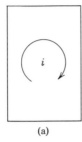
(a)

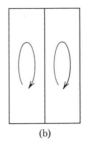
(b)

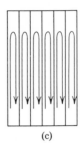
(c)

Fig. 16.7   Eddy currents.

loss was due to hysteresis, but the major part was due to the fact that a
changing magnetic flux induces voltages in the core material itself.   In a
conducting iron core, induced voltages cause localized *eddy currents* and
the resulting $i^2R = v^2/R$ power appears as heat.   As shown in Fig. 16.7a,
a changing flux (directed into the paper) induces a net current within
the core material.   The power loss can be reduced by decreasing v and
increasing R.   If, instead of a solid iron core, thin laminations are used
(Fig. 16.7b), the effective induced voltage is decreased and the resistance
of the effective path is increased.   (What effect does laminating the core
have on eddy-current path length?   On cross-sectional area?)   The
laminations, perhaps 0.02 in. thick, are electrically insulated from each
other by a thin varnish or just the scale produced in heating and rolling.
For a given core, the eddy-current power loss is given by†

$$P_e = K_e f^2 B_m{}^2 \tag{16-12}$$

Since induced voltage is proportional to fB_m (Eq. 16-2) and the loss varies
as the square of the voltage, we expect the power loss to vary as $f^2B_m{}^2$.
The constant K_e depends on the resistivity of the core material and the
thickness of the laminations.   How would you expect K_e to vary with
lamination thickness?   (See Problem 4.)

EXAMPLE 3

An iron-core inductor is designed to operate at 120 V at 60 cps.   Estimate the
effect on hysteresis and eddy-current losses of operating at 150 V at 50 cps.

SOLUTION.   Neglecting the IR drop, the induced voltage must be equal to
the applied voltage, and by Eq. 16-2, the flux density must be

$$B_m = k\frac{V}{f}$$

---

† See p. 392 of Timbie, Bush and Hoadley, *Principles of Electrical Engineering*, 4th ed.,
John Wiley and Sons, New York, 1951.

where the constant k includes the number of turns and the core area. The ratio of the new B_m' to the old B_m is

$$\frac{B_m'}{B_m} = \frac{V'}{V} \cdot \frac{f}{f'} = \frac{150}{120} \cdot \frac{60}{50} = \frac{3}{2}$$

By Eq. 16-11 (assuming $n = 1.6$),

$$\frac{P_h'}{P_h} = \frac{f'}{f} \cdot \left(\frac{B_m'}{B_m}\right)^{1.6} = \left(\frac{5}{6}\right)\left(\frac{3}{2}\right)^{1.6} = 1.6$$

By Eq. 16-12,

$$\frac{P_e'}{P_e} = \left(\frac{f'}{f}\right)^2 \left(\frac{B_m'}{B_m}\right)^2 = \left(\frac{5}{6}\right)^2 \left(\frac{3}{2}\right)^2 = 1.56$$

The operation of electromagnetic devices can be greatly affected by relatively small changes in operating conditions. (How is I' related to I?)

TRANSFORMER OPERATION

The transformer is an electromagnetic energy converter whose operation can be explained in terms of the behavior of a magnetic circuit excited by an alternating current. In its most common form, the transformer consists of two (or more) multiturn coils wound on the same magnetic core but insulated from it. A changing voltage applied to the input or *primary* coil causes a changing current to flow thus creating a changing magnetic flux in the core. Due to the changing flux, voltage is induced in the output or *secondary* coil. No electrical connection between input and output is necessary; the transformer may be used to insulate one circuit from another while permitting an exchange of energy between them. Since only changing currents are transformed, an output circuit can be isolated from a direct-current component of the input.

By adjusting the ratio of the turns on the two coils, we can obtain a voltage "step up" or "step down." The same device can be used to obtain a current step up or step down. In addition to transforming voltage or current, a transformer may be used to transform impedance to obtain maximum power transfer through impedance matching. Because these functions are performed efficiently and precisely, the transformer is an important energy conversion device and careful study of its behavior is justified.

Construction

In the basic configuration, two coils are wound on a common core. For power applications in the 25- to 400-cps frequency range, close coupling is

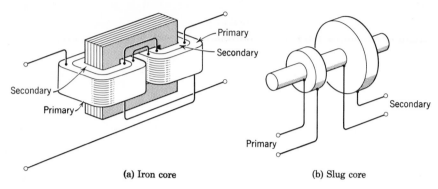

(a) Iron core　　　　　　　　　　　(b) Slug core

Fig. 16.8　Two transformers.

desired and the coils are intimately wound on a highly permeable closed iron core (Fig. 16.8a). Special design refinements make iron-core transformers useful over the audio-frequency range (20 to 20,000 cycles). For high frequencies (hundreds of kilocycles) and loose coupling, coils may be wound on a powdered iron "slug" (Fig. 16.8b) or with an air core.

To minimize resistance losses, the coils are usually wound with high-conductivity copper. In power and audio transformers, the cores are of high-permeability steel selected for low hysteresis loss and laminated to minimize eddy-current loss. The sum of hysteresis and eddy-current power is called *core loss* or *iron loss* in contrast to the *copper loss* due to the I^2R power in the windings.

Voltage Relations

In practice, the two coils are placed close together so that they link nearly the same flux. For clarity, in Fig. 16.9a the primary and second-

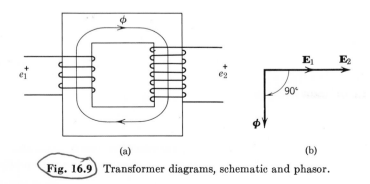

(a)　　　　　　　　　　　　　　　　(b)

Fig. 16.9　Transformer diagrams, schematic and phasor.

ary are shown on separate legs of the core, but it is assumed that both coils link the same flux. The voltage induced by the changing flux we call an *electromotive force* (emf) represented by the symbol e to avoid confusion with the terminal voltage v.

Assuming a sinusoidal variation in magnetic flux of the form $\phi = \Phi_m \sin \omega t$, the induced emfs are

$$e_1 = N_1 \frac{d\phi}{dt} = N_1 \omega \Phi_m \cos \omega t = \sqrt{2}\, E_1 \cos \omega t \qquad \text{(16-13a)}$$

and $\qquad\qquad \Phi_m = \dfrac{\sqrt{2}\, E_1}{N_1 \omega}$

$$e_2 = N_2 \frac{d\phi}{dt} = N_2 \omega \Phi_m \cos \omega t = \sqrt{2}\, E_2 \cos \omega t \qquad \text{(16-13b)}$$

where E_1 and E_2 are the rms values of the sinusoidal emfs. Therefore,

$$\frac{e_2}{e_1} = \frac{E_2}{E_1} = \frac{N_2}{N_1} \qquad \text{(16-14)}$$

or the emf ratio is just equal to the *turn ratio*. The relation between emf and magnetic flux phasors is shown in Fig. 16.9b. Since $\sin \omega t = \cos(\omega t - 90°)$, the emf phasor leads the flux phasor by 90°.

In practical transformers, the terminal voltages differ only slightly from the induced emfs and the terminal voltage ratio is approximately equal to the turn ratio. As an illustration, there may be a transformer on a power pole on your rear property line to transform the voltage from an efficient transmission value of 4400 V to a safe working value of 220 V. Approximately what turn ratio is required?

Exciting Current

With the secondary open-circuited, the emf E_2 appears across the terminals, V_2 is just equal to E_2, and V_1 is approximately equal to E_1. The current which flows in the primary when the secondary is open-circuited is called the *exciting current*. As shown in Fig. 16.10, the exciting current I_E consists of two parts. One component, the *magnetizing current* I_M, establishes the

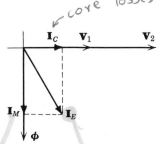

Fig. 16.10 Exciting current.

necessary flux to satisfy Eq. 16-13a and can be calculated when the properties and dimensions of the iron core are known. As expected, I_M is in phase with ϕ which it produces. The other component, the *core loss current* I_C, represents the power dissipated in hysteresis and eddy-current loss.   As expected, I_C is in phase with voltage V_1 so that the product is power.

In an efficient transformer the core loss is small and I_E is approximately equal to I_M.   Strictly speaking, the magnetizing current is not sinusoidal for sinusoidal voltage and flux because of the nonlinear relation between $H = Ni/l$ and $B = \phi/A$.   However, for many transformers the magnetizing current is relatively small, and it is convenient to assume that I_M is sinusoidal and can be represented by a phasor.

Current Relations

To develop the relation between primary and secondary currents under load conditions, let us assume that $V_2 = E_2$, $V_1 = E_1$, and $I_E = I_M$. When load Z_2 is connected across the secondary by closing switch S, a current $I_2 = V_2/Z_2$ flows.   (In Fig. 16.11b, θ_2 is assumed to be about $30°$ and the turn ratio $N_2/N_1 \cong 2$.)   The load current I_2 produces an mmf N_2I_2 which *tends* to oppose the magnetic flux which produces it. (Using the right-hand rule, check the directions of the mmfs produced by positive currents in the primary and secondary coils.)   But the flux cannot change if E_1 is to equal V_1, and therefore additional primary current I_1' must flow.   To maintain the core flux, the new net mmf must equal the mmf due to I_M alone or

$$N_1I_M - N_2I_2 + N_1I_1' = N_1I_M \qquad (16\text{-}15)$$

or

$$N_2I_2 = N_1I_1'$$

and

$$\frac{I_1'}{I_2} = \frac{N_2}{N_1} \qquad (16\text{-}16)$$

We conclude that a secondary current I_2 causes a component of primary current I_1'.   These currents are in phase and their ratio is just equal to the turn ratio.   (The ratio I_2/I_1' is the *reciprocal* of the turn ratio.)

Strictly speaking, some of the mmf N_2I_2 goes to produce the leakage flux shown in Fig. 16.11a; also, all the flux produced by the primary does not link the secondary.   In a well-designed transformer, however, the leakage flux is small and there is little error in Eqs. 16-14 and 16-16.

Because the transfer of the effect of a load across the output of a transformer to the source supplying the input is a difficult concept to grasp, let us describe the process again in different words.   With the secondary open (the transformer unloaded), the input current is just the exciting current which establishes the necessary magnetic flux (so that $E_1 \cong V_1$) and supplies the core losses.   The no-load power input is essentially the

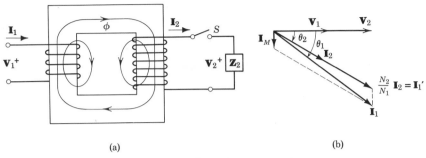

(a)   (b)

Fig. 16.11

power dissipated in the core. For a given V_2, the secondary current which flows when a load is connected is determined in magnitude and angle by Z_2. To maintain the magnetic flux at the required value, the mmf $N_2 I_2$ produced by the secondary current must be offset by an equal and opposite mmf $N_1 I_1'$ produced by additional primary current I_1'. To the source supplying the transformer, the increased primary current represents an increase in apparent power. The total power input to the transformer is $P_1 = V_1 I_1 \cos \theta_1$, where I_1 is the phasor sum of the exciting current and the load current transferred to the primary.

EXAMPLE 4

The laminated silicon steel core of a transformer has a mean length of 0.6 m and a cross section of 0.005 m². There are 150 turns on the primary and 450 turns on the secondary. The input is 200 V (rms) at 60 cps. Estimate the primary current (a) with the secondary open and (b) with a resistance load of 120 Ω connected across the secondary.

SOLUTION. The necessary maximum flux is, by Eq. 16-13,

$$\Phi_m = \frac{\sqrt{2}\, E_1}{N_1 \omega} = \frac{\sqrt{2} \times 200}{150 \times 2\pi \times 60} = 5 \times 10^{-3}\ \text{Wb}$$

The flux density is

$$B_m = \frac{\Phi_m}{A} = \frac{5 \times 10^{-3}}{5 \times 10^{-3}} = 1\ \text{T}$$

For silicon steel (Fig. 15.11) at this density, $H = 200$ A-t/m. The rms value of the magnetizing current is

$$I_M = \frac{1}{\sqrt{2}} \frac{\mathcal{F}}{N_1} = \frac{Hl}{\sqrt{2}\, N_1} = \frac{200 \times 0.6}{\sqrt{2} \times 150} \cong 0.6\ \text{A}$$

(a) Since silicon steel has low hysteresis loss and the laminated core has low eddy-current loss, and since an approximate answer is acceptable, we assume that $I_E = I_M = 0.6$ A.

(b) Assuming that the voltage ratio is equal to the turn ratio,

$$V_2 = \frac{N_2}{N_1} V_1 = \frac{450}{150} \times 200 = 600 \text{ V}$$

and

$$I_2 = \frac{V_2}{R_2} = \frac{600 \text{ V}}{120 \ \Omega} = 5 \text{ A}$$

The component of primary current due to the load is

$$I_1' = \frac{N_2}{N_1} I_2 = \frac{450}{150} \times 5 = 15 \text{ A}$$

Since the exciting current is small and is to be added at nearly right angles to I_1' (see Fig. 16.11b), it is neglected and the primary current with load is estimated to be 15 A.

LINEAR CIRCUIT MODELS

In deriving the voltage and current relations for a transformer and in solving Example 4, we made many simplifying assumptions. With just a little effort we can derive a model which provides much greater precision. Furthermore, in spite of the nonlinearity of the magnetic circuit and the vagaries of the hysteresis effect, precise results over a wide range of operating conditions can be obtained using a linear model. Finally, and this is important to engineers, the model parameters for a given transformer can be determined by two simple tests which can be performed with readily available instruments.

The Transformer as a Two-Port

In deriving a linear circuit model, we use the approach which worked so well with tubes and transistors and incorporate our understanding of transformer operation. In wiring diagrams, an iron-core transformer is represented by the schematic symbol in Fig. 16.12a. In the two-port

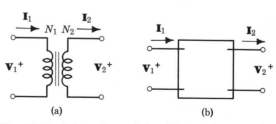

(a)   (b)

Fig. 16.12   Schematic symbol and two-port representation.

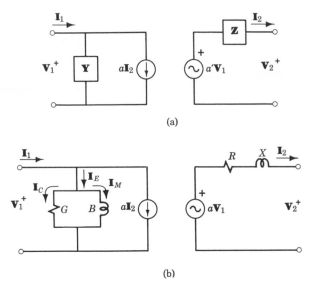

(a)

(b)

Fig. 16.13 Hybrid parameter model.

representation of Fig. 16.12b, we follow convention and show I_2 as the current *out* because the transformer is considered to be a source supplying a load connected to the output port. Since transformers work only with changing currents, usually sinusoidal, we think in terms of phasor quantities and complex immittances.

In deriving a circuit model, we can choose any two independent variables and the choice determines the nature of the model parameters. Let us choose V_1 and I_2 (see Eq. 10-3) and write

$$\begin{cases} I_1 = f_1(V_1, I_2) = YV_1 + aI_2 & (16\text{-}17) \\ V_2 = f_2(V_1, I_2) = a'V_1 - ZI_2 & (16\text{-}18) \end{cases}$$

In these relations we recognize four hybrid parameters which are constant in a linear model. The reason for the minus sign becomes clear as we interpret these equations in circuit form. The first equation indicates that I_1 has two components and suggests a parallel circuit. The second equation indicates that V_2 has two components and suggests a series circuit. The result is shown in Fig. 16.13; note that there is no electrical connection between input and output.

What is the physical nature of each of the four parameters? With the secondary open circuited, $I_2 = 0$ and I_1 is just equal to I_E, the exciting current.   By Eq. 16-17,

$$\mathbf{Y} = \frac{\mathbf{I}_E}{\mathbf{V}_1} = \frac{I_C}{V_1} - j\frac{I_M}{V_1} = G + jB \qquad (16\text{-}19)$$

where I_C is the core-loss current,

I_M is the magnetizing current,

G is an admittance accounting for power loss, and

B is an inductive (negative) susceptance accounting for energy storage.

Since the open-circuit secondary voltage is approximately the primary voltage times the turn ratio, Eq. 16-18 indicates that

$$a' = \frac{N_2}{N_1} \qquad (16\text{-}20)$$

With a current $\mathbf{I}_2$ flowing in the secondary, we expect (Eq. 16-16) a component $\mathbf{I}_1'$ equal to $(N_2/N_1)\mathbf{I}_2$ to appear in the primary.   Therefore,

$$a = \frac{N_2}{N_1} = a' \qquad (16\text{-}21)$$

With the transformer loaded, i.e., $\mathbf{I}_2 \neq 0$, the power lost in the resistance of the windings and the energy stored in the leakage fields (Fig. 16.11a) become appreciable.   These effects are accounted for by the impedance

$$\mathbf{Z} = R + jX = R + j\omega L \qquad (16\text{-}22)$$

where R is an equivalent resistance including the effects of both windings,

X is an equivalent reactance, and

L is an equivalent leakage inductance.

As a result of this impedance, the output voltage changes with variations in load current.

Open- and Short-Circuit Tests

The parameters in the linear circuit model are easily and accurately determined by an ingenious laboratory procedure.   With the secondary open circuited, $\mathbf{I}_2 = 0$ and the transformer model is as shown in Fig. 16.14a.   Voltmeter VM_2 has a very high resistance and appears to be an open circuit.   Wattmeter WM measures the total power input, and VM_1 and AM_1 measure the primary voltage and exciting current, respectively.

In this *open-circuit test* the exciting current flows in the primary windings.   However, I_E is small and since power varies as the square of the

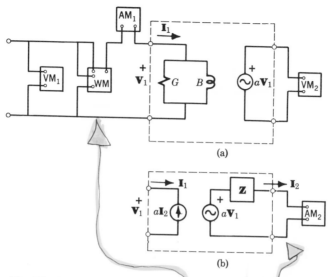

Fig. 16.14 Instrumentation for open- and short-circuit tests.

current, the power lost in the windings is negligible and WM indicates only the core loss.   Therefore,

$$G = \frac{P_{oc}}{V_{1o}^2} \tag{16-23}$$

and

$$B = -\sqrt{Y^2 - G^2} = -\sqrt{(I_{1o}/V_{1o})^2 - G^2} \tag{16-24}$$

$$a = \frac{V_{2o}}{V_{1o}} \tag{16-25}$$

Since the core loss is dependent on B_m (see Example 3), and therefore dependent on V_1, the open-circuit test is performed at rated voltage. (Transformer ratings are discussed on p. 533.)

In contrast, the *short-circuit test* is performed at rated current.   With the secondary short-circuited (ammeter AM_2 has a very low resistance and appears to be a short circuit), the transformer model is as shown in Fig. 16.14b.   Since I_2 is limited only by the small internal impedance Z, the primary voltage required for rated current is very small.   At this low voltage B_m is very small, the core loss is very small, and the exciting admittance Y is omitted from the model.

With the instruments of Fig. 16.14a applied to the short-circuited model, wattmeter WM indicates only the copper loss. Since

$$P_{sc} = I_{2s}^2 R = (I_{1s}/a)^2 R$$

$$R = \frac{a^2 P_{sc}}{I_{1s}^2} \tag{16-26}$$

Then

$$Z = \frac{a V_{1s}}{I_{2s}} = \frac{a V_{1s}}{I_{1s}/a} = a^2 \frac{V_{1s}}{I_{1s}} \tag{16-27}$$

and

$$X = \sqrt{Z^2 - R^2} = \sqrt{(a^2 V_{1s}/I_{1s})^2 - R^2} \tag{16-28}$$

Ammeter AM_2 is not essential, but the ratio I_{1s}/I_{2s} provides a check on the value of a determined from V_{2o}/V_{1o} in the open-circuit test.

There are two main reasons for representing a device by a linear model. First, the model permits general analysis and the drawing of general conclusions. Second, once the parameters are determined, the behavior of the device under various operating conditions can be predicted.

EXAMPLE 5

The primary of a transformer is rated at 10 A and 1000 V. On open circuit, instruments connected as in Fig. 16.14a indicate: $V_1 = 1000$ V, $V_2 = 500$ V, $I_1 = 0.42$ A, $P_{oc} = 100$ W. On short circuit, the readings are: $I_1 = 10$ A, $V_1 = 126$ V, $P_{sc} = 400$ W. Determine the hybrid parameters, predict the output voltage across a load impedance $Z_L = 15 + j9$ Ω, and draw a phasor diagram.

SOLUTION. The parameters are determined from the test data. From open-circuit data,

$$G = \frac{P_{oc}}{V_{1o}^2} = \frac{100}{(1000)^2} = 100 \times 10^{-6} = 100 \ \mu\mho$$

$$Y = \frac{I_{1o}}{V_{1o}} = \frac{0.42}{1000} = 420 \ \mu\mho$$

$$B = -\sqrt{Y^2 - G^2} = -\sqrt{(420)^2 - (100)^2} \times 10^{-6} \cong -400 \ \mu\mho$$

and

$$a = \frac{V_{o2}}{V_{o1}} = \frac{500}{1000} = \frac{1}{2}$$

From short-circuit data,

$$R = \frac{a^2 P_{sc}}{I_{1s}^2} = \frac{400}{4 \times 10^2} = 1 \ \Omega$$

$$Z = a^2 \frac{V_{1s}}{I_{1s}} = \frac{126}{4 \times 10} = 3.15 \ \Omega$$

$$X = \sqrt{Z^2 - R^2} = \sqrt{(3.15)^2 - (1)^2} \cong 3 \ \Omega.$$

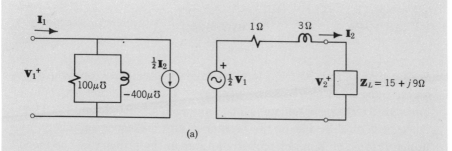

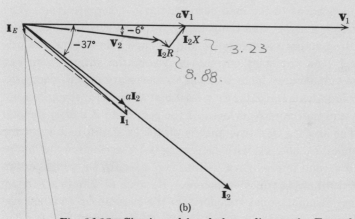

(b)

Fig. 16.15 Circuit model and phasor diagram for Example 5.

The labelled circuit model and specified load are shown in Fig. 16.15a. The secondary current under load is

$$I_2 = \frac{\frac{1}{2}V_1}{Z + Z_L} = \frac{\frac{1}{2} \times 1000 \underline{/0°}}{(1 + j3) + (15 + j9)} = \frac{500 \underline{/0°}}{16 + j12} = 25 \underline{/-37°} \text{ A}$$

and the output voltage is

$$V_2 = I_2 Z_L = (25 \underline{/-37°})(17.5 \underline{/+31°}) = 437 \underline{/-6°} \text{ V}$$

Note that under this overload, the terminal voltage ratio is appreciably less than the turn ratio.

The complete phasor diagram is shown in Fig. 16.15b with I_E exaggerated in scale. Note that aV_1 is equal to $V_2 + I_2Z$.

A More Precise Model

While the circuit model of Fig. 16.13 gives satisfactory results in many problems, a slight rearrangement provides a more precise model. The basis for rearrangement is suggested in Eq. 16.27, which can be rewritten as

$$\frac{\mathbf{V}_{1s}}{\mathbf{I}_{1s}} = \frac{\mathbf{Z}}{a^2} \tag{16-29}$$

We see that an impedance $\mathbf{Z}$ in the secondary circuit has the same effect as an impedance $\mathbf{Z}/a^2$ in the primary. This is another example of impedance transformation and could have been predicted from Eq. 11-21. Since part of $\mathbf{Z}$ is due to the resistance and leakage reactance of the primary, some of $\mathbf{Z}$ might properly appear in the primary of the model. Where?

A defect of the model of Fig. 16.13 is that it indicates that the exciting current is independent of the load current; this is not quite true. The induced emf $\mathbf{E}_1$ is smaller than the primary voltage $\mathbf{V}_1$ by the amount of the voltage drop across the resistance and leakage reactance of the primary winding. As the load current increases, the primary current increases, the voltage drop increases, and the necessary emf $\mathbf{E}_1$ decreases slightly. At high load currents, $\mathbf{E}_1$ is less than at no load, the necessary flux ϕ is less, and therefore $\mathbf{I}_E$ is less. If the portion of $\mathbf{Z}$ due to the primary resistance and leakage reactance is placed as shown in Fig. 16.16, the reduction of $\mathbf{E}_1$ and $\mathbf{I}_E$ with increasing $\mathbf{I}_1$ is accounted for automatically. A second improvement is that here $a = \mathbf{E}_2/\mathbf{E}_1$, which is just equal to the turn ratio and is constant. Because of practical design considerations, in commercial transformers the resistances and leakage reactances divide so that $R_1 \cong R_2/a^2$ and $X_1 \cong X_2/a^2$ (see Problem 7). In performing the short-circuit test, the impedance seen at the primary terminals is

$$\frac{\mathbf{V}_{1s}}{\mathbf{I}_{1s}} = \left(R_1 + \frac{R_2}{a^2}\right) + j\left(X_1 + \frac{X_2}{a^2}\right) \tag{16-30}$$

EXAMPLE 6

Using the data of Example 5, determine the parameters for the more precise model of Fig. 16.16.

SOLUTION. The values of G, B, and a are as previously calculated. Assuming the previously calculated resistance R and leakage reactance X, divide in the usual way,

$$R_2 = (\tfrac{1}{2})R = \tfrac{1}{2}(1) = 0.5 \ \Omega$$

and

$$R_1 = \frac{1}{a^2} R_2 = 4R_2 = 4 \times 0.5 = 2.0 \ \Omega$$

Also,

$$X_2 = \tfrac{1}{2}X = \tfrac{1}{2}(3) = 1.5 \ \Omega$$

and

$$X_1 = \frac{1}{a^2} X_2 = 4X_2 = 4 \times 1.5 = 6 \ \Omega$$

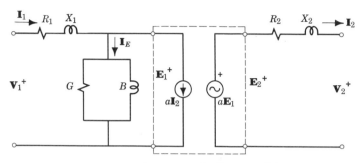

Fig. 16.16 A more precise linear model.

Other Circuit Models

The portion within the dotted line in Fig. 16.16 is called an *ideal transformer* because it provides for the transformation of voltage, current, and impedance without any of the imperfections of a real transformer. A real transformer approaches the ideal as the conductivity of the windings approaches infinity, the leakage flux approaches zero, the permeability of the core approaches infinity, and the core loss approaches zero. The ideal transformer is sometimes represented by adding the label "ideal" to the symbol in Fig. 16.12a, but its character is more clearly indicated by the symbolic representation in Fig. 16.17.

The ideal transformer and the precise model of Fig. 16.16 represent the extremes of complexity ordinarily employed in power transformer analysis. In a given situation, the best model to use is the one which gives the required degree of precision with a minimum of effort. The hybrid parameter model of Fig. 16.13 is one useful compromise. If the transformer is heavily loaded, the exciting admittance may be of negligible importance. If voltage variation is of greater interest than power dissipation, the resistive elements (R and G) can be neglected and only the relatively larger reactive elements (X and B) retained.

In the simplified circuit model of Fig. 16.18, the core loss has been neglected and the magnetizing circuit moved to the input terminals to

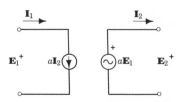

Fig. 16.17 An ideal transformer.

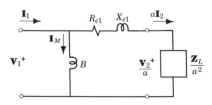

Fig. 16.18 A simplified circuit model.

simplify calculations. All quantities have been *referred* to the primary. Resistance R_{e1} is the equivalent resistance referred to the primary and is equal to $R_1 + R_2/a^2$. Similarly, voltage V_2/a is the secondary voltage referred to the primary and impedance Z_L/a^2 is the load impedance referred to the primary. Using this model, calculation of the input current for a given load impedance is straightforward.

Models for Communications Transformers

Power transformers are ordinarily operated at fixed frequencies and the circuit model reactances are constant. The input and output transformers used in audio-frequency applications (for example, in connecting a power transistor to a loud speaker) must handle signals from, say, 20 to 15,000 cps. Because of the wide variation in reactances, the circuit model applicable at low frequencies is quite different from that appropriate at high frequencies. In addition the *distributed capacitance* of the windings, unimportant in most power transformer applications, becomes significant at high frequencies.

A convenient model for an output transformer is shown in Fig. 16.19a.

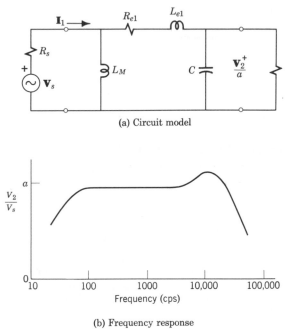

(a) Circuit model

(b) Frequency response

Fig. 16.19 An audio-frequency transformer.

This is derived from the model of Fig. 16.18 by including a lumped shunt capacitance C to represent all the distributed capacitive effects. Laboratory measurements on the actual transformer indicate a response curve like that shown in Fig. 16.19b. Could you have predicted this response on the basis of the model?

At moderate frequencies, corresponding to the mid-frequency range of an amplifier, the admittances of the shunt paths represented by L_M and C and the reactance of the series element L_{e1} are negligible. If R_s and R_{e1} are small, the mid-frequency voltage gain is just the turn ratio a. At low frequencies, the admittance $1/\omega L_M$ of the magnetizing circuit is high, part of the input current flows through this shunt path, and the output is reduced. At high frequencies, the effect of L_M is negligible, but the effects of L_{e1} and C are important. At the series resonant frequency of L_{e1} and C the voltage gain may be greater than a, but at higher frequencies the gain drops sharply. For quantitative analysis, the general model of Fig. 16.19a can be replaced by three simplified models which are applicable over restricted frequency ranges (see Exercise 20).

TRANSFORMER PERFORMANCE

For power applications the important external characteristics are voltage ratio, output power, efficiency, and the voltage variation with load. These may be obtained from manufacturer's specifications, from experimental measurements, or from calculations based on a circuit model.

Nameplate Ratings

The manufacturer of an electrical machine usually indicates on the *nameplate* the normal operating conditions. A typical nameplate might read: "Transformer, 4400/220 V, 60 cps, 10 kVA." The design voltages of the two windings are 4400 V and 220 V; either side may be the primary. At a frequency of 60 cps, the design voltages bring operation near the knee of the magnetization curve and exciting current and core losses are not excessive. Using either side as a secondary, the rated output of 10 kVA can be maintained continuously without excessive heating (and the consequent deterioration of the winding insulation). Because the heating is dependent on the square of the current, the output is rated in apparent power (kVA) rather than in power (kW). Supplying a zero power-factor load, a transformer can be operating at rated output while delivering zero power.

The cross section of the iron core is determined by the operating voltage and frequency. The cross section of the copper conductor is determined by the operating current. Knowing the effect of these factors, an engineer can *rerate* a device under changed operating conditions. For example, what should be the 50-cps rating of the transformer whose nameplate data are given in the preceding paragraph?

Efficiency

Efficiency is by definition the ratio of output power to input power. A convenient form is

$$\text{Efficiency} = \frac{\text{Output}}{\text{Input}} = \frac{\text{Output}}{\text{Output} + \text{Losses}} \tag{16-31}$$

Using the hybrid parameter model of Fig. 16.13, the output is $V_2 I_2 \cos \theta_2$ and the copper loss is $I_2{}^2 R$. The iron loss is independent of load current and is given by $V_1{}^2 G$ which is just equal to P_{oc} (Eq. 16-23).

By increasing the amount of copper, the $I^2 R$ loss is reduced; by increasing the amount (and quality) of iron, the eddy-current and hysteresis losses are reduced. The optimum design is based on economic considerations as well as technical factors. A *distribution* transformer which is always connected to the line should be designed with low iron losses. A *power* transformer which is only connected when in actual use usually has higher iron losses and lower copper losses than a comparable distribution transformer. It can be shown that for many engineering devices the maximum efficiency occurs when the variable losses are equal to the fixed losses (see Problem 8). In an *instrument* transformer which converts high voltages or high currents to lower values which are more easily measured, the important characteristic is a constant ratio of transformation.

Voltage Regulation

To hold the speed of a motor or the voltage of a generator constant under varying load we employ a *regulator*, and the variation in speed, or voltage, is expressed by the *regulation*. By definition the regulation is

$$\text{Regulation} = \frac{\text{No-load value} - \text{Full-load value}}{\text{Full-load value}} \tag{16-32}$$

The voltage regulation of a transformer, then, is the change in output voltage (produced by a change in load current from zero to rated value) divided by the rated voltage. The regulation may be either positive or negative and is usually expressed in percent.

The voltage regulation is defined for voltage *magnitudes*, but usually it is calculated from a phasor diagram based on a circuit model. The primary cause of voltage drop with load is leakage reactance and if high precision is not required, a simplified model can be used. Note that the regulation is positive if the voltage decreases with increasing load.

EXAMPLE 7

The 10-kVA, 60-cps, 1000/500-V transformer of Example 5 supplies a 0.5 leading pf load. Predict the voltage regulation and the full-load efficiency.

SOLUTION. The circuit model of Fig. 16.15 is repeated in Fig. 16.20. The internal impedance of the transformer is

$$Z = R + jX = \sqrt{1^2 + 3^2}\ \underline{/\tan^{-1} 3} = 3.16\ \underline{/+71.5°}\ \Omega$$

The output is rated at 500 V and 10 kVA; therefore, $V_2 = 500$ V and $I_2 = 10,000/500 = 20$ A.

Under full load at 0.5 leading pf, the voltage drop across the internal impedance of the transformer is

$$V_Z = I_2 Z = 20\ \underline{/+60°} \times 3.16\ \underline{/+71.5°} = 63.2\ \underline{/131.5°}\ V$$

The phasor diagram (Fig. 16.20b) is drawn with V_2 as a reference; it indicates that the no-load voltage is

$$aV_1 = V_2 + I_2 Z = (500 + j0) + (-41 + j48) \cong 462\ \underline{/6°}\ V$$

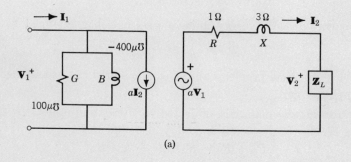

(a)

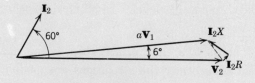

(b)

Fig. 16.20 Example 7.

The voltage regulation (Eq. 16-32) is

$$\text{VR} = \frac{aV_1 - V_2}{V_2} = \frac{462 - 500}{500} = -0.076 \text{ or } -7.6\%$$

The negative voltage regulation indicates a rise in output voltage due to the leading pf current in the leakage reactance X.

To determine efficiency, we note that the iron loss is given by the open-circuit test as $P_{oc} = 100$ W and the copper loss is $I_2{}^2R = (20)^2(1) = 400$ W. The output is $V_2I_2 \cos\theta = 500 \times 20 \times 0.5 = 5000$ W. By Eq. 16-31,

$$\text{Efficiency} = \frac{5000}{5000 + 100 + 400} \cong 0.91 \text{ or } 91\%$$

Even at this poor power factor the efficiency is quite high.

SUMMARY

◆ When an a-c voltage is applied to a coil, the magnetic flux in the core is just that required to induce a voltage approximately equal to the applied voltage.

For a linear magnetic circuit, the induced voltage is

$$v = N\frac{d\phi}{dt} = \frac{d\lambda}{dt} = L\frac{di}{dt}$$

For a flux $\phi = \Phi_m \sin 2\pi ft$

$$V(\text{rms}) = 4.44Nf\Phi_m$$

◆ The energy density (energy/unit volume) in a magnetic field is

$$W_v = \int_0^B H \, dB$$

In many practical problems all the energy stored can be assumed to be in the air gap.

◆ In ferromagnetic materials subjected to alternating mmfs, the iron losses are due to hysteresis and eddy currents, and

$$P_i = P_h + P_e = K_h f B_m{}^n + K_e f^2 B_m{}^2$$

◆ Transformers convert a-c power from one voltage, current, or impedance level to another level. In an ideal transformer,

$$\frac{V_2}{V_1} = \frac{N_2}{N_1} = a \qquad \frac{I_2}{I_1} = \frac{N_1}{N_2} \qquad \frac{Z_2}{Z_1} = \left(\frac{N_2}{N_1}\right)^2$$

In a practical transformer these relations are modified because of winding resistance, leakage reactance, and exciting current.

The exciting current includes magnetizing and core loss components.

♦ Transformer performance can be predicted on the basis of linear circuit models of varying complexity and precision. Open and short-circuit tests determine parameter values. Distributed capacitance is important at high frequencies.

♦ Transformers can operate at rated voltage and current continuously.

$$\text{Efficiency} = \frac{\text{Output}}{\text{Output} + \text{Iron loss} + \text{Copper loss}}$$

$$\text{Regulation} = \frac{\text{No-load value} - \text{Full-load value}}{\text{Full-load value}}$$

REVIEW QUESTIONS

1. Why were iron wires used in the Déri transformers?
2. What are the advantages of a closed core over an open core?
3. What determines the magnetic flux in a core excited by a direct voltage? An alternating voltage?
4. What is the effect on inductance of doubling the number of turns on a given core?
5. Describe an experimental method for measuring the energy stored in a given magnetic core.
6. How does the basic dictionary meaning of "hysteresis" apply to a magnetic material?
7. What are eddy currents? How are they minimized?
8. List four different functions of a transformer.
9. Sketch a core with two windings, one connected by means of switch S_1 to a voltage source V_1 and the other connected by means of switch S_2 to a resistance R_2.
   (a) Explain the electric and magnetic behavior when S_1 is closed.
   (b) Explain the behavior when S_2 is then closed.
10. What assumptions are made in deriving the model in Fig. 16.13b?
11. Can a 240/120-V transformer be used to step up 120 V to 240 V? To step up 240 V to 480 V?
12. What is the distinction between exciting and magnetizing currents?
13. Outline the procedure and draw the circuit connections in the experimental determination of circuit model parameters.
14. Draw from memory three circuit models of increasing precision.
15. What is meant by "rated kVA"? Why not "rated kW"?
16. Define the speed regulation of an electric motor driving a saw.

EXERCISES

1. From the definition of inductive reactance X_L and Eq. 16-2 derive an expression for inductance in terms of magnetic flux.

2. Compute the inductance of the toroid in Example 2 of Chapter 15.

3. Compute the inductance of a 1000-turn coil wound on the silicon sheet steel core of Exercise 11 of Chapter 15.

4. An inductance coil for 120-V, 60-cps operation is to be wound on a silicon steel core 4 cm × 5 cm in cross section and 40 cm in mean length. The maximum allowable flux density in the core ($\mu_r \cong 4000$) is 1.2 T.

    (a) How many turns are required?

    (b) What exciting current flows?

5. Repeat Exercise 4 for the case of a 5-mm air gap in the core.

6. Calculate the maximum energy stored in the air and in the iron in Exercise 5. Could the energy stored in either be neglected?

7. An iron-core inductance coil operates at 120 V and 60 cps with a hysteresis loss of 100 W and an eddy-current loss of 180 W. Estimate the losses for operation:

    (a) At 120 V and 50 cps.

    (b) At 100 V and 50 cps.

    (c) At 120 V and 72 cps.

8. The number of turns is increased by 20% on the core of Exercise 7. For operation at 120 V and 60 cps, estimate the new hysteresis and eddy-current losses.

9. Locate a transformer of any type or size and examine it carefully. Draw a sketch with approximate dimensions and list the purpose, manufacturer, approximate weight, and voltage and current specifications if available.

10. A 125/500-V, 60-cps transformer with a silicon steel core 10 cm² in cross section and 20 cm long is to supply a 200-W resistive load.

    (a) If the maximum allowable flux density is 1 T, approximately how many primary and secondary turns are required?

    (b) Approximately what is the magnetizing current?

    (c) Approximately what are the full-load primary and secondary currents?

11. A power transformer (in a radio) with 200 primary turns operates at 120 V and 60 cps. One secondary supplies 600 V at 100 mA and another secondary supplies 6 V at 2 A (at unity pf).

    (a) Estimate the number of turns on the secondaries.

    (b) Estimate the full-load primary current.

12. Tests are made on a 220/2200-V, 60-cps transformer. Open-circuit data are: $V_1 = 220$ V, $I_1 = 2$ A, $W_1 = 120$ W, $V_2 = 2200$ V. Short-circuit data are: $V_1 = 11$ V, $I_1 = 70$ A, $W_1 = 200$ W. Determine the values for a hybrid parameter model of this transformer.

13. A 400-Ω resistance is connected across the secondary of the transformer in Exercise 12.

    (a) Determine the actual primary voltage to produce 2200 V across the load and the resulting primary current.

    (b) Show all quantities on a clearly drawn phasor diagram.

14. Repeat Exercise 13 for a load of $300 + j400$ Ω.

15. Measurements on a 2500/250-V transformer indicate parameter values (see Fig. 16.16) of: $R_1 = 10$ Ω, $R_2 = 0.1$ Ω, $X_1 = 20$ Ω, $X_2 = 0.2$ Ω, $B = -50$ $\mu\mho$, $G \cong 0$.

    (a) Draw a clearly labeled model.

(b) Estimate the no-load primary (2500-V winding) current.

(c) Draw a simplified model neglecting the magnetizing current and referring all quantities to the primary.

(d) Using the simplified model, predict the primary current with $Z_L = 4.8 - j0.4$ Ω connected across the secondary.

16. Tests are made on a 200-kVA, 4000/1000-V, 60-cps transformer. Open-circuit data are: $V_2 = 1000$ V, $I_2 = 8$ A, W_2 not measured. Short-circuit data are: $V_1 = 224$ V, $I_1 = 50$ A, $W_1 = 10$ kW.

(a) Determine the parameters for the simplified model of Fig. 16.18.

(b) For a 200-kW resistance load sketch the phasor diagram.

(c) Determine the volage regulation for part (b).

17. The tests of Exercise 16 are completed and $W_2 = 3$ kW. Predict:

(a) The efficiency for a 200-kW resistance load.

(b) The efficiency for a load of 200 kVA at 0.6 lagging pf.

18. Predict the efficiency and voltage regulation of the transformer of Exercise 12 with a 15-kVA resistance load.

19. A transformer is to be used to couple a transistor audio amplifier with a mid-frequency output resistance of 1000 Ω to a 16-Ω loudspeaker. Specify the turn ratio and express the power gain (in db) obtained by using the transformer instead of connecting the loudspeaker directly across the amplifier.

20. Sketch the appropriate circuit models to represent the transformer of Exercise 19 at low, moderate, and high frequencies.

PROBLEMS

1. You are to design a transformer to operate on regular house current. Available is a laminated silicon steel core similar to Fig. 16.8a; the cross section is 20 cm^2 and the mean length is 40 cm. *State* all assumptions.

(a) Estimate the maximum allowable flux density without an excessive value of H.

(b) Specify the number of turns for the primary. (Remember this is sinusoidal current.)

(c) Estimate the rms value of the no-load primary current.

(d) Estimate the number of secondary turns to supply 1 kW to a 250-Ω resistor.

(e) Predict the full-load primary current.

(f) Predict the flux density with full-load current in the primary.

(g) What size wire should be used? (Consult a handbook.)

2. A coil of N turns is wound on a magnetic core of negligible reluctance. A tap (connection) is made N_2 turns from the end to form an *autotransformer*, and a resistance R is connected across the N_2 turns. A voltage V (rms) is applied across the entire winding of N turns. Sketch the circuit and predict the current I_R in the resistance and the input current I.

3. A core of silicon sheet steel is similar to that in Fig. 15.16 but with no air gap. The dimensions are $a = c = 10$ cm, $b = 60$ cm, and $d = 70$ cm. A coil of 100 turns is wound on the core and a voltage of 320 V (rms) at 60 cps is applied.

(a) Determine the maximum magnetic flux and maximum current.

(b) Sketch current and voltage waveforms approximately to scale.

(c) Describe the current in terms of harmonics.

4. Using dimensional analysis, derive an expression for K_e in Eq. 16.12 in terms of lamination resistivity and thickness. (*Hint:* See Examples in Chapter 2. Let P_e be the loss per unit volume. Determine the dimensions of K_e, resistivity ρ, and thickness x. Let $[K_e] = [\rho]^a[x]^b$ and evaluate a and b by inspection of the dimensional equation.)

5. A low-resistance 100-turn coil is wound on a silicon sheet-steel core with cross section of 10 cm² and mean length 20 cm. Determine the coil voltage for:

(a) A current $i = 1 \cos 300t$ A, and

(b) A current $i = 0.8 + 1 \cos 300t$ A, and compare the results.

6. An inductance coil consists of 500 turns of No. 24 copper wire wound on a high-permeability core 1 cm² in cross section and 10 cm in mean length with an air gap 1 mm long. Stating any assumptions, estimate the inductance.

7. Show that for symmetrically arranged coils and equal current density in primary and secondary windings $R_2 = a^2R_1$ in Fig. 16.16.

8. Prove that in a transformer maximum efficiency occurs when the variable losses are equal to the fixed losses.

9. A transformer is labeled: 10 kVA, 120/240 V, 60 cps. It is assumed to be well designed with optimum use of wire size and core size. (*Note:* Any practical insulation will stand 500 V.) You are asked if it can operate satisfactorily under the following conditions:

Frequency (cps)	60	60	60	120	120	30	30
Pri. voltage (V)	120	60	240	120	240	120	60

For each permissible condition, give the effective kVA rating.

10. The nameplate of a transformer with four separate coils reads: 5 kVA, 60 cps, 440/220/220/110 V.

(a) Interpret this nameplate and sketch the connection to provide a step down from 440 V to 110 V.

(b) What are the current ratings of the individual coils?

11. A transformer rated at 10 kVA, 2200/220 V is known to have a maximum efficiency of 96% at a load of 5 kVA unity pf. Predict the efficiency at a load of 10 kVA at 0.5 pf.

CHAPTER 17

Principles of Electromechanics

In electromechanical energy conversion the coupling may be through the medium of an electric field or a magnetic field. Practical devices employ a variety of physical phenomena. The $q\mathcal{E}$ force on a charge in an electric field is used in a cathode-ray tube for electron acceleration, in a condenser microphone for acoustoelectric conversion, and in proposed space craft for propulsion. The *piezoelectric* effect, whereby certain crystalline materials distort under the action of electric fields, is used in crystal pickups and microphones. The *electrostriction* effect, whereby dielectric materials change dimension in the presence of electric fields, is used in vibration instruments. The analogous deformation of ferromagnetic materials, called *magnetostriction*, is used in supersonic underwater signaling. At the present time, these phenomena are limited in application to rather special situations.

In contrast, the generation of an electromotive force in a moving conductor in a magnetic field and the reverse process of development of a mechanical force by sending a current through a similar conductor find very wide application in instrumentation, automation, and power generation. These electro*magneto*mechanical phenomena are emphasized in this book, but the techniques developed for their analysis are useful in analyzing the behavior of devices employing other phenomena as well.

The purpose of this chapter is to present basic principles and show their application to elementary forms of practical devices. Familiar techniques are used to derive linear models for devices employing translation and rotation. New methods are introduced for analyzing the behavior of iron elements moving in magnetic fields. The emphasis throughout is on principles and techniques useful in subsequent chapters for predicting the behavior of practical machines.

TRANSLATIONAL TRANSDUCERS

A device for changing energy from electrical to mechanical form or vice versa is called an electromechanical *transducer*. Usually such a transducer will operate as a *motor* changing electrical energy to mechanical, or as a *generator* changing mechanical energy to electrical. Let us consider how a conductor moving in a magnetic field performs these functions.

Electromotive and Mechanical Forces

In Fig. 17.1 a conductor of length l is moving at velocity u normal to a magnetic field of density B directed into the paper. Each charged particle in the conductor experiences a force

$$\mathbf{f}_q = q(\mathbf{u} \times \mathbf{B}) \tag{17-1}$$

The force on a positive charge is in the direction of advance of a right-hand screw if $\mathbf{u}$ is imagined to rotate into $\mathbf{B}$. By this rule, positive charges are forced upward and negative charges downward, and the net result (whether this is a metal or a semiconductor) is a difference of potential across the conductor. What is the magnitude of the emf generated?

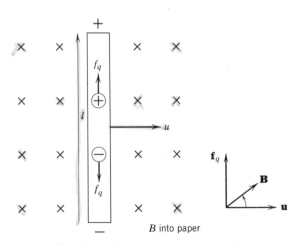

Fig. 17.1   Moving-conductor transducer.

The magnitude of the emf e can be determined by noting that charge separation continues until the force of the electric field produced is just equal to the force of the magnetic field causing it. Under equilibrium, the electric force per unit charge (or voltage gradient) is just equal to the magnetic force per unit charge or

$$\frac{\text{Electric force}}{\text{Charge}} = \varepsilon = \frac{e}{l} = \frac{\text{Magnetic force}}{\text{Charge}} = \frac{quB}{q} = Bu \quad (17\text{-}2)$$

For this case where $\mathbf{u}$, $\mathbf{l}$, and $\mathbf{B}$ are mutually perpendicular, the emf is

$$e = Blu \quad (17\text{-}3)$$

One interpretation of Eq. 17-3 is that the emf is just equal to the rate at which magnetic flux is being "cut" by the conductor. In general, the emf, a scalar, is given by the vector expression

$$e = \mathbf{B} \cdot (\mathbf{l} \times \mathbf{u}) = Blu \cos \alpha \sin \beta \quad (17\text{-}4)$$

where α is the angle from $\mathbf{B}$ to the normal to the plane containing $\mathbf{l}$ and $\mathbf{u}$, and β is the angle from $\mathbf{l}$ to $\mathbf{u}$. In most engineering devices the elements are arranged in the optimum orientation with $\alpha = 0°$ and $\beta = 90°$ and Eq. 17-3 applies.

If a path is provided for current flow (Fig. 17.2), there is a component of charge velocity u' in the direction of positive current and the charges experience a force f_d which is transmitted to the atoms in the lattice of the conductor and therefore to the conductor itself. Since $qu' = il$ (see Eq. 15-4), the *developed force* is

$$\mathbf{f}_d = i(\mathbf{l} \times \mathbf{B}) \quad (17\text{-}5a)$$

directed to the left. In general, $f_d = Bli \sin \gamma$ where γ (gamma) is the

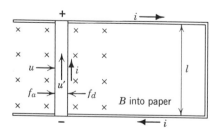

Fig. 17.2 Conductor moving on rails.

angle from l to $\mathbf{B}$. For l perpendicular to $\mathbf{B}$, the usual case, $\gamma = 90°$ and the magnitude of the developed force is

$$f_d = Bli \qquad (17\text{-}5b)$$

To cause motion in the direction of u, there must be an equal and opposite *applied* force f_a as shown.

Note that the current i produces a magnetic field and this must be considered in some practical machines; here we assume that it is negligibly small compared to B. Note also that the conductor of length l moving at velocity u sweeps out an area $dA = lu\,dt$ in time dt. For uniform B, the rate of change of flux linked by the one-turn closed path in Fig. 17.2 is

$$\frac{d\lambda}{dt} = \frac{d\phi}{dt} = B\frac{dA}{dt} = Blu = e \qquad (17\text{-}6)$$

As Faraday would have predicted, the emf is just equal to the rate of change of flux linkage.

Bilateral Energy Conversion

With a path provided for current flow the moving conductor is a source of electrical energy, and

$$\text{Electrical power} = P_e = ei = Blu\,i \qquad (17\text{-}7)$$

The necessary mechanical input is positive since the applied force is in the direction of the velocity, or

$$\text{Mechanical power} = P_m = f_a u = Bli\,u \qquad (17\text{-}8)$$

As expected from the principle of energy conservation, the mechanical power in newton-meters/sec is identically equal to the electrical power in watts.

The generated emf can be used to charge a battery as shown in Fig. 17.3. In this case

$$i = \frac{e - V}{R} \qquad (17\text{-}9)$$

For $e = Blu > V$, current i is positive and the transducer is a *generator*. At a lower velocity, $e < V$, current i is negative, and the developed force is reversed. The con-ductor is forced to the right, the mechan-

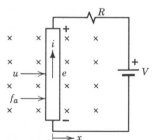

Fig. 17.3 Translational transducer.

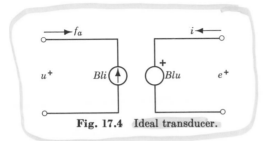

Fig. 17.4   Ideal transducer.

ical power input is negative, and the transducer is acting as a *motor.*
The moving conductor transducer is said to be *bilateral;* the energy flow
may proceed in either direction.

The Transducer as a Two-Port

Here, just as in the transformer, the magnetic field provides the coupling between input and output ports.   Using familiar techniques, we
should be able to derive a circuit model for this two-port device.   The
fact that mechanical force is dependent on a variable in the electrical
portion of the system and electromotive force is dependent on a variable
in the mechanical portion suggests the use of controlled sources.   One
possibility is shown in Fig. 17.4.

This ideal transducer is what Lynch and Truxal† call an "electromechanical ideal transformer."   In this representation, force is analogous to current and velocity is analogous to voltage (see Fig. 5.18).
What corresponds to the turn-ratio?   The change in the polarity of the
force generator Bli is due to the change in the assumed direction of i (see
Fig. 16.17).

A real transducer can be represented by considering the mass M of the
conductor and the coefficient of sliding friction D.   Then the governing
equation for the mechanical side becomes

$$f_a - M\frac{du}{dt} - Du = -f_d = -Bli \qquad (17\text{-}10)$$

Considering the terminal voltage v, the resistance R, and also the inductance L of the conductor, the governing equation for the electrical side
becomes

$$v - L\frac{di}{dt} - Ri = e = Blu \qquad (17\text{-}11)$$

What circuit configuration would satisfy this set of equations?

---

† W. A. Lynch and J. G. Truxal, *Principles of Electronic Instrumentation* (p. 477),
McGraw-Hill Book Co., New York, 1962.

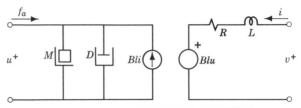

Fig. 17.5   Model of a real transducer.

The symbols shown in Figs. 17.5 and 17.6 are conventional for representing M and D in mechanical circuits. Application of d'Alembert's principle to the parallel mechanical circuit yields Eq. 17-10; application of Kirchhoff's voltage law to the series electrical circuit yields Eq. 17-11. We conclude that this circuit model represents the electromechanical system described by the equations. This model is analogous to the hybrid parameter model proposed for a real transformer (Fig. 16.13). What corresponds to the core loss? To the exciting current? Note that the ideal transducer represents the reversible portion of the energy conversion occurring in a real transducer.

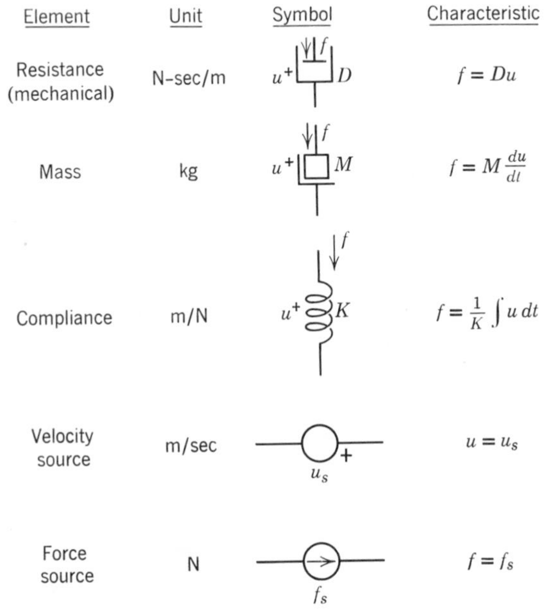

Element	Unit	Symbol	Characteristic
Resistance (mechanical)	N-sec/m	$u^+\!\boxed{}D$	$f = Du$
Mass	kg	$u^+\!\boxed{}M$	$f = M\frac{du}{dt}$
Compliance	m/N	$u^+\!\!\lessgtr K$	$f = \frac{1}{K}\int u\, dt$
Velocity source	m/sec	u_s	$u = u_s$
Force source	N	f_s	$f = f_s$

Fig. 17.6   Conventional symbols for mechanical circuits.

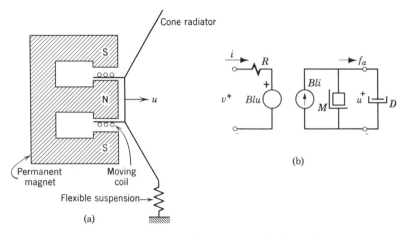

Fig. 17.7 Dynamic loudspeaker and simplified circuit model.

The Dynamic Transducer

The *moving-coil* or *dynamic* transducer is a practical form of the translational transducer. It is used in such devices as loudspeakers, disk recording heads, and phonograph pickups. The essential elements of a dynamic loudspeaker are shown in Fig. 17.7. The permanent magnet establishes an intense radial field in the annular air gap (shown in section). The moving coil consists of a few turns of fine wire wound on a light form and supported in the air gap. The coil form is attached to a light, stiff cone supported by a flexible suspension which keeps the cone and coil in place without restricting the axial motion.

An alternating current in the so-called *voice* coil develops a force which is transmitted to the cone. The cone produces air pressure waves and acoustic energy is radiated. In the simplified circuit model of Fig. 17.7b, the inductance of the moving coil and the effect of the cone suspension have been neglected. The elements M and D represent inertia effects and the loading effect of the air. At low frequencies the cone moves as a rigid piston, and the electrical energy is efficiently converted into sound waves if the cone is sufficiently large. At higher frequencies the effective mass of the cone presents a large mechanical admittance and the output is greatly reduced. In some high-fidelity systems the low-frequency signals are reproduced by a speaker with a large cone, the *woofer*, and the high-frequency signals are reproduced by the smaller *tweeter*. A *cross-over* network separates the sound into two bands; the signals below 1000 cps, say, are filtered out by a frequency-selective network and sent to the woofer.

EXAMPLE 1

The voice coil of a dynamic loudspeaker consists of 20 turns of diameter 2 cm in a field of $B = 0.5$ T. The effect of air loading on the cone can be represented by a mass M and a resistance coefficient D. Derive an electric circuit model for determining frequency response.

SOLUTION. For low and medium frequencies we shall neglect the inductance of the voice coil and the effects of the flexible suspension and work from the simplified circuit model of Fig. 17.7b. To facilitate analysis we wish to refer all mechanical quantities to the electrical side. Bearing in mind the comparable process in a transformer, we note that the energy stored in the mass M could be represented by an equal energy stored in the analogous capacitance C. Therefore,

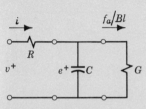

Fig. 17.8 Example 1.

$$\tfrac{1}{2}Mu^2 = \tfrac{1}{2}Ce^2 = \tfrac{1}{2}C(Blu)^2 \quad \text{and} \quad C = \frac{Mu^2}{(Blu)^2} = \frac{M}{(Bl)^2}$$

as shown in Fig. 17.8. The power dissipated in element D is represented by an equal power dissipation in the analogous conductance G. Therefore,

$$f_a u = u^2 D = e^2 G = (Blu)^2 G \quad \text{and} \quad G = \frac{u^2 D}{(Blu)^2} = \frac{D}{(Bl)^2}$$

For this device the "turn ratio" Bl is

$$Bl = B \times N\pi d = 0.5 \times 20 \times \pi \times 0.02 = 0.2\pi \text{ T-m}$$

and a force f_a in the mechanical side corresponds to a current f_a/Bl in the electrical side.

The Dynamic Pickup

The dynamic loudspeaker mechanism can also be used for a microphone. In fact, in some intercommunication systems the same device serves as microphone and speaker. Sound waves striking the cone cause motion of the coil in the magnetic field. In a well-designed microphone, the emf produced is an accurate replica of the sound signal for frequencies from 40 to 10,000 cps.

In the dynamic phonograph pickup, the lateral movement of the needle is transmitted to a tiny coil supported in the field of a permanent magnet. The small voltage generated is then amplified in a *preamplifier* which raises the signal above the *hum* level and also corrects the frequency distortion inherent in this type of pickup. The hum is due to voltages induced in the cable from pickup to amplifier by changing magnetic fields set up around transformers and other a-c components. The frequency distortion is due to the fact that this type of pickup is *velocity-sensitive,* as illustrated in the following example.

EXAMPLE 2

A dynamic phonograph pickup consists of a 20-turn coil (length of each turn = 1 cm) in a field of $B = 0.2$ T. If the maximum allowable recording amplitude is 0.02 mm, predict the output voltage at 1000 cps and at 100 cps.

SOLUTION. The effective length of conductor in the moving coil is $l = 20$ turns $\times$ 1 cm/turn = 20 cm = 0.2 m. For a sinusoidal displacement of amplitude 2×10^{-5} m,

$$x = A \sin \omega t = 2 \times 10^{-5} \sin \omega t$$

and the velocity at 1000 cps is

$$u = \frac{dx}{dt} = A\omega \cos \omega t = 2 \times 10^{-5} \times 2\pi \times 10^3 \cos \omega t \text{ m/sec}$$

Neglecting internal impedance, the output voltage is

$$v = e = Blu = 0.2 \times 0.2 \times 4\pi \times 10^{-2} \cos \omega t \text{ V}$$

The rms value of output voltage at 1000 cps is

$$V = \frac{0.2 \times 0.2 \times 4\pi \times 10^{-2}}{\sqrt{2}} \cong 0.0035 \text{ V} = 3.5 \text{ mV}$$

At 100 cps the output voltage for the same recording amplitude is only 1/10 as great. Since the amplitude is limited by the distance between grooves, some frequency compensation in the preamplifier is desirable.

ROTATIONAL TRANSDUCERS

In practice, translational transducers are limited to applications involving vibratory motion with relatively low displacement. To develop appreciable voltages, velocities must be high and this means relatively high frequencies. In contrast, an electromechanical transducer employing rotation of conductors in a magnetic field can produce large low-frequency or direct voltages (or torques) in easily constructed configurations.

The d'Arsonval Mechanism

The mechanism of the ordinary d-c ammeter was invented nearly a hundred years ago, but it is still one of our best current-measuring devices. The d'Arsonval movement is widely used in instrumentation, and it is a good illustration of a simple rotational transducer.

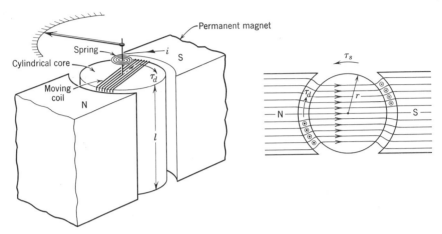

Fig. 17.9   The d'Arsonval meter movement.

As shown in Fig. 17.9, a moving coil is wound on a rectangular form which is supported on jeweled bearings in the air gap between the poles of a permanent magnet and a stationary iron core.   Current flowing in the coil produces forces which tend to rotate the coil assembly.   The current is conducted to and from the coil by two fine springs which also supply a restoring torque to oppose rotation of the coil.   A lightweight pointer attached to the assembly indicates the angular deflection on a calibrated scale.

Analysis of the behavior of the mechanism is simplified if we note that rotation is restricted, by means of mechanical stops, to the region of uniform radial magnetic field.   If there are N turns ($2N$ conductors) of length l normal to the magnetic field at a radius r, the torque τ_d (tau) developed by a current i is

$$\tau_d = f \cdot r = B(2Nl)i \cdot r = 2NBlri = k_m i \qquad (17\text{-}12)$$

The combined effect of the two spiral springs is a restoring torque τ_s which is proportional to angular deflection or

$$\tau_s = \frac{\theta}{K_r} \qquad (17\text{-}13)$$

where K_r is the rotational compliance in radians (or degrees) per newton-meter.   Under equilibrium conditions, the restoring torque is just equal to the developed torque, and

$$\theta = 2NBlrK_r \cdot i = k_\theta i \qquad (17\text{-}14)$$

The deflection is directly proportional to the current in the moving coil, and the meter scale is linear.

EXAMPLE 3

A d'Arsonval ammeter (Fig. 17.9) has a rectangular coil form with $l = 1.25$ cm and $w = 2r = 2$ cm. Each spiral spring has a compliance of $K_r = 16 \times 10^7$ °/N-m. A uniform flux density of 0.4 T is supplied by the permanent magnet. Determine the number of turns so that full-scale deflection of 100° is obtained with a current of 1 mA.

SOLUTION. Noting that two springs are only half as compliant as one and then solving Eq. 17-14,

$$N = \frac{\theta}{2Blri(K_r/2)} = \frac{100}{2 \times 0.4 \times 0.0125 \times 0.01 \times 0.001 \times 8 \times 10^7} = 12.5 \text{ turns}$$

(Is it convenient to construct a coil with an extra half turn?)

Meter Application and Response

The movement in Example 3 provides full-scale deflection with a current of 1 mA. How could it be used in a 0- to 5-A ammeter? In the connection of Fig. 17.10a, some of the meter current is *shunted* through R_s and only a part of the current to be measured flows through the moving coil. If the coil resistance R_c is 20 Ω, then full-scale deflection requires a voltage of

$$V = I_c R_c = 0.001 \times 20 = 0.020 \text{ V}$$

For full-scale deflection with a meter current of 5 A, the current in the *shunt* R_s is $5 - 0.001 = 4.999$ A. The resistance of the shunt should be

$$R_s = \frac{V}{I_s} = \frac{V}{I - I_c} = \frac{0.02}{4.999} \cong 0.004 \text{ Ω}$$

A sturdy and precisely adjusted resistance may be mounted inside the meter case or be available for external connection.

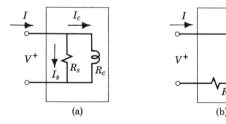

(a)   (b)

Fig. 17.10   Ammeter and voltmeter connections.

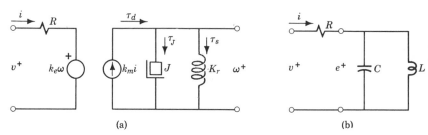

(a)   (b)

Fig. 17.11   Circuit model of a d'Arsonval movement.

Could this same movement be used in a voltmeter?   The d'Arsonval mechanism is essentially a current-measuring instrument, but it can be used as a voltmeter by adding a series resistance as in Fig. 17.10b.   For a 0- to 300-V voltmeter, full-scale deflection is obtained with 1 mA in the moving coil and a voltage drop of 0.02 V; the remainder of the voltage must appear across the *multiplier* resistance.   Therefore,

$$R_m = \frac{V_m}{I_c} = \frac{V - V_c}{I_c} = \frac{300 - 0.02}{0.001} \cong 300{,}000 \ \Omega$$

In a *multimeter*, several shunts and multipliers are mounted within the meter case and are connected at will by a selector switch (see Fig. 21.2).

In addition to providing a convenient method of solution, a model should give insight into the general behavior of a device.   What can we learn from the general model of a d'Arsonval movement?   Neglecting the small inductance of the moving coil and the friction in the jeweled bearings, the model is as shown in Fig. 17.11a.   For rotation, the appropriate mechanical variables are torque τ and angular velocity ω.   The element J represents the rotational inertia of the coil assembly and K_r is the combined spring compliance.   The mechanical proportionality constant $k_m = \tau_d/i$ is defined by Eq. 17-12.   The electrical proportionality constant k_e is defined as

$$k_e = \frac{e}{\omega} = \frac{2NBlu}{\omega} = 2NBlr = k_m \qquad (17\text{-}15)$$

and we see that in this electromechanical transducer also there is a simple "turn ratio."

Using the turn-ratio concept (see Example 1), the rotational admittances on the mechanical side can be referred to the electrical side as in Fig. 17.11b.   Suddenly connecting the instrument in a line corresponds to the application of a step current to the circuit model.   What is the dynamic response of the movement? Using the approach of Chapter 4, we can express the admittance of the *parallel portion* as

$$Y(s) = sC + \frac{1}{sL} = \frac{s^2LC + 1}{sL} \qquad (17\text{-}16)$$

Because the admittance function indicates purely imaginary zeros, we expect an undamped sinusoidal response.

If the only mechanical resistance is that due to bearing friction, the needle will indeed oscillate widely. How could the long wait for a steady reading be reduced? There are two commonly used methods for introducing the necessary damping. One is to mount a large but light vane on the coil assembly and introduce air-friction damping. Another is to make the coil form of a conducting material, such as aluminum. The coil form then becomes a shorted turn, and coil motion induces an emf which results in energy dissipation. How would this effect be represented in the circuit model of Fig. 17.11? How is the admittance function altered?

In a properly designed meter movement with optimum damping, the needle quickly reaches a steady reading. In the steady state, $\omega = 0$, $e = k_e\omega = 0$, and $\tau_J = J\,d\omega/dt = 0$. The model then indicates that

$$k_m i = \tau_s = \frac{1}{K_r} \int \omega \, dt = \frac{\theta}{K_r}$$

which agrees with Eq. 17-14. The dynamic response of electromechanical transducers is treated in more detail in Chapter 22.

The Elementary Dynamo

Rotation of the coil in a d'Arsonval mechanism is limited to something less than 180°. If we are to realize the advantages of this configuration, we must permit continuous rotation. One possibility is to mount a rectangular coil on a shaft and connect the ends of the coil to conducting *sliprings* attached to the shaft but insulated from it as in the elementary *dynamo* of Fig. 17.12. As the N-turn coil rotates at angular velocity ω in a uniform magnetic field B, the generated emf e is connected to the external circuit by fixed *brushes* sliding on the rotating sliprings.

Electromotive Force. The polarity of the generated emf is determined by considering the force on positive charges in the moving conductors. The right-hand rule indicates that the force on positive charges in the upper conductors in Fig. 17.12b is into the paper; therefore, the front slip ring is negative at the instant shown. (What is the direction of the

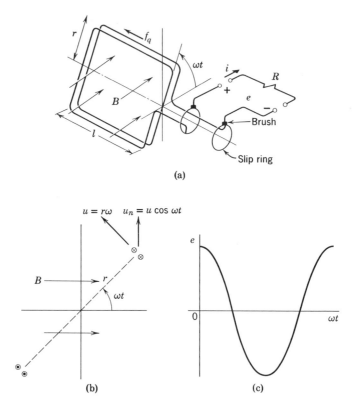

Fig. 17.12   Elementary dynamo construction and operation.

force in the lower conductors?)   The magnitude of the emf can be determined by any of the three expressions employed so far.   For $2N$ conductors of length l moving at velocity u in a magnetic field of density B,
the emf (Eq. 17-4) is

$$e = 2NBlu \cos \alpha \sin \beta = 2NBlr\omega \cos \omega t \sin 90°$$

$$= 2NBlr\omega \cos \omega t = NBA\omega \cos \omega t \qquad (17\text{-}17)$$

The rate at which flux is being cut by $2N$ conductors (Eq. 17-3) is

$$e = 2NBlu_n = 2NBlr\omega \cos \omega t = NBA\omega \cos \omega t \qquad (17\text{-}18)$$

The rate of change of flux linkage (Eq. 17-6) is

$$e = \frac{d\lambda}{dt} = NB\frac{d(A \sin \omega t)}{dt} = NBA\omega \cos \omega t \qquad (17\text{-}19)$$

Equation 17-19 shows that, in a uniform magnetic field, the emf is
determined by the area A of the coil and not the particular shape or

dimensions. The same emf or torque is developed by a circular coil, say, of the same area. Equations 17-12 and 15 were derived for rectangular coils in a uniform field; a more general formulation is

$$k_m = \frac{\tau_d}{i} = k_e = \frac{e}{\omega} = NBA \tag{17-20}$$

Torque. In the d'Arsonval movement there is a uniform radial field and Eq. 17-20 indicates that

$$e = k_e\omega = NBA\omega \tag{17-21}$$

Comparing Eqs. 17-17 and 20 and reasoning by analogy with Eq. 17-12, we anticipate that in the elementary dynamo

$$\tau_d = k_m i \cos \omega t = NBAi \cos \omega t \tag{17-22}$$

What is the direction of this torque? The direction depends on the direction of the current. If the coil is rotating in the direction shown in Fig. 17.12a and if a resistance R is connected across the terminals, the current will flow as shown and the right-hand rule indicates a clockwise torque. This is a *developed* torque which must be overcome by the mechanical power source. If an electrical power source is used, this torque is available for doing mechanical work.

EXAMPLE 4

The elementary dynamo of Fig. 17.12 is driven at constant angular velocity by a mechanical source. The output terminals are connected to a load resistance R. Determine the electrical power supplied to the load and the mechanical power required.

SOLUTION. Assuming that the resistance and inductive reactance of the coil are small compared to R, all the emf appears across R and the current is

$$i = \frac{e}{R} = \frac{NBA\omega \cos \omega t}{R} = I_m \cos \omega t$$

The average electrical power is

$$P_e = \left(\frac{I_m}{\sqrt{2}}\right)^2 R = \frac{(NBA\omega)^2}{2R}$$

The applied torque must be equal and opposite to the developed torque, and its magnitude (see Fig. 17.13) is

$$\tau_a = NBA \cos \omega t \cdot i = NBA \cos \omega t \frac{NBA\omega \cos \omega t}{R}$$

The average mechanical power is the product of the average torque times the angular velocity of rotation or

$$P_m = T_{\text{ave}}\omega = \frac{\omega}{2} \frac{(NBA)^2}{R} \omega = \frac{(NBA\omega)^2}{2R} = P_e$$

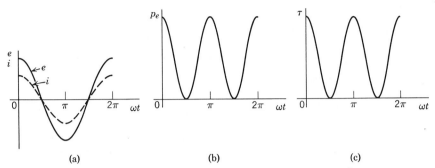

(a)   (b)   (c)

Fig. 17.13   Power and torque relations in an elementary dynamo.

We conclude from Example 4 that the ideal elementary dynamo is another bilateral electromechanical energy converter.

A General Torque Equation

As preparation for the analysis of a variety of rotating machines we need a general expression for torque.   A single, simple relation which would apply to a-c or d-c machines employing electro- or permanent magnets in various configurations would be very convenient.   Let us take another look at the elementary dynamo and try to abstract the essential idea.

As shown in Fig. 17.14b, a current i_2 out of the upper conductor of length l in a field of uniform magnetic flux density B_1 develops a force

$$\mathbf{f} = i_2(\mathbf{l} \times \mathbf{B_1})$$

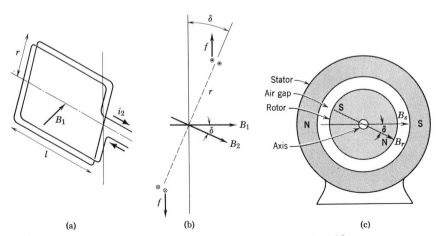

(a)   (b)   (c)

Fig 17.14   Torque on a coil in a magnetic field.

and the torque developed by an N-turn coil of width $2r$ is

$$\tau_d = 2NB_1 l i_2 \cdot r \sin \delta = B_1 A \cdot N i_2 \cdot \sin \delta \qquad (17\text{-}23)$$

where $A = 2lr$ is the area of the coil and δ (delta) is the angle between $\mathbf{B}_1$ and the normal to the plane of the coil. But what is $N i_2$? This is the mmf of the coil and establishes a flux density $\mathbf{B}_2$ in the direction shown. Alternative forms of Eq. 17-23 are

$$\tau_d = k_a B_1 i_2 \sin \delta = k_b B_1 B_2 \sin \delta \qquad (17\text{-}24a,b)$$

In words, the torque can be considered as due to the *interaction of an electric current and a magnetic field* or to the *interaction of two fields*. But B_1 itself is but a manifestation of a current i_1, either in a coil or in the atoms of a magnet, so the torque can also be considered as due to the *interaction of two currents*. A third formulation of the basic relation is

$$\tau_d = k_c i_1 i_2 \sin \delta \qquad (17\text{-}24c)$$

The angle δ is called the *torque angle* or *power angle*. The torque increases with $\sin \delta$ and reaches a maximum at $\delta = 90°$. Figure 17.14c symbolizes the general rotating machine. The stationary portion or *stator* sets up the field B_s and the rotating portion or *rotor* sets up the field B_r. Either or both of these fields may be established by electric currents in a practical machine. For a given current (or amount of copper) and a given flux (or amount of iron), the machine designer realizes the maximum torque if he arranges for δ to be 90°. For continuous torque, $\sin \delta$ must not change sign. These are critical considerations and dictate the mechanical arrangement and electrical connection of most practical rotating machines.

Rotating Machines

A rotating electromechanical converter has several important advantages. Torques and velocities can be constant instead of pulsating, and high velocities are possible without the high accelerating and decelerating forces inherent in translational devices. High velocities permit high voltages and, therefore, higher electrical power per unit weight. Because frictional losses increase rapidly with velocity, the bearings are placed on shafts of small radius (and low linear velocity) and the active conductors are at a much larger radius.

A-C Machines. A sinusoidal emf is generated when the coil of an elementary dynamo is turned at constant angular velocity in a uniform magnetic field. A more effective arrangement of copper and iron is

shown in Fig. 17.15. Direct current is supplied to the field windings
on the rotor through brushes and sliprings. The small air gap minimizes
the magnetizing current required for
a given flux density. The a-c emf
($e = d\lambda/dt$) is generated in conductors
connected in series and placed in slots
in the stator. Having the high-power
conductors stationary minimizes the
problems of insulation, centrifugal
force, and electrical connection. By
distributing the turns along the periphery of the stator and shaping the
air gap properly, the output voltage
can be made to approximate a sinusoid.
Most of the world's electrical power is
generated in more elaborate versions
of this basic alternator.

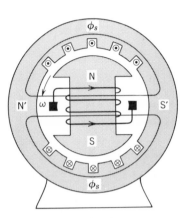

Fig. 17.15   An alternator.

Under what conditions can the
alternator function as a motor? If
the field is energized to establish B_r and a direct current is supplied to the
stator to establish B_s, the rotor will turn until $\delta = 0$ and then stop.
When the fields are aligned, $\sin \delta = 0$ and there is no torque; this is a
position of equilibrium. But motoring action is possible if we can upset
the equilibrium in just the right way. Assume that at a particular
instant the current is out of the upper conductors and into the lower
conductors in Fig. 17.15. This creates a stator field with poles N' and S'
as shown and $\delta = 90°$. The developed torque tends to turn the rotor
clockwise (in the $-\omega$ direction). Because of inertia the rotor will rotate
past the position of $\delta = 0$. If at that instant the current in the stator is
reversed, the new torque is also clockwise and the rotor continues to turn.
The stator current can be reversed by a mechanical switch, or an alternating current of just the right frequency can be used. The latter
arrangement is the basis of the *synchronous motor* treated in more detail
in Chapter 18.

D-C Machines.   To obtain unidirectional torque from direct currents,
we use a rotating mechanical switch called a *split-ring commutator*. The
same device permits the generation of direct currents in a rotating
machine. In d-c machines, the *field* winding is stationary and the
assembly of conductors and commutators, called the *armature*, rotates.
The operation of the commutator is indicated in Fig. 17.16. At the

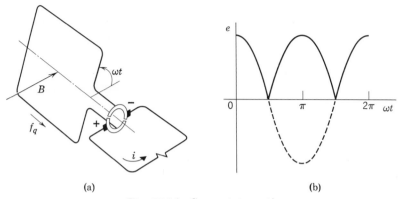

(a)   (b)

Fig. 17.16 Commutator action.

instant shown, the coil emf is decreasing. At $\omega t = \pi/2$, the emf is zero and the coil is shorted by the brushes. An instant later the lower conductor begins to move up across the flux and the generated emf is reversed; but the lower conductor has automatically been switched to the negative brush and the terminal polarity is unchanged. The commutator is a synchronous full-wave rectifier.

In the more practical form of Fig. 17.17a, the armature conductors are embedded in a cylindrical iron rotor. The stationary field windings establish a high and nearly uniform flux density in the small air gap. The emf generated in a single conductor (number 1) is shown in Fig. 17.17b; instant ωt_a corresponds to the left-hand figure with conductor 1 just

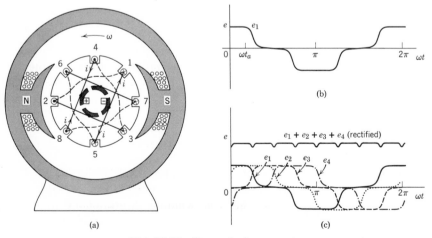

(a)   (c)

Fig. 17.17 Two-pole d-c generator.

leaving the S pole. Starting at the negative brush (drawn on the inside of the commutator but actually riding on the outside), we see that conductors 1, 2, 3, and 4 are connected in series. The sum of the individual emfs appears at the positive brush. Going in the other direction from the negative brush, we see that the other four conductors are connected in series. In this winding there are two *parallel paths*. As the armature rotates, carrying the segmented commutator with it, conductor 1 is switched out of one path and conductor 8 takes its place.

In a practical machine there are many conductors and many commutator segments. At any instant many coils are connected in series between brushes and a few coils are short-circuited (by the brushes) as they are being switched from one circuit to another. As each coil is switched, there is a momentary drop in terminal voltage, resulting in what is called commutator *ripple*, but this is small compared to the total effect of many coils in series.

As indicated in Fig. 17.17a, the current is into the paper in all conductors moving upward, and out of the paper in all conductors moving downward. The net result of all the currents is a flux density distribution which can be represented by a vector directed upward. As the armature rotates, this flux density *remains fixed in space* at the optimum torque angle $\delta = 90°$. The resulting developed torque is clockwise and, in a generator, must be overcome by the mechanical power source. If direct current from an electrical source is introduced at the brushes, a constant unidirectional torque is developed and the machine functions as a motor.

The two-pole commutator machine resembles the d'Arsonval mechanism in many ways. As would be expected from Eq. 17-22, for constant flux density in the air gap

$$K_m = \frac{T}{I} = K_e = \frac{E}{\Omega} \tag{17-25}$$

where the capital letters indicate direct or average values of torque T, current I, emf E, and angular velocity Ω. If field current, and therefore flux density and total flux per pole Φ, is a variable, the expressions for torque and emf are

$$T = K\Phi I \quad \text{and} \quad E = K\Phi\Omega \tag{17-26}$$

The steady-state model of a commutator machine is shown in Fig. 17.18. In the steady state, energy storage terms are not significant and only the rotational mechanical friction D_r and electrical resistance R are considered. The value of K depends on the machine construction and the electrical connection, as illustrated in the following example.

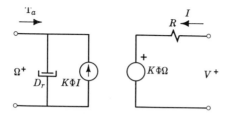

Fig. 17.18 Steady-state model of a commutator machine.

EXAMPLE 5

In a machine similar to that in Fig. 17.17, the armature is wound on a laminated iron cylinder 15 cm long and 15 cm in diameter. The N and S pole faces are 15 cm long (into the paper) and 10 cm along the circumference. The average flux density in the air gap under the pole faces is 1 T. If there are 80 conductors in series between the brushes and the machine is turning at $n = 1500$ rpm, predict the no-load terminal voltage.

SOLUTION. The average or d-c voltage can be predicted in any of the three ways expressed in Eqs. 17-17, 17-18, and 17-19. In this case the rate of flux cutting is a convenient approach. For N_s conductors (*not* coils) in series, the average emf is

$$E = N_s \frac{\Delta \Phi}{\Delta t} \left(\frac{\text{Wb}}{\text{sec}}\right) = N_s \times \Phi \left(\frac{\text{Wb}}{\text{pole}}\right) \times p \left(\frac{\text{poles}}{\text{revolution}}\right) \times \frac{n}{60} \left(\frac{\text{revolutions}}{\text{sec}}\right)$$

or

$$E = \frac{N_s \Phi p n}{60} \text{ volts} \tag{17-27}$$

Here the flux per pole is

$$\Phi = BA = 1 \times 0.15 \times 0.1 = 0.015 \text{ Wb}$$

Therefore,

$$E = 80 \times 0.015 \times 2 \times \frac{1500}{60} = 60 \text{ V}$$

Equation 17-27 can be derived directly from Eq. 17-18 by taking into account the number of poles and recognizing that the d-c voltage is just the average of a rectified sinusoid. The value of K in Eq. 17-26 can be derived from Eq. 17-27 by noting that $\Omega = 2\pi n/60$. Solving,

$$K = \frac{E}{\Phi \Omega} = \frac{N_s p}{2\pi} \tag{17-28}$$

The number of conductors in series is conveniently determined from $N_s = Z/p'$ where Z is the total number of conductors and p' is the number of parallel paths. In one common type of winding, $p' = p$ the number of poles.

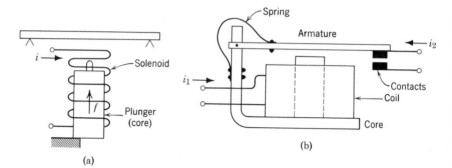

Fig. 17.19   (a) Door chime and (b) relay.

MOVING-IRON TRANSDUCERS

Most of the devices described so far employ a moving conductor in a magnetic field.   The elementary alternator of Fig. 17.15 differs in that the iron rotor, which could be a permanent magnet, moves past the stationary conductors; but this is essentially just a convenient method of obtaining relative motion of the conductors with respect to the field. There is another type of electromagnetomechanical energy converter which employs an initially unmagnetized iron member moving in the direction of a magnetic field.   Such *moving-iron* transducers cannot be analyzed conveniently in terms of forces on currents; a different approach is required.

Examples of moving-iron transducers are shown in Figs. 17.19 and 20. In the simple door chime, part of an iron core or plunger is within the

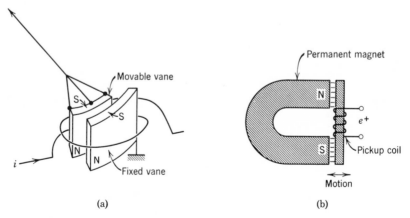

Fig. 17.20   (a) Iron-vane instrument and (b) reluctance pickup.

solenoid. When a current i flows in the solenoid, the plunger is accelerated upward and strikes the chime. To design such a chime we need to
know the force on the core as a function of position. A relay is a control
device whereby the current in circuit 2 can be turned on or off by a
current in circuit 1. In Fig. 17.19b, a current i_1 energizes the coil and
moves the armature against the restraining force of the spring. The
movable contact meets the fixed contact and circuit 2 is closed. Mechanical stops (not shown) limit the armature travel. Relay specifications
include the *pickup* or closing current and the *dropout* or opening current.
How could these currents be predicted?

The *iron-vane* mechanism of Fig. 17.20a is another form of the moving-
iron transducer. Current in a multiturn coil magnetizes two soft-iron
elements. Since the polarities are the same and like poles repel, the
movable vane rotates with respect to the fixed vane. The developed
torque (opposed by a spring not shown) is always in the same direction;
therefore, this is a good mechanism for measuring alternating currents.
In a *reluctance pickup* (Fig. 17.20b), a vibratory motion of the small iron
armature changes the air gap and, therefore, the reluctance of the magnetic circuit. The flux established by the permanent magnet changes
and a voltage is induced in the pick-up coil. Is the generated emf proportional to the displacement, velocity, or acceleration of the armature?

Virtual Work Method

One approach to the quantitative analysis of an electromechanical
transducer employs the principle of *virtual work*. We are interested in
determining a force; therefore, we assume that a small displacement takes
place, calculate the work that would be done in such a virtual displacement, and then determine the actual force.

If the plunger of Fig. 17.19a were to move an infinitesimal vertical distance dx, the work done on the plunger would be $f\,dx$. Where does this
energy come from? It must come from the electrical input. Does all
the electrical input appear as mechanical work? No, some of it appears
as heat from electrical resistance and mechanical friction, and some of it
may be stored in the magnetic field. Let us minimize i^2R by using high-
conductivity wire and minimize mechanical friction by proper design.
Then practically all the electrical input appears as either mechanical work
or as an increase in energy stored in the magnetic field.

In a linear magnetic system, the energy stored is $\frac{1}{2}Li^2$; if the current is
constant at a value I, the change in energy stored is $\frac{1}{2}I^2\,dL$. (Does the
inductance change as the core moves?) The electrical input is $p\,dt =$
$ei\,dt = (N\,d\Phi/dt)I\,dt = I\,d(N\Phi)$ where $d(N\Phi)$ is the change in flux link-

age associated with a virtual displacement dx. But $N\Phi = LI$ (Eq. 16-4) and if I is constant, $I\,d(N\Phi) = I^2\,dL$. Expressing the idea in the previous paragraph, we write

Electrical input = Work done + Increase in energy stored   (17-29)

or

$$I^2\,dL = f\,dx + \tfrac{1}{2}I^2\,dL$$

and

$$f = \frac{I^2\,dL - \tfrac{1}{2}I^2\,dL}{dx} = \tfrac{1}{2}I^2\frac{dL}{dx} \qquad (17\text{-}30)$$

This is a relation of great simplicity and, it turns out, of considerable generality. *The force is directly proportional to the rate of change of inductance and in the direction associated with an increase in inductance* (since I^2 is always positive). Reasoning by analogy, what result would you anticipate for a rotational transducer? A similar analysis yields

$$\tau = \tfrac{1}{2}I^2\frac{dL}{d\theta} \qquad (17\text{-}31)$$

Another basic conclusion is that in such a linear magnetic system, half the electrical energy input is converted to mechanical energy and the other half appears as an increase in the energy stored in the magnetic field.†

EXAMPLE 6

A magnetic circuit is completed through a soft-iron rotor as shown in Fig. 17.21. Derive an expression for torque as a function of angular position.

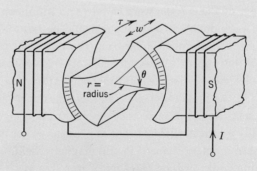

Fig. 17.21   Example 6.

---

† See Chapters 4 and 5 of H. H. Skilling, *Electromechanics*, John Wiley and Sons, New York, 1962.

SOLUTION. To simplify the analysis, let us assume:
1. All the reluctance of the magnetic circuit is in the air gaps of length l.
2. There is no fringing so the effective area of each gap is the area of overlap = $A = r\theta w$.

The total reluctance for two gaps in series is

$$\mathcal{R} = \frac{2l}{\mu_o A} = \frac{2l}{\mu_o r w \theta}$$

The inductance is

$$L = \frac{N\Phi}{I} = \frac{N\mathfrak{F}}{I\mathcal{R}} = \frac{N^2 I}{I\mathcal{R}} = \frac{N^2 \mu_o r w \theta}{2l}$$

By Eq. 17-31 the torque is

$$\tau = \tfrac{1}{2}I^2 \frac{dL}{d\theta} = \frac{\mu_o N^2 I^2 r w}{4l}$$

or the torque is independent of θ under the assumed conditions. Actually, there is some positive torque for negative values of θ. (Why?) Also note that there is no torque when overlap is complete because $dL/d\theta$ drops to zero.

The *reluctance torque* evaluated in Example 6 is important in practical machines. Small electric-clock motors operate on this principle. Some medium-size synchronous motors are pulled into synchronism by reluctance torque, and in large machines the reluctance effect contributes a significant part of the total torque.

Energy Balance Method

Equation 17-29 is an abbreviated *energy balance* based on the law of conservation of energy. In general, the energy added to a system goes to increase the energy stored within the system or appears as an output from the system. Some of the chemical energy of the fuel supplied to a diesel-electric system is stored in the kinetic energy of the flywheel, or as thermal energy evidenced by an increase in temperature, and the remainder appears as useful electrical output or unavailable heat radiated or carried away in the exhaust. In dealing with electromagnetomechanical converters it is convenient to write the energy balance as

$$\frac{\text{Mechanical}}{\text{input}} + \frac{\text{Electrical}}{\text{input}} = \frac{\text{Mechanical}}{\text{storage}} + \frac{\text{Magnetic}}{\text{storage}} + \text{Heat} \quad (17\text{-}32)$$

This equation applies to all types of converters. In a generator, mechanical input is positive and electrical input is negative. In a d'Arsonval movement, electrical input is positive, mechanical input is zero, and mechanical energy is stored in the springs. During current changes, the kinetic energy of the moving coil may be significant. In a relay, the change in energy stored in the air gap just balances the mechanical output (see Eq. 17-33). Also, in every real device some energy is converted into heat in irreversible processes. Copper loss, hysteresis and eddy-current losses, and bearing and air-friction losses must all be considered. The energy-balance approach is particularly useful in situations in which overall effects are more easily handled than detailed phenomena.

EXAMPLE 7

A commutator machine is rated at 5 kW, 250 V, 2000 rpm. The armature resistance R_a is 1 Ω. Driven from the electrical end at 2000 rpm, the no-load power input to the armature is $I_a = 1.2$ A at 250 V with the field winding ($R_f = 250$ Ω) excited by $I_f = 1$ A. Estimate the efficiency of this machine as a 5-kW generator.

SOLUTION. The wiring diagram and the steady-state circuit model (see Fig. 17.18) are shown in Fig. 17.22.

An input power of $I_f{}^2 R_f = 1^2 \times 250 = 250$ W is required to provide the necessary magnetic flux. This is power lost and it appears as heat.

In no-load steady-state operation there is no output and no change in energy storage; therefore, the armature input of 1.2 A at 250 V = 300 W is all loss. A small part ($I_a{}^2 R_a = 1.2^2 \times 1 = 1.44$ W) is copper loss, but most of the input power goes to supply air, bearing, and brush friction and the eddy-current and hysteresis losses associated with flux changes in the rotating armature core. All these losses are dependent on speed, but are nearly independent of load.

At full-load of 5 kW, $I_a = 5000$ W/250 V = 20 A and the armature copper loss is $I_a{}^2 R_a = 20^2 \times 1 = 400$ W.

With the generator driven from the mechanical end, the rotational losses can be assumed to be equal to the no-load armature input and are represented by D_r in the model. Then the energy balance (Eq. 17.32) is

$$\text{Mech.} \atop \text{input} + \begin{bmatrix} \text{Field} \\ \text{input} \end{bmatrix} - \begin{matrix} \text{Elec.} \\ \text{output} \end{matrix} \end{bmatrix} = 0 + 0 + \begin{bmatrix} \text{Field} & + & \text{Arm.} & + & \text{Rotat.} \\ \text{loss} & & \text{loss} & & \text{loss} \end{bmatrix}$$

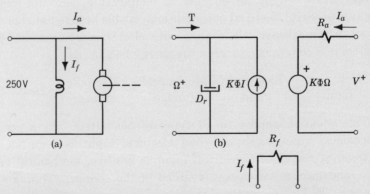

Fig. 17.22 Wiring diagram and circuit model for Example 7.

and

$$\frac{\text{Mech.}}{\text{input}} + [250 - 5000] = [250 + 400 + 300]$$

or

$$\text{Mech. input} = 5000 + 250 - 250 + 400 + 300 = 5700 \text{ W}$$

(Note that field input is all loss and appears on both sides.)   Then

$$\text{Efficiency} = \frac{\text{Output}}{\text{Input}} = \frac{\text{Elect. output}}{\text{Mech. input} + \text{Elect. input}} = \frac{5000}{5700 + 250} = 0.84$$

The Electromagnet

A versatile example of the moving-iron transducer is the electromagnet shown in Fig. 17.23.   An electric current, alternating or direct, develops a pull on the pivoted armature and raises the mass M a distance dl. Motion of the armature may be used to close or open contacts, to open or close valves, or to engage mechanisms.   The important design criterion is the force developed for a given current.

Considering the region within the dashed line as an electromechanical system, we see that there is electrical energy input and mechanical energy output, we suspect that there is energy stored, and we know there is energy lost irreversibly.   In terms of the energy-balance equation, the mechanical input for a virtual displacement dl is $-(f\,dl)$ since the work is actually done *by* the system.   If during this infinitesimal displacement we adjust the current so that the magnetic flux remains constant, $N\,d\phi/dt$ is zero and there is no induced emf in the coil.   Then the electrical input is just $i^2R\,dt$, where dt is the time required for displacement dl.   (How

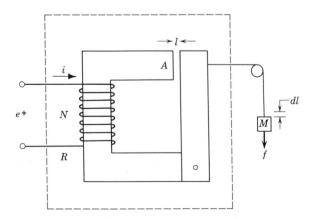

Fig. 17.23   Electromagnet with pivoted armature.

are these conditions different from those imposed in deriving Eq. 17-30?)

If the motion of the armature is horizontal, there is no change in potential energy stored; and if the motion is slow, there is no change in kinetic energy stored. The energy stored in the magnetic field does change. From Eq. 16-7 we know that the energy per unit volume is $\frac{1}{2}B^2/\mu$. If ϕ and B are constant, there is no change in the energy stored in the iron; but the energy stored in the air gap *decreases* by $(\frac{1}{2}B^2/\mu_o)A\,dl$, where A is the area of the gap if fringing is neglected.

The final term in the energy balance is primarily the $i^2R\,dt$ loss in the coil winding. With a frictionless pivot there is no mechanical friction loss, and with no change in ϕ there is no eddy-current or hysteresis loss. (Was this a convenient condition?) Equation 17.32 becomes

$$-f\,dl + i^2R\,dt = 0 - \frac{1}{2}\frac{B^2}{\mu_o}A\,dl + i^2R\,dt \qquad (17\text{-}33)$$

Actually, current i is a variable, but since the same term appears on both sides of the equation its evaluation is unimportant. Solving for the developed force in newtons,

$$f = \frac{B^2A}{2\mu_o} \qquad (17\text{-}34)$$

This result is general and does not require that ϕ (and B) be constant (see Exercise 17.25). Since the flux density possible in practical materials is limited by saturation, this relation places an upper limit on the force developed by an electromagnet of a given cross section.

To determine the relation between force and current, we assume that the permeability of the iron is so high that all the mmf in the magnetic circuit appears across the reluctance of the air gap. Then

$$B = \frac{\phi}{A} = \frac{\mathfrak{F}}{\mathfrak{R}_aA} = \frac{Ni}{(l/\mu_oA)A} = \frac{\mu_oNi}{l}$$

and Eq. 17-34 becomes

$$f = \frac{\mu_oN^2i^2A}{2l^2} \qquad (17\text{-}35)$$

where μ_o is the permeability of free space $= 4\pi \times 10^{-7}$ H/m,

N is the number of turns on the coil,

i is the current in amperes,

A is the area of the air gap in meters^2, and

l is the length of the gap in meters.

Note that the force increases as the armature moves and the air gap length decreases. For very small air gaps the assumptions must be reexamined.

EXAMPLE 8

In the relay shown in Fig. 17.24, the contacts are held open by a spring exerting a force of 0.2 N. The gap length is 4 mm when the contacts are open and 1 mm when closed. The coil of 5000 turns is wound on a core 1 cm² in cross section. Predict the pickup and dropout currents for this relay.

SOLUTION. To simplify the solution, we assume:

1. All reluctance is in a uniform air gap.
2. Fringing is negligible so that $A = 10^{-4} \text{ m}^2$.
3. Spring force is constant and acts at a distance equal to half the distance from the pivot to the air gap.
4. Friction and inertia effects are negligible.

For pickup or closing, the gap length is 4×10^{-3} m and the required force is $\frac{1}{2} \times 0.2 \text{ N} = 0.1 \text{ N}$. Solving Eq. 17-35 for current,

$$i = \sqrt{\frac{2l^2f}{\mu_o N^2 A}} = \sqrt{\frac{2 \times 16 \times 10^{-6} \times 0.1}{4\pi \times 10^{-7} \times 25 \times 10^6 \times 10^{-4}}} \cong 0.032 \text{ A}$$

The closing current is approximately 32 mA. Since current is directly proportional to gap length, the opening or dropout current is approximately $32/4 = 8$ mA.

To check the adequacy of the core area and the validity of the reluctance assumption, we note that

$$B = \frac{\mu_o N i}{l} = \frac{4\pi \times 10^{-7} \times 5 \times 10^3 \times 32 \times 10^{-3}}{4 \times 10^{-3}} = 0.05 \text{ T}$$

a very conservative value.

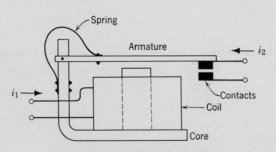

Fig. 17.24 Relay for Example 8.

SUMMARY

♦   A conductor moving in a magnetic field generates an emf

$$e = \mathbf{B} \cdot (\mathbf{l} \times \mathbf{u}) = Blu \cos \alpha \sin \beta$$

and develops a force

$$\mathbf{f} = i(\mathbf{l} \times \mathbf{B}) \qquad \text{where } f = Bli \sin \gamma$$

The translational transducer is a bilateral energy converter which can be represented by a two-port model with

$$P_e = ei = P_m = fu = Bliu$$

The dynamic transducer used in loudspeakers and pickups consists of a coil in translation in a transverse magnetic field.

♦   The d'Arsonval mechanism widely used in instrumentation consists of a coil in rotation in a magnetic field; the coil generates an emf $e = NBA \ \omega$ and develops a torque $\tau = NBA \ i$.

♦   A coil rotating in a uniform magnetic field generates an emf $e = NBA\omega \cos \omega t$ and develops a torque $\tau = NBAi \cos \omega t$.

The emf can be evaluated in terms of the velocity of moving conductors, the rate at which flux is cut, or the rate of change of flux linkage.

The torque can be evaluated in terms of the interaction of two electric currents, the interaction of two magnetic fields, or the interaction of a current and a field.

♦   A useful form of the general torque equation is

$$\tau = kB_r B_s \sin \delta$$

♦   An alternator with direct current supplied to the rotor generates a sinusoidal emf in the stator.

The alternator can operate as a motor if the rotor turns at synchronous speed and alternating current is supplied to the stator.

♦   The commutator permits the generation of direct current and the production of unidirectional torque; as the rotor turns, conductors are automatically switched to the proper circuit.

$$\frac{T}{I} = \frac{E}{\Omega} = K\Phi = \frac{N_s p}{2\pi} \Phi$$

♦   The method of virtual work and the energy-balance concept are particularly useful in analyzing moving-iron transducers; in general,

$$f = \tfrac{1}{2} I^2 \frac{dL}{dx} \qquad \text{and} \qquad \tau = \tfrac{1}{2} I^2 \frac{dL}{d\theta}$$

♦   The force developed by an electromagnet is approximately

$$f = \frac{B^2 A}{2\mu_o} = \frac{\mu_o N^2 i^2 A}{2l^2}$$

REVIEW QUESTIONS

1. List four basically different reversible electromechanical phenomena.

2. On a transducer, terminal A is positive with respect to terminal B. If an ammeter indicates current is flowing *out* of terminal B, is this transducer acting as a motor or as a generator? Explain.

3. Explain how, in a moving current-carrying conductor in a magnetic field, positive charges are forced in one direction and the conductor in another.

4. Outline the steps in deriving an expression for emf generated in a moving conductor.

5. In Fig. 17.5, what corresponds to the turn ratio in a transformer?

6. Draw and label a mechanical circuit model to represent a device governed by the equation $Bli = M \, du/dt + Du + \int u \, dt/K$.

7. An advertisement says: "The superior tone quality is due to the highly compliant suspension and massive magnet structure of the speaker." Analyze this statement. What does it mean?

8. A loudspeaker has two coils; one consists of a few turns in an air gap and the other consists of many turns on an iron core. What function is served by each?

9. What frequency-response characteristic is desirable in the preamplifier following a dynamic phonograph pickup?

10. Why is the current to a d'Arsonval instrument carried by the spiral springs? What is the maximum possible deflection?

11. Write an expression for sensitivity ($°/A$) for a d'Arsonval mechanism.

12. How can the same instrument measure voltage and current?

13. Explain the concept of a "turn ratio" in a rotating coil transducer.

14. How is the circuit of Fig. 17.11b altered by movement damping?

15. Write three different expressions for the emf generated in a coil moving with respect to a permanent magnet.

16. Write an expression for torque in an ideal dynamo which does not include any magnetic factors. Explain the energy basis.

17. What is the torque angle? How does it affect machine design?

18. What advantages do rotational devices have over translational devices?

19. What condition is necessary if a machine with direct current in the rotor and alternating current in the stator is to develop useful torque?

20. Draw a sketch of an actual commutator (auto generator or starter motor) showing segments, insulation, and brushes.

21. Explain the operation of a commutator in a d-c motor.

22. Are there eddy-current or hysteresis losses in a d-c generator? Why?

23. Given a bar of soft iron in a magnetic field; is the torque in such a direction as to increase or decrease the stored magnetic energy?

24. What is the meaning of "virtual"? What is "virtual work?"

25. Explain the operation of a reluctance clockmotor.

26. Make an energy balance for a d-c generator which is accelerating; clearly identify each term.

27. How would the energy balance (Eq. 17-33) differ for current held constant?

28. How is the lifting force of an electromagnet affected by a slight reduction in pole-face area?

EXERCISES

1. The line in Fig. 17.25 represents a long, straight conductor carrying a current I in air.

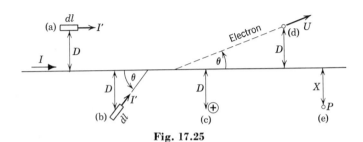

Fig. 17.25

(a) Express the force on element a of length dl carrying current I' and indicate its direction.

(b) Repeat for element b.

(c) Repeat for a similar element c carrying current into the paper.

(d) Repeat for an electron d moving with velocity U in the direction shown.

(e) Express the magnetic flux density and the magnetic field intensity at point P and indicate their directions.

2. A hot, corrosive liquid (such as molten sodium) is to be pumped by the scheme shown in Fig. 17.26.

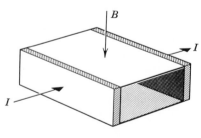

Fig. 17.26

(a) How would such a device work?

(b) For flow out of the paper, what should be the sign of I?

(c) Estimate the pressure rise in a 5-cm $\times$ 20-cm pipe with $B = 1$ T and $I = 1000$ A.

3. In the transducer of Fig. 17.2, the resistance of the rails is negligible compared to the resistance R of the conductor of mass M which slides without friction on the rails. The conductor is initially at rest and a constant force f_a is applied at time $t = 0$.

(a) Draw an appropriate circuit model.

(b) Determine the velocity u as a function of time.

4. The conductor in the transducer of Fig. 17.3 moves so that its position is $x = 100t^2$ m, where t is in sec. Length $l = 0.5$ m, mass $M = 0.1$ kg, $B = 0.8$ T, $V = 24$ V, and $R = 0.5$ Ω.

(a) Find velocity u.

(b) Define the regions for operation as a motor and as a generator. (Assume positive current i corresponds to generator action.)

(c) Predict the power supplied to the battery at $t = 1$ sec.

(d) Neglecting friction, predict the applied force required at $t = 1$ sec.

5. Derive the model shown in Fig. 17.5, starting from general two-port considerations, and explaining your choice of independent variables.

6. Draw a clearly labeled sketch of an ideal gear train consisting of two gears with N_1 and N_2 teeth, respectively, and derive a mechanical circuit model.

7. Examine a dynamic speaker and draw a sketch showing magnet structure, voice coil, and cone suspension. Estimate weight and dimensions.

8. A dynamic speaker is shown in Fig. 17.7. A *maximum* force of 0.2 ounce is required to provide adequate acoustic power. The 15-turn coil is in a magnetic flux density of $B = 0.4$ T. The annular air gap has a radius of 1 cm, a length of 2 mm, and a depth (in the direction of u) of 1 cm.

(a) Determine the rms value of the necessary sinusoidal current.

(b) Estimate the magnetomotive force required to provide the design flux density.

(c) If an electromagnet is used instead of a permanent magnet, where should the magnetizing coil be placed?

9. A dynamic phonograph pickup is similar to the speaker in Fig. 17.7. The displacement of the needle is transmitted directly to the 20-turn coil which vibrates in a field of $B = 0.10$ T. Each turn of the coil is 3 cm long.

(a) How many grooves per centimeter are there on a typical 33 rpm record? (What is the playing time?)

(b) If approximately 80% of the space per groove is available for recording, what is the maximum peak-to-peak displacement allowable?

(c) What is the maximum voltage (rms value) generated in this pickup at 100 cps? At 10,000 cps?

(d) For a uniform response (output voltage versus frequency), what provisions in regard to amplitude of vibration should be made in recording?

10. A d'Arsonval type ammeter (Fig. 17.9) is to have a full-scale deflection of 2 rad with a current of 5 A. A permanent magnet can supply a flux density of 0.2 T through a 7.5-turn square coil 2 cm on a side. What remains to complete the design? Complete the specifications.

11. A d'Arsonval movement provides full-scale deflection with a current of 5 mA or an applied voltage of 50 mV. Specify the shunt and multiplier to provide ranges of 0 to 3 A and 0 to 150 V.

12. Repeat Exercise 11 for ranges of 0 to 10 A and 0 to 300 V.

13. Redraw Fig. 17.11a to include the effect of a conducting coil form and derive Eq. 17.16 for this case.

14. A magnetic field out of the paper (Fig. 17.27) is independent of distance y, but linearly dependent on distance x so that $B = 2x + 1$ T, where x is in meters. A coil l meters on a side (l is small compared to the dimensions of the field) lies in the plane of the paper with its center at the origin. Calculate the emf induced in the coil as a function of time for each of the following motions:
   (a) Rotation about the y axis at angular velocity Ω rad/sec.
   (b) Translation along the y axis so that the ordinate of the center is $y = \sin \Omega t$ m.
   (c) Translation along the x axis so that the abscissa of the center is $x = \sin \Omega t$ m.

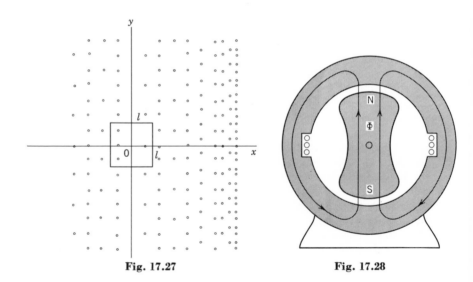

Fig. 17.27   Fig. 17.28

15. A tachometer consists of a voltmeter and the device shown in Fig. 17.28. The permanent magnet provides a total flux Φ, all of which links the N-turn stator coil in the position shown. The voltmeter is connected to the coil. Stating any necessary assumptions, derive the relation between shaft speed in rpm and voltmeter reading. What type of voltmeter is required?

16. An alternator similar to Fig. 17.15, but with 4 poles on the rotor, is driven at 1500 rpm. Sketch the alternator, labeling the poles, and predict the output frequency.

17. To turn the alternator of Exercise 16 at 1500 rpm with no output current requires a torque of 2 N-m. With an output current of 2 A, the required torque is 4 N-m. Neglecting stator resistance, estimate the generated emf.

18. A d-c generator similar to Fig. 17.17, but with four stator poles, turns at 1800 rpm. Each pole face (at the air gap) is 10 cm × 10 cm and $B = 1$ T. Between brushes there are 100 turns effectively in series, and each turn has a total length of 38 cm. Estimate the emf generated.

19. If the generator of Exercise 18 supplies a current of 50 A, what torque is developed?

20. Inductance data for a solenoid and plunger are plotted in Fig. 17.29. For a constant current of 5 A, plot a curve of solenoid pull as a function of plunger position and determine the maximum pull.

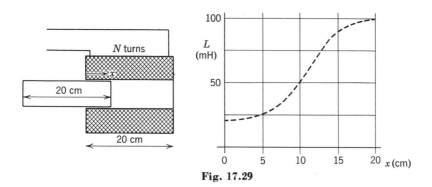

Fig. 17.29

21. In the a-c ammeter of Fig. 7.4b, the total inductance with all coils aligned is 10 mH, and with the rotating coil reversed, 6 mH. Assuming that $L = L_s + L_r + 2M \sin \theta$, estimate the torque developed by a current of 2 A when the rotating coil is normal to the stationary coil $\theta = 0°$.

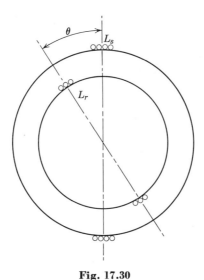

Fig. 17.30

22. In the cylindrical device shown in Fig. 17.30, the inductance L_s of the stator winding is 2 H and L_r of the rotor winding is 1.6 H. The emf induced in the rotor is $M \, di_s/dt$ where mutual inductance $M = 0.8 \cos \theta$ H. Resistances are negligibly small.   The stator current is $i_s = 2 \sin \omega t$ A and the rotor winding is short-circuited.

   (a) Write the voltage equation for the short-circuited rotor.

   (b) Derive and sketch the variation in rotor torque as angle θ is slowly changed.

   (c) Compare this equation to Eq. 17-24c and explain any difference.

23. Assuming linearity, derive expressions for the energy stored in:

   (a) A compressed spring of compliance K.

   (b) A mass M in translation.

   (c) A solid cylinder of mass M and radius r in rotation about its axis.

   (d) A magnetic field in terms of reluctance $\mathfrak{R}$.

24. Make an energy balance for a d'Arsonval ammeter while current is increasing.

25. In Fig. 17.23 assume that current i is held constant.

   (a) Make an energy balance, stating necessary assumptions.

   (b) Derive Eq. 17-35 for this condition.

26. A magnetic contactor used to close circuits carrying heavy currents is similar to Fig. 17.23 with contacts mounted on the pivoted armature.   The cross section of the core is 5 cm² and the length is 20 cm.   Estimate the current required in a 500-turn coil to develop a force of 20 N across a 1-cm gap.

27. A relay similar to Fig. 17.19b requires a current of 36 mA to close the contacts when the air gap is 3 mm.   Estimate the current required if the gap is reduced to 2 mm.

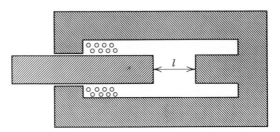

Fig. 17.31

28. The solenoid in Fig. 17.31 is drawn full scale.   The silicon steel sections are 1 cm thick into the paper.   The coil consists of 160 turns of copper wire. Estimate the current required to produce a pull of 5 N (a little over a pound) when $l = 1.5$ cm.

   (a) State any simplifying assumptions desirable.

   (b) Estimate the required current.

   (c) Calculate (for this current) the pull for several values of l and plot a graph of pull f versus gap length l.

   (d) What happens to the force when the gap length goes to zero?

PROBLEMS

   1. The device whose characteristics are shown in Fig. 17.32b is to be used as a velocity sensor.   The operating point is defined by I_o, X_o.   Represent the

device, for small variations in x, by a circuit model consisting of a controlled voltage source e in series with an inductance L. Write a general equation for v as a function of i and x and evaluate L and e.

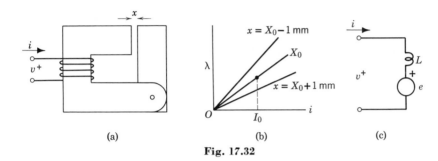

(a)   (b)   (c)

Fig. 17.32

2. In a simplified form of magnetohydrodynamic generator (see Fig. 14.6) the electrodes are parallel and of length $l = 30$ cm. A field of $B = 1$ T (into the paper) exists in the channel which has a square cross section $b = 10$ cm on a side. The plasma has a resistivity $\rho = 10^{-5}$ Ω-m and an average velocity $U = 10$ m/sec.

(a) Explain why an emf should be developed across the electrodes.

(b) Derive a literal expression for the electrode voltage indicated by a high-resistance voltmeter.

(c) Estimate the maximum power obtainable from this generator under the given conditions.

(d) What nonelectrical measurements would reveal this power?

3. The displacement of the needle of a dynamic pickup is $x = X \sin \omega t$ m. The output of the pickup is fed into a transistor preamplifier whose input is a pure resistance at medium frequencies. Stating any necessary assumptions, sketch the displacement and the output voltage as functions of time. Repeat for a displacement $x = X \sin \omega t + 0.3 X \sin 3 \omega t$ m. For "high-fidelity," what provision should be made?

4. A d'Arsonval instrument can be employed to measure slowly changing currents. Investigate the response of such an instrument to alternating voltages of the form $v = V_m \cos \omega t$. Work in terms of phasors, using θ for angular displacement and $\dot{\theta}$ for angular velocity to distinguish from frequency ω. Neglect the inductance of the moving coil and the frictional resistance of the bearings.

(a) Draw an appropriate circuit model, clearly labeled, and derive an expression for the input impedance.

(b) Sketch the variation in impedance magnitude Z as a function of frequency ω, labeling significant values of Z and ω.

(c) Derive an expression for the ratio θ/V and sketch a graph of the ratio θ_m/V_m as a function of ω.

5. Derive Eq. 17-2 by equating the work done by an external agency to the work done on the moving charges.

6. Prepare a chart summarizing the characteristics of some of the devices studied so far. Rule a page into 4 columns headed Device, Input, Output, and Function. Provide 10 rows for the following devices: Amplifier, Rectifier, Modulator, Transformer, Loudspeaker, Pickup, Ammeter, Relay, Commutator Motor, and Alternator. Complete the chart by filling in the blanks with brief statements (10 words or less).

7. In the motor of Fig. 17.33, the reluctance $\mathfrak{R}$ of the magnetic circuit is a function of deflection angle θ. Make an energy balance and prove that the developed torque is $\tau_d = -\frac{1}{2}\phi^2 \, d\mathfrak{R}/d\theta$. Explain the minus sign.

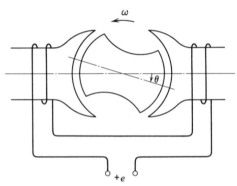

Fig. 17.33

8. You are to derive an expression for the average torque developed by the motor of Fig. 17.33. The reluctance of the magnetic circuit is a minimum at $\theta = 0°$. Assume that the rotor shape is such that $\mathfrak{R} = \mathfrak{R}_0 - \mathfrak{R}_a \cos 2\theta$. (Does this look reasonable?) If the impedance of the winding is negligibly small, $v = e$ and a sinusoidal voltage produces a sinusoidal magnetic flux $\phi = \Phi_m \cos \omega t$. Since unidirectional torque is produced only if the speed of rotation is synchronized with the alternation of the flux, let $\theta = \omega t - \delta$. What is θ when the flux is maximum? If instantaneous torque is represented by the sum of components of various frequencies, which component corresponds to average torque?

9. The *shaker* in Fig. 17.34 is used in vibration-testing electronic devices. The spring of compliance K holds the plunger of mass M at a displacement X_0 when a steady polarizing current I_0 is supplied. A varying current i in the N-turn coil develops a varying force f on the soft iron plunger.

(a) Sketch a family of curves of F versus X for various values of I. Label an operating point defined by X_0 and I_0.

(b) Sketch a family of curves for flux linkage λ versus I for various values of X. Label the operating point.

(c) Stating any necessary assumptions and letting i and x be small variations, write an expression for λ in terms of $I_0 + i$, $X_0 - x$ and two arbitrary constants. Then express $e = d\lambda/dt$.

(d) Stating any necessary assumptions, write an expression for the "small-signal" variation in force f in terms of i and x and two arbitrary constants.

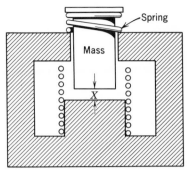

Fig. 17.34

(e) Write an expression relating the available force f_a to the inertia force due to M and the restoring force due to K.

(f) On the basis of equations c, d, and e (replacing dx/dt with u), draw and label an appropriate circuit model.

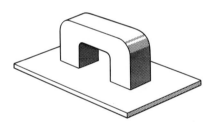

Fig. 17.35

10. An electromagnet to lift steel plate is made of silicon sheet steel in the shape shown in Fig. 17.35. The square pole pieces are 10 cm on a side and the effective length of the core is 40 cm. To allow for scale and surface irregularities, an air gap of 1 mm must be assumed.

(a) Design the coil for this electromagnet (What must be specified?) to provide for lifting plates weighing 2000 lb. (Do both gaps lift?) State all simplifying assumptions.

(b) How should the design be modified to lift 4000-lb plates? (*Careful;* look at those assumptions!)

(c) It is proposed to use the electromagnet of Part a to lift clean smooth plates where the air gap is negligible. What weight plates can be lifted under these conditions? (Is your answer reasonable?)

◆ DIRECT-CURRENT MACHINES
◆ SYNCHRONOUS MACHINES
◆ INDUCTION MOTORS

CHAPTER **18**

Steady-State Performance of Rotating Machines

The rotating machine is preeminent as a means for converting great amounts of electromechanical energy. The design of efficient and economical machines is a highly developed art, demanding specialized training and extensive experience; the number of engineers who *design* electrical machines is small. In contrast, engineers in all branches of engineering and in nearly all functional classifications *use* electrical machines. This chapter is concerned with the use of existing machines in steady-state applications under normal conditions of operation.

Our purpose here is to provide the background necessary to select machines to meet general requirements and to predict the behavior of the machines selected. Electrical machines vary widely in operating characteristics, power requirements, flexibility, ruggedness, and cost; therefore, the features of the most common types of machines are described in some detail. Prediction of the precise behavior of a given machine is quite difficult. By making simplifying assumptions, however, we can derive relatively simple models which give satisfactory results under most conditions. Being aware of the effect of the assumptions made, we can (with more training) modify the results if greater precision is required.

From Chapter 17 we know the principles of emf generation and torque development which apply to all rotating electromagnetic devices. Now we are going to investigate the construction features and operating characteristics of the most important types of machines. Our procedure, as

581

with transistors and transformers, is to derive circuit models and use these to predict steady-state performance. Later (in Chapter 22) we shall study the dynamic behavior of machines as preparation for applications in control systems.

Classification of Electrical Machines

The rotating machine consists essentially of axial conductors moving in a magnetic field that exists in a cylindrical gap between two iron cores, but in practice it takes on a great variety of forms. One basis of classification is in terms of the current flowing in the stator and rotor windings. On this basis:

Direct-current machines—direct current in both stator and rotor.
Synchronous machines—alternating current in one, direct in the other.
Induction machines—alternating current in both stator and rotor.

We start our study with d-c machines; the construction is complicated, but a relatively simple model is quite satisfactory. In contrast, the construction of an induction motor is quite simple, but the prediction of performance is fairly complicated.

DIRECT-CURRENT MACHINES

The stator or *field* of a d-c generator or motor (Fig. 17.17) consists of an even number of magnetic poles (alternating N and S around the circumference) excited by direct current flowing in the field windings. The rotor or *armature* consists of a cylindrical iron core carrying the active conductors embedded in slots and connected to the segments of the commutator. Direct current is carried to and from the armature by stationary brushes riding on the commutator. The commutator automatically switches the conductors so that the external current from a generator or the torque from a motor is steady and unidirectional. The location of the brushes insures that the torque angle δ is 90°.

Basic Relations

The emf generated in each conductor can be calculated from $e = Blu$ and the total emf is determined by the number of conductors in series at any time. The torque developed in any conductor can be calculated from $\tau_d = Blir$ and the total torque is the summation of the individual contributions. For a given machine in the steady state, the basic relations are:

$$E = K\Phi\Omega \quad \text{and} \quad T_d = K\Phi I \tag{18-1}$$

where E is the generated emf in volts,

Φ is the air gap flux per pole in webers,

Ω is the angular velocity in radians/second,

T_d is the developed torque in newton-meters,

I is the armature current in amperes, and

K is a constant for the given machine (see Eq. 17-28).

Equations 18-1 apply *at the air gap;* the terminal voltage differs from the generated emf by the armature resistance voltage drop and the shaft torque differs from the developed torque by the mechanical resistance torque.

The d-c machine is a bilateral energy converter so that at the air gap the developed mechanical power is just equal to the generated electrical power or

$$T_d\Omega = EI \qquad (18\text{-}2)$$

The air gap power represents only the reversible portion of the electromechanical energy conversion.   Losses due to irreversible energy transformations occur in all practical machines.

Circuit Model of a Generator

For a d-c generator in the steady state, the circuit model of Fig. 18.1 is applicable.   Under steady-state conditions, currents and velocities are constant (or changing very slowly) so that there are no changes in mechanical or magnetic energy storage to consider.   This means that the rotational inertia and electrical inductance terms are omitted from the model.   The field resistance R_f must be considered in efficiency calculations.

In the linear model, the mechanical resistance term D represents all rotational losses.   It can be evaluated by measuring the no-load power

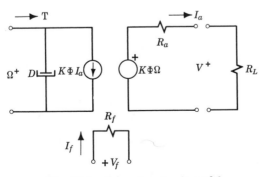

Fig. 18.1   Generator circuit model.

input when the machine is operated at rated speed Ω and rated voltage E (and, therefore, rated air gap flux Φ). Included in the rotational losses are: bearing and brush friction, air friction or *windage*, and core losses due to hysteresis and eddy-currents in regions of changing magnetic flux. (Where?)

The electrical resistance R_a is an effective resistance which takes into account the d-c resistance of the armature winding, the effect of non-uniform current distribution in the armature conductors, the brush-contact loss, and the resistance of any auxiliary windings in the armature circuit. It also could include *stray-load* loss which arises from the distortion of flux and current distribution under heavy load. Here we assume that R_a is a fixed, measurable value.

EXAMPLE 1

A d-c generator is rated at 10 kW, 200 V, and 50 A at 1000 rpm. $R_a = 0.4\ \Omega$ and $R_f = 80\ \Omega$. Predict the no-load voltage at 1000 rpm and the full-load voltage at 800 rpm if the field current is kept constant.

SOLUTION. For constant-speed operation (resulting from a governor on the driving engine), the mechanical portion of the circuit model is not significant in the calculation of electrical quantities. From the model of Fig. 18.2 we see that the terminal voltage is

$$V = K\Phi\Omega - I_a R_a = E - I_a R_a$$

At no load, $I_a = 0$ and $V = V_{nl} = E$. Therefore

$$V_{nl} = E = V_{fl} + I_a R_a = 200\ \text{V} + 50 \times 0.4 = 220\ \text{V}$$

If the field current is constant, the generated emf E is directly proportional to speed; therefore, at 800 rpm

$$E' = E \times \tfrac{800}{1000} = 220 \times \tfrac{800}{1000} = 176\ \text{V}$$

The terminal voltage at 800 rpm under full load (50 A) is

$$V'_{fl} = E' - I_a R_a = 176 - 50 \times 0.4 = 156\ \text{V}$$

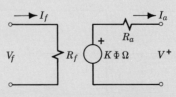

Fig. 18.2   Example 1.

In the model of Fig. 18.1 we assume that D, R_a, R_f, and K are constants; therefore, this is a linear model. To minimize errors, we should determine the constants under rated conditions; for small variations from a chosen operating point, linearity can be assumed with little error. The *external characteristic* is defined by

$$V = E - I_a R_a = K\Phi\Omega - I_a R_a \qquad (18\text{-}3)$$

Under certain conditions we may choose to assume that the magnetic circuit also is linear. Then the magnetic flux is directly proportional to field current and

$$V = K' I_f \Omega - I_a R_a \qquad (18\text{-}4)$$

Field Excitation

One basis for classifying d-c machines is according to the arrangement for field excitation. While motors almost always receive field current from the same power source which supplies the armature, generators may be *separately excited* or *self-excited*. The conventional symbols for field and armature are shown in Fig. 18.3a; here the field is separately excited by connecting it to an independent source. A field winding for *shunt* connection directly across the armature usually consists of many turns of fine wire, and I_f is a few percent of I_a. A field winding for *series* connection consists of a few turns of heavy wire since it carries the entire armature current. Series generators are unsatisfactory for most applications, but series motors are widely used.

In *compound*-connected machines all field poles have both shunt and series turns. The total mmf is either the sum or difference of $N_{sh} I_f$ and

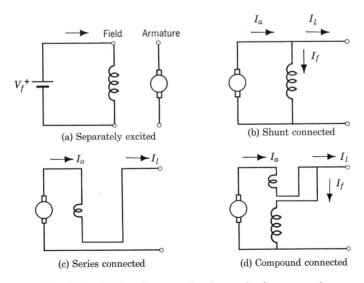

(a) Separately excited

(b) Shunt connected

(c) Series connected

(d) Compound connected

Fig. 18.3 Wiring diagrams showing excitation connections.

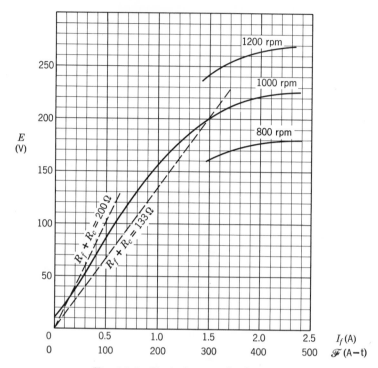

Fig. 18.4   Typical magnetization curve.

$N_{ser}I_a$ as desired.   The relative influence of the shunt windings can be adjusted by means of a variable resistor or *control rheostat* in the shunt field circuit.   The series field mmf is a function of load current, but its relative effect can be reduced by connecting a low-resistance *diverter* across the series field.

The relation between generated emf and field current is defined by a *magnetization curve* (Fig. 18.4).   Since E is proportional to Φ and I_f is proportional to $\mathcal{F}$, this is similar to a Φ-$\mathcal{F}$ curve for a magnetic circuit with an air gap.   It is easily obtained experimentally by measuring no-load voltage as a function of field current at a constant speed.   Curves for any other speed are obtained by direct proportion.   Due to *residual magnetism*, a small emf is generated even with zero field current.   Over a wide range the curve is nearly linear.   At high values of E corresponding to high values of B, *saturation* of the iron core has an appreciable effect.

The Self-Excited Shunt Generator

The magnetization curve is independent of the source of I_f.   In a separately excited generator, I_f is controlled by the operator and, within

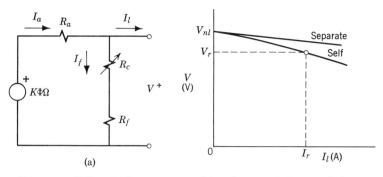

Fig. 18.5 Self-excited generator model and external characteristics.

limits, the no-load voltage can be set to any value. In a self-excited generator the no-load voltage is determined by the magnetization curve and the total resistance of the field circuit. If the very small $I_a R_a$ drop (Fig. 18.5a) is neglected, the generated emf $E = K\Phi\Omega$ appears across R_f and R_c, the resistance of the control rheostat, and

$$E = (R_f + R_c)I_f \qquad (18\text{-}5)$$

This represents a straight line with a slope $R_f + R_c$. But E is also a function of I_f as defined by the magnetization curve. The intersection of these curves is the simultaneous solution of the two relations.

EXAMPLE 2

The d-c generator of Example 1 is rated at 10 kW, 200 V, and 50 A at 1000 rpm. $R_a = 0.4\ \Omega$ and $R_f = 80\ \Omega$. The magnetization curve is shown in Fig. 18.4. Predict the values of R_c to yield a no-load voltage of 200 V and a full-load voltage of 200 V.

SOLUTION. For a speed of 1000 rpm (Fig. 18.4), $E = V_{nl} = 200$ V when $I_f = 1.5$ A; therefore, solving Eq. 18-5 yields

$$R_c = \frac{E}{I_f} - R_f = \frac{V_{nl}}{I_f} - R_f = \frac{200}{1.5} - 80 = 53\ \Omega$$

For a full-load voltage of 200 V, the generated emf (see Example 1) must be 220 V. Figure 18.4 indicates a field current of 2 A; therefore,

$$R_c = \frac{V_{fl}}{I_f} - R_f = \frac{200}{2} - 80 = 20\ \Omega$$

The process of voltage buildup in a self-excited generator can be explained in terms of Fig. 18.4. With the generator rotating, a small voltage (about 10 V here) exists due to residual magnetism. When the field circuit is closed, this voltage causes a small field current which increases the flux which increases the voltage, etc. This cumulative process continues until the stable operating point is reached; at this point the voltage generated is just that required to produce the current to establish the necessary flux. No further increase in voltage is possible, except by lowering the resistance of the field circuit. Note that if the field circuit resistance is increased slightly, to 200 Ω in Example 2, the no-load terminal voltage is drastically reduced. (What would happen if the polarity of the residual voltage was opposite to that assumed here?)

The Compound Generator

The variation in terminal voltage with a change in load current is usually undesirable. As indicated in Fig. 18.5b, the drop in voltage in a separately excited generator is primarily due to $I_a R_a$. In a self-excited generator the drop in terminal voltage decreases the field current and reduces the generated voltage still further. In contrast, the excitation provided by a series winding increases with armature current. A compound generator with the shunt and series windings properly proportioned produces a full-load voltage just equal to the no-load value; such a machine is said to be *flat-compounded*.

EXAMPLE 3

The generator of Examples 1 and 2 is to be operated with the shunt field (200 turns per pole) separately-excited.
(a) Design a series winding (Fig. 18.6a) to provide flat compounding.
(b) Predict the full-load terminal voltage if the series winding is incorrectly connected.

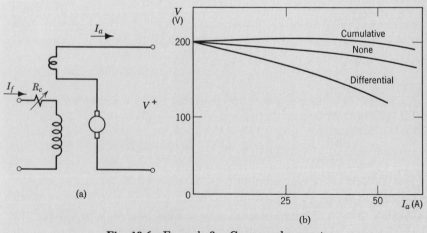

Fig. 18.6   Example 3.   Compound generator.

SOLUTION. (a) We assume that the resistance of the series winding is negligible. From Example 2 (or reading from Fig. 18.4), the required mmf is:
For 200 V at no-load, $NI_f = 200 \times 1.5 = 300$ A-t/pole.
For 200 V at full-load, $NI_f = 200 \times 2 = 400$ A-t/pole.
The difference of $400 - 300 = 100$ A-t is to be supplied by an armature current of 50 A; therefore, the series winding should provide

$$\frac{100 \text{ A-t/pole}}{50 \text{ A}} = 2 \text{ turns/pole}$$

(b) Knowing the number of turns per pole on the shunt winding used in determining the magnetization curve, we could convert the horizontal scale to mmf. In *cumulative* compounding the mmfs of the shunt and series windings add. In *differential* compounding the series winding is connected so that the series mmf is in opposition to that produced by the shunt field. For differential compounding with $I_f = 1.5$ A and $I_a = 50$ A, the net mmf per pole is

$$200 \times 1.5 - 2 \times 50 = 300 - 100 = 200 \text{ A-t}$$

This corresponds to $I_f = 1$ A (in the 200-turn shunt winding) and the magnetization curve indicates $E \cong 156$ V. Then

$$V = E - I_a R_a = 156 - 50 \times 0.4 = 136 \text{ V}$$

The external characteristics of the generator of Example 3 are shown in Fig. 18.6b. Under certain circumstances the "drooping" characteristic of the differentially compounded generator may be desirable. The degree of compounding can be reduced by use of a diverter. Under other circumstances a rise in voltage with load may be desirable and the machine is *over-compounded*.

Armature Reaction

In deriving the basic relations for a conductor moving in a magnetic field, we assumed that the field due to current in the conductor itself was negligibly small. In a loaded machine, this is no longer true. As shown in Fig. 18.7a, the armature current establishes an appreciable magnetic field directed at right angles or *in quadrature* with respect to the main field. The result of this *armature reaction* is a distortion of the flux distribution (Fig. 18.7b) with two practical results.

In the first place, commutation is affected adversely because the point of zero generated emf is shifted (in the direction of rotation in a generator). In some machines, the position of the brushes can be shifted under load to avoid shorting turns with appreciable emf. More commonly, a small auxiliary field winding carrying the load current is placed midway between the main poles. Such *commutating poles* oppose and nullify the mmf of the armature. Another practical arrangement is to

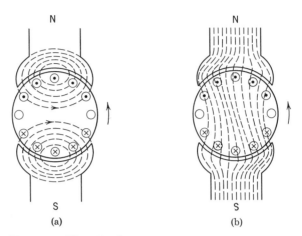

Fig. 18.7   Flux distribution showing armature reaction.

place conductors carrying armature current in the faces of the main poles. Such *compensating windings* oppose the armature mmf and reduce the distortion of the flux distribution.

A second effect of armature reaction is a reduction in generated emf due to a reduction in the average flux density.   Because the magnetic circuit is nonlinear, the increase in flux density in regions of high mmf is less than the decrease in regions of low mmf.   The total flux per pole is reduced and therefore the emf.   This effect contributes to the curvature in the external characteristics in Fig. 18.6b.

Armature reaction is of great importance in the design and performance of large machines, and certain devices such as the automobile generator voltage regulator depend on armature reaction for their operation.   In most of our problems, however, the additional complexity of considering armature reaction is not justified and we shall neglect its effect.

The Shunt Motor

If electrical power is supplied to a d-c machine, it can operate as a motor.   The essential difference between a motor and a generator is in the direction of armature-current flow.   The same circuit model is applicable to a motor, or it can be turned around as in Fig. 18.8.   D-c motors are classified as shunt, series, or compound, according to the method of field connection.   Since torque depends on field flux and armature current, the operating characteristics of the various types differ widely.

In the *shunt motor* (Fig. 18.9), the field circuit is connected directly

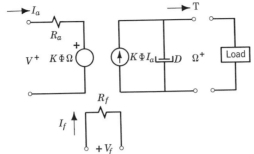

Fig. 18.8 Motor circuit model.

across the supply line and therefore the field current is constant (but adjustable by means of the rheostat R_c). The basic relations (Eqs. 18-1) apply, but it is usually more convenient to work with speed in rpm. Letting $\Omega = n \times 2\pi/60$, the basic equations are:

$$E = K\Phi \frac{2\pi n}{60} = kn\Phi \quad \text{and} \quad T_d = K\Phi I_a \quad (18\text{-}6)$$

where n is the speed in rpm and k is a new constant.

On the basis of Fig. 18.8, the voltage equation becomes

$$V = E + I_a R_a = kn\Phi + I_a R_a \quad (18\text{-}7)$$

The speed characteristic is revealed by solving Eq. 18-7 so that

$$n = \frac{V - I_a R_a}{k\Phi} \quad (18\text{-}8)$$

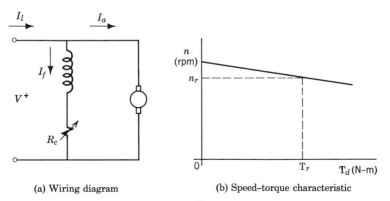

(a) Wiring diagram (b) Speed–torque characteristic

Fig. 18.9 Shunt motor.

Except for the effect of armature reaction, Φ remains constant. Since even at full load $I_a R_a$ is a small percentage of V, the shunt motor is essentially a constant-speed machine. At any given load, however, the speed is readily adjusted, within limits, by changing the field current with a control rheostat.

A specific expression for speed as a function of developed torque is obtained by solving the torque equation for I_a and substituting in Eq. 18-8 to yield

$$n = \frac{V}{k\Phi} - \frac{R_a}{kK\Phi^2} \mathrm{T}_d = n_{nl} - m\mathrm{T}_d \qquad (18\text{-}9)$$

Equation 18-9 indicates a straight-line relation between speed and developed torque (Fig. 18.9b).

Just how does a machine adjust to an increased load? As torque is applied to the shaft the motor slows down and the emf decreases. A small decrease in emf results in a large increase in I_a (Eq. 18-7) and a large increase in developed torque. The motor slows down just enough to develop the required torque. If the shaft load is reduced, the motor speeds up slightly and the armature current (representing power input) is reduced.

EXAMPLE 4

The d-c machine of the previous Examples is to be used as a shunt motor. No-load tests indicate that the rotational losses at rated speed are 1100 W. With a terminal voltage of 220 V, (a) predict the field current for a full-load speed of 1000 rpm, and (b) estimate the no-load speed.

SOLUTION. (a) Solving Eq. 18-7, for $I_a = 50$ A and $R_a = 0.4\ \Omega$,

$$E = V - I_a R_a = 220 - 50 \times 0.4 = 200 \text{ V}$$

The magnetization curve (Fig. 18.4) indicates $I_f = 1.5$ A for $E = 200$ V at a full-load speed of 1000 rpm.

(b) To supply the rotational losses, the armature input must be 1100 W (plus negligibly small $I_a{}^2 R_a$ loss). Therefore, at no load,

$$I_a = \frac{P_{nl}}{V} = \frac{1100}{220} = 5 \text{ A}$$

The no-load speed could be determined by solving Eq. 18-8, using the value of $k\Phi$ determined from full-load data. A simpler approach is to use the proportionality between E and n which leads to

$$n_{nl} = \frac{E_{nl}}{E_{fl}} \times n_{fl} = \frac{(V - I_a R_a)_{nl}}{(V - I_a R_a)_{fl}} \times n_{fl} = \frac{220}{200} \times 1000 = 1100 \text{ rpm}$$

As indicated by Example 4, the variation in speed of a shunt motor under load is quite small. The *speed regulation,* analogous to the voltage regulation of a transformer or generator, is defined as

$$SR = \frac{n_{nl} - n_{fl}}{n_{fl}} \qquad (18\text{-}10)$$

For the shunt motor of Example 4, the speed regulation is 10%. Typical values for shunt motors are in the range from 5 to 12% and justify classifying the shunt motor as a constant-speed machine.

The Series Motor

If a field winding consisting of a few turns of heavy wire is connected in series with a d-c armature (Fig. 18.10), the resulting *series motor* has characteristics quite different from those of a shunt motor. The basic equations (Eq. 18-6) still apply, but now magnetic flux is dependent on load current.

To simplify the analysis, we shall assume that the series motor is operating on the linear portion of the magnetization curve and $\Phi = k_1 I_a$. Then the emf and torque equations become

$$E = kn\Phi = knk_1I_a = k_E n I_a \qquad (18\text{-}11a)$$

and

$$T_d = K\Phi I_a = Kk_1 I_a{}^2 = k_T I_a{}^2 \qquad (18\text{-}11b)$$

Equation 18-11b indicates that the torque developed by a series motor is proportional to the square of the armature current. (How does this compare with the performance of a shunt motor?) To determine the speed-torque characteristic, we note that

$$V = E + I_a(R_a + R_s) = (k_E n + R_t)I_a \qquad (18\text{-}12)$$

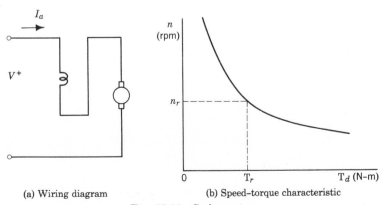

(a) Wiring diagram   (b) Speed–torque characteristic

Fig. 18.10 Series motor.

where $R_t = R_a + R_s$, the total resistance of the armature circuit.   Solving Eq. 18-12 for I_a and substituting in Eq. 18-11b,

$$\mathrm{T}_d = k_T \frac{V^2}{(k_E n + R_t)^2} \qquad (18\text{-}13)$$

For values of n such that $k_E n \gg R_t$, Eq. 18-13 indicates that the developed torque is inversely proportional to the square of the speed.   This relation is displayed in Fig. 18.10b.   The series motor is *not* a constant-speed machine; this is not necessarily a disadvantage, but it does limit the application of series motors.

EXAMPLE 5

The d-c machine of the previous Examples is to be operated as a series motor. The resistance of the series winding is estimated to be 0.2 Ω.
(a) Design the series winding.
(b) Predict the torque developed at rated speed and at twice rated speed.
SOLUTION.   (a) Assuming that the machine is to be rated at 220 V and 50 A at 1000 rpm, at full load the emf must be

$$E = V - I_a(R_a + R_s) = 220 - 50(0.4 + 0.2) = 190 \text{ V}$$

The magnetization curve (Fig. 18.4) indicates a required mmf of $NI_f = 200 \times$ 1.4 = 280 A-t.   Then the series winding must provide

$$N_s = \frac{280 \text{ A-t}}{50 \text{ A}} \cong 5\tfrac{1}{2} \text{ turns per pole}$$

If this is not convenient, 6 turns can be wound per pole and a diverter used to insure 280 A-t.

(b) To determine torque we must evaluate two machine constants.   We assume operation on the linear portion of the magnetization curve.   (Is this a reasonable assumption for currents lower than rated?   See Fig. 18.4.)   From Eq. 18-6, using rated values,

$$K\Phi = \frac{60 \ E}{2\pi n} = \frac{60 \times 190}{2\pi \times 1000} = \frac{5.7}{\pi}$$

and the rated value of developed torque is

$$\mathrm{T}_r = K\Phi I_a = \frac{5.7}{\pi} \times 50 \cong 91 \text{ N-m}$$

From Eq. 18-11a,

$$k_E = \frac{E}{n I_a} = \frac{190}{1000 \times 50} = 0.0038$$

Equation 18-13 indicates that at twice rated speed,

$$\mathrm{T}_r = \mathrm{T}_r \frac{(k_E n + R_t)_r{}^2}{(k_E n + R_t)_2{}^2} = 91 \left(\frac{3.8 + 0.6}{7.6 + 0.6}\right)^2 \cong 26 \text{ N-m}$$

In Example 5, if the torque drops to approximately 30% of the full-load value, the machine speed doubles; to prevent excessive speeds, series motors are always mechanically coupled to their loads.

Starting and Speed Control

At starting the speed is zero, the emf of a d-c machine is zero, and the applied voltage appears across the armature resistance (see Eq. 18-7 or Fig. 18.8). To prevent excessive armature current, the starting voltage must be reduced. Usually a starting resistance is placed in series with the armature to limit the current. Since the torque of a series motor varies as the square of the current (neglecting saturation), for a given starting current the starting torque of a series motor is greater than that of a comparable shunt motor (see Fig. 18.11a). For high starting torque and rapid acceleration of a shunt motor, full voltage should be applied to the field. In a series motor, the field current is subject to the same limitations as the armature current. Special *starting boxes* for d-c motors provide a variable starting resistance and protection against loss of voltage and loss of field current. (See Exercise 14.) Reversing either the armature or the field connection, but not both, changes the direction of rotation.

One of the chief virtues of the shunt motor is the ease with which the speed can be adjusted. Equation 18-8 indicates that the speed is inversely proportional to Φ and therefore to I_f. Over a limited range, the speed can be controlled by adjusting R_c, the control rheostat; the lowest speed possible corresponds to the maximum current which flows when $R_c = 0$. Higher speeds are obtained by reducing the field current.

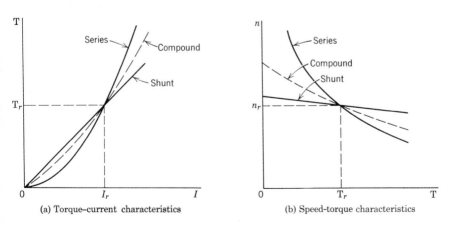

(a) Torque–current characteristics   (b) Speed-torque characteristics

Fig. 18.11   Operating characteristics of d-c motors.

What would happen if the field circuit were opened accidentally? Equation 18-8 also indicates that the speed can be controlled by varying the terminal voltage or the resistance in the armature circuit. The first is more expensive and the second is less efficient than field control. (Why?) Adding resistance in the armature circuit also increases the speed regulation.

The speed of a series motor is dependent on the load and is not so easily controlled. Under heavy torque loads, the series motor slows down, the emf decreases, and the armature current increases until sufficient torque is developed. A variable voltage supply or a series resistor can be used to vary the speed. On street cars or trolley buses, a common application of series motors, the motorman uses a variable resistor to control the speed.

The *compound motor* has a shunt and a series field connected so that their mmfs add. The operating characteristics are intermediate between those of shunt and series motors (see Fig. 18.11). By adjusting the relative strength of the shunt and series fields, a motor can be designed to provide a desired compromise.

Performance of D-C Motors

Previous examples have illustrated the approach to calculating speed and torque. To compute output and efficiency, the mechanical and electrical losses must be taken into account. The parameters in the circuit model may be computed by using rather elaborate formulas, or they may be measured in the laboratory. A no-load test of a rotating machine is similar to the open-circuit test of a transformer and yields analogous data. Full-load tests may be performed, using a *dynamometer* to measure the shaft torque.

The *power-flow diagram* in Fig. 18.12 is an aid in visualizing the energy conversion processes in a machine. The power-flow diagram, the energy balance, and the circuit model are closely related. Under dynamic conditions additional terms must be introduced to account for changes in

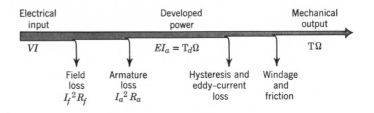

Fig 18.12   Power-flow diagram for a d-c motor.

magnetic and mechanical energy storage. The midpoint of the diagram corresponds to the air gap with iron losses entered on the mechanical side.

EXAMPLE 6

The d-c machine of Example 4 is rated at 220 V, 50 A, at 1000 rpm. $R_f =$ 80 Ω and $R_a = 0.4\ \Omega$. At rated speed, the field current is 1.5 A and the rotational losses are 1100 W. Determine the output under rated conditions and predict the full-load efficiency. (Do not charge $I_f{}^2R_c$ losses to the machine.)

SOLUTION. The circuit model of Fig. 18.8 is applicable. At rated current and voltage,

$$E = V - I_a R_a = 220 - 50 \times 0.4 = 200\ \text{V}$$

By Eq. 18-6,

$$K\Phi = \frac{60E}{2\pi n} = \frac{60 \times 200}{2\pi \times 1000} = \frac{6}{\pi}$$

and the rated value of developed torque is

$$\text{T}_d = K\Phi I_a = \frac{6}{\pi} \times 50 = \frac{300}{\pi} = 95.5\ \text{N-m}$$

The developed mechanical power at the air gap is

$$P_m = \text{T}_d\Omega = K\Phi I_a\Omega = \frac{300}{\pi} \times \frac{2\pi \times 1000}{60} = 10{,}000\ \text{N-m/sec}$$

Alternatively, the developed mechanical power is equal to the electrical power at the air gap or

$$P_m = P_e = EI_a = 200 \times 50 = 10{,}000\ \text{W} = 10{,}000\ \text{N-m/sec}$$

Subtracting the rotational losses, the power available at the shaft is

$$P = 10{,}000 - 1100 = 8900\ \text{W} = \tfrac{8900}{746} = 11.9\ \text{hp}$$

The overall efficiency is

$$\frac{\text{Output}}{\text{Input}} = \frac{\text{Shaft Output}}{VI_a + I_f^2 R_f} = \frac{8900}{220 \times 50 + 1.5^2 \times 80} = \frac{8900}{11{,}180} \cong 0.8\ \text{or}\ 80\%$$

While d-c motors are less common than a-c motors, they are ideally suited to certain applications. The commutator makes the d-c machine relatively high in first cost and in maintenance, and an enclosure must be used where there is moisture, dust, or explosive vapor. However, the d-c motor provides good speed regulation, high torque, high efficiency, and great flexibility. D-c motors range in size from tiny units turning fans in electronic apparatus to 10,000-hp motors driving the rolls in steel mills. Other applications include ship propulsion, fork lifts, and punch presses.

SYNCHRONOUS MACHINES

In the synchronous machine, direct current is supplied to the rotor and alternating current flows in the stator winding. The same machine can function as an *alternator* or as a *synchronous motor;* the only difference is in the direction of energy flow. Current is transferred to the rotor by stationary brushes riding on sliprings (Fig. 18.13). Because the required field power is much less than that associated with the armature, placing the field on the rotor is the most practical arrangement. A recent innovation is the use of transformer action to transfer alternating current to the rotor and there convert it to direct current, using semiconductor diodes mounted on the rotor. This eliminates the necessity for any sliding contacts and greatly reduces maintenance problems.

As pointed out in connection with Fig. 7.24, the emf generated in each turn of the 4-turn coil shown is slightly out of phase with the emf generated in its neighbor because it experiences maximum flux density at a different instant. By proper distribution of the turns and shaping of the field pole the total emf can be made to approach a sinusoid. Two other similar windings (not shown) occupy the remainder of the periphery of

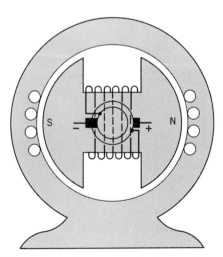

Fig. 18.13 Elementary 2-pole synchronous machine.

the stator and the result is a balanced set of three sinusoids which can be connected in Y or Δ (see Figs. 7.25 and 7.27).

Basic Relations

·In this discussion the emphasis is on three-phase machines although two-phase machines are sometimes used, particularly in control systems. For convenience we assume that all machines are Y-connected and balanced, and we work in terms of one phase; the phase voltage is the line-to-neutral voltage ($V_p = V_l/\sqrt{3}$) and the phase torque is just one-third of the total torque. Voltages and currents are sinusoidal and are represented by phasors. Assuming linear magnetic circuits greatly simplifies the mathematics and leads to results which are quite satisfactory for our purposes.

On the basis of these assumptions the basic relations for generated emf and developed torque are:

$$E = kn\Phi \quad \text{and} \quad T_d = k_T \Phi_r \Phi_s \sin \delta \quad (18\text{-}14)$$

where E and Φ are rms values, T_d is an average value, and δ is the torque angle. The net air-gap flux Φ is due to d-c field current I_f in the rotor and the armature reaction effect of a-c current I flowing in the stator. In generator operation, the frequency of the emf is directly related to the speed of rotation. A complete cycle of emf is generated as a pair of magnetic poles pass a given coil; therefore, the frequency in cps is

$$f = \frac{n}{60}\frac{p}{2} \quad (18\text{-}15)$$

In motor operation, to develop unidirectional torque the rotor must turn at *synchronous speed n_s* given by

$$n_s = \frac{120f}{p} \quad (18\text{-}16)$$

It is convenient to remember that for 60-cps operation the highest synchronous speed is 3600 rpm, obtained with a 2-pole machine ($p = 2$).

Circuit Model of an Alternator

For steady-state operation, the circuit model (quite similar to that for the d-c machine in Fig. 18.1) for the synchronous machine is as shown in Fig. 18.14. The phasors **E**, **I**, and **V** are rms values of per-phase quantities. The *armature resistance R_a* is an effective resistance which represents copper losses and takes into account nonuniform distribution of current in the armature conductors. The *synchronous reactance X_s* represents the effect of armature reaction and leakage inductance.

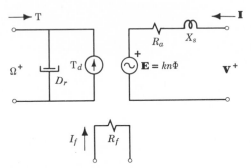

Fig. 18.14 Steady-state circuit model of a synchronous machine.

Armature reaction results in a component of flux which induces a voltage in quadrature with the current and therefore can be represented by an inductive reactance. The effect of stator leakage flux which does not react with the rotor is also represented by an inductive reactance. In our simplified approach, these two effects are combined into a single reactance X_s which is assumed to be constant.†

The assumption regarding X_s holds fairly well for a machine with a uniform air gap. In such a *cylindrical-rotor* machine, the field windings are embedded in slots in an otherwise smooth rotor. The assumption is inaccurate for the more typical *salient-pole* machine shown in Fig. 18.13. In either case, the machine constants can be determined by open- and short-circuit tests just as for the transformer. In all but the smallest machines, the synchronous reactance is much larger than the armature resistance; therefore, we neglect R_a except in calculating losses.

Alternator Characteristics

In considering the electrical characteristics of an alternator driven at constant speed, the simplified model of Fig. 18.15a is satisfactory. Note that R_a is neglected and $E = k'I_f$ for a linear magnetic circuit. The external characteristic is defined by

$$\mathbf{V} = \mathbf{E} - \mathbf{I}(R_a + jX_s) \cong \mathbf{E} - j\mathbf{I}X_s \qquad (18\text{-}17)$$

or

$$\mathbf{E} = \mathbf{V} + j\mathbf{I}X_s \qquad (18\text{-}18)$$

The corresponding phasor diagram for an inductive load is shown in Fig. 18.15b. Phasor **V** is taken as a horizontal reference and **I** is drawn

---

† For a more complete discussion of synchronous reactance see Chapter 10 of Robertson and Black, *Electric Circuits and Machines* (2nd ed.), D. Van Nostrand, New York, 1957.

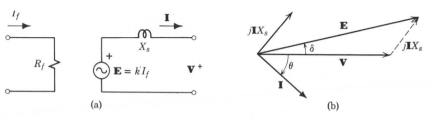

Fig. 18.15   Alternator model and phasor diagram.

at a lagging angle θ. The $j\mathbf{I}X_s$ drop is 90° ahead of $\mathbf{I}$ and $\mathbf{E}$ is the sum of $\mathbf{V}$ and $j\mathbf{I}X_s$. Since $\mathbf{E}$ is directly determined by rotor flux Φ_r and $\mathbf{V}$ bears a similar relation† to air gap flux Φ_s linking the stator, the angle between $\mathbf{E}$ and $\mathbf{V}$ is just equal to δ, the angle between Φ_r and Φ_s.

The behavior of the alternator under various power factor conditions is illustrated in Fig. 18.16. We assume that the alternator is supplying a

---

† This statement assumes that the effects of leakage reactance and armature resistance are neglected.

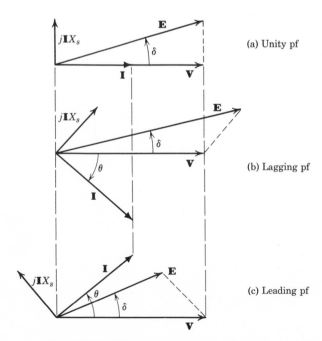

Fig. 18.16   Effect of load power factor on alternator operation.

constant power $P = VI \cos \theta$, at a fixed voltage and frequency, as the power factor is changed. At unity pf, E and V are approximately equal in magnitude. For lagging-pf operation, E is considerably larger than V; therefore, I_f must be increased above the value required for a unity-pf load. For leading-pf operation, E is considerably smaller than V and less field current is required. A physical explanation for this behavior is that the leading current in the stator produces a component of mmf (by armature reaction) which aids the mmf established by the field current; therefore, less I_f and E are required for the same V.

EXAMPLE 7

A three-phase 6-pole alternator is rated at 10 kVA, 220 V, at 60 cps. Synchronous reactance is $X_s = 3\ \Omega$. The no-load terminal voltage (rms) follows the magnetization curve of Fig. 18.4. Determine the rated speed and predict the field current required for full-load operation at 0.8 lagging pf.

SOLUTION. The rated speed is given by (Eq. 18-16)

$$n_s = \frac{120f}{p} = \frac{120 \times 60}{6} = 1200 \text{ rpm}$$

Assuming Y connection, the phase voltage is $220/\sqrt{3} = 127$ V, the rated phase current is

$$I = \frac{P_A/3}{V_p} = \frac{10,000/3}{127} = 26.2 \text{ A}$$

and the voltage drop across the synchronous reactance is

$$IX_s = 26.2 \times 3 = 78.6 \text{ V}$$

The phasor diagram for 0.8 lagging-pf operation is shown in Fig. 18.17. The necessary value of generated emf is

$$\mathbf{E} = \mathbf{V} + j\mathbf{I}X_s = \mathbf{V} - IX_s \sin\theta + jIX_s \cos\theta$$
$$= 127 + 47.2 + j62.9 \cong 184\ \underline{/20°} \text{ V}$$

An rms voltage of 184 V at 1200 rpm corresponds to $184 \times \frac{10}{12} = 153$ V at 1000 rpm, and Fig. 18.4 indicates $I_f = 1.0$ A.

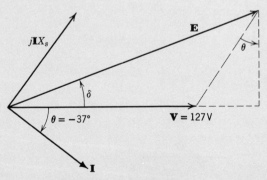

Fig. 18.17 Phasor diagram for Example 7.

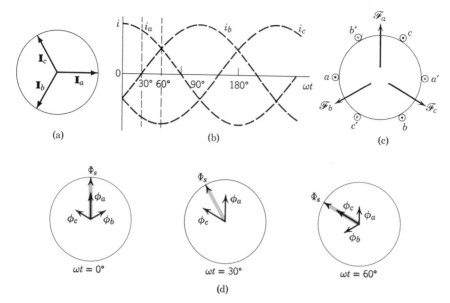

(a)　　　(b)　　　(c)

$\omega t = 0°$　　　$\omega t = 30°$　　　$\omega t = 60°$

(d)

Fig. 18.18　Production of a rotating stator field.

The Rotating Field

For unidirectional torque, sin δ must not change sign (Eq. 18-14) and therefore the stator field must rotate at the same speed as the rotor field. How can a rotating field be produced by stationary coils? This concept is fundamental to the operation of synchronous and induction motors. It can be explained in terms of the mmf contributed by the three balanced currents in Fig. 18.18a. The instantaneous values of the currents are shown in (b). Positive currents in the concentrated windings produce mmfs in the directions indicated in (c). At the instant $\omega t = 0°$, say, i_a is a positive maximum and i_b and i_c are negative and one-half maximum. Assuming a linear magnetic circuit, the principle of superposition applies, and the flux contributions of the three currents are as shown in (d). The stator flux is the vector sum of the three contributions. At $\omega t = 30°$, the relative magnitudes of the three currents have changed and the position of the resulting stator flux has shifted 30°. We say that a rotating magnetic field exists because the position of maximum flux rotates at synchronous speed.

It was pointed out in Chapter 7 that in a balanced three-phase circuit power is constant rather than pulsating, as in a single-phase circuit.

We should have expected that an alternator supplying constant electrical power at a constant speed would develop a constant torque.   For constant torque, δ must remain constant or the stator flux must move in synchronism with the rotor flux.   Figure 18.18 is a demonstration of a situation which we could have anticipated.

Motor Characteristics

Another feature of synchronous machines, which should come as no surprise, is that by changing the direction of power flow the alternator becomes a motor.   In a d-c machine, the direction of current flow is reversed by changing the field current and thereby changing the generated emf.   But Fig. 18.16 indicates that in a synchronous machine there may be large changes in **E** with no change at all in the power delivered by the alternator.   How can such a machine be made to deliver torque to a load?

Consider an alternator driven at synchronous speed by a gasoline engine.   The output terminals of the alternator are connected to the three-phase line of the local power company.   Referring to the model in Fig. 18.19, let **V** be one phase voltage and let I_f be adjusted so that **E** = **V**.   Under this condition, **I** = 0 and there is no power transfer

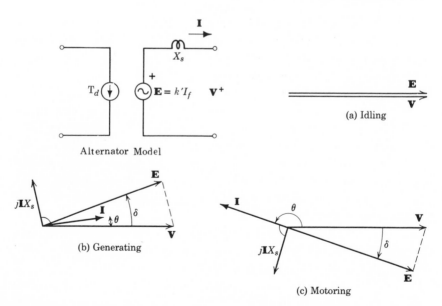

Fig. 18.19   Power flow in a synchronous machine.

between the alternator and the line; the alternator is idling. Now let us open the throttle of the gasoline engine and attempt to accelerate the rotor. As the rotor is driven ahead of the stator field, there is a voltage difference between **E** and **V**, and current **I** flows to satisfy Eq. 18-18. (Note that the magnitude of **E** does not change.) The electrical power output must be matched by a corresponding mechanical input or

$$P_e = 3VI \cos \theta = P_m = 3\mathrm{T}_d\Omega \qquad (18\text{-}19)$$

where $\mathrm{T}_d = k_\mathrm{T}\Phi_r\Phi_s \sin \delta$ as before. The increase in developed torque associated with angle δ equals the increase in applied torque and the average speed of the engine-alternator combination does not change. The forward shift in δ† accompanying mechanical input is clearly visible when the rotor is illuminated by a stroboscopic light.

If the engine throttle is returned to the idle position, the torque angle returns to zero and the rotor continues to turn at synchronous speed. If the throttle is closed, the rotor tends to slow down; the engine is now, in effect, an air compressor acting as a load on the synchronous machine. As the rotor shifts back through an angle δ (Fig. 18.19c), the emf **E** is retarded in phase with respect to **V** and a voltage difference exists across X_s. The resulting current **I** is nearly 180° out of phase with **V**. The electrical *output* $VI \cos \theta$ is *negative*, or the machine is absorbing electrical power from the line and delivering mechanical power to the shaft. It is operating as a *synchronous motor*.

A more convenient model for a synchronous motor is shown in Fig. 18.20a. Here the reference direction of I has been changed and in-phase

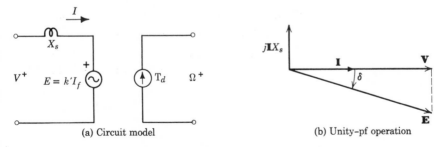

(a) Circuit model   (b) Unity-pf operation

Fig. 18.20   The synchronous motor.

---

† Note that δ is in "electrical degrees" where there are 180° electrical between adjacent magnetic poles. In a 4-pole machine, one revolution corresponds to $\dfrac{p}{2} \times 360 = 720$ electrical degrees.

current represents positive electrical input.   In general, the input power per phase is

$$P = VI \cos \theta \qquad (18\text{-}20)$$

The voltage relation for a motor (Fig. 18.20a) is

$$\mathbf{V} = \mathbf{E} + j\mathbf{I}X_s \qquad (18\text{-}21)$$

and the current is

$$\mathbf{I} = \frac{\mathbf{V} - \mathbf{E}}{jX_s} \qquad (18\text{-}22)$$

if the armature resistance is neglected.   On the basis of this simple model, as interpreted by these equations, the behavior of synchronous motors under various operating conditions can be predicted.

EXAMPLE 8

The alternator of Example 7 ($X_s = 3 \ \Omega$) is rated at 10 kVA, 220 V, and 26.2 A at 1200 rpm.   Predict the torque angle and the field current for unity-pf operation as a motor at rated load.

SOLUTION.   The phasor diagram for unity-pf operation is shown in Fig. 18.20b. A slight increase in $\mathbf{E}$ over the idling value (Fig. 18.19a) is required.   Solving Eq. 18-21,

$$\mathbf{E} = \mathbf{V} - j\mathbf{I}X_s = 127 - j26.2 \times 3 \cong 150 \ \underline{/32°} \ \mathrm{V}$$

and the torque angle δ is 32°.

Referring again to the magnetization curve of Fig. 18.4, we see that an rms voltage of 150 V at 1200 rpm corresponds to $150 \times \frac{10}{12} = 125$ V at 1000 rpm, and the required field current is $I_f \cong 0.75$ A.

Power Relations

Since torque varies as the sine of the angle δ, there is a maximum possible developed torque and power.   If the load on a motor is increased continuously, the rotor field drops further and further behind the stator field until this maximum is reached.   Any further increase in load torque pulls the rotor into a position of less than maximum developed torque, and the rotor falls out of step and out of synchronism.   At less than

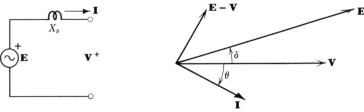

Fig. 18.21   Derivation of developed power.

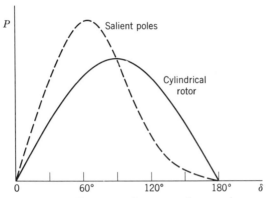

Fig. 18.22 Power angle curves for synchronous motors.

synchronous speed the developed torque is first in one direction and then in the other, and the machine comes to a shuddering halt. What would happen if the input to an alternator were increased continuously?

An approximate expression for the maximum electrical power developed in an alternator can be derived by using the simplified model and phasor diagram of Fig. 18.21. By Eq. 18-18,

$$\mathbf{I} = \frac{\mathbf{E} - \mathbf{V}}{jX_s} = -j\left[\frac{E\,\underline{/\delta}}{X_s} - \frac{V\,\underline{/0°}}{X_s}\right] = -j\left[\frac{E(\cos\,\delta + j\,\sin\,\delta)}{X_s} - \frac{V}{X_s}\right]$$

The real part of $\mathbf{I}$ is $(E/X_s)\sin\,\delta$ which is equal to $I\cos\,\theta$. Then the electrical power developed per phase is $VI\cos\,\theta$ or

$$P = \frac{VE}{X_s}\sin\,\delta \qquad (18\text{-}23)$$

The product of torque and speed is mechanical power which equals electrical power at the air gap. Therefore,

$$\mathrm{T}_d = \frac{P}{\Omega} = \frac{VE}{\Omega_s X_s}\sin\,\delta \qquad (18\text{-}24)$$

In a motor the electrical power developed is negative, which is consistent with the negative value of δ associated with mechanical power output.

The solid line in Fig. 18.22 is the power angle curve based on Eq. 18-23 and holds for cylindrical-rotor machines. Most synchronous motors have salient poles and the reluctance torque contribution is appreciable. It can be shown (see Problem 8 in Chapter 17) that the reluctance torque varies as sin 2δ; the dashed line in Fig. 18.22 shows the variation expected

in salient-pole machines. The advantages of salient-pole construction
are a higher maximum or *pull-out* torque and a smaller torque angle for a
given load in the normal operating region (below $\delta \cong 30°$).

EXAMPLE 9

Predict the pull-out torque for the motor of Example 7 operating at unity pf.
SOLUTION. Assuming cylindrical-rotor construction, Eq. 18-23 applies.
Under unity-pf conditions, $E = 150$ V. For $\delta = 90°$, the total power is

$$P_{max} = 3\,\frac{VE}{X_s} = \frac{3 \times 127 \times 150}{3} \cong 19,000 \text{ W or N-m/sec}$$

At 1200 rpm, the pull-out torque is

$$T_{max} = \frac{P_{max}}{\Omega_s} = \frac{P_{max} \times 60}{2\pi n_s} = \frac{19,000 \times 60}{2\pi \times 1200} \cong 150 \text{ N-m}$$

Note that the maximum power is nearly twice the rated value. How does the
associated $I^2 R_a$ loss compare to the rated value?

Reactive Power Relations

A unique feature of the synchronous motor is its ability to carry shaft
load and draw a leading current. In an industrial plant operating at
a lagging power factor, use of some relatively expensive synchronous
motors may be justified by the savings resulting from improved power
factor. (See the discussion preceding Example 4 in Chapter 7.)

The effect of varying field current on the power factor of an unloaded
motor is displayed by the phasor diagrams in Fig. 18.23. Because the
motor carries no shaft load, the torque angle is zero; for normal excitation $E = V$ and the motor draws no current. If, as in Fig. 18.23b,
the field current is increased, E exceeds V and the resulting current is
determined by Eq. 18-22. Such an *over-excited* machine draws a leading
current, i.e., the sinusoidal current reaches its maximum 90° ahead of
the sinusoidal terminal voltage. The power drawn is still zero since
$VI \cos \theta = 0$, but the reactive power $P_X = VI \sin \theta$ is appreciable.
These conditions are characteristic of a capacitor (or condenser) and
therefore a rotating machine of this type is called a *synchronous condenser*.

If the field current is below normal, E is less than V and a lagging
current flows (Fig. 18.23c). Such an *under-excited* machine draws a
negative reactive power and could be called a *synchronous inductor;* however, under-excited machines do not offer advantages comparable to those
of the synchronous condenser. The phasor diagrams in Fig. 18.23 are
drawn for a motor with no shaft load; in general, there is shaft load and
I has an in-phase component.

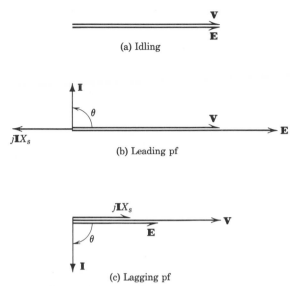

(a) Idling

(b) Leading pf

(c) Lagging pf

Fig. 18.23 Effect of excitation on the power factor of an unloaded synchronous motor.

In d-c machines, the direction of power flow is determined by the relative magnitude of E and V and can be controlled by I_f. In a synchronous machine, changing the relative magnitude of E affects only the reactive power flow. To change the direction of power flow requires a change in the torque angle δ and this is accomplished by changing the mechanical power supplied to the shaft. Opening the throttle of the driving engine advances the rotor and increases δ, and electrical power is produced. Loading the shaft retards the rotor and increases δ in a negative direction, and mechanical power is produced.

EXAMPLE 10

A three-phase induction furnace (Fig. 18.24a) draws 7.5 kVA at 0.6 lagging pf. A 10-kVA synchronous motor is available. If the overall pf of the combination is to be unity, estimate the mechanical load which can be carried by the motor.

SOLUTION. The reactive power of the furnace is

$$P_X = -7.5 \sin (\cos^{-1} 0.6) = -6 \text{ kVAR}$$

as shown in Fig. 18.24b. By operating at leading pf, the synchronous motor can supply this reactive power. If losses are neglected, the available power of the synchronous motor is

$$P_{\text{SM}} = \sqrt{P_A{}^2 - P_X{}^2} = \sqrt{10^2 - 6^2} = 8 \text{ kW}$$

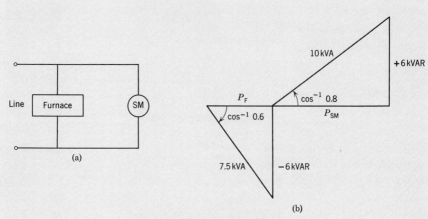

Fig. 18.24   Example 10.

At the cost of a small increase in copper loss in the motor field windings, the necessary reactive power is supplied to the furnace and 80% of the motor rating is available for any mechanical load.

Performance of Synchronous Motors

The synchronous motor is a constant-speed device with a relatively high efficiency, a controllable power factor, and a relatively high first cost. Since it has no inherent starting torque, special starting provisions are required. Most synchronous motors are started by the induction motor action described in the next section. Commercial designs provide starting torques of the order of 120% of rated and pull-out torques of the order of 175% of rated. One feature is that by increasing the number of poles, low constant speeds are available without gearing. Synchronous motors find application wherever their virtues offset their disadvantages. They are found in all types of industrial plants, and are used to drive compressors, blowers, and mixers.

INDUCTION MOTORS

In any rotating machine, we can conceive of torque as a result of the interaction of a current and a magnetic field, and we can write $T_d = k_a B_1 I_2 \sin \delta$ (Eq. 17-24a). In a d-c machine, direct current is supplied to the stator to establish B_1 and to the rotor as I_2, and the commutator maintains δ at the optimum 90° at any speed. In a synchronous machine, polyphase alternating current supplied to the stator produces a

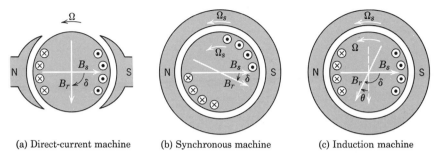

(a) Direct-current machine   (b) Synchronous machine   (c) Induction machine

Fig. 18.25   Torque production in rotating machines.

rotating magnetic field, and the d-c rotor field established by I_2 rotates at synchronous speed to develop a torque proportional to sin δ (Fig. 18.25b). In an induction machine, polyphase alternating current supplied to the stator produces a rotating magnetic field (just as in the synchronous machine), and alternating currents are induced in the rotor by transformer action.   The interaction between the induced rotor currents and the stator field produces torque.

Because the synchronous machine is much better for generating alternating current, the induction generator is not commercially significant and therefore our emphasis is on the three-phase induction motor.   This simple, rugged, reliable, inexpensive device consumes the major part of all the electric energy generated.   It is built in sizes ranging from a fraction of one horsepower to many thousand horsepower.   The transformer makes it possible to transmit large quantities of power over long distances; the induction motor makes it desirable.   This important electromagnetic device deserves our attention.

Operating Principles

In its most common form, the rotor consists of axial conductors shorted at the ends by circular connectors to form a *squirrel cage* (Fig. 18.26). The stator is identical to that of a synchronous motor.   As the stator field moves past the rotor conductors, emfs are induced by transformer action.   The induced emf is a maximum in the rotor conductors under the poles, as shown in Fig. 18.25c.   Because of the reactance of the rotor windings, the current and therefore the rotor field lag the emf by angle θ, and the torque angle is greater than 90°.

The stator field rotates at synchronous speed Ω_s determined by the frequency and number of poles (Eq. 18-16).   The rotor always turns at a lower speed Ω; if the rotor turned at synchronous speed, there would be no change in flux linkage, no induced current, and no torque.   The small

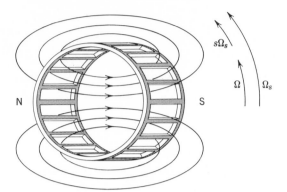

Fig. 18.26   Squirrel-cage rotor.

difference in speed which produces flux cutting and motor action is called the *slip*.   By definition, the slip is

$$s = \frac{\Omega_s - \Omega}{\Omega_s} = \frac{n_s - n}{n_s} \qquad (18\text{-}25)$$

and is usually expressed in percent.   The slip at full load for a squirrel-cage motor is typically 2 to 5%.   Note that the rotor field created by the induced rotor currents moves ahead at a speed $s\Omega_s$ relative to the rotor structure.   The absolute speed of the rotor field is

$$\Omega_{rf} = \Omega + s\Omega_s = \Omega_s \qquad (18\text{-}26)$$

as required for unidirectional torque.   In other words, the magnetic pole induced in a portion of the rotor is always of the proper polarity to react with the stator pole passing by.   The flexibility of the induction motor, in contrast to the fixed-speed character of the synchronous motor, is due to this principle.

EXAMPLE 11

A three-phase, 220-V, 60-cps induction motor runs at 1140 rpm.   Determine the number of poles, the slip, and the frequency of the rotor current.

SOLUTION.   Since the synchronous speed must be slightly higher than the running speed and because at 60 cps the only possibility is 1200 rpm (Eq. 18-16), we conclude that this is a 6-pole machine.   At 1140 rpm the slip is

$$s = \frac{n_s - n}{n_s} = \frac{1200 - 1140}{1200} = 0.05 \qquad \text{or } 5\%$$

The induced emf in the rotor is due to the slip speed and therefore

$$f_2 = sf = 0.05 \times 60 = 3 \text{ cps}$$

Note that at starting $n = 0$ and $s = 1$; therefore, the frequency of the induced current is 60 cps.

Basic Relations

The induction motor is essentially a transformer with a rotating secondary. The force between primary and secondary coils in a transformer appears as useful torque in an induction motor. If the rotor is held stationary (by the inertia of a starting load or by an applied brake), the passing stator field induces in one phase of the rotor winding an emf of magnitude E_2 and frequency f. The current which flows at standstill is

$$\mathbf{I}_2 = \frac{E_2}{R_2 + j2\pi f L_2} = \frac{E_2}{R_2 + jX_2} \tag{18-27}$$

where R_2 and L_2 are the effective resistance and inductance of the rotor winding on a per-phase basis.

Now we are going to take advantage of an ingenious method for representing the power-developing capability of a short-circuited coil. At standstill, the slip $s = 1$ and the rotor frequency is just the stator frequency f. At any other speed, the slip is s, the induced emf is sE_2, the rotor frequency is sf, and the rotor reactance is sX_2. The rotor current can be expressed as

$$\mathbf{I}_2 = \frac{sE_2}{R_2 + jsX_2} = \frac{E_2}{R_2/s + jX_2} = \frac{E_2}{R_2 + jX_2 + R_2[(1 - s)/s]} \tag{18-28}$$

since

$$R_2\frac{1 - s}{s} = \frac{R_2}{s} - R_2 \tag{18-29}$$

Then Eq. 18-28 can be rewritten as

$$\mathbf{E}_2 = \mathbf{I}_2(R_2 + jX_2) + \mathbf{I}_2 R_2\frac{1 - s}{s} = \mathbf{I}_2 \mathbf{Z}_2 + \mathbf{E}_g \tag{18-30}$$

Two circuit models satisfying Eq. 18.30 are shown in Fig. 18.27. The

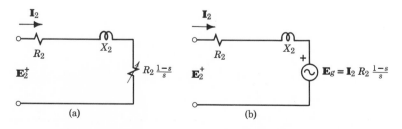

Fig. 18.27 Circuit models of rotor of induction motor.

first looks like the secondary of a transformer with a variable load resistance; the second represents the load as a reversible energy transformation. In each model, the electrical power transferred to the rotor is $E_2I_2 \cos \theta_2$. The power lost irreversibly is $I_2{}^2R_2$; the remainder, E_gI_2, is converted into mechanical power.

In analyzing the energy conversion taking place in an induction motor, the basic relations are

$$E_g = I_2R_2 \frac{1-s}{s} \quad \text{and} \quad T_d = \frac{E_gI_2}{\Omega} \qquad (18\text{-}31)$$

The first of these relations results from a consideration of electrical energy in the rotor; the second results from the application of the energy-conservation principle to the electromechanical conversion process. To obtain an expression for torque in the form of Eq. 17.24a, consider the total electrical power transferred from the stator at Ω_s to the rotor. From either model of Fig. 18.27 this is $P_2 = E_2I_2 \cos \theta$. But E_2 is the rms value of an induced emf directly proportional to B_1, and $\cos \theta$ is just equal to $\sin \delta$ (Fig. 18.25c); therefore,

$$T_2 = \frac{P_2}{\Omega_s} = \frac{1}{\Omega_s} E_2I_2 \cos \theta_2 = k_aB_1I_2 \sin \delta \qquad (18\text{-}32)$$

The developed torque T_d is less than T_2 by an amount corresponding to the $I_2{}^2R_2$ power loss.

Circuit Model of an Induction Motor

The model for the rotor (Fig. 18.27) resembles that of the secondary of a transformer. If we use the complete transformer model of Fig. 16.16, the circuit model of an induction motor is as shown in Fig. 18.28. Since R_2 and X_2 are important only insofar as they affect input electrical power, it is convenient to assume that the turn ratio a is unity and to define R_2 and X_2 on that basis. If this is done, the ideal transformer

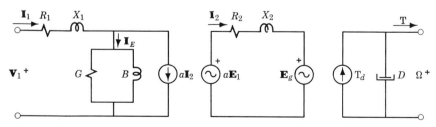

Fig. 18.28 A general circuit model for an induction motor.

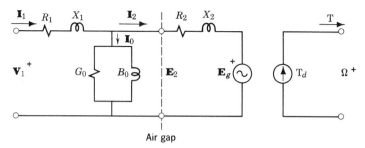

Fig. 18.29   A circuit model based on no-load measurements.

consisting of aI_2 and aE_1 is superfluous and can be omitted.   The dashed line in Fig. 18.29 corresponds to the air gap across which energy is coupled to the rotor.   A further simplification results if we transfer the rotational losses $\Omega^2 D$ to the primary and combine them with the stator core loss represented by G.   (The rotor core loss is usually negligibly small because of the low rotor frequency.)   The sum of rotational loss and core loss is conveniently determined by measuring the no-load input where I_0 is the no-load current.

One other modification reduces the labor of performance calculations and simplifies the general analysis without introducing excessive error. Just as for the transformer (see Fig. 16.18), moving the elements representing no-load loss to the input terminals results in a circuit consisting of two branches in parallel across a fixed voltage.   In the transformer the reluctance of the magnetic circuit is small and the exciting current is only a small percentage of rated current.   In an induction motor, however, the air gap raises the reluctance and the rotational loss adds to the core loss.   As a result, the no-load current is 20 to 40% of rated current, and this is too large to neglect.   The effect of the no-load current can be taken into account by adjusting the terminal voltage to account for the $I_0(R_1 + jX_1)$ drop as indicated in the following example.

EXAMPLE 12

The parameters of a 25-hp, 220-V, 60-cps induction motor are: $R_1 = 0.05\ \Omega$, $R_2 = 0.06\ \Omega$, $X_1 = 0.23\ \Omega$, $X_2 = 0.23\ \Omega$.   The no-load power input is 690 W at 220 V and 20 A.   Calculate the adjusted voltage V_a in Fig. 18.30 and determine the error made by using an algebraic rather than a phasor calculation.

SOLUTION. $R_1 + jX_1 = 0.05 + j0.23 \cong 0.25\ \underline{/78°}\ \Omega$

$$P_0 = 3V_1I_0 \cos\theta_0 \quad \text{or} \quad \theta_0 = \cos^{-1}(690/3 \times 127 \times 20) = -85°$$

$$V_a = V_1 - I_0(R_1 + jX_1) = 127\underline{/0°} - 20\underline{/-85°}\ (0.25\ \underline{/78°})$$

$$= 127\underline{/0°} - 5\underline{/-7°} = 127 - 4.9 + j0.6 = 122.1 + j0.6 \cong 122.1\ \text{V}$$

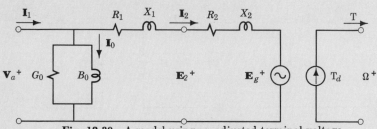

Fig. 18.30   A model using an adjusted terminal voltage.

Algebraically,

$$V_a = V_1 - I_0 \sqrt{R_1{}^2 + X_1{}^2} \tag{18-33}$$

$$= 127 - 20 \sqrt{(0.05)^2 + (0.23)^2} = 127 - 20(0.25) = 122 \text{ V}$$

The error is very small.

As indicated by Example 12, the error made in using an algebraic calculation of V_a is negligibly small and therefore Eq. 18-33 is satisfactory. (Draw the phasor diagram approximately to scale and you will see why.) In many cases R_1 can be neglected compared to X_1 in this calculation, and in some cases use of the unadjusted terminal voltage is satisfactory.

One final simplification is desirable. Combining Eqs. 18-25 and 31, we can write

$$\mathrm{T}_d = \frac{E_g I_2}{\Omega} = \frac{I_2{}^2 R_2[(1 - s)/s]}{\Omega_s(1 - s)} = \frac{I_2{}^2 R_2}{s\Omega_s} \tag{18-34}$$

Since $E_g = I_2 R_2(1 - s)/s$, the total series resistance is

$$R_1 + R_2 + R_2 \frac{1 - s}{s} = R_1 + \frac{R_2}{s} \tag{18-35}$$

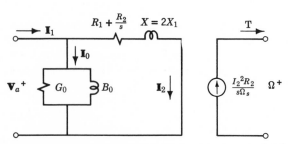

Fig. 18.31   A simplified circuit model for an induction motor.

The reactances X_1 and X_2 are difficult to separate and usually they are assumed equal; the sum is then $X = 2X_1$. The result is the simplified circuit model of Fig. 18.31. On the basis of this model we can predict the performance of induction motors under varying conditions.

Induction Motor Characteristics

An important characteristic of any motor is the speed-torque relation. For the induction motor, the total torque T is $3T_d$ or

$$T = \frac{3I_2{}^2R_2}{s\Omega_s} = \frac{3V_a{}^2}{\Omega_s}\frac{R_2/s}{(R_1 + R_2/s)^2 + X^2} \qquad (18\text{-}36)$$

The speed-torque curve for a typical squirrel-cage motor is plotted in Fig. 18.32. Under normal operating conditions the slip is small (less than 5%) and the induction motor is essentially a constant-speed machine under load. For s small, R_2/s is large compared to R_1 and to X, and a good approximation is

$$T_{\text{normal}} \cong \frac{3V_a{}^2 s}{\Omega_s R_2} \qquad (18\text{-}37)$$

In the normal operating range, torque is directly proportional to slip. Another conclusion from Eq. 18-37 is that at normal speeds the torque is inversely proportional to R_2. The use of larger rotor conductors permits larger induced currents and greater torque is developed at a given slip.

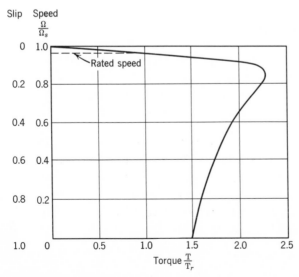

Fig. 18.32 Typical speed-torque curves for a squirrel-cage induction motor.

When the speed is low, $s \cong 1$ and the reactive term in Eq. 18-36 is large compared to the resistive term. An approximation for low-speed torque is

$$T_{\text{low speed}} \cong \frac{3V_a{}^2 R_2}{s\Omega_s X^2} \tag{18-38}$$

and we see that near standstill, torque varies inversely with slip. At standstill, $s = 1$ and Eq. 18-38 becomes

$$T_{\text{starting}} \cong \frac{3V_a{}^2 R_2}{\Omega_s X^2} \tag{18-39}$$

We conclude that starting torque is directly proportional to $V_a{}^2$ and to R_2.

Maximum torque occurs at an intermediate speed; how could this maximum be predicted? If we differentiate Eq. 18-36 with respect to slip and set the derivative equal to zero, the slip for maximum torque is found to be

$$s = \frac{R_2}{\sqrt{R_1{}^2 + X^2}} \tag{18-40}$$

At this value of slip, the maximum or *breakdown* torque is

$$T_m = \frac{3V_a{}^2}{2\Omega_s(R_1 + \sqrt{R_1{}^2 + X^2})} \tag{18-41}$$

An analysis of the effect of R_2 leads to the following conclusions:

1. At normal speeds, torque is inversely proportional to R_2.
2. At low speeds, torque increases with increasing R_2.
3. The slip for maximum torque is directly proportional to R_2.
4. The maximum torque is independent of R_2.

These conclusions are supported by the speed-torque curves for similar motors with varying values of R_2 shown in Fig. 18.33. Apparently the design of the squirrel-cage rotor is a compromise. Low rotor resistance results in low slip for a given torque and high operating efficiency; high rotor resistance results in high starting torque and relatively low starting current. (Why?)

EXAMPLE 13

Predict the starting torque and maximum torque for the 6 pole motor of Example 12, and estimate the rotor resistance for maximum torque at starting.

SOLUTION. From Example 12, $R_1 = 0.05\ \Omega$, $R_2 = 0.06\ \Omega$, $X = 0.46\ \Omega$, and $V_a = 122$ V. By Eq. 18-39, the starting torque is

$$T_{\text{starting}} \cong \frac{3V_a{}^2 R_2}{\Omega_s X^2} = \frac{3(122)^2 0.06}{[(1200 \times 2\pi)/60](0.46)^2} = 101 \text{ N-m}$$

By Eq. 18-41, the maximum torque is

$$T_m = \frac{3V_a{}^2}{2\Omega_s(R_1 + \sqrt{R_1{}^2 + X_2{}^2})} \cong \frac{3(122)^2}{2 \times 40\pi(0.05 + 0.46)} \cong 360 \text{ N-m}$$

since $R_1{}^2$ is small compared to $X_2{}^2$. To obtain maximum torque at starting, R_2 is given by Eq. 18.40 for $s = 1$ or

$$R_2 = \sqrt{R_1{}^2 + X^2} = \sqrt{(0.05)^2 + (0.46)^2} \cong 0.46\ \Omega$$

Motors with Variable Rotor Resistance

How can the insertion of additional resistance in the rotor increase the starting torque? At first thought it would seem that insertion of resistance would decrease the induced current and therefore the torque. But at starting, $s = 1$ and $R_2/s = R_2$, which is small compared to X_2, so the magnitude of the current (Eq. 18-28) is affected only slightly by an increase in R_2. In contrast, the power factor ($\cos\theta$ in Eq. 18-32) is greatly improved and the torque is increased. An alternative viewpoint is that δ is brought closer to 90° and the current I_2 bears a more favorable relation to the flux density B_1.

How can the resistance be increased during starting for high torque and reduced to a minimum during normal operation for low slip and high

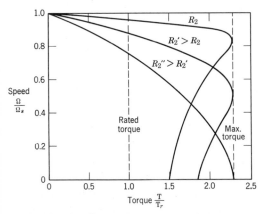

Fig. 18.33 Effect of R_2 on speed-torque curves.

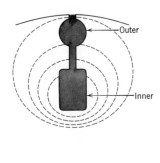

Fig. 18.34 Double-rotor conductors and leakage flux.

efficiency?   One method is to arrange connections to the rotor coils (by using sliprings and brushes) so that additional resistances can be connected in series.   In such a *wound-rotor* motor, the rotor winding is similar to that on the stator; an auxiliary *controller* permits the insertion of variable external resistances corresponding to R_2' and R_2'' in Fig. 18.33. The wound-rotor motor provides optimum starting conditions and also provides a measure of speed control, since for a given torque the speed depends on rotor resistance.   The disadvantages of the wound-rotor motor include higher first cost, higher maintenance cost, and lower efficiency during variable-speed operation.

The *double-squirrel-cage* motor is a clever design for obtaining the advantages of variable resistance without the disadvantages.   Each rotor conductor consists of two parts, one in the normal location and a second deeply imbedded in the rotor iron (Fig. 18.34).   The leakage reactance and therefore the impedance of the inner conductor are higher than that of the outer conductor.   At starting, rotor frequency is high and little current flows in the inner conductor; the effective rotor resistance is high.   At normal speeds, slip is low, rotor frequency is low, the two conductors are in parallel, and the effective rotor resistance is low. How would the speed-torque curve of such a motor differ from those in Fig. 18.33?

Performance of Induction Motors

The similarity between the induction motor and the transformer has been noted; in fact, a wound-rotor motor can be used as a static transformer with a three-phase secondary voltage available at the sliprings. Another similarity is in the method of determining the machine parameters in the circuit model.   A *no-load* motor test provides data for the determination of G_0 and B_0 just as an open-circuit transformer test. Corresponding to the short-circuit transformer test is the *blocked-rotor* test; with the rotor held stationary, all the input power is dissipated as losses and R and X can be determined.

The stator reactance X_1 is usually assumed to be half of X, but the division of R must be done carefully because R_2 is a key factor in motor performance.   One approach is to measure the d-c resistance between terminals which gives an approximate value for $2R_1$, assuming a Y-connected stator.   The d-c value is then corrected empirically to give an effective a-c value of R_1 and the remainder of R is the effective value of R_2 referred to the stator circuit (see Problem 19).   When the model parameters are known, the performance of any motor may be predicted from the mathematical relations or from the circuit model itself.

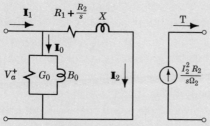

Fig. 18.35 Example 14.

EXAMPLE 14

Predict the input, output, and efficiency of the 1200-rpm motor in Example 12 at a slip of 2.8%.

SOLUTION. The parameters for the model in Fig. 18.35 are: $V_a = 122$ V, $R_1 = 0.05$ Ω, $R_2 = 0.06$ Ω, and $X = 0.46$ Ω. The no-load power input is 690 W at 20 A and 220 V. At $s = 2.8\%$, the rotor current is

$$\mathbf{I}_2 = \frac{V_a}{R_1 + R_2/s + jX} = \frac{122\;\underline{/0°}}{0.05 + 0.06/0.028 + j0.46} = \frac{122\;\underline{/0°}}{2.19 + j0.46} \cong 54.4\;\underline{/-12°}\;\text{A}$$

and

$$\mathbf{I}_1 = \mathbf{I}_0 + \mathbf{I}_2 = 20\;\underline{/-85°} + 54.4\;\underline{/-12°} = 63.1\;\underline{/-29.5°}\;\text{A}$$

The total input power is

$$3V_1I_1\cos\theta = 3 \times 127 \times 63.1 \times 0.87 = 20.9\;\text{kW}$$

The total developed torque is (by Eq. 18-36)

$$T = \frac{3I_2{}^2R_2}{s\Omega_s} = \frac{3(54.4)^2 \times 0.06}{0.028 \times 40\pi} \cong 152\;\text{N-m}$$

and the output power is

$$P_{hp} = \frac{T\Omega}{746} = \frac{152 \times (1 - 0.028)40\pi}{746} \cong 25\;\text{hp}$$

The efficiency is

$$\frac{\text{Output}}{\text{Input}} = \frac{25 \times 0.746}{20.9} = 0.89\;\text{or}\;89\%$$

The polyphase squirrel-cage induction motor is a rugged, efficient, easily started, nearly constant-speed machine that is applicable to many purposes. The wound-rotor version provides control of speed and starting torque in return for an increased investment. Induction motors are particularly useful for hoists, mixers, or conveyors which must start under load.

Single-Phase Induction Motors

To obtain the rotating field necessary for unidirectional torque, a poly-phase winding is required. With a single-phase winding, an oscillating field is possible, but the axis of the stator field remains fixed in space. If a squirrel-cage rotor is turning in such an oscillating field, a pulsating torque is developed, which tends to bring the rotor to nearly synchronous speed. If the rotor is stopped and then started in the opposite direction, the developed torque is in the opposite direction and again the rotor is accelerated. The problem in single-phase motor design is to get the rotor started.

There are several ingenious methods for doing this.† In the *shaded-pole* motor, a heavy copper coil is wound around half of each salient stator pole. Induced currents in the shorted turn delay the buildup of magnetic flux in that region of the pole. The magnetic flux vector appears to shift as a function of time and the rotor experiences the effect of a partially rotating field.

The *split-phase* motor employs two separate windings having different reactance-resistance ratios. The current reaches its maximum in the high-reactance winding at a later time and the rotor experiences a shift in magnetic field which provides the necessary starting torque. When the motor is nearly up to speed, the high-resistance winding is disconnected by a centrifugal switch.

The *capacitor* motor employs a capacitor in series with an auxiliary winding to provide the necessary phase shift. For improved performance two capacitors are used. The larger provides good starting torque and then is switched out by a centrifugal switch. The smaller remains in the circuit to provide good operating efficiency and power factor.

SUMMARY

◆ In a direct-current machine, the basic steady-state relations are:
$$E = K\Phi\Omega \quad \text{and} \quad T_d = K\Phi I$$

◆ In a d-c generator, the external characteristics are defined by:
$$V = E - I_a R_a \quad \text{and} \quad T_d = T_a - \Omega D$$

Generators may be separately excited or self-excited. The magnetization curve defines E as a function of I_f.

---

† For further description see Ch. 9 of Skilling, *op. cit.*, or Chapter 12 of Robertson and Black, *op. cit.*

Self-excited voltage buildup stabilizes where the field-resistance line intersects the magnetization curve.

In a flat-compounded generator the increase in series field mmf $N_s I_a$ offsets the drop in armature voltage $R_a I_a$.

Armature reaction results in a distortion of flux distribution.

♦ A d-c motor differs from a generator only in the direction of I_a;

$$E = kn\Phi = V - I_a R_a \qquad T_d = K\Phi I_a = T_a + \Omega D$$

SHUNT MOTOR	SERIES MOTOR
Flux: Constant but adjustable	Varies with I_a
Emf: $E = kn\Phi$	$E = k_E n I_a$
Torque: $T_d = K\Phi I_a$	$T_d = k_T I_a{}^2$
Speed: $n = \dfrac{V - I_a R_a}{k\Phi}$	$T_d = k_T \dfrac{V^2}{(k_E n + R_t)^2}$
$n = n_{nl} - k' T_d$	$\dfrac{n}{n_r} \cong \left(\dfrac{T_{dr}}{T_d}\right)^{1/2}$
Nearly constant	Widely varying
Speed Control: Efficient over limited range by varying I_f	Inefficient by insertion of R_{ser}
Starting Torque: Fair; $\dfrac{T}{T_r} = \dfrac{I_a}{I_{ar}}$	Good; $\dfrac{T}{T_r} = \left(\dfrac{I_a}{I_{ar}}\right)^2$

Starting: $E = 0$ at $n = 0$ ∴ must insert series R to limit I_a and $I_a{}^2 R_a$ heating.

Speed regulation defined as $SR = \dfrac{n_{nl} - n_{fl}}{n_{fl}}$.

Characteristics of a compound motor are intermediate between those of shunt and series motors.

♦ In a synchronous machine, the basic relations are:

$$E = kn\Phi = k' I_f \qquad \text{and} \qquad T_d = k_T \Phi_r \Phi_s \sin \delta$$

The speed of the rotating stator field is $n_s = 120\ f/p$.

Unidirectional torque is developed only when the rotor turns at n_s.

The direction of power flow depends on torque angle δ.

In the simple model, R_a is negligible compared to X_s.

X_s represents armature reaction and leakage inductance.

Power transformations are explained by phasor diagrams.

♦ In an alternator, $\mathbf{E} = \mathbf{V} + j\mathbf{I}X_s$ and δ is positive.

The pf of the load determines the required E and I_f.

Mechanical power is absorbed when the rotor is advanced.

$$P_m = 3\mathrm{T}_d\Omega = P_e = 3VI\cos\theta = 3\frac{VE}{X_s}\sin\delta$$

◆ In a synchronous motor, $\mathbf{V} = \mathbf{E} + j\mathbf{I}X_s$ and δ is negative.
Motor pf is determined by E and therefore by I_f.
An over-excited synchronous condenser draws leading current.
Electrical power is absorbed when the rotor is retarded.
Pull-out torque occurs at $\delta = 90°$ with cylindrical rotor.
No starting torque; usually employs induction motor action.

◆ In an induction motor, the slip of the rotor coils behind the rotating stator field induces rotor currents which develop torque.
The slip is $s = (\Omega_s - \Omega)/\Omega_s = (n_s - n)/n_s$ where $n_s = 120\,(f/p)$.
The basic energy conversion relations are:

$$E_g = I_2 R_2 \frac{1-s}{s} \quad \text{and} \quad \mathrm{T}_d = \frac{E_g I_2}{\Omega} = \frac{I_2{}^2 R_2}{s\Omega_s}$$

◆ The circuit model of an induction motor is similar to that of a transformer.
Use of an adjusted voltage V_a simplifies the model.
In terms of model parameters the total three-phase torque is

$$\mathrm{T} = \frac{3V_a{}^2}{\Omega_s} \frac{R_2/s}{(R_1 + R_2/s)^2 + X^2}$$

Useful approximations for normal operation and for starting are:

$$\mathrm{T}_{\text{normal}} \cong \frac{3V_a{}^2 s}{\Omega_s R_2} \quad \text{and} \quad \mathrm{T}_{\text{starting}} \cong \frac{3V_a{}^2 R_2}{\Omega_s X^2}$$

Torque is zero at synchronous speeds, increases linearly with slip at normal speeds, reaches a maximum, and decreases at high slip. Maximum torque is independent of R_2, but it occurs at a speed determined by R_2. In the wound-rotor motor, R_2 is variable.

◆ Single-phase induction motors depend on partial rotation of the stator field for starting torque; running torque is pulsating.

REVIEW QUESTIONS

1. Explain the statement: "The air-gap power represents the reversible portion of electromechanical energy conversion."

2. Outline a laboratory procedure for determining D in Fig. 18.1.

3. Why and where are there eddy-current and hysteresis losses in a d-c machine?

4. Given the rated voltage of a generator, estimate the no-load voltage.

5. On a compound generator, how could you distinguish between the series and shunt field windings by inspection?

6. Draw a wiring diagram of a compound generator showing control rheostat and diverter; what is the function of each?

7. What would happen if the polarity of the residual magnetism in a self-excited generator were reversed?

8. Explain the operation of a flat-compounded generator.

9. Why is an under-compounded generator more stable than an over-compounded machine? Sketch their V-I characteristics.

10. What is armature reaction and why is it of concern to designers?

11. Sketch speed-torque curves for series, shunt, and compound motors.

12. What happens if the field connection of a fully loaded shunt motor is accidentally broken? Repeat for a lightly loaded motor.

13. How does a series motor react (electrically) to increased load?

14. In starting a shunt motor, should V_f be maximum or minimum? Why?

15. In comparison to I_f control of speed, why is V_a control more expensive and R_a control less efficient?

16. Distinguish between a salient-pole and a cylindrical-rotor machine.

17. Explain the nature of synchronous reactance X_s.

18. Why is the angle between **E** and **V** equal to that between Φ_r and Φ_s?

19. What happens to alternator voltage when the load pf. changes?

20. Explain the production of a rotating field by stationary coils.

21. How does a synchronous motor react to an increase in shaft load?

22. What happens if the input to an alternator is increased continuously?

23. How does reluctance torque affect the pull-out torque of a motor?

24. How can a synchronous motor be used to correct power factor?

25. How would you reverse the rotation of a synchronous motor? An induction motor?

26. Discuss and compare the value of δ in commutator, synchronous, and induction motors.

27. Explain how a short-circuited rotor produces torque.

28. Specify several possible operating speeds for 50-cps motors.

29. Why is the rotor core loss usually negligibly small?

30. Draw the phasor diagram for Example 12 to scale.

31. Why is induction-motor torque directly proportional to slip at some speeds and inversely proportional at other speeds?

32. Outline an experimental procedure for determining induction-motor parameters.

33. Examine and classify a single-phase motor and explain its operation.

EXERCISES

1. A separately excited d-c generator has the magnetization curve shown in Fig. 18.36. Predict the no-load voltage at 1000 rpm with $I_f = 2$ A.

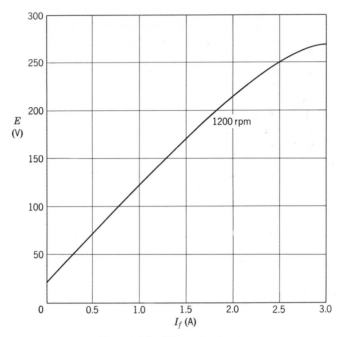

Fig. 18.36   Magnetization curve.

2. Repeat Exercise 1 at 1500 rpm and $I_f = 1.5$ A.

3. The magnetization curve for a d-c generator is shown in Fig. 18.36.   The generator is run at 800 rpm and is rated at 125 V, 40 A. $R_a = 0.1\ \Omega$ and $R_f = 50\ \Omega$.

    (a) Sketch the magnetization curve for 800-rpm operation.

    (b) Estimate the field current for rated conditions.

    (c) Predict the no-load voltage for separate excitation.

4. A self-excited d-c generator operates at 1200 rpm (see Fig. 18.36).   Predict the no-load voltage if the total resistance of the field circuit is 100 Ω.

5. A self-excited d-c generator, known to be in good mechanical condition, fails to generate anywhere near rated voltage when driven by a motor.   List four possible causes for this unsatisfactory operation and indicate the steps you would take to eliminate each.

6. A 2000-rpm compound generator has 200 turns/pole on the shunt field and 2 turns/pole on the series field. $R_a = 0.8\ \Omega$ and $R_s = 0.2\ \Omega$.   Operated separately excited with $I_f = 1$ A, the no-load voltage is 100 V.   (State any necessary assumptions.)

    (a) Under separate excitation with $I_f = 1$ A, estimate the terminal voltage at a load current of 10 A.

    (b) Repeat part (a), assuming compound excitation.   How would you describe the degree of compounding?

7. A 1200-rpm d-c shunt generator is rated at 25 kW at 250 V.   When operated self-excited with $I_f = 4$ A in the 200-turn field winding, $V_{nl} = 250$ V and $V_{fl} = 220$ V.

(a) Determine the effective resistance of the armature.

(b) Assuming a linear magnetic circuit, express the terminal voltage in terms of the field and armature currents.

(c) Specify the number of series field turns to provide flat compounding.

8. Let V = terminal voltage, I_a = armature current, I_f = field current, n = speed, T = load torque, and P = power output. State how I_a and n of a typical d-c shunt motor would be affected (approximately) by the following changes in operating conditions:

(a) Keeping I_f and T constant, and halving V.

(b) Keeping I_f and P constant, and halving V.

(c) Keeping V and T constant, and doubling I_f.

(d) Keeping P constant, and halving I_f and V.

9. State how I_a and n (see Exercise 8) of a typical d-c series motor would be affected (approximately) by halving the terminal voltage if:

(a) T remains constant.

(b) P remains constant.

(c) T varies as the square of n.

10. A d-c shunt motor has a no-load speed of 1000 rpm at 200 V and no external field resistance ($R_f = 100$ Ω and $R_a = 0.5$ Ω). The load torque on the shaft is increased until the total line current is 52 A.

(a) Draw and label an appropriate circuit model.

(b) Estimate the new speed and the developed torque.

(c) Estimate the no-load speed with a control rheostat set at 25 Ω inserted in the field circuit.

11. A d-c shunt motor is rated at 10 hp, 240 V, 42 A, and 1500 rpm. Rated field current is 2 A and $R_a = 0.4$ Ω.

(a) Predict the speed regulation.

(b) Predict the speed when operated at 200 V and the line current is 22 A.

12. A 220-V series motor ($R_t = 0.3$ Ω) draws 50 A while hoisting a given weight at 300 ft/min. Assuming linearity, specify the resistance to be placed in series with the armature to slow the hoisting speed to 200 ft/min.

13. A 220-V series motor is rated at 75 A while delivering 20 hp at 1200 rpm ($R_t = 0.2$ Ω). Assuming linearity, estimate the speed and power output at a current of 50 A.

14. Figure 18.37 shows a *starting box* connected to a shunt motor. The motor is started by closing switch S and moving contact lever L to the first button

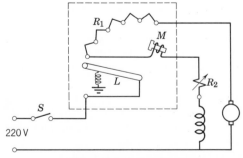

Fig. 18.37 Starting box.

on R_1. As the motor speeds up, the lever is advanced; at the last button it is held in position by magnet M against the pull of a spring. Explain the functions of R_1, R_2, and M in terms of desired starting conditions for a d-c motor.

15. In starting the motor of Exercise 13, it is desired to limit the starting current to twice rated current.

(a) Draw a schematic wiring diagram showing a starting resistance and specify the value.

(b) Estimate the starting torque, *stating* any necessary assumptions.

16. Calculate the full-load efficiency of the motor in Exercise 11 and predict the efficiency at 5-hp output.

17. Given a self-excited shunt generator,

(a) Draw an appropriate steady-state circuit model.

(b) Draw a clearly labeled power-flow diagram with input on the left.

18. A 10-hp, 250-V, 2000-rpm shunt motor with $R_f = 125$ Ω and $R_a = 0.5$ Ω requires a no-load total input of 6 A.

(a) Predict the full-load efficiency.

(b) Predict the speed regulation.

19. Determine the speed for 50-cps operation of a three-phase, 8-pole, 220-V alternator.

20. A conveyor belt is to be driven at a constant velocity of 471 ft/min by means of a pulley 6″ in diameter. The force required is estimated to be 350 lb. Specify the type of motor, the hp, the frequency, and the number of poles.

21. A power plant consists of four 3-phase hydrogen-cooled alternators rated at 156,250 kW each at 18,000 V line-to-line and 0.85 pf lagging, direct-connected to four 3600-rpm, 21-stage, 1800-psig steam turbines. The synchronous reactance per phase is 1 Ω.

(a) Determine the number of poles and rated current of each alternator.

(b) Estimate the generated emf and power angle under rated conditions. Draw a labelled phasor diagram.

22. A 3-phase, 8-pole synchronous machine is rated at 20 kVA, 220 V, 60 cps. The magnetization curve is similar to Fig. 18.4 and X_s per phase is 2 Ω.

(a) Draw an appropriate circuit model for alternator operation.

(b) Estimate the field current for rated voltage at no load.

(c) Repeat (b) for full load at 0.8 pf leading.

(d) Repeat (b) for full load at 0.8 pf lagging.

23. The machine of Exercise 22 is operating as a synchronous motor at rated voltage and current. The field current is decreased and it is noticed that the stator current decreases. Draw an appropriate phasor diagram and determine whether the motor is operating with unity, lagging, or leading power factor. Explain your reasoning.

24. A synchronous motor carries a load which results in a power angle $\delta = 15°$; field current is adjusted for minimum stator current.

(a) Draw a labeled model and phasor diagram for this condition.

(b) If the load torque is doubled, predict the effect on speed, power angle, power factor, and line current.

25. A synchronous motor is operating near unity pf at rated voltage, frequency, excitation, and load. Predict the effect on power and reactive power of:

(a) A 10% reduction in a-c line voltage.

(b) A 10% reduction in a-c voltage and frequency.

26. A synchronous motor is delivering 100 kW to a constant load; I_f is adjusted for minimum stator current and $\delta = 15°$. Explaining your reasoning with a large-scale phasor diagram, predict the effect of a 20% decrease in I_f on (a) speed, (b) power angle, (c) power factor, (d) line current.

27. A 3-phase, 500-V (line-to-neutral), 6-pole, 60-cps synchronous motor (per phase $X_s = 6\ \Omega$) is rated at 60 kW output at 0.8 leading pf.

(a) Draw a simplified model and calculate the rated line current.

(b) Draw a phasor diagram and estimate the generated emf and the torque angle under rated conditions.

(c) Estimate the pull-out torque for this machine.

(d) List all assumptions made in the previous calculations.

28. A 3-phase, 60-cps, 6-pole synchronous motor has per-phase ratings of 300 V, 20 A, and $X_s = 10\ \Omega$. Field current for minimum stator current with no shaft load is 1.2 A. For operation as a synchronous condenser, estimate the field current required for full-rated kVAR. Draw a labeled phasor diagram.

29. The nameplate of an induction motor states: 10 hp, 220 V, 60 cps, 1740 rpm.

(a) Determine the number of poles, the rated slip, and the frequency of the rotor currents at rated load.

(b) Estimate the speed at an output of 5 hp.

30. A 3-phase, 60-cps induction motor develops rated output at 855 rpm. Determine the number of poles and the rated slip.

31. For the motor of Exercise 30 at rated load, determine:

(a) The speed of the rotor with respect to the stator (rpm).

(b) The speed of the rotor *field* with respect to the rotor.

(c) The speed of the rotor field with respect to the stator *field*.

(d) The frequency of the currents in the rotor.

32. The rotor of the motor in Exercise 29 is 20 cm in diameter and 15 cm long. The maximum air-gap flux density is 1 T. Stating any necessary assumptions, estimate the emf (rms) induced in each rotor conductor at standstill and at full load.

33. Draw a phasor diagram for Example 12 to scale.

34. Draw labeled power-flow diagrams for a motor based on:

(a) The model of Fig. 18.28.

(b) The model of Fig. 18.30.

35. The maximum torque of a 60-cps squirrel-cage motor is 3 × rated torque and occurs at 85% of synchronous speed. The starting torque is 1.5 × rated.

(a) Predict the effect on starting torque of operating at 50 cps.

(b) Predict the effect on maximum torque of operating at 50 cps.

36. A 6-pole induction motor has a speed-torque characteristic like Fig. 18.32. Predict the operating slip when the motor is connected to a load defined by $T_l = 10^{-3} T_r n$ where n is in rpm.

37. Repeat Exercise 36 for a load defined by $T_l = 10^{-6} T_r n^2$.

38. A 12-pole, 60-cps, 15-hp induction motor is rated at 5% slip. Estimate the power output at a speed of 580 rpm.

39. A 440-V, 60-cps, 4-pole, 3-phase induction motor has the following per-phase parameters: $R_1 = 0.6\ \Omega$, $R_2 = 0.4\ \Omega$, $X_1 = 2\ \Omega$, $X_2 = 2\ \Omega$, $B_0 = 30$ m℧, and $G_0 = 10$ m℧.

(a) Estimate the no-load input current and power.

(b) Predict the power output at 5% slip.

(c) Predict the motor power factor at 5% slip.

40. For the induction motor in Exercise 39 estimate:

(a) The power output at 4% slip.

(b) The no-load speed, assuming that half the no-load input is due to rotational losses.

41. For the induction motor in Exercise 39 estimate:

(a) The starting torque.

(b) The starting torque if the line voltage drops to 400 V.

42. Derive Eqs. 18-40 and 18-41.

43. Reproduce Fig. 18.33 and add a speed-torque curve for a double-squirrel-cage motor. Explain your reasoning.

44. If a synchronous motor is to be started by induction motor action, what modification of the salient poles is necessary?

45. Consider the transformer, induction motor, and synchronous motor.

(a) What determines the power factor of each (as a load)?

(b) What range of power factors is expected in each?

46. Two squirrel-cage induction motors are identical except that the rotor of motor A is made of aluminum of conductivity σ and the rotor of motor C is made of copper of conductivity 1.5 σ. The starting torque of motor A is 60 N-m. Predict the starting torque of motor C.

PROBLEMS

Note: In solving the following problems, be sure to *state* any necessary assumptions.

1. The magnetization curve for a 1200-rpm shunt generator is shown in Fig. 18.36. Machine constants are: $R_a = 0.5$ Ω, $L_a = 0.5$ H, $R_f = 100$ Ω, and $L_f = 30$ H. For self-excited operation:

(a) Estimate the steady-state no-load terminal voltage.

(b) Predict the time required for the voltage to build up to 80% of its ultimate no-load value. (*Hint:* What voltage is available to cause di/dt?)

2. A d-c shunt generator is rated at 10 kW, 200 V, at 1200 rpm. There are 500 turns per pole on the field winding, $R_f = 100$ Ω, and $R_a = 0.4$ Ω.

(a) Draw and label an appropriate steady-state circuit model for self-excited operation and estimate the no-load terminal voltage.

(b) Specify a series winding to provide flat compounding.

3. A d-c shunt motor is rated at 10 hp, 200 V, at 1200 rpm. $R_f = 100$ Ω and $R_a = 0.4$ Ω.

(a) Estimate the no-load speed.

(b) Estimate the no-load speed with a 50-Ω control rheostat in the field circuit.

4. A series motor used in a control application drives a load which is primarily friction. For small variations in voltage V and speed N, the corresponding variation in torque is $\tau = Av - Bn$. If a small low-frequency voltage $v = V_m \sin t$ is superimposed on the d-c voltage applied to the motor, predict the corresponding variation in motor speed. Draw an appropriate model.

5. A d-c series motor, rated at 20 hp at 240 V and 1000 rpm, drives a constant-torque load (independent of speed). Predict the speed if the line voltage drops to 210 V.

6. The torque required by a blower is defined by $T = 6 \times 10^{-5} n^2$ N-m where n is in rpm. Available are a shunt motor ($R_a = 0.4$ Ω) and a series motor ($R_t = 0.6$ Ω), each rated at 10 hp and 1200 rpm at 240 V.

(a) Predict the operating speeds of the two different motors driving this blower.

(b) Estimate the copper losses of the two motors.

(c) Convert the copper losses to a percentage of rated copper loss and draw a conclusion regarding the two machines.

7. A nameplate reads: D-c Shunt Motor, 25 hp, 250 V, 92 A, 1750 rpm. At no-load, rated speed requires $I_f = 2$ A and $I_a = 8$ A. You are to predict the steady-state performance of this machine.

(a) Draw a clearly labeled schematic wiring diagram, an appropriate circuit model, and a power-flow diagram.

(b) Mechanical load is applied to the shaft until the total line current is 102 A. Predict the speed, developed torque, mechanical power output in hp, and the overall efficiency.

8. Available are two d-c shunt generators: one rated at 200 V at 5 A with $I_f = 0.5$ A and the other rated at 200 V at 100 A with $I_f = 5$ A. Show how these could be connected as a two-stage power amplifier. Estimate the d-c power gain possible.

9. Predict the dynamic behavior of a synchronous motor with rotor inertia J turning at speed Ω_s when a sudden load ΔT is applied to the shaft.

(a) Write a simplified expression for T_d as a function of δ for constant V and Φ_r and *small* values of δ.

(b) Write an expression for Ω during the time δ is changing to accommodate an increased load.

(c) Neglecting frictional resistance to changes in δ, derive an equation governing the behavior under a suddenly applied torque.

(d) Determine the *form* of the variation of δ with time after the torque is applied and draw a conclusion.

10. The inductive element in Fig. 18.38 might be a transmission line or the air gap of a rotating machine. If $\mathbf{E}_1 = E_1 \underline{/0°}$ and $\mathbf{E}_2 = E_2 \underline{/\alpha}$ where E_1 and

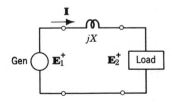

Fig. 18.38 Power transfer.

E_2 are constant and α is a variable angle, derive a general expression for the power transferred and determine α for maximum power transfer.

11. Without automatic controls and systematic procedures it would be possible for an operator at a nearby facility (a linear accelerator) to throw a sudden overload on the power plant of Exercise 21 and pull its alternators out of synchronism. Predict the total pull-out power of the four alternators.

12. A plant load consisting of 420 kW at 0.6 lagging pf is supplied by a 750-kVA transformer. An additional 200 kW of power is required. If the additional load is carried by synchronous motors at 0.8 pf leading, will a new transformer be required? What will be the new plant pf?

13. Specify the type of electric motor which will meet the following requirements best:

(a) Provide constant speed under all loads.

(b) Provide an easily adjusted speed which remains nearly constant (within 10%) over a wide range of loads.

(c) Operate from ordinary "house current" and be cheap. (Starting torque is not important.)

(d) Operate from a d-c line and provide relatively high starting torque.

(e) Provide rugged, maintenance-free operation and nearly constant speed (within 5%) over a wide range of loads.

(f) Operate from the single-phase a-c line and provide relatively high starting torque.

(g) Operate on ac, provide high starting torque, and permit some variation of speed under load.

(h) Draw a leading pf. current while driving a mechanical load.

14. Prepare a chart comparing the characteristics of different types of electric motors. List power supply, starting characteristics, speed-torque characteristics, special advantages, disadvantages, and typical applications for:

(a) D-c shunt motors.

(b) D-c series motors.

(c) Reluctance motors.

(d) Synchronous motors.

(e) Polyphase induction motors.

(f) Single-phase induction motors.

15. Four different electric motors are operating at rated torque at rated speed. The load torque is increased 10%. Estimate the new speed for the shunt motor, the series motor, the synchronous motor, and the induction motor.

16. Sketch characteristic load curves for a squirrel-cage induction motor, showing efficiency, speed, line current, and power factor as functions of output power. Justify the shape of each curve; express each variable as a dimensionless ratio.

17. A certain class of squirrel-cage induction motors is designed to provide a starting torque equal to 1.5 × rated and a breakdown torque equal to 2.5 × rated. A 6-pole, 60-cps motor of this class is to supply a starting torque of 75 N-m and operate on a duty cycle requiring 15 hp for 4 sec, 20 hp for 12.5 sec, and idle for 43.5 sec. Specify the hp rating of the appropriate motor.

18. A 3-phase induction motor is designed for 500 V at 60 cps.

(a) Sketch the speed-torque curve for rated operation.

(b) Sketch the speed-torque curve for 450-V, 60-cps operation.

(c) Sketch the speed-torque curve for 500-V, 50-cps operation.

(d) Estimate the effect on line current of operating at rated torque at 10% below rated voltage.

19. Laboratory test of a three-phase, Y-connected, 6-pole, 75-hp, 2000-V induction motor gave the following results:

> No-load: 2000 V, 7 A, 3.5 kW
>
> Blocked rotor: 670 V, 32 A, 9.1 kW
>
> Effective a-c resistance between terminals = 0.7 Ω

(a) Determine the model parameters.

(b) Predict the power output at 1152 rpm.

(c) Predict the efficiency and power factor at rated load.

20. Reasoning from basic principles, explain how an induction motor could serve as a source of electrical power, i.e., as a generator.

PART IV

SYSTEMS

Feedback in Amplifiers

An important component of many systems is a provision whereby part of the output is returned or fed back to the input in order to improve the performance of the system. The concept of *feedback* is not new; it is inherent in many natural biological processes and it occurs in the operation of well established social systems. However, the formulation of the principles of feedback is a recent achievement and exploitation of this new understanding has come in the last few years.

An irritating case of feedback occurs in a public address system in which the input microphone can pick up some of the output energy from the loudspeaker. The first sound into the microphone is highly amplified, converted into acoustic energy in the loudspeaker, transmitted back to the microphone, and amplified again. The cyclical process is repeated again and again and builds up a "squeal." The frequency of the squeal is determined by the parameters of the electro-acoustic system and the amplitude is limited by nonlinearity in the system response.

A desirable type of feedback occurs when a service organization, such as an airline, makes a change in its operating policy, investing income in free in-flight movies, for example, and later notes an overall increase in revenue. To reduce the time delay between policy change and observed result, a shorter *feedback loop* may be provided by means of questionnaires filled out by passengers and returned directly to the home office.

In electrical systems there are two general categories of feedback applications. One is concerned with the use of feedback for purposes of com-

parison and subsequent control.   In the automatic control system called
an "autopilot," the desired attitude of an airplane is represented by an
input or reference signal; the actual attitude of the airplane is sensed by
a gyro and represented by an output signal which is fed back and compared to the input.   The difference is amplified and used to correct the
actual attitude until the difference is zero.   The analysis of the behavior
of such systems is the subject of Chapter 22.

A second application of feedback is to improve the performance or
characteristics of a device or system.   Through the intentional use of
feedback, the gain of amplifiers can be made much greater, or more stable,
or less sensitive to change, or less dependent on frequency.   On the other
hand, amplifier designers must take steps to prevent unintentional feedback from degrading the performance of their products.   In this chapter
we study the basic concept of feedback, learn how to reduce complicated
systems to the basic form, investigate the general benefits of *positive* and
negative feedback, and then look at some practical applications of this
important concept to amplifiers.

Basic Feedback System

A transistor amplifier with feedback is represented by the circuit
model of Fig. 19.1.   The voltage gain of the amplifier alone, called the
forward gain, is defined by

$$\mathbf{G} = \frac{\mathbf{V}_2}{\mathbf{V}_1} \qquad (19\text{-}1)$$

where $\mathbf{V}_1$ and $\mathbf{V}_2$ are phasors and $\mathbf{G}$ is a complex function of frequency.

The voltage divider consisting of R_1 and R_2 provides a means of tap-
ping off a portion $\mathbf{V}_f$ of the output voltage $\mathbf{V}_2$ and feeding it back into
the input.   The *feedback factor* is

$$\mathbf{H} = \frac{\mathbf{V}_f}{\mathbf{V}_2} \qquad (19\text{-}2)$$

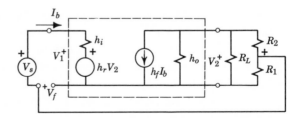

Fig. 19.1   Transistor amplifier with voltage feedback.

In general, $\mathbf{H}$ is a complex quantity although here $\mathbf{H} = R_1/(R_1 + R_2)$ is a real number.

Now the amplifier input $\mathbf{V}_1$ is the sum of the signal $\mathbf{V}_s$ and the feedback voltage $\mathbf{V}_f$ or

$$\mathbf{V}_1 = \mathbf{V}_s + \mathbf{V}_f \tag{19-3}$$

The output voltage is now

$$\mathbf{V}_2 = \mathbf{GV}_1 = \mathbf{G}(\mathbf{V}_s + \mathbf{V}_f) = \mathbf{G}(\mathbf{V}_s + \mathbf{HV}_2) = \mathbf{GV}_s + \mathbf{GHV}_2$$

Solving,

$$\mathbf{G}_f = \frac{\mathbf{V}_2}{\mathbf{V}_s} = \frac{\mathbf{G}}{1 - \mathbf{GH}} \tag{19-4}$$

where $\mathbf{G}_f$ is the gain with feedback.

Equation 19-4 is the basic equation for system gain with feedback, and by studying this equation some of the possibilities of such a system can be foreseen. If the complex quantity $\mathbf{GH}$ is positive, as it approaches unity the gain increases without limit. If $\mathbf{GH}$ is just unity, the gain is infinite and there is the possibility of output with no input; the amplifier has become a self-excited *oscillator*. If $\mathbf{GH}$ is negative, the gain is reduced, but accompanying benefits may offset the loss in gain. For example, if $\mathbf{GH}$ is very large with respect to unity, $\mathbf{G}_f \cong \mathbf{G}/\mathbf{GH} = 1/\mathbf{H}$, or the gain is independent of the gain of the amplifier itself. (In what way might this be beneficial?)

BLOCK DIAGRAMS

Before investigating the specific behavior of feedback systems, we need a simplified notation which will permit us to disregard the details of circuits and devices and focus our attention on system aspects. Also, our approach should emphasize the paths whereby signals are transmitted.

Block Diagram Representation

Let us represent linear two-port devices by *blocks* labeled to indicate the functions performed and with single-line inputs and outputs labeled to indicate the signals at those points. The amplifier whose small-signal circuit model is within the dashed line in Fig. 19.1 is represented symbolically by the block of Fig. 19.2a.

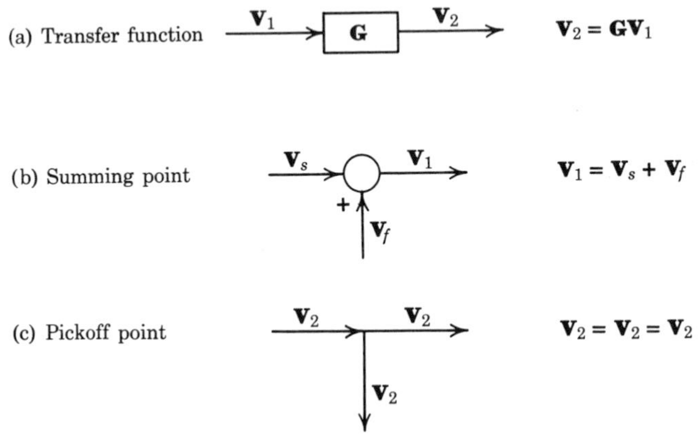

(a) Transfer function $\mathbf{V}_1 \rightarrow \boxed{\mathbf{G}} \rightarrow \mathbf{V}_2$ $\mathbf{V}_2 = \mathbf{G}\mathbf{V}_1$

(b) Summing point $\mathbf{V}_1 = \mathbf{V}_s + \mathbf{V}_f$

(c) Pickoff point $\mathbf{V}_2 = \mathbf{V}_2 = \mathbf{V}_2$

Fig. 19.2   Block diagram symbols and defining equations.

Such a symbol can represent any two-port device for which the output signal is a known function of the input signal. In representing a d-c generator with constant field current, the input signal could be a speed variation n and the output a voltage variation e. The block would be labeled $k\Phi$ since $e = k\Phi n$. In general, the ratio of output signal to input signal is called the *transfer function*.

To be represented by such a block, a device must be linear. Also, it is assumed that each device has infinite input impedance and zero output impedance, so that devices may be interconnected without loading effects. In the system of Fig. 19.1, $R_1 + R_2$ must be large with respect to R_L, so that the amplifier gain is unaffected by the feedback connection. If this amplifier is to provide the input to another device which draws an appreciable current, a transistor amplifier, for example, transfer function $\mathbf{G}$ must be recalculated, taking into account the finite nput impedance of the next device. When these conditions are met, the blocks are said to be *unilateral;* linear unilateral blocks may be interconnected freely.

Two different types of connection are possible. A *summing point* (Fig. 19.2b) has two or more inputs and a single output. The output is the sum or difference of the inputs, depending on the signs; a plus sign is assumed if no sign is indicated. In contrast, from a *pickoff point* (Fig. 19.2c) the signal can be transmitted undiminished in several directions. Physically this is illustrated by a voltage which can serve as input to several devices with high input impedances, or by a tachometer which senses the speed transmitted by a shaft without diminishing the speed.

Using block diagram notation, the amplifier of Fig. 19.1 is represented as in Fig. 19.3. In this case, all variables are voltages but, in general, different variables may appear on the diagram. (All signals entering a summing point must have the same units.) The amplifier block represents Eq. 19-1 and the feedback block represents Eq. 19-2. In this case, **G** is a voltage gain, but in general it is a transfer function. The summing point fulfills Eq. 19-3, and Eq. 19-4 gives the gain of the system. This basic system appears so frequently that Eq. 19-4 should be memorized.

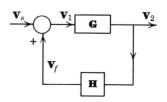

Fig. 19.3 Block diagram of basic feedback system.

EXAMPLE 1

An amplifier consists of three identical stages for which the voltage gain is -100. A voltage divider in which $R_1/(R_1 + R_2) = 0.01$ provides feedback. Predict the overall gain without and with feedback.

SOLUTION. Because G and H are pure numbers, we can work with rms signals. With switch S open, the circuit of Fig. 19.4 is operating without feedback. Therefore,

$$V_4 = (-100)V_3 = (-100)^2 V_2 = (-100)^3 V_1$$

$$G = \frac{V_4}{V_1} = -10^6$$

With switch S closed, there is feedback and, from Eq. 19-4, the gain is

$$G_f = \frac{G}{1 - GH} = \frac{-10^6}{1 - (-10^6)(0.01)} = -\frac{10^6}{1 + 10^4} \cong -100$$

The overall gain has been reduced to that of a single stage. What could justify this sacrifice in gain?

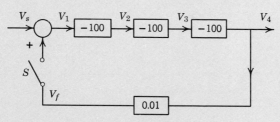

Fig. 19.4 Example 1.

Block Diagram Algebra

Analysis of the behavior of complicated systems can be simplified by following a few rules for manipulating block diagram elements. These rules are based on the definitions of block diagram symbols and could be derived each time, but it is more convenient to demonstrate their validity once and list them for ready reference.

Rule I.   *Any closed-loop system can be replaced by an equivalent open-loop system.*

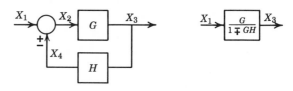

Fig. 19.5   Rule I: $\dfrac{X_3}{X_1} = \dfrac{G}{1 \mp GH}.$

Rule II.   *The gain of cascaded blocks is the product of the individual gains.*

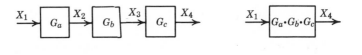

Fig. 19.6   Rule II: $\dfrac{X_4}{X_1} = \dfrac{X_2}{X_1} \cdot \dfrac{X_3}{X_2} \cdot \dfrac{X_4}{X_3} = G_a \cdot G_b \cdot G_c.$

Rule III.   *The order of summing does not affect the sum.*

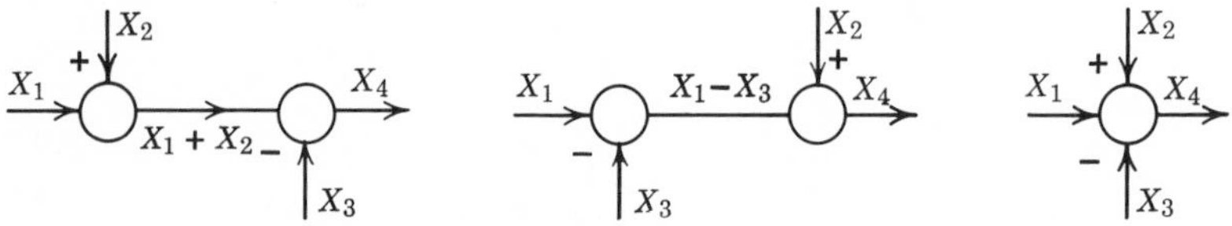

Fig. 19.7.   Rule III: $X_4 = X_1 + X_2 - X_3.$

Rule IV. *Shifting a summing point beyond a block of gain G_a requires the insertion of G_a in the variable added.*

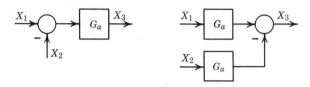

Fig. 19.8 Rule IV: $X_3 = G_a(X_1 - X_2) = G_aX_1 - G_aX_2$

Rule V. *Shifting a pickoff point beyond a block of gain G_a requires the insertion of $1/G_a$ in the variable picked off.*

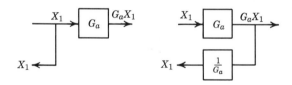

Fig. 19.9 Rule V: $X_1 = (1/G_a)G_aX_1$

These rules and the corollaries of Rules IV and V are illustrated in the following example.

EXAMPLE 2

Determine the overall gain of the system shown in Fig. 19.10a.

SOLUTION. It would be possible to determine the gain by writing the equation for each element in turn and solving simultaneously. A preferable procedure is to simplify the system by block diagram algebra. Applying Rule V, the pickoff point is moved beyond G_c with the result as shown in Fig. 19.10b. Applying the inverse of Rule IV permits shifting the summing point for the lower loop before G_a. Applying Rules III and II, the reduced diagram is put into the basic form and the overall gain can be written by inspection as

$$G_{61} = \frac{X_6}{X_1} = \frac{G_aG_bG_c}{1 - (G_aG_b)(G_d/G_a - 1)}$$

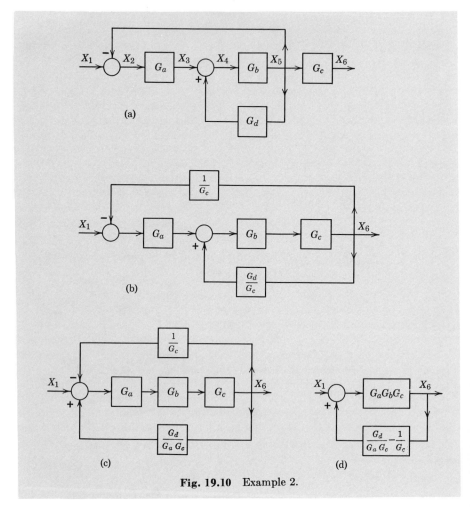

Fig. 19.10   Example 2.

Positive Feedback

By using the rules of block diagram algebra, all linear feedback networks can be reduced to the basic system of Fig. 19.10d, for which the gain is $G_f = G/(1 - GH)$. The behavior of the system can be predicted by examining the quantity $1 - GH$. In a complicated network, the denominator will be a polynomial, as in Example 2, and its poles and zeros will correspond to critical points in the behavior pattern.

For GH positive but less than unity, the denominator will be less than unity and the system gain is greater than the forward gain G. This condition of *positive feedback* was used in early radio receivers, called "regenerative receivers," to provide high gain when electronic amplifiers were poor and signals were weak. Operation with positive feedback becomes less stable as GH approaches unity, so regenerative receivers required constant adjustment.

If the value of **GH** approaches $1 + j0$, the denominator approaches zero and the overall gain increases without limit. An amplifier of infinite gain can provide an output with no input; such a device is called an *oscillator* or signal generator and is an important part of many electronic systems. On the other hand, in a linear amplifier such oscillations are undesirable and special provisions may be necessary to prevent them.

Oscillation

Consider a three-stage RC-coupled amplifier. For one stage the high-frequency gain is, by Eq. 11-38,

$$\mathbf{A}_h = A_o \frac{1}{1 + j\omega C_p R_o} = A_o \frac{1}{1 + j\omega/\omega_2}$$

where ω_2 defines the upper cutoff frequency. At a slightly higher frequency where $\omega = \sqrt{3}\,\omega_2$,

$$\mathbf{A}_h = \frac{A_o}{1 + j\sqrt{3}} = \frac{A_o}{2}\underline{/-\tan^{-1}\sqrt{3}} = \frac{A_o}{2}\underline{/-60°}$$

For three stages, at this frequency,

$$\mathbf{G} = \left(\frac{A_o}{2}\right)^3 \underline{/3(-60°)} = \left(\frac{A_o}{2}\right)^3 \underline{/-180°} = -\left(\frac{A_o}{2}\right)^3 + j0$$

Assuming feedback is present and $\mathbf{H} = 0.008$,

$$\mathbf{GH} = -0.008\left(\frac{A_o}{2}\right)^3 + j0 = -\left(\frac{A_o}{10}\right)^3$$

For oscillation, $\mathbf{G}_f$ must be infinite or the denominator must be zero, or

$$\mathbf{GH} = -\left(\frac{A_o}{10}\right)^3 = +1 + j0 \quad \text{and} \quad A_o = -10$$

This is interpreted as follows: In a three-stage amplifier with a per-stage gain of -10, if 0.8% of the output voltage is fed back to the input, oscillation is possible at a frequency for which the per-stage phase shift is $60°$. In practice, there is a range of frequencies which will be amplified, but one of these will be maximized and the level of oscillation will build up until A_o is just equal to -10.

Another way of looking at the phenomenon of oscillation is to recognize that in any impulsive input, such as turning on a switch, components of energy corresponding to all frequencies are present. Also small voltages are generated by the random motion of electrons in conductors. Any such action can initiate the small signal which builds up and up through amplification and feedback to the equilibrium level. For small signals, A_o is usually quite large (much greater than -10); as the signal level increases, the gain decreases due to nonlinearity and the amplitude of oscillation stabilizes at the equilibrium level.

The preceding illustration indicates that a circuit arranged for amplification may produce oscillation if some small part of the output is coupled or fed back to the input with the proper phase relation. Opportunities for such coupling exist in the form of stray electric and magnetic fields or through mutual impedances of common power supplies. Amplifier designers use shielding and filtering to minimize coupling and reduce the possibility of oscillation.

Oscillators

When a circuit is designed to oscillate,† special provision is made to feed back a portion of the output signal in the correct phase and amplitude to make the **GH** product just equal to $1 + j0$. By making **GH** frequency dependent, oscillation can be obtained at a single desired frequency. Either **G** or **H** can be the frequency-dependent element of the feedback system.

The oscillator of Fig. 19.11 is basically an amplifier with a parallel resonant circuit for a load impedance. Gain is a maximum for signals at the resonant frequency of the collector circuit. This is called a *tuned* amplifier because the frequency for maximum amplification can be

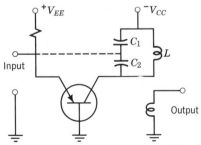

Fig. 19.11   Resonant-circuit oscillator.

---

† The fact that stable operation occurs in the nonlinear region of the device characteristic complicates the design and analysis of oscillators.

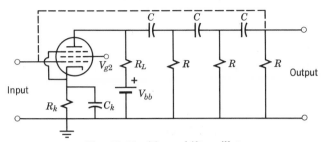

Fig. 19.12 Phase-shift oscillator.

selected by varying the capacitance. Such an amplifier is used in a radio receiver to amplify the signals transmitted by a selected station while rejecting all others. To create a "self-excited amplifier" or oscillator, the connection shown by the dotted line is added and part of the voltage across the tuned circuit is fed back into the input. In this case, **G** is a sensitive function of frequency.

For audio frequencies, the values of L and C required for a resonant circuit are impractically large. The *phase-shift oscillator* of Fig. 19.12 avoids this requirement and is fairly common for the generation of audio frequency signals. The output of the pentode amplifier appears across R_L. The first RC section constitutes a phase-shifting network in that the voltage across R is from 0° to 90° ahead of the voltage across R_L depending on the frequency. For a particular frequency, the three RC sections produce a total phase shift of 180°; the additional 180° required for oscillation is inherent in the grid voltage-plate voltage relations in a triode. In this case, H is the frequency sensitive element of the feedback system.

Negative Feedback

Negative feedback, where the amplitude and phase of the signal fed back are such that the overall gain of the amplifier is less than the forward gain, may be used to advantage in amplifier design. Since additional voltage or current gain can be obtained easily with transistors or tubes, the loss in gain is not important if significant advantages are obtained. Among the possible improvements in amplifier performance are:

1. Gain can be made practically independent of device parameters; gain can be made insensitive to temperature changes, aging of components, and variations from typical values.

2. Gain can be made practically independent of reactive elements and, therefore, insensitive to frequency.

3. The time constant of a circuit component can be modified to obtain faster response.

4. Gain can be made selective to discriminate against noise, distortion, or system disturbances.

5. The input and output impedance of an amplifier can be improved greatly.

NEGATIVE FEEDBACK APPLICATIONS

Stabilizing Gain

For precise instrumentation or long-term operation, amplifier performance must be predictable and stable. However, amplifier components such as transistors and vacuum tubes vary widely in their critical parameters. By employing negative feedback and sacrificing gain (which can be made up readily) stability can be improved.

EXAMPLE 3

An amplifier with an initial gain $G_1 = 100$ undergoes a 10% reduction in gain when a faulty transistor is replaced. Predict the stabilizing effect of a feedback loop where $H = -0.09$.

SOLUTION. Using the basic equation for gain with feedback, the initial gain is

$$G_{f1} = \frac{G_1}{1 - G_1 H} = \frac{100}{1 - 100(-0.09)} = 10$$

If gain is reduced by 10% to $G_2 = 90$,

$$G_{f2} = \frac{G_2}{1 - G_2 H} = \frac{90}{1 - 90(-0.09)} = 9.9$$

The change in gain with feedback is 1% or only $\frac{1}{10}$ as great as it is in the amplifier alone.

It can be shown (see Exercise 20) that, for small changes in G, the fractional change in overall gain with feedback is equal to the change in G divided by $1 - GH$. By definition, the *sensitivity* of gain to change is

$$\frac{dG_f/G_f}{dG/G} = \frac{1}{1 - GH} \tag{19-5}$$

In words, the sensitivity of the gain to change is reduced by the factor $1 - GH$.

Improving Frequency Response

No amplifier amplifies equally well at all frequencies; at the upper cutoff frequency, for example, the voltage gain is down to 70.7% of the midfrequency value. By sacrificing gain, however, the upper cutoff frequency can be raised. In the practical case, gain can be made insensitive to frequency over the range of interest by using negative feedback.

Using system notation, the gain **G** is frequency dependent because of storage effects in the electronic device and reactive elements in the circuit. The feedback factor **H** however, can be obtained through purely resistive elements. If **H** is obtained by means of a voltage divider tap on a precision noninductive resistor, then $\mathbf{H} = H$, a constant. If **GH** is very large at the frequency of interest, the basic gain equation becomes

$$\mathbf{G}_f = \frac{\mathbf{G}}{1 - \mathbf{GH}} \cong \frac{\mathbf{G}}{-\mathbf{GH}} = -\frac{1}{H} \qquad (19\text{-}6)$$

and the gain is independent of frequency, temperature, or aging.

EXAMPLE 4

An amplifier whose high-frequency response is given by $\mathbf{G} = A_o/[1 + j(\omega/\omega_2)]$ is employed in the basic feedback circuit (Fig. 19.3). If $A_o = 1000$, $\omega_2 = 10^4$ rad/sec, and $H = -0.009$, derive an approximate expression for high-frequency response with feedback and predict the new upper cutoff frequency.

SOLUTION. With feedback,

$$\mathbf{G}_f = \frac{\mathbf{G}}{1 - \mathbf{GH}} = \frac{\dfrac{1000}{1 + j(\omega/\omega_2)}}{1 + \dfrac{9}{1 + j(\omega/\omega_2)}} = \frac{1000}{1 + j\left(\dfrac{\omega}{\omega_2}\right) + 9} = \frac{100}{1 + j\left(\dfrac{\omega}{10\omega_2}\right)}$$

For ω small compared to $10\omega_2$,

$$\mathbf{G}_f \cong 100$$

At the new cutoff frequency, gain will be down by a factor of $\sqrt{2}$. Therefore, $\omega/10\omega_2 = 1$, or

$$\omega = 10\omega_2 = 10(10^4) = 10^5 \,\text{rad/sec},$$

In Example 4, the midfrequency gain is decreased by a factor of $1 - GH$, and the bandwidth has been increased by the same factor. As is usual in such cases, we have traded gain for bandwidth.

Reducing Time Constants

The speed of response of control elements is usually a limiting factor in the performance of control systems. An actuating motor with inertia takes a finite time to come up to a given speed, and it takes a finite time for the level in a chemical tank to drop a given amount. By using feedback principles, the speed of response can be greatly increased or, in other words, the time constant of the system can be reduced. The control

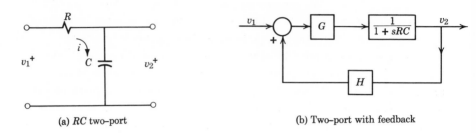

(a) RC two–port   (b) Two–port with feedback

Fig. 19.13   Reduction of time constant by means of feedback.

system applications of this concept are treated in Chapter 22.   Here we are interested in the application to electrical circuits.

To illustrate the powerful effect of feedback on the time constant of an electrical circuit, consider the RC two-port of Fig. 19.13a.   For exponential functions, the transfer function can be derived as

$$\frac{v_2}{v_1} = \frac{(1/sC)i}{(R + 1/sC)i} = \frac{1}{1 + sRC} \tag{19-7}$$

The time constant RC is a measure of the time for v_2 to approach v_1 if v_1 is a suddenly applied d-c voltage, for example.   (Or it is a measure of the time required for a motor to reach operating speed or a liquid level to drop to a new value.)

If amplification (G) and feedback (H) are provided, the system is described by the block diagram of Fig. 19.13b.   For this system,

$$\frac{v_2}{v_1} = \frac{\dfrac{G}{1 + sRC}}{1 - \dfrac{GH}{1 + sRC}} = \frac{G}{1 + sRC - GH} = \frac{G}{1 - GH + sRC} \tag{19-8}$$

If we define a new input

$$v_1' = v_1 \frac{G}{1 - GH}$$

then, by Eq. 19-8,

$$\frac{v_2}{v_1'} = \frac{v_2}{v_1} \cdot \frac{v_1}{v_1'} = \frac{1}{1 + s\dfrac{RC}{1 - GH}} \tag{19-9}$$

and the time constant has been reduced by the factor $(1 - GH)$.   As in the preceding illustration, a desirable result has been achieved at the expense of amplification.

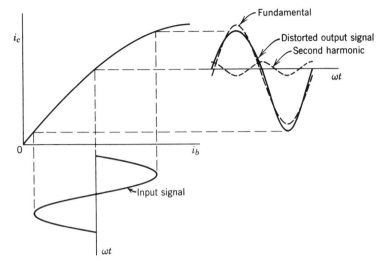

Fig. 19.14 Nonlinear distortion introducing second harmonic.

Reducing Distortion

Distortion-free amplification is obtained easily at low signal levels. In the last power amplifier stage, however, efficient performance usually introduces nonlinear distortion because of the large-signal swings. A common type of distortion results in the introduction of a second harmonic as shown in Fig. 19.14.

A nonlinear amplifier can be represented by the system of linear blocks shown in Fig. 19.15a with switch S open. The distortion component V_d is introduced in the output with no corresponding component in the input V_i. Without feedback, the output signal is

$$V_o = GV_i + V_d \qquad (19\text{-}10)$$

and the distortion in percent is $(V_d/GV_i) \times 100$. Closing the switch S

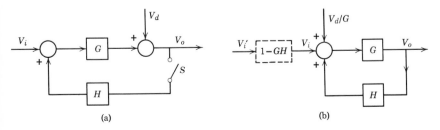

Fig. 19.15 Block diagram representation of distortion component.

introduces feedback. In Fig. 19.15b, using the corollary of Rule IV, the distortion component V_d has been shifted ahead of G by inserting the factor $1/G$. Now

$$V_o = \frac{G(V_i + V_d/G)}{1 - GH} = \frac{G}{1 - GH} V_i + \frac{V_d}{1 - GH}$$

If another stage of low-level, distortionless amplification with a gain of $1 - GH$ is added, the new output is

$$V_o = GV_i' + \frac{V_d}{1 - GH} \qquad (19\text{-}11)$$

The relative amplitude of the distortion component compared to the desired component has been reduced by the factor $1 - GH$ which may be 10 to 100 or so.

EXAMPLE 5

The output of a power amplifier contains a 10-V, 1000-cps fundamental and "20% second-harmonic distortion." The gain $\mathbf{G} = 100 \underline{/0°}$. Predict the effect of negative feedback on the distortion if $H = -0.19$.

SOLUTION. The block diagram for the system is as shown in Fig. 19.16a. Blocks G and H are linear models so the distortion component V_d is introduced as an extraneous signal not present in the input to the amplifier. By definition, 20% second-harmonic distortion indicates the presence of a 2000-cps signal of magnitude

$$V_d = 0.20 V_{b1} = 0.20 \times 10 = 2 \text{ V}$$

Applying Rule IV, the summing point for V_d is shifted in front of G and the block diagram is that of Fig. 19.16b. With feedback, the gain is

$$G_f = \frac{G}{1 - GH} = \frac{100}{1 + 19} = 5$$

To retain the original power output, the input signal must be increased to

$$V_i = \frac{V_{o1}}{G_f} = \frac{10}{5} = 2 \text{ V at 1000 cps}$$

The output is now G_f times the equivalent input or

$$V_o = G_f(V_i + V_d/100)$$

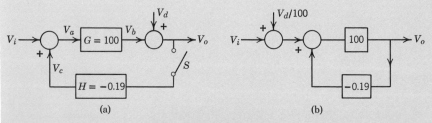

(a)   (b)

Fig. 19.16 Example 5.

At 1000 cps, $V_{o1} = G_f V_i = 5 \times 2 = 10$ V
At 2000 cps, $V_{o2} = G_f V_d/100 = 5 \times 0.02 = 0.1$ V
The percentage of second-harmonic distortion is now

$$\frac{V_{o2}}{V_{o1}} \times 100 = \frac{0.1}{10} \times 100 = 1\% \text{ (a tolerable amount)}$$

Originally the required input signal was $V_{o1}/100 = 0.1$ V; therefore, additional, distortionless, voltage gain of $2V/0.1V = 20$ is necessary but this is easily obtainable at these low levels.

To dispel some of the mystery in the reduction of distortion by negative feedback, study the voltage distributions for Example 5 shown in Fig. 19.17. Since the blocks are linear, the superposition principle is applicable and the two signals can be handled separately.

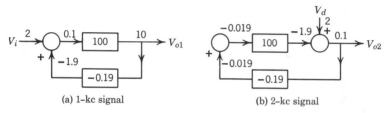

(a) 1–kc signal   (b) 2–kc signal

Fig. 19.17 Voltage distributions for fundamental and second harmonic in Example 5.

Improving Impedance Characteristics

To minimize the loading effect on the signal source the input impedance of an electronic device, such as an amplifier, should be high. A vacuum tube with negative grid is very good in this respect, but a transistor is not. Also, to provide efficient power transfer to the load, the output impedance of the device should be small. Neither the vacuum tube nor the transistor is optimum in this respect. By using negative feedback the input and output impedances can be dramatically improved. A particularly useful form of feedback circuit is the *cathode follower* or its transistor counterpart, the *emitter follower*.

FOLLOWERS

The Cathode Follower

In the vacuum-tube amplifier of Fig. 19.18, the load resistor R_k is in series with the cathode and the plate is tied directly to V_{bb}, an a-c ground.

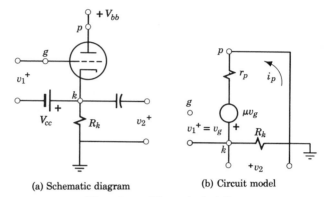

(a) Schematic diagram   (b) Circuit model

Fig. 19.18   The cathode follower.

As indicated in the small-signal model for midfrequencies, when $v_1 = v_g$ is positive, i_p is positive and v_2 is positive.   As the signal voltage v_1 changes, the voltage of the cathode with respect to ground "follows," hence the name *cathode follower*.   By inspection, the output voltage is

$$v_2 = i_p R_k = \frac{\mu v_g}{r_p + R_k} R_k$$

and the gain is

$$G = \frac{v_2}{v_g} = \frac{\mu R_k}{r_p + R_k} \tag{19-12}$$

If the circuit is rearranged as shown in Fig. 19.19, the a-c linear model indicates that the output voltage has been fed back into the grid-cathode circuit in opposition to the input voltage.   In the alternate form of the

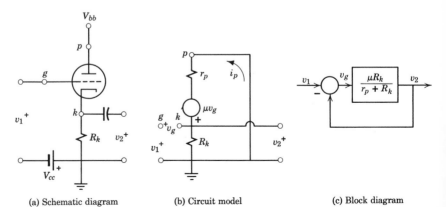

(a) Schematic diagram   (b) Circuit model   (c) Block diagram

Fig. 19.19   The cathode follower as a feedback circuit.

basic feedback circuit in Fig. 19.5, $H = +1$ and the equivalent block diagram is as shown in Fig. 19.19c. From the alternate form of the basic feedback equation,

$$G_f = \frac{G}{1 + GH} = \frac{\dfrac{\mu R_k}{r_p + R_k}}{1 + \dfrac{\mu R_k}{r_p + R_k}} \qquad (19\text{-}13)$$

Since μ, r_p and R_k are all positive quantities, the gain is always less than unity and only approaches unity as μR_k becomes large compared to $r_p + R_k$.

In spite of its lack of gain, a cathode follower is usually the first stage of a cathode-ray oscilloscope. For a tube operating in the negative grid region, the input impedance is very high; and, therefore, the instrument does not load the signal being measured. Since only the difference between v_1 and v_2 appears across the grid-cathode terminals, large voltage inputs can be handled. Also, and this is the chief advantage of the cathode follower, the output impedance is low so that signals are faithfully transmitted to the next stage.

The output impedance (a resistance at moderate frequencies) can be determined for the equivalent Thévenin generator of Fig. 19.20. Under open-circuit conditions Eq. 19-13 can be rearranged to give

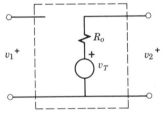

Fig. 19.20 Thévenin equivalent circuit.

$$v_{oc} = v_2 = \frac{\mu R_k v_1}{(1 + \mu)R_k + r_p}$$

When v_2 and R_k are shorted, $v_g = v_1$ and the short-circuit current is

$$i_{sc} = i_p = \frac{\mu v_1}{r_p}$$

Then

$$R_o = \frac{v_{oc}}{i_{sc}} = \frac{R_k r_p}{(1 + \mu)R_k + r_p} = \frac{R_k \dfrac{r_p}{1 + \mu}}{R_k + \dfrac{r_p}{1 + \mu}} \qquad (19\text{-}14)$$

It is seen that the output impedance consists of R_k in parallel with an impedance $r_p/(1 + \mu)$ instead of R_L in parallel with r_p as for the

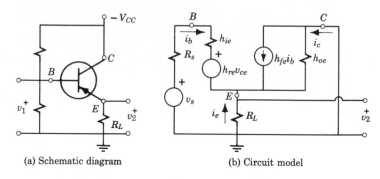

| (a) Schematic diagram | (b) Circuit model |

Fig. 19.21   Common-collector amplifier.

grounded-cathode configuration.   For a triode with $\mu = 55$, $r_p = 5.5$ kΩ, and $R_k = 100$ Ω, the output impedance is less than 50 Ω.

The Emitter Follower

The common-collector amplifier or *emitter follower* offers similar advantages when transistors are used.   The transistor is inherently a feedback device since some of the output is coupled back into the input.   Disregarding the biasing network, the small-signal model for moderate frequencies is as shown in Fig. 19.21b.   The analysis of this circuit model is not difficult, but the algebra is needlessly complicated.   Two simplifications are justified by practical considerations.   First, h_{re} is always small and here it is negligible.   Second, h_{oe} is negligibly small compared to $1/R_L$ with which it is in parallel.

Proceeding as with the cathode follower, the simplified circuit model is first drawn without feedback in Fig. 19.22a.   Inspection of the circuit

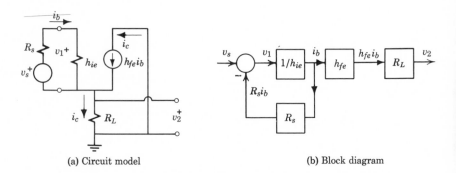

| (a) Circuit model | (b) Block diagram |

Fig. 19.22   Simplified common-collector amplifier without feedback.

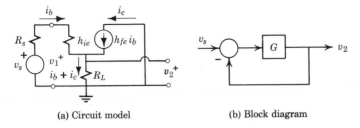

(a) Circuit model   (b) Block diagram

Fig. 19.23   Common-collector amplifier with feedback.

indicates that

$$i_b = \frac{v_s}{R_s + h_{ie}} \quad \text{and} \quad i_c = h_{fe}i_b$$

Then

$$v_2 = i_c R_L = \frac{h_{fe}v_s R_L}{R_s + h_{ie}}$$

and the voltage gain is

$$G = \frac{v_2}{v_s} = \frac{h_{fe}R_L}{R_s + h_{ie}} \tag{19-15}$$

When feedback is introduced as in Fig. 19.23, the block diagram shows that v_2 is fed back in opposition to v_1 ($H = +1$ in the alternate form), and the voltage gain of the emitter follower is

$$G_f = \frac{G}{1 + GH} = \frac{\dfrac{h_{fe}R_L}{R_s + h_{ie}}}{1 + \dfrac{h_{fe}R_L}{R_s + h_{ie}}} \tag{19-16}$$

If h_{fe} is large (50 to 150) and if R_L is of the same order of magnitude as $(R_s + h_{ie})$, then G_f approaches unity, but it can never exceed unity.

The virtue of an emitter follower is not in providing voltage gain. It does provide a current gain of $h_{fe} + 1$ and a corresponding power gain, but its greatest usefulness is in providing impedance transformation. From Fig. 19.23a,

$$v_1 = i_b h_{ie} + (i_b + i_c)R_L = i_b h_{ie} + i_b R_L + h_{fe}i_b R_L$$

By definition, the input resistance is

$$R_i = \frac{v_1}{i_b} = h_{ie} + (h_{fe} + 1)R_L \cong (h_{fe} + 1)R_L \tag{19-17}$$

The effective output resistance can be evaluated from open- and short-circuit conditions.   With the output terminals open-circuited,

$$v_{oc} = v_2 \cong v_s$$

since the gain is approximately unity (Eq. 19-16).

With the output terminals shorted (shorting R_L),

$$i_b = \frac{v_s}{R_s + h_{ie}}$$

and

$$i_{sc} = i_b + i_c = (h_{fe} + 1)i_b = \frac{h_{fe} + 1}{R_s + h_{ie}} v_s$$

Then

$$R_o = \frac{v_{oc}}{i_{sc}} = \frac{R_s + h_{ie}}{h_{fe} + 1} \tag{19-18}$$

From Eqs. 19-17 and 19-18, it is clear that the emitter follower acts as an impedance transformer with a ratio of transformation approximately equal to $h_{fe} + 1$.   With a load resistance R_L, the resistance seen at the input terminals is $(h_{fe} + 1)$ times as great.   With the input circuit resistance $R_s + h_{ie}$, the effective output resistance is only $1/(h_{fe} + 1)$ times as large.

EXAMPLE 6

A 2N1893 transistor ($h_{ie} = 2.8$ kΩ, $h_{fe} = 70$) is used as an amplifier with $R_L = 4$ kΩ.   Compare the input resistances in the common-emitter and common-collector configurations.

SOLUTION.   Using the simplified circuit of Fig. 19.24a, the input resistance in the common-emitter configuration is

$$R_{ie} = \frac{v_1}{i_b} = h_{ie} = 2.8 \text{ k}\Omega$$

Using Eq. 19-17, the common-collector input resistance is

$$R_{ic} = h_{ie} + (h_{fe} + 1)R_L = 2.8 + (70 + 1)4 = 287 \text{ k}\Omega$$

The common-collector input resistance is over 100 times as great.

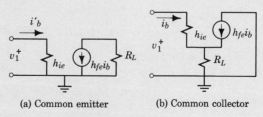

(a) Common emitter   (b) Common collector

Fig. 19.24   Example 6.

SUMMARY

◆ Feedback is important in biological, social and technical processes and systems. Its principal virtue is the ability to provide satisfactory operation of a system under widely varying conditions, even when parameters of the system itself are changed.

◆ In a closed-loop system, a portion of the output is fed back and compared to or combined with the input.

◆ Where G is the forward gain (or transfer function) and H is the feedback factor, the gain of the basic feedback system is

$$G_f = \frac{G}{1 - GH} \quad \text{or} \quad G_f = \frac{G}{1 + GH}$$

depending on the sign ($\pm$) of the feedback connection.

◆ Complicated systems which can be analyzed into linear, unilateral two-port elements are conveniently represented by simple diagrams consisting of blocks, summing points, and pickoff points.

◆ Block diagrams can be manipulated according to the following rules and their corollaries:

    I. Any closed-loop system can be replaced by an equivalent open-loop system.

    II. The gain of cascaded blocks is the product of the individual gains.

    III. The order of summing does not affect the sum.

    IV. Shifting a summing point beyond a block of gain G_a requires the insertion of G_a in the variable added.

    V. Shifting a pickoff point beyond a block of gain G_a requires the insertion of $1/G_a$ in the variable picked off.

◆ The quantity $1 - GH$ is the key to the behavior of closed-loop systems.

For $|1 - GH| < 1$, positive feedback occurs and the system gain is greater than the forward gain.

For $|1 - GH| = 0$, the system gain increases without limit and oscillation is possible.

For $|1 - GH| > 1$, negative feedback occurs and the system gain is less than the forward gain.

◆ An oscillator is a self-excited amplifier in which a portion of the output signal is fed back in the correct phase and amplitude to make $\mathbf{GH} = 1 + j0$.

By making G or H frequency dependent, oscillation at a single frequency can be obtained.

◆   Important advantages of negative feedback compensate for the loss
    in gain.
    Gain can be made insensitive to device parameters.
    Gain can be made insensitive to frequency.
    Time constants of components can be modified.
    Noise and distortion can be discriminated against.
    Input and output impedances can be improved.

◆   In cathode and emitter followers, the entire output is fed back into
    the input so that gain is less than unity but input and output
    impedances are optimized.

◆   The emitter follower acts as an impedance transformer with a ratio
    of approximately $h_{fe} + 1$.

REVIEW QUESTIONS

1. Cite an example of feedback in a biological system and describe its operation.
2. Cite an example of feedback in a social system and describe its operation.
3. Cite an example of feedback in each of the following branches of engineering:
aeronautical, chemical, civil, industrial, and mechanical.
4. If the speaker of a public address system is moved farther away from the
microphone, what is the effect on the possibility of a "squeal," the frequency
of the squeal if it does develop, and the amplitude of the squeal?
5. Differentiate between the two general categories of feedback applications
in electrical systems described in the introduction to this chapter.
6. From memory, draw and label a basic feedback system and write the expression for overall gain.
7. Draw a circuit in which H is a complex quantity.   Under what circumstances
might this be desirable?
8. Given a two-stage pentode amplifier, under what circumstances would G
be a complex quantity?
9. What is the physical meaning for $GH = 1$?   What is the a-c *power* gain
around the closed loop for this situation?
10. List three conditions which must be met if a system is to be represented by a
block diagram.
11. Differentiate between a summing point and a pickoff point.
12. Differentiate between a gain and a transfer function.
13. Write the corollaries to block diagram algebra rules IV and V.
14. Draw a complicated system with two pickoff points and two summing points.
Using the rules of block diagram algebra, reduce the system to an open-loop
equivalent.
15. Define positive feedback and negative feedback.
16. Is oscillation possible in an ordinary two-stage RC-coupled audio amplifier?
Explain.
17. Explain how a multistage audio amplifier may become an oscillator at a
certain frequency.

18. A portable high-gain amplifier tends to become oscillatory as the batteries age. It is known that the internal resistance of batteries increases with age. Explain the connection between these phenomena.

19. Draw a simplified circuit diagram of a transistor oscillator in which the frequency dependent element is a parallel LC circuit in the collector and feedback to the base is accomplished inductively.

20. List five specific benefits which may result from negative feedback and indicate where they would be important.

21. List three reasons why the gain of a transistor amplifier without feedback might change in normal operation.

22. Explain the expression "trading gain for bandwidth."

23. Explain on a physical basis the operation of feedback in reducing the time constant in Fig. 19.13. Consider voltages at various times at various points.

24. Draw a block diagram to represent a "noisy" amplifier in which noise (perhaps an objectionable hum) appears in the output without a corresponding input. Suggest a means for reducing such noise.

25. Explain how an amplifier can be made insensitive to the effect of increased temperatures on transistor parameters.

26. Define the impedance characteristics of an ideal amplifier and explain your answer.

27. Why is a common-plate amplifier called a cathode follower?

28. Cite two virtues of the cathode follower.

29. Explain why a "transistor is inherently a feedback device."

30. Explain how an emitter follower functions as an impedance transformer. Where in a "hi-fi" set would this property be valuable?

EXERCISES

1. The circuit model of a triode with tapped load resistor is shown in Fig. 19.25.

(a) Label polarities of voltage drops in terms of positive I_p and determine the voltage feedback factor H.

(b) From circuit equations derive an equation for overall midfrequency gain V_3/V_1 for this amplifier.

(c) Draw a carefully labeled block diagram with feedback.

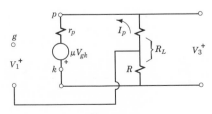

Fig. 19.25

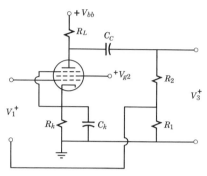

Fig. 19.26

2. Draw an a-c circuit model for the pentode amplifier of Fig. 19.26 and repeat Exercise 1.

3. Given the block diagram of Fig. 19.27, calculate the transfer functions Y/X_2 ($X_1 = 0$) and Y/X_1 ($X_2 = 0$). Determine Y in terms of X_1 and X_2.

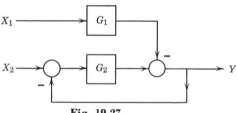

Fig. 19.27

4. Draw a labelled circuit model for a self-excited d-c generator operating at constant speed with no load. Assume linear operation and slow changes (neglect L_f and L_a). Write the governing equation for each component and for any summation present. Draw and label an appropriate block diagram.

5. Repeat Exercise 4 assuming operation with a load R_L.

6. A driver on a freeway wishes to keep his left fender two feet from the white line. Draw a labeled block diagram for the closed-loop system he uses.

7. Reduce the block diagram of Fig. 19.28 to the basic feedback system of Fig. 19.3 and indicate the values of G and H. Determine the gain of the system.

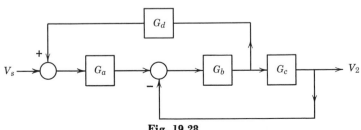

Fig. 19.28

8. Repeat Exercise 7 for the block diagram of Fig. 19.29.

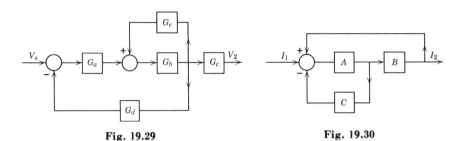

Fig. 19.29   **Fig. 19.30**

9. Repeat Exercise 7 for the block diagram of Fig. 19.30.

10. Given a system described by the following equations:

$$V_2 = V_1 + V_4 - AV_3 \qquad V_3 = BV_2 \qquad V_4 = CV_3$$

where V_1 is the input and V_4 is the output. Draw a labeled block diagram representing this system.

11. Given a system described by the following equations:

$$I_2 = I_1 + V_3/R_3 \qquad I_3 = V_3/B \qquad V_2 = R_2I_2$$

$$V_4 = AV_3 \qquad V_3 = V_2 - V_4$$

where I_1 is the input and I_3 is the output. Draw a labeled block diagram representing this system.

12. Draw a labeled block diagram for the circuit of Fig. 19.26.

(a) Derive an expression for overall midfrequency gain.

(b) Compare result to that for part (b) of Exercise 2.

13. A common-emitter amplifier with load R_L is represented by a T-equivalent linear model with a current generator controlled by I_s, the effective value of the input signal.

(a) Write the equations governing the amplifier.

(b) Draw and label an appropriate block diagram, using I_s as input and V_L as output. Is feedback present?

14. Repeat Exercise 13, considering I_s is obtained from a source of voltage V_s in series with R_s. Use V_s as input and V_L as output. Can you identify the feedback factor physically?

15. A feedback system is represented by Fig. 19.3 with $\mathbf{H} = 0.01\underline{/180°}$. Define the conditions necessary for oscillation.

16. A feedback system is represented by Fig. 19.30 with $\mathbf{A} = 100\underline{/90°}$ and $\mathbf{B} = 10\underline{/90°}$. Determine the value of $\mathbf{C}$ necessary for oscillation.

17. In the tuned oscillator of Fig. 19.11, $C_1 = C_2 = 500$ pF and $L = 10$ mH. Define the frequency of oscillation in words and symbols and estimate its value in cps.

18. In the phase-shift oscillator of Fig. 19.12, $R = 100$ kΩ and $r_p = R_L = 10$ kΩ.

(a) Determine the approximate value of C for oscillation at 50 cps. State any simplifying assumptions made.

(b) If oscillation at 50 cps is to be determined by a resonant circuit with $L = 1\text{H}$, approximately what value of C is required? Is this a reasonable value for a variable capacitor?

19. A common-emitter small-signal amplifier (Fig. 11.20b) uses a 2N699B with $I_C = 1$ mA and $V_{CE} = 5$ V. $R_L = 5$ kΩ and $R_B = 20$ kΩ.

(a) Through what range can the mid-frequency current gain vary without departing from the manufacturer's specifications (min. to max.)?

(b) Introduce current feedback with $H = -0.1$ and recalculate the range of current gain.

(c) How could the loss in current gain due to the introduction of negative feedback be made up?

20. Consider the basic feedback system of Fig. 19.3. Assuming small changes in G, derive a general expression for the fractional change in overall gain with feedback (dG_f/G_f) in terms of the change in forward gain (dG/G) and the values of G and H.

21. A common-emitter transistor amplifier uses a 2N525 with $R_L = 4$ kΩ. The voltage source has negligible internal resistance.

(a) Predict the approximate voltage gain using typical parameters, and then repeat the calculation assuming h_{fe} is actually 20% less than typical.

(b) Provide feedback with $H = -0.05$ and repeat part (a). Compare results.

22. A transistor amplifier has a high-frequency response defined by $\mathbf{A} = A_o/(1 + j\omega/\omega_2)$ where $A_o = 100$ and $\omega_2 = 40$ krad/sec.

(a) Plot a couple of points and sketch a graph of A/A_o versus ω with ω on a logarithmic scale.

(b) Assume that a feedback loop with $H = -0.05$ is provided and repeat part (a). Label this graph "With feedback."

23. A transistor amplifier has a low-frequency response defined by $\mathbf{A} = A_o/(1 - j\omega_1/\omega)$ where $\omega_1 = 100$ rad/sec and $A_o = 140$.

(a) Plot a couple of points and sketch a graph of A/A_o versus ω with ω on a logarithmic scale.

(b) Assume that a feedback loop with $H = -0.05$ is provided and repeat part (a). Label this graph "With feedback."

24. An amplifier has a midfrequency gain of 100 but the gain is only 60 at 100 kc. Devise a feedback system and specify a real value of H so that the gain at 100 kc is within 5% of the new midfrequency gain.

25. Given the circuit of Fig. 19.31, what assumptions can be made regarding C_C and C_k at mid-frequencies?

(a) Replace the tube with a linear model, draw the small-signal circuit model for the amplifier, and derive an equation for midfrequency gain.

(b) Construct a block diagram with feedback for the circuit of part (a), reduce this to a single block, and compare the result with that of part (a).

26. Remove C_k from the circuit of Fig. 19.31 and repeat Exercise 25.

27. In Fig. 19.16, consider V_d to be the input and V_o the output and redraw the block diagram. Calculate the gain V_o/V_d for this system and interpret the result.

28. An audio amplifier with a voltage gain of 60 has an output of 5 V, but superimposed on the output is an annoying 60-cycle hum of magnitude 0.3 V.

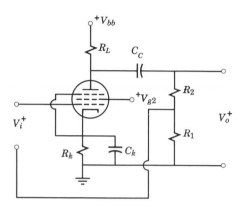

Fig. 19.31

(a) Devise a feedback system and specify H so that with the same 5-V output, the hum component is reduced to 0.02 V.

(b) Draw separate block diagrams for the audio signal and the hum component, showing the actual voltages at each point in the system.

29. A cathode follower uses a tube for which $\mu = 99$ and $r_p = 5$ kΩ. If $R_k = 1$ kΩ, calculate the gain and the output resistance. What is the input resistance?

30. A triode cathode follower with feedback (Fig. 19.19) with $\mu = 20$ and $r_p = 8$ kΩ is to supply a load of 200 Ω.

(a) If the load resistance is to be matched for maximum power transfer what value of R_k is appropriate?

(b) The voltage across the load resistance is the input to a next stage with an input resistance $R_g = 200$ kΩ and a total shunt capacitance of 100 pF. Predict the upper cutoff frequency.

31. A 2N525 transistor is to be used as an emitter follower. It is supplied by a source defined by $V_s = 2$ mV and $R_s = 1$ kΩ, and it uses a load resistor of 2 kΩ in the emitter circuit. Determine the voltage output and the input and output resistances by using the simplified model.

32. A 2N699B transistor is used to follow a high impedance source where $R_s = 100$ kΩ.

(a) Devise a circuit and specify R_L so that the input resistance seen by the source is approximately 100 kΩ.

(b) Predict the output resistance of the transistor under these circumstances.

33. In deriving Eq. 19.18 for R_o, it was assumed that $v_2 \cong v_s$ under open-circuit conditions. Determine a more precise value of v_{oc} and show that for $h_{fe} = 50$, $h_{ie} = 2$ kΩ, and $R_L = 2$ kΩ the approximation was justified.

PROBLEMS

1. A lightly loaded shunt motor M is controlled by a speed regulator as shown in Fig. 19.32. T is an electric tachometer and A is an amplifier. *Stating* any

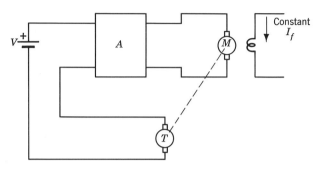

Fig. 19.32

necessary assumptions, draw a labeled block diagram for the system under conditions of *slow* changes.

2. An amplifier with a gain $G_1 = 500$ is subject to a 10% change in gain due to part replacement. Design an amplifier (in block diagram form) which provides the same overall gain but in which similar part replacement will produce a change in gain of only 0.1%. Use amplifier G_1 as part of your design.

3. A compound-wound d-c generator has a separately excited shunt field and a series field carrying armature current. *Stating* any necessary assumptions, represent the generating system by a block diagram. Under what conditions would this system be unstable?

4. A class-A power amplifier is to supply 200 V (rms) of signal across a 4000-Ω load resistance.

(a) How much a-c power is required? To get this much output with the available tube, the grid must be driven into non-linear regions. It is calculated that the major element of distortion is a 20-V second harmonic. Express this as "percent distortion."

(b) The source for the amplifier is a phono-pickup with an output of 8 mV. If the final power amplifier stage has a voltage gain of 20, how many transistor voltage amplifier stages of what voltage gain each do you recommend?

(c) It is suggested that the distortion can be reduced by providing feedback around the power amplifier. Specify the feedback factor necessary to reduce the distortion to 2%. To maintain the same output voltage, how must the voltage amplifiers be modified?

5. Consider the common-emitter T-equivalent circuit for a transistor with R_L in the collector circuit.

(a) Write the loop equations and draw the corresponding block diagram. Define the feedback factor. *Stating* any necessary assumptions, determine the voltage gain and input resistance.

(b) Convert to a common-collector circuit with the same R_L and repeat part (a). Compare the results.

♦ ANALOG COMPUTATION
♦ OPERATIONAL AMPLIFIERS
♦ ELECTRONIC ANALOG COMPUTERS

CHAPTER **20**

The Analog Computer

Recent advances in computation method and speed have led to increased understanding of physical phenomena and to improved engineering designs. The *digital computer* is preeminent in general purpose, high precision computation; it can be programmed to solve any problem which can be reduced to a sequence of arithmetic and logic operations on discrete data (see Chapter 13). In the *analog computer* numerical values are represented by continuously varying quantities such as displacements or voltages; its great virtue is in the rapid solution of complicated problems with a wide range of system parameters. Because it is so fast and so responsive to the operator's suggestions, the analog computer is an important tool for the research or the development engineer. In essence, it becomes a flexible model of the physical system being studied. By changing inputs, initial conditions, and parameter values and observing the results, the operator can rapidly determine the effects of such changes and quickly arrive at an optimum design.

By definition, physical systems are analogous if they are described by the same integrodifferential equations. In discussing circuits we emphasized the analogous relations between thermal, mechanical, electrical, and magnetic circuits. In analyzing electronic and electromagnetic devices we used analogous models to represent tubes, transistors, transformers, and motors. The treatment of the analog computer here is designed to emphasize further the importance of analogies in engineering analysis.

Another reason for its inclusion is that the modern analog computer is a good example of the use of feedback to obtain precision in electronic instrumentation. First, we look at the basic computation operations and see how they can be achieved by mechanical and electrical means. Then we learn how the electronic operational amplifier uses feedback to perform the same operations with great precision. Finally, we use the electronic computer in the solution of engineering problems.

ANALOG COMPUTATIONS

The sliderule is one of our oldest analog computers. Essentially, it is a device for adding lengths which are analogous to logarithms. On the C and D scales, for example, the ruling marked "2" designates a length (measured from the index) corresponding to log 2 and the ruling marked "3" designates a length corresponding to log 3. If the index of the C scale is placed over 2 on the D scale and the indicator moved to 3 on the C scale, the length indicated on the D scale corresponds to log 2 + log 3 which is equal to log (2 × 3) or log 6. Thus the sliderule is a mechanical computer which can be used to multiply two quantities. The other basic arithmetic operations are: addition, multiplication by a constant, differentiation, and integration.

Types of Analog Computers

In addition to electronic computing elements, there are mechanical, electromechanical, and electrical devices for performing the basic operations. Because each type possesses certain advantages, a complicated computer may contain more than one type of computing element.

Mechanical. Addition can be performed mechanically by combinations of linkages or gears. In the rack and spur gear in Fig. 20.1a, the output represented by translation of the gear is proportional to the sum of the inputs x and y. *Multiplication* by a constant is performed easily by a gear ratio or a lever system (Fig. 20.1b). Multiplication of two varia-

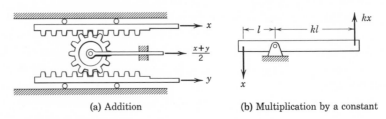

(a) Addition (b) Multiplication by a constant

Fig. 20.1 Mechanical computing elements.

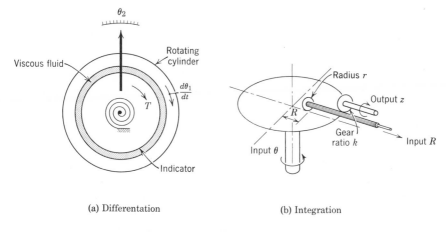

(a) Differentation   (b) Integration

Fig. 20.2 Mechanical calculating elements.

bles is more difficult. One method is to take advantage of the fact that in similar triangles $z/y = x/k$. If mechanical linkages are constrained by guides and bearings so that similar triangles are maintained, then $z = k'xy$ and the output is proportional to the product.

Mechanical differentiation of a variable with respect to time is easy if the variable can be represented by a displacement. In Fig. 20.2a the torque transmitted to the inner cylinder by the viscous fluid is proportional to the velocity of the outer cylinder and therefore to the derivative of the angular displacement. The first successful mechanical analog computers used refined versions of the simple disk-disk *integrator* in Fig. 20.2b. One input is the angular position θ (rad) of the large disk and the other is the radius R at which the small disk contacts the large one. Since $2\pi R\,d\theta = 2\pi(kr)\,dz$, the output position $Z = k'\int R\,d\theta$ and the device is an integrator.

Electromechanical. Many analog computers employ elements such as potentiometers (variable voltage dividers), recording pens, or motor drives in which signals are converted from electrical to mechanical form and vice versa. The motors used in computer mechanisms, sometimes called *instrument servos*, are designed for rapid response, high accuracy, and small size. For many purposes, the relatively slow response and high maintenance (even in well-designed units) make electromechanical devices undesirable as computing elements. In some training devices such as the space-flight simulator, however, servomechanisms are ideal to provide rolling and pitching sensations and to allow the trainee to alter the attitude of the simulator as if he were flying the spacecraft.

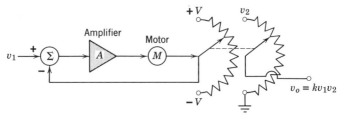

Fig. 20.3   A servomultiplier.

The *servomultiplier* of Fig. 20.3 is commonly applied in electromechanical computation at low frequencies. The control potentiometer and multiplying potentiometer are mechanically coupled and driven by a servomotor in which the output (angular position) is directly proportional to the input v_1. (How does feedback insure this relation?) The output voltage is proportional to potentiometer setting and to input v_2; therefore, $v_o = kv_1v_2$ and the device is a multiplier.

Electrical. We have already used electrical circuits for mathematical operations. Addition is accomplished easily in any linear circuit, and the primary function of a linear amplifier is to multiply by a constant. A potentiometer is simple and convenient for multiplying by an adjustable constant less than one. To multiply two variables, as in modulation, we took advantage of the nonlinear characteristic of a diode. (Could mechanical multiplication be achieved by using square-law cams in an analogous way?) Differentiation and integration are possible by using resistance and capacitance in the circuits of Figs. 13.2 and 13.3, but for precise results the operation must be restricted to the nearly straight portion of the response curves. For instrumentation we need a precise, stable device with high gain and a wide frequency response; these are the characteristics of an electronic amplifier with feedback.

Auxiliary Components

Before describing the electronic computational element we should note that a *function generator* is usually necessary to provide an input to the analog computer corresponding to the expected input to the real system. Trigonometric functions are encountered frequently and there are various methods for their generation. The *Scotch yoke* is a mechanical device for generating a sinusoidal displacement. Electronic signal generators are useful for sinewaves at ordinary frequencies and special circuits are available to generate tangents and secants. At low frequencies, motor-driven potentiometers with resistance elements tapered to give sinusoidal output voltages are useful.

Other functions can be generated mechanically by cams, noncircular gears, and various linkages. The wave-shaping properties of diode-resistance networks are useful in generating arbitrary functions (see Fig. 13.7). With the 10 diodes available in some commercial generators a wide variety of functions can be represented with errors of less than 1%. In the ingenious *photoformer*, an opaque mask is cut in the shape of the desired function and mounted between the face of a cathode-ray tube and a photocell. Using feedback control, the spot is moved along the edge of the curve and the required y-deflection voltage becomes the output of the function generator.

A *function plotter* is necessary to display the response of the analog computer. If the response can be repeated rapidly, a cathode-ray display tube is convenient. For a permanent record, a circular-chart, strip-chart, or x-y recording instrument is necessary. One problem with direct-acting instruments is that considerable energy is required to position a marking pen on the moving chart. In an indirect-acting instrument, the necessary power may be supplied through a feedback-controlled electronic amplifier. In Fig. 20.4, the input to the amplifier is the difference between v_1 and i_2R. At balance the error is zero and $i_2 = v_1/R$; therefore, the large current driving the recording instrument is directly proportional to the input signal, but little energy is required from the source.

The Operational Amplifier

The computing element in the electronic analog computer is a direct-coupled, high-gain voltage amplifier with a flat response from zero frequency to several kilocycles per second. Careful design is necessary to avoid any drift in operating point and to provide the stability essential in instrumentation. The voltage gain (assumed negative) is at least 10^5 and an odd number of stages is used to avoid oscillation due to positive feedback. A cathode-follower or emitter-follower is used in the last stage to provide a low output impedance and therefore eliminate any loading effect.

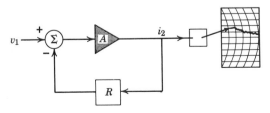

Fig. 20.4 Indirect-acting instrument with feedback.

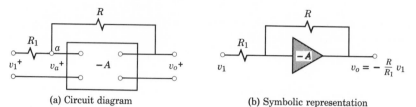

(a) Circuit diagram   (b) Symbolic representation

Fig. 20.5   Operational amplifier for multiplication by a constant.

Multiplication.   In the circuit of Fig. 20.5, block A represents the high-gain amplifier with high input impedance and low output impedance.   An input voltage v_1 is applied in series with input resistance R_1 and the feedback resistance R is connected between output and input. Because of the high input impedance to the amplifier, the amplifier input current is negligibly small.   Therefore, the input current is just equal to the feedback current and at node a we can write

$$\frac{v_1 - v_a}{R_1} + \frac{v_o - v_a}{R} = 0 \tag{20-1}$$

Since the gain of the amplifier is $-A$, $v_a = v_o/(-A)$ and Eq. 20-1 can be rewritten as

$$\frac{v_1}{R_1} + \frac{v_o}{R_1 A} + \frac{v_o}{R} + \frac{v_o}{RA} = 0 .$$

Solving for the amplifier output,

$$v_o = -\frac{v_1(R/R_1)}{1 + (1/A)(1 + R/R_1)} \tag{20-2}$$

Since A is at least 10^5 whereas R and R_1 are chosen to be of the same order of magnitude, $A \gg (1 + R/R_1)$ and the output is, with little error,

$$v_o = -\frac{R}{R_1} v_1 \tag{20-3}$$

Three mathematical operations are possible with the circuit of Fig. 20.5.

1. If $R = R_1$, the output is the negative of the input and the device is a sign changer or an *inverter.*

2. If $R/R_1 = K$, the output is the input multiplied by a constant K and the device is a *scale changer.*

3. If R and R_1 are replaced by $Z\underline{/\theta}$ and $Z\underline{/\theta_1}$, for sinusoids the gain becomes $\mathbf{G} = -\mathbf{V}_o/\mathbf{V}_1 = (-1)\underline{/\theta - \theta_1}$ and the device is a *phase shifter.*

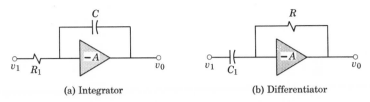

(a) Integrator   (b) Differentiator

Fig. 20.6 Electronic integration and differentiation.

Integration and Differentiation. The behavior of the operational amplifier is entirely different if the feedback element is a capacitance (Fig. 20.6a). One approach to the analysis is to use the general impedance concept. For exponentials of the form e^{st}, $Z_{R_1} = R_1$ and $Z_C = 1/sC$ and Eq. 20-3 becomes

$$v_o = - \frac{1/sC}{R_1} v_1 = - \frac{1}{R_1 C} \frac{1}{s} v_1 \qquad (20\text{-}4)$$

But $1/s$ corresponds to an integration for exponentials so the output voltage is proportional to the integral of the input or

$$v_o = - \frac{1}{R_1 C} \int v_1 \, dt \qquad (20\text{-}5)$$

and the device is an *integrator.* The same result is obtained if the current $i_R = (v_o - v_a)/R$ in Eq. 20-1 is replaced by $i_C = C d(v_o - v_a)/dt$.

Another possibility is to interchange the resistance and capacitance as in Fig. 20.6b. For exponentials $Z_{C_1} = 1/sC_1$ and $Z_R = R$ and Eq. 20-3 becomes

$$v_o = - \frac{R}{1/sC_1} v_1 = -RC_1 s v_1 = -RC_1 \frac{dv_1}{dt} \qquad (20\text{-}6)$$

and the output voltage is proportional to the derivative of the input. For practical reasons to be mentioned later, the *differentiator* is not so useful as the integrator.

Addition. If the circuit of Fig. 20.5 is modified to permit multiple inputs, the operational amplifier can perform addition. In Fig. 20.7, the

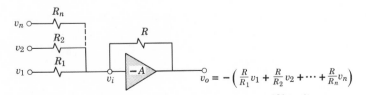

Fig. 20.7 Electronic summation.

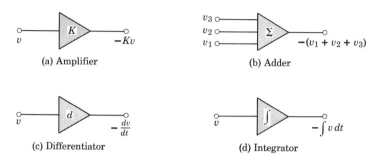

(a) Amplifier   (b) Adder

(c) Differentiator   (d) Integrator

Fig. 20.8   Symbolic representation of operational amplifiers.

input current is supplied by several voltages through separate resistances. If the input impedance of the amplifier is very high, the sum of the input currents is just equal and opposite to the feedback current or

$$\frac{v_1 - v_i}{R_1} + \frac{v_2 - v_i}{R_2} + \cdots + \frac{v_n - v_i}{R_n} = \frac{v_i - v_o}{R} \qquad (20\text{-}7)$$

Again the gain $-A$ is very large and since $v_i = v_o/(-A)$, v_i is very small compared to v_o, v_1, v_2, etc.   Neglecting v_i as before, Eq. 20-7 becomes

$$\frac{v_1}{R_1} + \frac{v_2}{R_2} + \cdots + \frac{v_n}{R_n} = -\frac{v_o}{R}$$

or

$$v_o = -\left(\frac{R}{R_1} v_1 + \frac{R}{R_2} v_2 + \cdots + \frac{R}{R_n} v_n\right) \qquad (20\text{-}8)$$

As would be expected from the theorem of superposition, the output of the amplifier is the weighted sum of the inputs or the device is an *adder*. Note that this is an analog adder in contrast to the digital adder shown in Fig. 13.24.   Note also that a signal is subtracted by first passing it through an inverter and then into an adder.   In block diagrams it is convenient to represent all operational amplifiers by the triangle symbol and designate the operations as shown in Fig. 20.8.

EXAMPLE 1

Predict the output voltage of the circuit shown in Fig. 20.9a where the block represents an ideal amplifier with A very large.

SOLUTION.   For A very large, v_i is very small and the representation as an integrator in Fig. 20.9b is accurate.   By the principle of superposition,

$$v_o = -\frac{1}{C} \int \left(\frac{v_1}{R_1} + \frac{v_2}{R_2}\right) dt = -\frac{1}{CR_1} \int \left(v_1 + v_2 \frac{R_1}{R_2}\right) dt = -\int (v_1 + 5v_2) \, dt$$

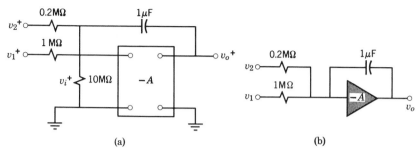

Fig. 20.9 Integration of a weighted sum.

All operational amplifiers perform inversion. In Example 1, the two input voltages provide an input current which represents a weighted sum. The combination of R and C results in integration of the weighted sum with respect to time.

THE ELECTRONIC ANALOG COMPUTER

The modern electronic analog computer is a precision instrument. Its basic purpose is to predict the behavior of a physical system which can be described by a set of algebraic or differential equations. The programming procedure is to arrange the operational amplifiers to perform the operations indicated in the describing equations and provide a means for displaying the solution.

In addition to the operational amplifiers, the practical computer includes an assortment of precision resistors and capacitors, a function generator to provide various inputs, means for introducing initial conditions, potentiometers for introducing adjustable constants, switches for controlling the operations, an oscilloscope or recorder for displaying the output, and a problem board for connecting the components in accordance with the program. In the hands of a skillful operator, the analog computer faithfully simulates the physical system, provides insight into the character of the system behavior, and permits the design engineer to evaluate the effect of changes in system parameters before an actual system is constructed

Solution by Successive Integration

In one common application the analog computer is used to solve linear integrodifferential equations. To illustrate the approach, let us predict

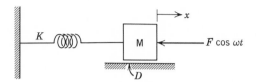

Fig. 20.10   A physical system.

the behavior of the familiar physical system shown in Fig. 20.10.   Assuming that mass is constant, that the spring is linear, and that friction force is directly proportional to velocity, the system is described by the linear differential equation

$$\Sigma f = 0 = -F \cos \omega t - M \frac{d^2x}{dt^2} - D \frac{dx}{dt} - \frac{1}{K} x \qquad (20\text{-}9)$$

The behavior of the system can be expressed in terms of displacement $x(t)$ or velocity $u(t)$ where $u = dx/dt$.   We wish to display this behavior so we proceed to program the computer to solve the equation.

The first step is to solve for the highest derivative.   Anticipating the inversion present in an operational amplifier we write

$$\frac{d^2x}{dt^2} = -\left(\frac{F}{M} \cos \omega t + \frac{D}{M} \frac{dx}{dt} + \frac{1}{KM} x\right) \qquad (20\text{-}10)$$

To satisfy this equation the mathematical operations required are: addition, integration, inversion, and multiplication by constants.   The required addition and the two integrations are shown in Fig. 20.11; in each operation there is an inversion.

The next step is to arrange the computer elements to satisfy the equation.   Knowing the required inputs to the adder, we can pick off the necessary signals (in the form of voltages) and introduce the indicated multiplication constants and inversions.   One possible program is outlined in Fig. 20.12.   Closing the circuit imposes the condition that the equation be satisfied.   A properly synchronized cathode-ray tube con-

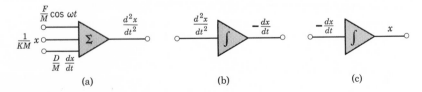

Fig. 20.11   Operations required in the solution of Eq. 20.10 by successive integration.

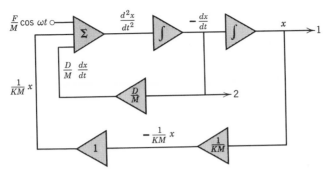

Fig. 20.12 Analog computer program for Eq. 20.10.

nected at terminal 1 would display the displacement $x(t)$. The velocity $u(t)$ is available at terminal 2, but an inversion would be necessary to change the sign. Here six operational amplifiers are indicated; by shrewd use of amplifier capabilities, the solution can be accomplished with only three operational amplifiers.

EXAMPLE 2

For the physical system in Fig. 20.10 mass $M = 1$ kg, friction coefficient $D = 0.2$ N-sec/m, and compliance $K = 2$ m/N. Devise an analog computer program using only three operational amplifiers to obtain the displacement and velocity for an applied force $f = F \cos \omega t$ N.

SOLUTION. From Example 1 we know that one operational amplifier can add and integrate the weighted sum. In this case, $M = 1$, $D/M = \frac{1}{5}$, and $1/KM = \frac{1}{2}$; after one integration Eq. 20-10 becomes

$$\frac{dx}{dt} = -\int \left(F \cos \omega t + \frac{1}{5}\frac{dx}{dt} + \frac{1}{2}x \right) dt \qquad (20\text{-}11)$$

A convenient reference is to let $RC = 1$ and specify resistances in megohms and capacitances in microfarads. For $C = 1$ μF and $R_1 = 1$ MΩ (see Fig. 20.9b), a pure integration is performed; for $R_2 = 0.2$ MΩ, v_2 has a weighting of 5 in the result. On that basis the appropriate values for Eq. 20-11 are as shown in Fig. 20.13.

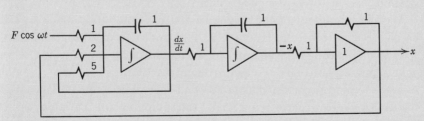

Fig. 20.13 Analog computer program for Eq. 20.11. (Resistances in MΩ and capacitances in μF.).

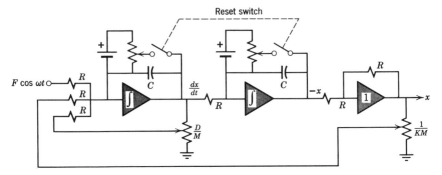

Fig. 20.14 A practical computer with provision for introducing initial conditions.

The Practical Computer

In the practical computer there are provisions and limitations which we have not considered. One provision is for inserting a variety of initial conditions. How could we impose the condition that the initial displacement in Example 2 is $X_o = 10$ m? In these programs, displacement is represented by a voltage at a particular point in the circuit. A convenient place to put an initial voltage is on a capacitor. Figure 20.9a indicates that since v_i is negligibly small because of the high gain A, the voltage across the 1-μF capacitor is just equal to v_o. An initial voltage of 10 V on the capacitor of the second integrator of Fig. 20.13 is analogous to an initial displacement of 10 m. The practical computer provides voltage sources and potentiometers (see Fig. 20.14) to introduce initial displacements or velocities by closing the *reset* switch. To *compute* the switch is opened.

Potentiometers also provide flexibility in the form of adjustable multiplying constants. By properly selecting the value of R in Fig. 20.14, the multiplying constants are less than unity and potentiometers are satisfactory. Using calibrated potentiometers, the designer has a continuous range of parameter values at his fingertips.

Another advantage of the analog computer is that the time scale can be changed at will. In Example 2, 1 second of computer time corresponds to 1 second of real time. To slow down an event which takes only a few milliseconds, we can arrange the *time scale* so that 1 millisecond of real time corresponds to 1 second of computer time. To change the time scale by a factor a, we can let the computer time variable $t_c = at$ and rewrite the differential equation. Increasing the integrator time constant RC by a factor a slows down the computer by the same factor.

Changing the time scale changes the voltage levels produced by integration and it may be necessary to modify the *amplitude scale*.

One limitation of the practical computer is that the amplifiers are linear over only a finite voltage range, usually around ± 100 V. To insure accuracy and to avoid possible damage, the amplifier outputs should never exceed the rated maximum value. On the other hand, if the signal voltage is too low at any stage, it may be masked by the *noise* voltages which are present in any electronic equipment. (One reason for preferring integration over differentiation in analog computation is that random noise voltages may have large time derivatives, while their integrated values are usually zero.) Once the time-scale factor has been established, an amplitude-scale factor can be introduced to keep signal voltages as large as possible without exceeding the rated values.

EXAMPLE 3

For the physical system in Fig. 20.10 mass $M = 1$ kg, friction coefficient $D = 2$ N-sec/m, and compliance $K = 0.0001$ m/N. Plan an analog computer program to obtain a record showing displacement and velocity for an applied force $f = -200 \cos 200t$ N.

SOLUTION. With this very stiff spring the governing equation becomes

$$\frac{d^2x}{dt^2} + 2\frac{dx}{dt} + 10{,}000x = -200 \cos 200t$$

The frequency of the applied force is 200 rad/sec or 32 cps. Reasoning by analogy from Eq. 4-24, we see that the undamped natural frequency of the system is

$$\omega_n = \frac{1}{\sqrt{KM}} = \frac{1}{\sqrt{0.0001}} = 100 \text{ rad/sec or 16 cps}$$

Because the pen recorder available will not follow such rapid variations, we wish to expand the time scale by a factor of 10. Letting computer time $t_c = 10t$, $u = dx/dt = 10\,dx/dt_c$ and $d^2x/dt^2 = 100\,d^2x/dt_c^2$. In terms of computer time,

$$100\frac{d^2x}{dt_c^2} + 20\frac{dx}{dt_c} + 5000x = -200 \cos 20t_c$$

or

$$\frac{d^2x}{dt_c^2} + 0.2\frac{dx}{dt_c} + 50x = -2 \cos 20t_c$$

The program for such a computation proceeds as in Example 2 (see Fig. 20.13). The resulting plot of displacement $x(t_c)$ must be interpreted in terms of the changed time variable.

The plot of velocity in Example 3 must be interpreted also since u_t is equal to $10u_c$. One possibility is to adjust the amplitude scale so that the output of the first integrator is $10\,dx/dt_c$ instead of dx/dt as shown in

Fig. 20.13. Since the force, velocity, and displacement are all repre-sented by voltages, provision must be made to place these at proper levels; in complicated systems, amplitude scaling becomes difficult. Fortunately, most commercial computers have overload indicators on each amplifier; the variable to any amplifier which shows overloading can be rescaled.

An interesting application of the analog computer is as a *function gener-ator*. A desired time function can be obtained as a solution to another equation. For example, the function $y = Y \cos \omega t$ can be obtained as the solution of the equation

$$\frac{d^2y}{dt^2} + \omega^2 y = 0$$

with the proper initial conditions (see Problem 3).

SUMMARY

◆ The analog computer is a flexible model of the system being studied; values are represented by continuously varying quantitie.

◆ The basic operations of addition, multiplication, differentiation, and integration can be performed by mechanical, electromechanical, elec-trical, or electronic devices, or by combinations of these.

◆ The operational amplifier, the basic element of the electronic analog computer, employs high gain and feedback to perform mathematical operations precisely. In general,

$$\frac{v_o}{v_1} = - \frac{Z(s)}{Z_1(s)}$$

where the character of Z and Z_1 determines the operation.

◆ Programming consists of arranging the operational amplifiers to per-form efficiently the operations indicated in the equations describing the system to be studied.

Integration is preferable to differentiation for practical reasons.

◆ In a practical computer there are provisions for introducing initial conditions and for adjusting parameter values.

Changes in time and amplitude scale may be necessary.

REVIEW QUESTIONS

1. What is the basic difference between digital and analog computers?
2. Sketch a simple mechanical computer for multiplying by a constant.
3. How can a variable represented by a translation be differentiated?

4. How is feedback employed in Fig. 20.3?
5. How is a nonlinear diode characteristic used in electronic multiplication?
6. What is a function generator? Why is it necessary in analog computation?
7. Explain the reasoning behind Eq. 20-1.
8. Why does $1/s$ correspond to an integration for exponentials?
9. Why is the differentiator less useful than the integrator in computation?
10. What is the difference between an analog computer and an analogous circuit on which measurements are taken?
11. Outline the procedure followed in programming an analog computer.
12. What would be needed to permit the solution of nonlinear equations?
13. What are the objectives of time scaling and amplitude scaling?

EXERCISES

1. Design and sketch a mechanical linkage employing similar triangles so that one displacement is proportional to the product of two variable displacements.
2. Explain the operations of each element in the feedback system of Fig. 20.3.
3. Assuming that means are available for obtaining $x + y$ and $x - y$ mechanically and that square-law cams can provide $z = w^2$, show mathematically how multiplication ($z = kxy$) is possible.
4. Referring to Fig. 20.5, let R_a the input resistance of the amplifier be 1 MΩ. For $R_1 = R = 1$ MΩ and $A = 10^5$, determine the error made in assuming that $v_o = -v_1(R/R_1)$.
5. In Exercise 4, it is assumed that the output impedance of the amplifier is negligible. Repeat the determination of error, using the given values and assuming $R_o = 10^3$ Ω.
6. Derive Eq. 20-5 following a general approach starting with Eq. 20-1.
7. Derive an equation in terms of s for v_o/v_i in Fig. 20.15.

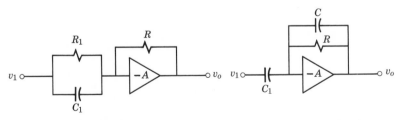

Fig. 20.15   **Fig. 20.16**

8. Derive an equation in terms of s for v_o/v_i in Fig. 20.16.
9. Draw block diagrams to show computer programs to solve the following sets of equations:

(a) $\begin{cases} 4x + 2y = 10 \\ 5x - y = 6\cos\omega t \end{cases}$ (b) $\begin{cases} x - 2y = 0 \\ 2x + y = t^2 \end{cases}$

10. Draw block diagrams to show efficient computer programs to solve the following equations:

(a) $2\dfrac{d^2x}{dt^2} + x = 4\cos \omega t$

(b) $\dfrac{d^3x}{dt^3} - 20\dfrac{dx}{dt} + x = 50$

(c) $\dfrac{d^3y}{dt^3} + 2\dfrac{d^2y}{dt^2} - 3\dfrac{dy}{dt} + y = 0$

11. Modify the diagram of Exercise 10b to provide that at $t = 0$, $x = 10$, $dx/dt = 2$, and $d^2x/dt^2 = 10$.

12. Draw block diagrams to show efficient computer programs to solve the following sets of equations:

(a) $\begin{cases} \dfrac{dx}{dt} + x - \dfrac{dy}{dt} = f(t) \\[2mm] \dfrac{dy}{dt} + 2y - 2x = 0 \end{cases}$ (b) $\begin{cases} \dfrac{dx}{dt} + 2x - 2y + 10 = 0 \\[2mm] y + \dfrac{dy}{dt} - \dfrac{dx}{dt} = \sin \omega t \end{cases}$

13. Write the equation whose analog is shown in Fig. 20.17.

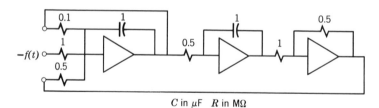

C in μF   R in MΩ

Fig. 20.17

14. Write the equation whose analog is shown in Fig. 20.18.

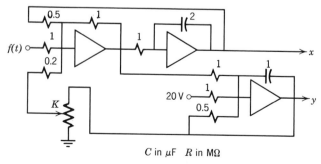

C in μF   R in MΩ

Fig. 20.18

PROBLEMS

1. An electromechanical integrator consists of an input voltage v_1, a motor which runs at a speed kv_1 and drives a tachometer which supplies an output voltage equal to $k_t \, d\theta/dt$, and a feedback circuit which insures that the tachometer output is always just equal to v_1. The motor also drives a potentiometer so that $v_o = \theta_p v_2$, where v_2 is the voltage across the potentiometer. Draw a block diagram of the integrator and demonstrate that the output is proportional to the integral of the input.

2. Devise a sweep circuit using an operational amplifier to provide an output voltage proportional to time. Show a reset switch to insure that $v_o = 0$ at $t = 0$.

3. Devise a function generator whose output is $20e^{-10t}$. Use an analog computer, programming the computer to solve an equation whose solution is the desired function. Draw a block diagram indicating the necessary input and initial conditions.

◆ **ELECTRICAL INDICATING INSTRUMENTS**
◆ **ELECTRONIC INDICATING INSTRUMENTS**
◆ **INSTRUMENTATION TRANSDUCERS**
◆ **INSTRUMENTATION SYSTEMS**

CHAPTER **21**

Instruments and Instrumentation Systems

All branches of experimental engineering depend on instrumentation. At one extreme in the scale of complexity is the mercury thermometer used in verifying a temperature. At the other extreme is the Mariner IV satellite, a space-going laboratory which after years of development, months of travel, and millions of dollars expended, sent back a few pictures of Mars as it passed by on its way into a permanent orbit around the sun.

Instruments and instrumentation systems are used for detecting, observing, measuring, controlling, computing, communicating, and displaying physical quantities. In a broad sense, instruments extend human sensing abilities by measuring more accurately, or more rapidly, or over greater ranges, or at greater distances, or by measuring quantities to which human beings are insensitive. While advances in instrumentation improve Man's control over his physical environment, they may, as in the case of automation, jeopardize his control over his social environment.

From the engineer's viewpoint, a knowledge of instrumentation principles and techniques is essential for studying the characteristics of existing devices in a test facility, for designing automatic operating and processing systems in an industrial plant, and for discovering new truths in a research laboratory. In any instrumentation system there is a flow of information in the form of signals. Because of the ease and precision with which electrical signals are processed, it is customary to convert physical variables into electrical form for measuring, communicating, and computing. The emphasis here, therefore, is on electrical instrumentation.

The information on circuits, electronic devices, electromagnetic devices, and feedback systems presented in this book provides an adequate background for the study of almost any instrumentation system. Our purpose here is to use this background in providing an introduction to instrumentation principles and techniques which will be valuable in undergraduate laboratory work, in graduate research projects, and as preparation for professional employment. The sophisticated instrumentation used in the various branches of science and engineering is highly specialized; here we can only look at a few of the more important instruments and methods.

First, we consider the basic electrical indicating instruments and their characteristics. Next, we look at the more sophisticated electronic instruments which provide greater accuracy, flexibility, or convenience. Then we study some common transducers for converting physical variables into electrical signals for processing. Finally, we consider the characteristics and components of comprehensive instrumentation systems.

ELECTRICAL INDICATING INSTRUMENTS

The d'Arsonval moving-coil mechanism (see Fig. 7.4a) is a versatile device for displaying electrical currents or other physical variables which are directly related to currents. In *indicating* instruments the moving coil carries a needle which gives a temporary indication of the current value; in *recording* instruments the moving coil actuates a pen or stylus so as to leave a permanent record.

D-C Measurements

An ordinary portable instrument may have a movement requiring about 50 μW for full-scale deflection. If many turns of fine wire are used on the moving coil, the resistance of the movement is high, but the current required for full-scale deflection, i.e. the current *sensitivity*, is low. Conversely, the coil may be of fewer turns and lower resistance, but a larger current is required for full-scale deflection. As pointed out in Chapter 17 (see Fig. 17.10), the same movement can be used for measuring current and voltage.

The Ammeter. Current in a branch is measured by an ammeter connected in series with the branch. Because the ammeter has some internal resistance, insertion of the ammeter may change the current in the

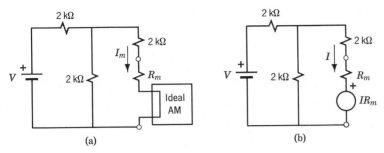

Fig. 21.1 Effect of an ammeter on a current.

branch from its original value. A useful model of a real ammeter consists of an ideal resistanceless ammeter in series with a resistance equal to the meter resistance (see Fig. 21.1a). Knowing the characteristics of the circuit, we can predict the effect of the ammeter or we can specify the maximum allowable meter resistance for a negligible effect.

EXAMPLE 1

The current in a branch of the circuit in Fig. 21.1a is to be measured by inserting a milliammeter with an estimated internal resistance $R_m = 200 \, \Omega$. The meter reads 0.937 mA. Predict the current without the ammeter.

SOLUTION. The compensation theorem† states that *the effect on any network of increasing the resistance of a branch (originally carrying a current I) by an amount R_m is the same as the effect of inserting an emf IR_m in the modified branch.* As shown in Fig. 21.1b, the voltage drop due to the insertion of the meter resistance R_m is just compensated by the addition of a fictitious emf IR_m. The increment of current due to the compensating emf is, by the theorem of superposition,

$$I_m' = \frac{IR_m}{R'} \tag{21-1}$$

where R' is the resistance seen by the ideal ammeter. The actual ammeter reading is

$$I_m = I - I_m' = I\left(1 - \frac{R_m}{R'}\right) = I\left(\frac{R' - R_m}{R'}\right) \tag{21-2}$$

and, therefore, the original current without the ammeter is

$$I = I_m\left(\frac{R'}{R' - R_m}\right) \tag{21-3}$$

---

† See p. 373 of H. H. Skilling, *Electrical Engineering Circuits*, 2nd edition, John Wiley and Sons, New York, 1965.

In this case $R' = 0.2 + 2 + (2 \times 2)/(2 + 2) = 3.2$ kΩ and

$$I = 0.937 \left(\frac{3.2}{3.2 - 0.2} \right) = 1 \text{ mA}$$

In Example 1, the insertion of the instrument introduced an error of greater than 6%. To keep this error less than 1%, Eq. 21-2 indicates that $R_m/R' \leq 0.01$ or $R_m \leq 0.01R' = 32$ Ω. A typical value for a portable 1-mA instrument might be around 25 Ω.

A circuit for a multirange ammeter is shown in Fig. 21.2a. Four shunts are available to give four ammeter ranges. A make-before-break selector switch selects the appropriate range. (Why is the make-before-break action necessary?) Initial current readings should always be made on the highest current range; a lower range can then be selected to obtain an easily read deflection.

The Voltmeter. Voltage across a branch is measured by a voltmeter in parallel with the branch. The d'Arsonval movement is converted to a voltmeter by inserting a current-limiting multiplier resistance in series with the moving coil. A 25-Ω instrument providing full-scale deflection with a current of 1 mA develops a voltage drop of $25 \times 0.001 = 0.025$ V. To convert this instrument to a 0- to 5-V voltmeter, the multiplier resistance must develop a voltage drop of $5 - 0.025 = 4.975$ V when the meter current is 1 mA. Therefore, $M = 4.975/0.001 = 4975$ Ω.

A circuit for a multirange voltmeter is shown in Fig. 21.2b. Four multiplier resistances are available to provide four voltmeter ranges. The values can be calculated from the equations

$$\frac{V_1}{I_m} = R_m + M_1 \qquad \frac{V_2}{I_m} = R_m + M_1 + M_2 \qquad (21\text{-}4)$$

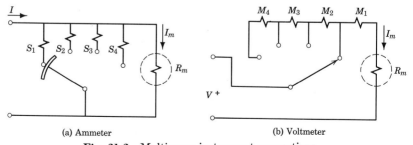

(a) Ammeter   (b) Voltmeter

Fig. 21.2 Multirange instrument connections.

and so forth. Initial voltage readings should always be made on the highest voltage range; a lower range can then be selected to obtain an easily read deflection. In a given measurement, the effect of connecting the voltmeter must be taken into account.

EXAMPLE 2

A voltmeter with a 1-mA movement (R_m = 5000 Ω on the 5-V scale) reads 2.5 V in the circuit of Fig. 21.3a. Predict the voltage without the meter.

SOLUTION. Following the same line of reasoning as in Example 1 (see Problem 1), the compensation theorem indicates that the effect of the voltmeter can be compensated by the insertion of a current source V/R_m as shown in Fig 21.3a. The actual voltmeter reading is

$$V_m = V\left(1 - \frac{R'}{R_m}\right) = V\left(\frac{R_m - R'}{R_m}\right) \qquad (21\text{-}5)$$

where R' is the resistance seen by the ideal voltmeter. Therefore, the original voltage without the voltmeter is

$$V = V_m\left(\frac{R_m}{R_m - R'}\right) \qquad (21\text{-}6)$$

In this case, R' is the equivalent resistance of the parallel combination of 2 kΩ, 2 kΩ, and 5 kΩ or R' = 0.833 kΩ and

$$V = 2.5\left(\frac{5}{5 - 0.833}\right) = 3 \text{ V}$$

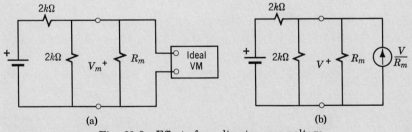

(a)   (b)

Fig. 21.3 Effect of a voltmeter on a voltage.

In Example 2 the connection of the voltmeter introduced an error of greater than 16%. To keep this error less than 1%, Eq. 21-5 indicates that $R_m/R' \geq 100$ or $R_m \geq 100R'$ = 83,300 Ω. For electronic circuit testing a typical instrument has a 50 μA movement and an internal resistance of 2000 Ω. When the proper multiplier is used to convert this instrument to a 5-V voltmeter, the effective meter resistance is $\frac{5}{50} \times 10^6$ or 100,000 Ω. When converted to a 1-mA milliammeter, the effective meter resistance is 2000 (50 μA/1 mA) = 100 Ω.

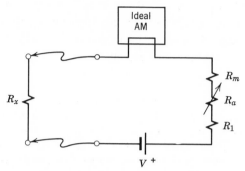

Fig. 21.4   Series-type ohmmeter.

The Ohmmeter.   A useful application of the d'Arsonval movement is in
measuring the d-c resistance of passive circuits.   A simple series-type
ohmmeter is shown in Fig. 21.4.   The battery (usually 1.5 V), a fixed
resistance R_1, and a variable "Ohms Adjust" resistor R_a are mounted
within the ohmmeter case.   With the test prods shorted, R_a is varied
until the ammeter reads full scale (usually 1 mA).   When the test prods
are across an unknown resistance R_x, the current read is less than full
scale and the meter can be calibrated to read resistance in ohms directly.
The scale is nonlinear since current is inversely proportional to the total
series resistance.

For a 1-mA movement and a 1.5-V battery, full-scale deflection corresponds to an internal resistance of 1500 Ω.   Half-scale deflection is
obtained with R_x equal to 1500 Ω; very high resistance readings are
crowded into the lower part of the scale.   To raise the resistance value
corresponding to half-scale deflection to 15,000 Ω and facilitate the reading of high resistances, a selector switch could change V to 15 V and
change the fixed resistance to R_2.   This requires a change in R_a which is
inconvenient; practical ohmmeters use a more complicated circuit† to
avoid this difficulty, but the general principle of resistance measurement
is the same.

Two precautions must be observed in using an ohmmeter.   First,
resistance measurements can only be made on passive circuits; active
sources would contribute currents which would upset the resistance-
current relation and perhaps damage the instrument.   Second, the ohmmeter should not be used to measure the resistance of elements which

---

† See Malmstadt, Enke, and Toren, *Electronics for Scientists*, W. A. Benjamin, Inc.,
New York, 1963.

would be damaged by the current employed; some semiconductor devices, meter movements, and fuses would be destroyed by a current of 1 mA or so.

The Multimeter. Since the same d'Arsonval movement can serve for current, voltage, and resistance measurements, an effective arrangement is to include shunts, multipliers, and battery in the same case along with the necessary selector switch. Such a combination volt-ohm-milliammeter (VOM) is called a *multimeter.* In addition to d-c quantities, a-c voltages can be measured by using a rectifier circuit. The precautions noted in connection with the individual instruments apply to the multimeter as well. When the multimeter is not in use, the selector switch should be turned to a high d-c voltage scale to avoid battery drain due to accidental short-circuiting of the terminals or damage of the rectifiers or movement by accidental connection to a d-c source.

Instrument Characteristics and Errors

The preceding discussion of d-c measurements provides a basis for a general description of instrument characteristics and measurement errors. The difference between the measured value and the true value of a quantity is called the *error.* Relatively constant errors which appear in all measurements in a series are called *systematic* errors; these may be due to such effects as miscalibration, nonlinearities, zero shift, or observer bias. Variable or accidental errors which appear in certain measurements are called *random* errors; these may be due to such effects as bearing stickiness, observer mistake, or to unknown causes.

No physical measurement is without error. The *accuracy* of a measurement is the ratio of the error in the measured value to the true value (usually defined by a more accurate measurement which in turn includes some error) and is usually expressed in percent. In producing a voltmeter with a specified accuracy of 0.5% of full scale, the manufacturer employs designs, fabrication processes, and testing procedures which insure that a certain fraction, say 98%, of all voltmeters produced are within the specified accuracy. The term *precision* is defined as a measure of the reproducibility of independent measurements by the same instrument and is not to be confused with accuracy.†

In making any measurement there is always some effect on the quantity being measured. For an accurate measurement of an electrical quan-

---

† For a more complete discussion see Ernest Frank: *Electrical Measurement Analysis,* McGraw-Hill Book Co., New York, 1959.

tity there are two possible approaches.   One is to make the measurement and then correct for the disturbance due to measuring.   The other is to make the measurement in such a way that the effect on the measured quantity is less than a certain acceptable amount.

Examples 1 and 2 illustrate these approaches.   Using the compensation theorem, the effect of connecting an ammeter or voltmeter can be estimated and the indicated current or voltage can be corrected.   This approach has wide application throughout engineering and science. Knowing the parameters of the circuit and the effect of connecting an ammeter or voltmeter, we can specify the characteristics of the measuring instrument.   From the examples we conclude that for negligible error an ammeter should have a low resistance compared to that seen by an ideal ammeter inserted at the same point and a voltmeter should have a high resistance compared to that seen by an ideal voltmeter connected to the same terminals.

There are other instrument characteristics which require attention but can only be mentioned here.   Since the *response* of an instrument is never instantaneous, the indicated value is never the true value when a variable is changing.   The time *lag* is dependent on the natural frequency of the instrument and the degree of damping.   Some instruments are subject to *hysteresis;* the response to a given signal depends on the previous condition.   Also there may be a slow change in properties with time, called *drift*, which influences the calibration.   Freedom from the influence of environmental conditions such as temperature or humidity is referred to as *stability*.

A-C Measurements

In the *iron-vane* instrument (see Fig. 17.20a), the developed torque is proportional to the square of the current and therefore alternating currents can be measured.   In the *thermocouple* instrument, a d'Arsonval movement is used to measure the emf generated at a junction of dissimilar materials; since the emf is dependent on the temperature rise which is nearly proportional to the square of the current flowing through the junction, the instrument can be calibrated in terms of rms currents.

Electrodynamometer Instruments.   In the *electrodynamometer* instrument (see Fig. 7.4b), the developed torque is proportional to the product of the current in a fixed coil and the current in the moving coil.   In an ammeter the same current flows in both coils and the torque is proportional to the square of the current; the inertia of the movement performs an averaging function and the indication is a true rms value.   In a watt-

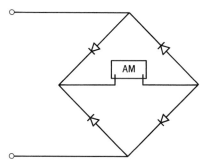

Fig. 21.5 Rectifier-type instrument.

meter the current in one coil is proportional to the instantaneous current and the current in the other coil is proportional to the instantaneous voltage; the torque is proportional to the instantaneous power and the indication is proportional to the average power. Electrodynamometer instruments are useful for accurate measurements at frequencies up to a few hundred cycles per second.

Rectifier Instruments. Semiconductor diodes can be used to convert alternating current to direct current which is measured by a d'Arsonval movement. In the full-wave bridge circuit of Fig. 21.5, an alternating current at the terminals produces a unidirectional current through the moving coil and the deflection is proportional to the average current. These instruments are calibrated on sinusoidal waves to read rms values. Since the rms value of the sinusoid is $0.707/0.636 = 1.11$ times the average value, the instrument indicates 1.11 times the average value of the rectified waveform of any applied current. It is accurate for sinusoids only; for any other waveform a correction must be applied.

EXAMPLE 3

A rectifier-type ammeter indicates a current of "2.22 A rms" when measuring the triangular wave of Fig. 21.6. Estimate the peak and rms value of the current.

SOLUTION. This instrument indicates 1.11 times the average of the rectified wave; therefore, the average is

$$I_{av} = \frac{2.22}{1.11} = 2 \text{ A}$$

and the peak value for the triangular wave is

$$I_{pk} = 2I_{av} = 4 \text{ A}$$

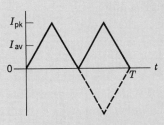

Fig. 21.6 Triangular wave.

The rms value is

$$I_{\text{rms}} = \sqrt{\frac{1}{T}\int_0^T i^2\,dt} = \sqrt{\frac{I_{\text{pk}}^2}{3}} = \sqrt{\frac{16}{3}} = 2.31\ \text{A}$$

For triangular waves the reading is approximately 4% low.

ELECTRONIC INDICATING INSTRUMENTS

The availability of stable, high-gain electronic amplifiers whose characteristics are known precisely has contributed greatly to the art of instrumentation.   One reason for using amplifiers is to reduce the power required from the system under observation; the power required to drive the indicating or recording instrument is provided by the amplifier.   A related advantage is that the input impedance of a vacuum-tube voltmeter, for example, can be millions of ohms instead of the few thousand ohms of a d'Arsonval instrument.   Another reason is that electronic devices can follow signal variations at frequencies of many megacycles per second.   Amplifiers are particularly valuable when the signal being measured is very small and might be lost in the *noise* generated by extraneous sources; a high *signal-to-noise ratio* is essential for accurate instrumentation or precise control.

The Vacuum-Tube Voltmeter

By using a negative-grid vacuum tube as an amplifier, a voltage can be measured with negligible loading effect.   In such a *vacuum-tube voltmeter* (VTVM), the voltage being measured is applied to the grid and the resulting change in plate current can be used to actuate a d'Arsonval movement (see Fig. 11.5a).   Because of the importance of this instrument, highly refined circuits have been developed to provide accuracy, flexibility, and stability.

One ingenious arrangement is the basic d-c vacuum-tube voltmeter circuit shown in Fig. 21.7b.   In this balanced d-c amplifier, the tubes and components are matched so that the only current flowing in the ammeter is due to the *difference* between input voltages V_1 and V_2; all quiescent effects are balanced out.   For VTVM application, the input to the second tube is short-circuited so that V_2 is zero; I_m is determined by V_1 and can be calibrated to read V_1 in volts.

To measure alternating voltages, a diode clamper is used (see explanation accompanying Fig. 13.8).   In Fig. 21.7a, capacitor C tends to charge up to the positive peak value V_s of the input voltage.   The diode

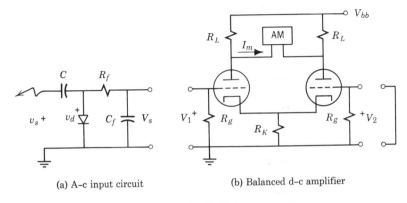

(a) A-c input circuit   (b) Balanced d-c amplifier

Fig. 21.7 Basic VTVM components.

voltage v_d is then equal to $v_s - V_s$ or the clamper output contains a d-c component equal to the peak value of the input. The combination of R_f and C_f is a filter which removes the a-c component, and d-c voltage V_1 is applied to the amplifier. This type of VTVM responds to peak values but is calibrated to read rms values of sinusoids; in other words, the meter indication is 0.707 times the positive peak value of the input. On other than sinusoids, a correction must be applied.

EXAMPLE 4

The triangular current wave of Example 3 indicated "2.22 A rms" on a rectifier-type ammeter. Predict the indication on a peak-responding VTVM connected across a 1-Ω resistor carrying this current.

SOLUTION. The peak value of the triangular voltage wave is $I_{pk}R = 4 \times 1 = 4$ V and the VTVM indicates 0.707 times the peak value or

$$V = 0.707 \times V_{pk} = 0.707 \times 4 = 2.83 \text{ V}$$

The rms value is 2.31 V (see Example 3); therefore, for triangular waves the indication is approximately 22% high.

On a commercial VTVM a switch converts the instrument from d-c to a-c operation. The input impedance is 10 megohms or more and remains constant up to frequencies of 5 megacycles or greater. For measuring small signals at high frequencies, the input diode is placed in the test probe itself and the effect of the capacitance of the leads is minimized.

The Cathode-Ray Oscilloscope

The cathode-ray tube (see Figs. 9.7, 9.8, and 9.9) provides a controlled spot of light where the electron beam strikes the fluorescent screen. The deflections of the spot are directly proportional to the voltages on the

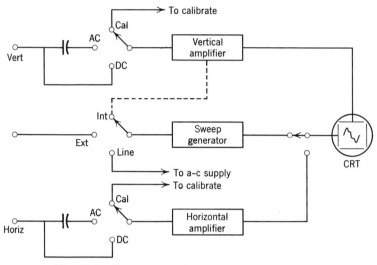

Fig. 21.8   Components of a cathode-ray oscilloscope.

horizontal and vertical deflecting plates. The *intensity* of the spot is determined by the accelerating potentials in the electron gun, and the *focus* is determined by the potentials on the focusing electrodes. ' The cathode-ray oscilloscope (CRO), consisting of the tube and appropriate auxiliary apparatus, is a precise and flexible laboratory instrument. The input impedance may be many megohms and the frequency response may extend to many megacycles.

The block diagram of Fig. 21.8 indicates the essential components. A signal applied to the "Vert" terminal causes a proportional vertical deflection of the spot; the calibration of the *vertical amplifier* can be checked against an internal calibrating signal. The *sweep generator* causes a horizontal deflection of the spot proportional to time; it is *triggered* to start at the left of the screen at a particular instant on the internal vertical signal ("Int"), an external signal ("Ext"), or the a-c supply ("Line"). Instead of the sweep generator, the *horizontal amplifier* can be used to cause a deflection proportional to a signal at the "Horiz" terminal.

Voltage Measurement. An illuminated scale dividing the screen into 1-cm divisions permits use of the CRO as a voltmeter. With the vertical amplifier sensitivity set at 0.1 V/cm, say, a displacement of 2.5 cm indicates a voltage of 0.25 V. Currents can be determined by measuring the voltage across a known resistance.

Time Measurement. A calibrated sweep generator permits time measurement. With the sweep generator set at 5 cm/msec, two events separated on the screen by 2 cm are separated in time by 0.4 msec.

Waveform Display. A special property of the CRO is its ability to display high-frequency or short-duration waveforms. With the sweep generator synchronized with a periodic input waveform, the repeated displays are superimposed and a stationary pattern is obtained. A *blanking circuit* turns off the electron beam at the end of the sweep so the return trace is not visible. Nonrepetitive voltages are made more visible by using a long persistence fluorescent material or a high-speed camera can be used for a permanent record.

X-Y Plotting. The relation between two periodic variables can be displayed by applying a voltage proportional to x to the horizontal amplifier and one proportional to y to the vertical amplifier. The characteristics of diodes or transistors are quickly displayed in this way. The hysteresis loop of a magnetic material can be displayed by connecting the induced emf (proportional to B) to the vertical amplifier and an iR drop (proportional to H) to the horizontal amplifier. Since the two amplifiers usually have a common internal ground, some care is necessary in arranging the circuits.

Phase-Difference Measurement. If two sinusoids of the same frequency are connected to the X and Y terminals, the phase difference is revealed by the resulting pattern. For voltages $v_x = V_x \cos \omega t$ and $v_y = V_y \cos (\omega t + \theta)$, it can be shown that the phase difference is

$$\theta = \sin^{-1} \frac{A}{B} \tag{21-7}$$

where A is the y deflection when the x deflection is zero and B is the

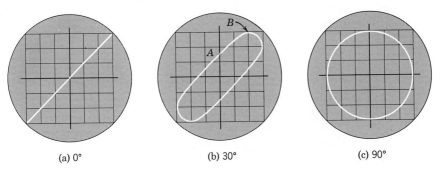

(a) 0°   (b) 30°   (c) 90°

Fig. 21.9 Phase difference as revealed by CRO patterns.

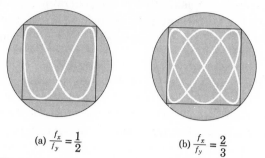

(a) $\dfrac{f_x}{f_y} = \dfrac{1}{2}$　　　　　　　　(b) $\dfrac{f_x}{f_y} = \dfrac{2}{3}$

Fig. 21.10 Lissajous figures for frequency comparison.

maximum y deflection.   The parameters of the circuit are useful in determining whether the angle is leading or lagging.

Frequency Comparison.   When the frequency of the sinusoid applied to one input is an exact multiple of the frequency of the other input, a stationary pattern is obtained.   For a 1:1 ratio, the so-called Lissajous patterns are similar to those in Fig. 21.9.   For 1:2 and 2:3 ratios, the Lissajous figures might be as shown in Fig. 21.10.   For a stationary pattern, the ratio of the frequencies is exactly equal to the ratio of the number of tangencies to the enclosing rectangle.   Patterns can be predicted by plotting x and y deflections from the two signals at corresponding instants of time.

The Electronic Counter

A recent instrumentation development of great value is the electronic counter diagrammed in Fig. 21.11.   The events to be counted—meteorites, heartbeats, or revolutions—are transduced into electrical signals which are then transformed into sharp pulses.   A precision time base is established, perhaps by a controlled oscillator, and used to open and close the gate to the cascaded scale-of-ten counters for display.   The counters consist of four flip-flops (see Example 4 in Chapter 13) with feedback loops to convert from a scale-of-sixteen to a decimal scale.   In counting, the gate is held open for a precise fraction of a second, the events are counted, and then the gate is closed and the total count displayed.

The same unit can be adapted to measure the elapsed time between similar events.   In this mode of operation, an event is used to open the gate and the cycles of the timing generator are counted until the next event closes the gate.   In this manner the period of an electrical signal can be counted by determining the time between corresponding points on the wave.   If the timing generator operates at a frequency of 10 Mc

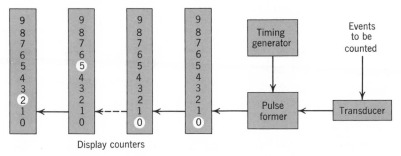

Display counters

Fig. 21.11 Elements of an electronic counting system.

(accurate to ± 1 cps), and if 2500 pulses are counted during a given time interval, the time interval is 0.0002500 sec. If this represents the period of a sine wave, the frequency is 4000 cps and the counter is performing frequency measurement.

INSTRUMENTATION TRANSDUCERS

The convenience of the vacuum-tube voltmeter, the versatility of the cathode-ray oscilloscope, and the speed and precision of the electronic counter are available for measuring any physical variable which can be transduced to electrical form. The *transducers* or *sensors* employ a great variety of physicoelectric phenomena, but they can be classified into two general categories.

Active Transducers

A sensing element which generates an emf or current is called an *active transducer*. The electrical power generated may be sufficient to drive a d'Arsonval movement as in the case of a thermocouple, or it may be so minute that special high-impedance amplifiers must be used as in the case of the pH probe. Useful active transducers include the following.

Thermoelectric. The emf developed across a junction of two dissimilar materials is a sensitive function of temperature. If a circuit contains two junctions at different temperatures, a net emf is developed. In practice, the reference junction is maintained at a known temperature and the other junction is exposed to the temperature to be measured (see Fig. 21.12). For commercial *thermocouples* tables are available for direct conversion of the observed emf to the corresponding temperature difference. Thermocouples are rugged and accurate, but the fairly long response time constant prevents accurate measurement of rapidly changing temperatures.

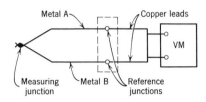

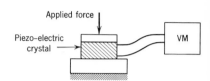

Fig. 21.12 Thermocouple circuit.   **Fig. 21.13** Piezoelectric transducer.

Piezoelectric. Certain crystalline materials, natural and synthetic, develop an emf when they are deformed. This *piezoelectric* effect is used in microphones and phonograph pickups and also in instruments measuring displacement or pressure (see Fig. 21.13). The small size and very good high-frequency response of crystal elements make them valuable in dynamic measurements.

Photoelectric. The sensitivity of cathode surfaces and semiconductor junctions to illumination permits the use of *phototubes* and *photojunction cells* as optical transducers. In the phototube, incident photons cause the emission of electrons with sufficient energy to move to the anode and contribute to an external current. In the photojunction cell, high-energy photons create electron-hole pairs in the depletion region and contribute to an external current just as in the solar cell (see Fig. 14.3).

Electromagnetic. The moving coil in a magnetic field employed in the dynamic microphone (see Example 2 in Chapter 17) is a velocity-sensitive transducer. Linear displacement and acceleration measurements can be obtained by electronically integrating and differentiating the output of a velocity transducer.

Angular velocity can be measured by using d-c or a-c *tachometer* generators with permanent magnets; the generated emf is directly proportional to the velocity. The output of an a-c tachometer is usually rectified and measured on a d-c instrument. Another method of measuring angular velocity is shown in Fig. 21.14. The projecting teeth vary the reluctance

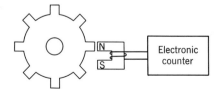

Fig. 21.14 Electromagnetic revolution counter.

in the air gap of the permanent magnet, inducing pulses which are counted by an electronic counter.

Passive Sensors

Any physical effect which changes an electrical circuit parameter can be used in sensing. In such *passive sensors* a source of electrical energy must be available.

Resistance. The resistance of a conductor may be affected by temperature, mechanical strain, or illumination. The *resistance thermometer* is widely used for precise continuous and remote temperature measurement. The *hot-wire anemometer* uses a variable resistance to measure the velocity of the air stream in which it is immersed. A fine wire is heated by an electric current and the voltage drop observed; the voltage and the resistance are dependent on wire temperature which is governed by the cooling effect of the moving air. In the *strain gauge*, stretching a fine wire increases its length, reduces its cross section, and changes its conductivity; the resulting change in resistance is approximately proportional to the strain. In the *photoconductive cell* an increase in illumination increases the rate of generation of electron-hole pairs and increases the conductivity. In the circuit of Fig. 21.15, the voltage-divider is adjusted until the transistor is cut off with the photoconductive cell dark; illumination results in a change in emitter-base bias and a large increase in collector current.

Inductance. The common *variable reluctance* sensor uses the displacement of a magnetic armature to change the reluctance and thereby alter the self-inductance of a coil. Any quantity such as force, pressure,

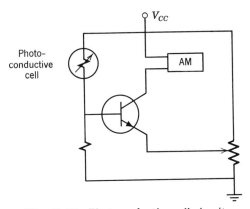

Fig. 21.15   Photoconductive cell circuit.

acceleration, or velocity which can be converted to a displacement can be measured indirectly. A unique application is the measurement of the thickness of paint on magnetic materials; when the U-shaped core is placed on a flat surface, the paint forms two gaps in the magnetic circuit. In the important *differential transformer* (discussed in the following section), mutual inductance is varied by the displacement of a magnetic core linking two coils.

Capacitance. The capacitance of a parallel-plate unit is dependent on the plate separation and the dielectric material. In the *capacitance pressure* sensor (Fig. 21.16a), a variation in pressure flexes a conducting diaphragm and decreases its separation from a fixed plate. In the *liquid level gauge* (Fig. 21.16b), the liquid has access to the space between two parallel plates; since the dielectric constant of the liquid differs from that of air, the capacitance of the unit is a function of liquid height. The variation in capacitance can be used to change the response of a parallel circuit as shown in Fig. 21.16c or change the frequency of a resonant circuit.

Bridge Measurements

With a passive sensor, an external electrical source is required. One possibility with a resistance thermometer, for example, is to use a d-c supply and measure the change in current resulting from the change in resistance (as in the ohmmeter). But when the expected change in current is small, even a good ammeter cannot provide an accurate measurement. For accurate measurement of passive elements, the *bridge* circuit is an excellent arrangement.

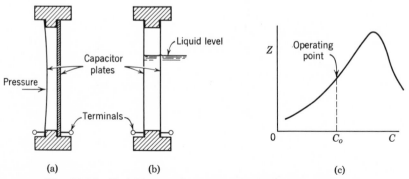

Fig. 21.16   Variable-capacitance transducers and characteristic.

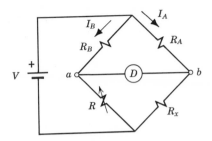

Fig. 21.17 Wheatstone bridge.

The Wheatstone Bridge. In the basic Wheatstone bridge shown in Fig. 21.17, R_A, R_B, and R are standard resistances, and R_x is the resistance to be measured. The *null detector* D is a sensitive galvanometer which reads zero when the bridge is *balanced*. At balance there is no current from a to b; therefore, nodes a and b are at the same potential and

$$I_A R_A = I_B R_B$$
$$I_A R_x = I_B R \tag{21-8}$$

Dividing the first equation by the second and solving,

$$R_x = R \frac{R_A}{R_B} \tag{21-9}$$

The three standard resistances are known within about 0.01%, so if the null point is established precisely, the unknown resistance can be measured with a high degree of accuracy. Modifications of this basic bridge circuit provide for measurement of large and small resistances and of small changes in resistance such as those encountered in strain gauge measurements. Note that balance is independent of the applied voltage; a stable, precisely known voltage is not required. If an a-c source is used, the detector can be an earphone. The combination of a simple transistor and an earphone can provide the same sensitivity as an expensive galvanometer.

EXAMPLE 5

An unknown resistance is measured on a Wheatstone bridge and a null is obtained with $R_A = 500\ \Omega$, $R_B = 5000\ \Omega$, and $R = 270.4\ \Omega$. The fixed resistors are accurate within $\pm 0.01\%$ and the variable resistor within $\pm 0.02\%$. Determine the unknown resistance.

SOLUTION. Assuming the null point is precisely determined, from Eq. 21-9,

$$R_x = R \frac{R_A}{R_B} = 270.4(1 \pm 0.0002) \frac{500(1 \pm 0.0001)}{5000(1 \pm 0.0001)}$$

The worst case is that in which R and R_A are in error in one direction and R_B in the other. In this case the errors add and

$$R_x = 27.04(1 \pm 0.0004) = 27.04 \pm 0.01\ \Omega$$

In computing errors, as in Example 5, two approximate formulas are useful. For x, y, and z very small compared to 1,

$$(1 + x)(1 + y) = 1 + x + y + xy \cong 1 + x + y$$

and

$$\frac{1}{1 + z} = (1 + z)^{-1} = 1 - z + z^2 - \cdots \cong 1 - z \tag{21-10}$$

The Impedance Bridge. The same bridge circuit can be arranged to measure impedances as shown in Fig. 21.18. Here a null is obtained when

$$\mathbf{Z}_x = \mathbf{Z} \frac{R_A}{R_B} \tag{21-11}$$

Since $\mathbf{Z}_x = R_x - j(1/\omega C_x)$, Eq. 21-11 is satisfied only if

$$R_x = R \frac{R_A}{R_B} \quad \text{and} \quad C_x = C \frac{R_B}{R_A} \tag{21-12}$$

In words, the real and imaginary components of impedance must balance separately.

In deriving Eqs. 21-12 it is assumed that the unknown consists·of a series combination of R_x and C_x. Various forms of the basic bridge have been invented to measure unknown impedances accurately and conveniently. In the *Maxwell bridge* of Fig. 21.19, a standard capacitor C permits the measurement of an unknown inductive impedance. It can be shown (see Exercise 16) that the balance equations for this circuit are:

$$R_x = R \frac{R_A}{R_B} \quad \text{and} \quad L_x = C_B R R_A \tag{21-13}$$

This is convenient because standard fixed capacitors are less expensive than standard variable inductors.

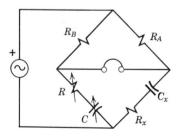

Fig. 21.18 Impedance bridge.

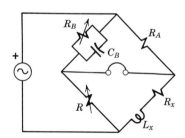

Fig. 21.19 Maxwell bridge.

Dynamic Bridge Response. The null method works well in making static measurements, but it cannot be used in measuring rapidly changing parameters. In determining the dynamic stresses in a structure, using strain gauges, for example, a practical method is to balance a Wheatstone bridge under static conditions and then use the unbalanced bridge as a dynamic transducer. A convenient approach is to represent the bridge by a Thévenin equivalent circuit.

For the special case of $R_A = R_B = R$, the Wheatstone bridge is as shown in Fig. 21.20. To determine the signal voltage v due to a very small resistance change ΔR, we note that

$$V_1 = \frac{R}{2R} V = \frac{V}{2}$$

and

$$V_2 = \frac{R + \Delta R}{R + R + \Delta R} V = \frac{V}{2} \frac{1 + \Delta R/R}{1 + \Delta R/2R} = \frac{V}{2} \frac{1 + \delta}{1 + \delta/2}$$

where $\delta = \Delta R/R$ the fractional unbalance. Using Eqs. 21-10,

$$V_2 \cong \frac{V}{2} (1 + \delta) \left(1 - \frac{\delta}{2}\right) \cong \frac{V}{2} \left(1 + \frac{\delta}{2}\right)$$

and

$$v = V_2 - V_1 \cong \frac{V}{2} \left(1 + \frac{\delta}{2}\right) - \frac{V}{2} = V \cdot \frac{\delta}{4} = \frac{V}{4} \frac{\Delta R}{R} \qquad (21\text{-}14)$$

The resistance looking into the bridge with the source voltage removed is just $2(R/2) = R$ and the Thévenin equivalent is as shown in Fig. 21.20b. The output signal is small, but it is easily amplified and recorded or displayed on an oscilloscope. Another possibility is to excite the bridge with a high-frequency a-c source; in this case the output is an amplitude-modulated wave particularly well-suited to telemetering. The dynamic stresses in a manned spacecraft during take-off can be measured in this way.

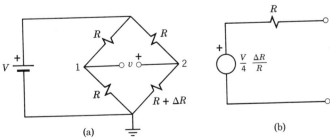

Fig. 21.20 Unbalanced bridge and Thévenin equivalent.

Potentiometer Measurements

In bridge measurements an unknown impedance is compared to a standard. The same approach is employed in the analytical balance where an unknown weight is compared to a standard weight under conditions of balance. Such *comparison methods* are capable of great accuracy and are widely used in science and engineering. The *potentiometer*† is a useful instrument for measuring voltages by comparison and is frequently used in conjunction with active transducers.

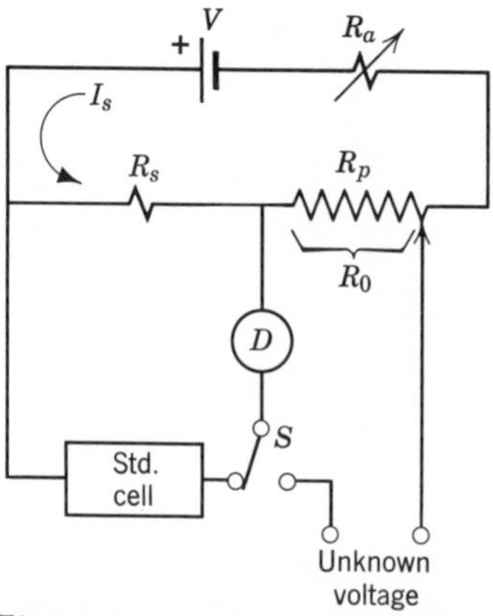

The Slide-Wire Potentiometer. If an accurately known voltage is connected across a linear resistance, such as a uniform wire, a variable standard voltage is available for comparison with an unknown. One practical form of this arrangement is shown in Fig. 21.21. A source V supplies a standard current I_s through a uniform potentiometer resistance R_p, an adjustable resistance R_a, and a standard resistance R_s. A *standard cell* provides a precisely known emf V_s when no current is drawn. To set the current to the standard value, switch S is placed in the position shown, and R_a is adjusted until detector D indicates that $I_s R_s$ is equal to the emf of the standard cell.

Fig. 21.21 Slidewire potentiometer.

With $I_s = V_s/R_s$ accurately known, the potentiometer voltage $V_0 = I_s R_0$ is determined solely by the position of the sliding contact. To measure an unknown voltage, switch S is thrown and the sliding contact is moved until the detector indicates a null. In practical form, R_p is a compact multiturn resistance with a continuously variable tap; the dial is calibrated to read voltage directly. For greater accuracy a series combination of fixed and variable resistances is used for R_p. For greater convenience the voltage source V can be replaced by a Zener-diode regulated voltage supply and the standard cell omitted.

Self-Balancing Potentiometer. For automatic control and continuous recording the self-balancing potentiometer is widely used. In the simpli-

---

† Here *potentiometer* refers to a measuring instrument employing a voltage divider; the voltage divider itself is also called a potentiometer.

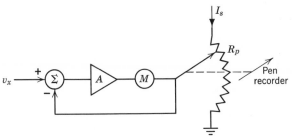

Fig. 21.22   Self-balancing potentiometer.

fied block diagram of Fig. 21.22, the difference between the input voltage
and the potentiometer voltage is amplified and used to drive the bal-
ancing motor M. Rotation of the motor shaft is always in such a direction as to decrease the unbalance between the potentiometer voltage and
the voltage being measured. When the system is in balance, the position
of the shaft indicates the input voltage (from a thermocouple, for example) and the pen provides a record (of temperature) on a strip chart. In
one type of X-Y recorder, self-balancing potentiometers provide vertical
and horizontal deflections proportional to input voltages corresponding
to the two variables being plotted on the stationary paper.

The Strain-Gauge Transducer

Two passive transducers are used so widely that they deserve further
discussion. One is the *bonded resistance strain gauge* consisting of a grid
of fine resistance wire cemented or bonded to a thin paper backing (Fig.
21.23). When the gauge is cemented to a structural member under test,
any deformation of the member results in a change in dimensions and
therefore a change in resistance of the gauge. The relation between
strain ϵ and resistance change is

$$\epsilon = \frac{\Delta l}{l} = K_g \frac{\Delta R}{R} \qquad (21\text{-}15)$$

where K_g is the gauge factor. For most metallic elements the gauge
factor is between 2 and 4; semiconductor strain gauges are available with
gauge factors of several hundred.

Since the strain $\Delta l/l$ is usually very small, the change in resistance is
small and bridge methods are indicated. In the arrangement shown in
Fig. 21.23c, R_x is the resistance of the gauge. If the bridge is initially
balanced with standard resistance R_s, the change in gauge resistance is

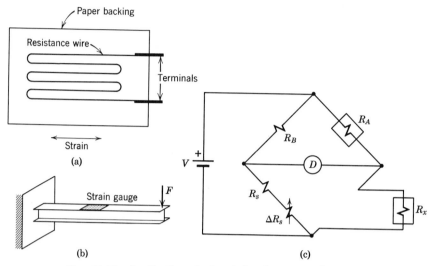

Fig. 21.23   Application of a bonded resistance strain gauge.

measured accurately by the resistance ΔR_s needed for rebalancing after strain occurs.

One problem is that the bridge cannot distinguish between changes in resistance due to strain and those due to temperature changes. The effect of temperature can be reduced by using materials having very low temperature coefficients of resistance. A clever arrangement is to use for R_A an unstressed dummy gauge exposed to the same temperature as R_x. Another possibility is to mount the second gauge symmetrically with respect to the first so that when one is in tension the other is in compression. The effects of temperature and gauge lead wire are cancelled out and the sensitivity of the bridge is doubled. (How would such an arrangement effect the Thévenin equivalent circuit of Fig. 21.20b?)

Although the strain gauge is directly responsive to small displacements, it can be used for indirect measurement of other variables, such as pressure or acceleration, which can produce strain in an auxiliary mechanism. In wind-tunnel tests of aircraft models, for example, the model is supported by a beam or *sting* with several degrees of freedom. Strain gauges properly placed on the beam permit the determination of lift, drag, and lateral forces and roll, pitch, and yaw torques.

The Differential Transformer

Another very useful device for conversion of mechanical displacements into electrical signals is the *linear differential transformer* shown in Fig.

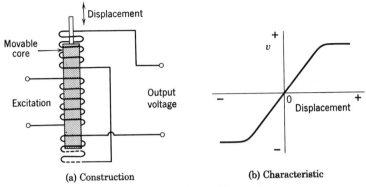

(a) Construction   (b) Characteristic

Fig 21.24 The differential transformer.

21.24. The transformer consists of a primary and two identical secondaries connected in series opposition. With the freely moving iron core in dead center, the voltages induced in the two secondaries just cancel and the output is zero. An upward displacement increases the coupling with the upper secondary and decreases the coupling with the lower secondary. A downward displacement produces the opposite effect. The result is an output voltage dependent upon core position.

The differential transformer is a low-impedance device producing an output of several volts. With proper design the output voltage is a linear function of displacement over a range which may be a few microinches or several inches. This transducer is particularly useful in measuring displacements larger than those for which the strain gauge is suitable. With appropriate auxiliary mechanisms it can be used to measure velocity, acceleration, force, pressure, liquid level, or rate of flow.

INSTRUMENTATION SYSTEMS

An instrumentation system is an assemblage of components arranged to perform an overall measurement function. But the components must not only perform their individual functions well, they must also work effectively with the associated components. In this sense an instrumentation system is more than the sum of its parts.

System Aspects

In an instrumentation system there is a flow of information in the form of signals. Systems are usually characterized by size and complexity, and in a typical instrumentation system the signals may be transformed many times and into many forms.   For example, pressure may affect the position of a diaphragm, whose movement changes the mutual inductance in a differential transformer and modulates the excitation voltage, which controls the frequency of a carrier current, which creates an electromagnetic wave which is radiated through space.   After transmission, reception, and demodulation, the resulting current may deflect a galvanometer, which moves a light beam across photographic paper and leaves a record in the form of a chemical change.

Each component modifies the signal.   The signal may deteriorate as a result of time lag or distortion, or the information content may be enhanced by amplification or filtering.   For maximum power transfer or optimum response the components must be matched.   If the system is to supply data to or receive instructions from a human being, its design must reflect the physical, physiological, and psychological characteristics of the operator.   The decision speed, reaction time, and susceptibility to fatigue of human operators are particularly important when the cost of error is high and the margin of safety is low, as in the control of aircraft or spacecraft.   Where a human serves as a link in an instrumentation system, the color of a dial, the shape of a knob, or the pitch of a warning signal may be a critical design element.

Sensors and Transducers

In describing the components of a general data-acquisition system (see Fig. 21.25), let us start with the sensors which detect and respond to the physical variables to be measured.   The essential characteristic of a good sensor is that it responds in a predictable and useful way to the quantity being observed; for example, a bimetallic strip bends a known amount in response to a given change in temperature.   As mentioned previously, many different physical phenomena are employed in sensors.

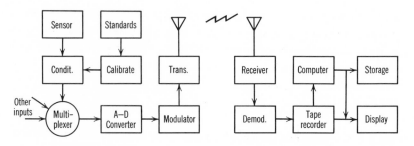

Fig. 21.25   A data-acquisition and reduction system.

Usually we want the response in the form of an electrical signal. The combination of a bimetallic strip and the contacts of an electrical switch provides such an electrical output. In addition to the active transducers previously described, passive sensors such as strain gauges and differential transformers can provide electrical outputs when properly excited. So-called *conditioning equipment* includes the power supplies for bridges, the excitation carriers for differential transformers, the voltage references for potentiometers, and the temperature controlling devices for thermocouples.

Calibrating Equipment

An important part of the "count-down" in a missile firing or any other comprehensive test is the calibration of the sensing elements. Calibration usually involves comparison against a standard. Standards of great precision are available for time, frequency, and voltage. *Atomic clocks* employing the natural resonance frequency of excited atoms keep time with less than 0.01 sec deviation per year. The National Bureau of Standards broadcasts over station WWV time signals accurate to 1 μ sec and audio frequencies accurate to 1 part in 50 million. The primary standard of voltage in this country is a group of 47 Weston cells with a precision of the order of 1 μV.

In the calibration procedure, a series of standard inputs is applied to each channel of the data-acquisition system. The responses are recorded and provide the basis for calibration. Sensing elements which cannot be calibrated in position are periodically calibrated in a testing laboratory and before and after critical measurements.

Analog-to-Digital Converters

Digital signals are less susceptible than analog signals to deterioration by noise or stray pickup or by attenuation in long cables and radio links. Since each binary digit or *bit* of information exists in one of only two states, rather large changes in waveform or amplitude can be tolerated without loss of information. Another reason for converting signals from analog sensors into digital form is to obtain data acceptable to digital computers.

A direct method of converting analog to digital numbers is the shaft position *encoder* shown in Fig. 21.26. The conducting pattern in contact with the brushes provides the code which changes as the commutator position (the analog quantity) changes. In the position shown, the brushes are in contact with segments corresponding to 16, 8, and 2 outputs so the total read-out number is 26. Commercial encoders are avail-

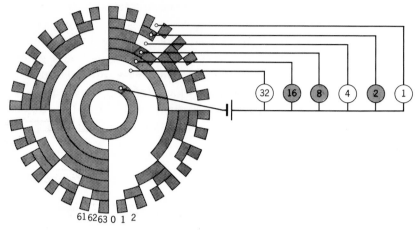

61 6263 0 1 2

Fig. 21.26   Analog-to-binary encoder reading 26.

able which provide over 1000 positions per revolution.   As the commutator rotates, there are positions of ambiguity where brushes of finite
width give misleading indications.   Several arrangements have been
devised to eliminate such ambiguities by mechanical means or by logic
circuit operations.

An analog signal in the form of a varying frequency can be converted
into digital form with the aid of an electronic counter.   The gate is held
open for a fixed interval of time and the number of cycles of the signal
frequency fed into a binary counter is a measure of the analog signal.

One method of converting analog voltages into digital form uses a
linear sweep circuit as shown in Fig. 21.27.   When the sweep voltage
crosses the axis at point 1, a gate is opened and a counter starts to count
pulses from the timing generator.   When the sweep voltage equals the
analog signal voltage, the count is stopped.   The analog voltage determines the length of time the gate is open and therefore determines the

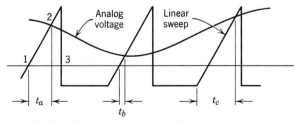

Fig. 21.27   Time-base analog-to-digital conversion.

number of pulses counted by the binary counter. At point 3 the counter of this *time-base encoder* is reset.

Telemetering Equipment

The communication of data from the point of measurement to the point of processing or display is an important element in any instrumentation system. Data transmission to a remote location in the form of electrical signals is called *telemetry* and may be by radio wave or by telephone-type land lines. Land-line telemetry is used in oil refineries, chemical processing plants, electrical power systems, and pipe-line transmission systems. Radio telemetry is used for in-flight tests of aircraft and satellites and for data transmission over great distances or rough terrain.

In radio telemetry the high-frequency carrier wave is modulated by subcarriers upon which the data are superimposed. A great variety of modulation or coding systems is available. To accommodate data from more than one sensor, the capacity of a channel is shared in the process called *multiplexing*. In a *time-division* multiplex system the signals corresponding to data from a particular sensor occupy a certain segment of the data sampling cycle. Time division can be achieved mechanically using a one-bar commutator which successively contacts the brushes connected to the various inputs. In an AM *frequency-division* multiplex system, each input modulates a subcarrier at a relatively low frequency. The modulated subcarriers are then combined and used to modulate the radio carrier. The signals corresponding to data from a particular sensor occupy a certain side band. At the receiver the carrier is demodulated and the signals separated by frequency-selective band-pass filters.

Tape Recorders

The magnetic tape recorder has completely changed the character of data processing. This widely used recording instrument has a great dynamic range over a wide frequency range with low distortion and great flexibility. The recorded signal can be stored permanently or played back immediately at the recording speed or a more convenient speed.

The operation of the recorder is indicated in Fig. 21.28. A flexible magnetic tape is moved past a *recording head* at constant speed by the *tape transport*. Variations in the signal current produce variations in the flux density at the gap and therefore variations in the magnetization of the tape material. To avoid distortion due to the nonlinearity of the magnetic circuit, the input signal is superimposed on a high-frequency constant-amplitude bias current. The peak values of the total signal (note that this is not amplitude modulation) lie on the linear portion of

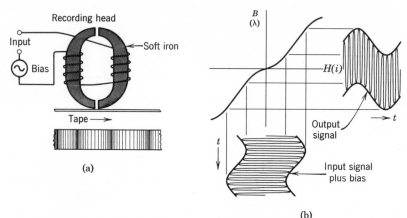

Fig. 21.28   Magnetic tape recording.

the magnetization curve.   The *reproducing head,* identical to the recording head, produces a signal in response to the flux density variation.
The high-frequency bias component is removed by a low-pass filter and
the output signal resembles the input.

For a sinusoidal input current the peak value of the residual magnetism in the tape is of the form

$$B = B_0 + kI_m \cos \omega t + k_b I_b \cos \omega_b t \qquad (21\text{-}16)$$

where I_b is the bias current.   The emf induced in the reproducing head is

$$e = \frac{d\lambda}{dt} = NA \frac{dB}{dt} = k'\omega I_m \sin \omega t + k_b' I_b \omega_b \sin \omega_b t \qquad (21\text{-}17)$$

After the bias frequency component is removed by filtering, the rms value
of the signal is

$$E = k''fI \qquad (21\text{-}18)$$

The voltage reproduced is directly proportional to frequency, so the output amplifier must introduce a compensating frequency characteristic to
provide an overall linear response.

In addition to tape recorders, instrumentation systems employ galva-
nometer-actuated oscillographs, pen-type strip-chart recorders, X-Y plot-
ters, punched cards, and cathode-ray oscilloscopes with cameras.   Indicating instruments are also used at this stage for continuous monitoring.

Computers

Data reduction is an important part of a general instrumentation system. General purpose digital computers are employed extensively, but special purpose digital or analog computers may be more effective. To conserve expensive computer time, the recorded data may be reviewed in graphical form and only a small fraction selected for complete analysis. Where only a small amount of data is to be analyzed or where the data are obscured by noise, manual reading may be preferable to computer analysis. Digital-to-analog conversion may be desirable at certain stages of the data reduction.

Where the computation involves complicated calculations or where the same computer can be used for several functions, the general purpose electronic digital computer is used. The essential units are: input, memory, arithmetic, control, error-checking, and output. Such a computer can accept data and programmed instructions, perform thousands of arithmetic operations per second, check the computations, and present the results in tabular or graphical form or store them for future reference.

In the instrumentation systems described here, it is desirable that the variables being measured be disturbed as little as possible. In the automatic control systems described in the next chapter, the same components are employed for a quite different purpose. In forcing a physical system to behave in a prescribed way, problems of response and stability arise which do not occur in data-acquisition systems.

SUMMARY

◆ All branches of experimental engineering depend on instrumentation to extend human abilities to detect, observe, measure, control, compute, communicate, and display physical quantities.

◆ The d'Arsonval movement responds to direct current, but it can be used to measure voltage and resistance as well.
   The effect of an instrument on the circuit being tested can be taken into account using the compensation theorem.

◆ A-c quantities can be measured directly by iron-vane or electrodynamometer instruments or indirectly by rectifier-type instruments. For other than sinusoids, a correction may be necessary.

◆ The vacuum-tube voltmeter employs electronic circuitry to provide high input impedance, accuracy, flexibility, and stability.

◆ The cathode-ray oscilloscope measures voltage and time, displays waveforms, and compares phase and frequency.

◆ The electronic counter employs a time base and gating circuit to determine the number of events per unit time or the time between events.

◆ Instrumentation transducers convert physical variables to electrical form.

Active transducers include: thermocouples, piezoelectric pickups, phototubes, photojunction cells, dynamic pickups, and tachometers. Passive transducers include: resistance thermometers, hot-wire anemometers, strain gauges, photoconductive cells, variable-reluctance elements, differential transformers, and liquid-level gauges.

◆ Bridge measurements based on null conditions are highly accurate. A slightly unbalanced bridge can be used as a transducer.

◆ Potentiometer measurements use voltage comparisons for high accuracy.

Self-balancing potentiometers are valuable for recording and control.

◆ The strain gauge and bridge measures small displacements accurately. The differential transformer measures larger displacements accurately.

◆ In an instrumentation system all components must work together effectively.

Such a system may include sensors and transducers, calibrating equipment, analog-to-digital and digital-to-analog converters, telemetering equipment, multiplexers, computers, recorders, and indicators.

REVIEW QUESTIONS

1. Define instrument sensitivity, error, accuracy, and precision.
2. How is a circuit affected by an ammeter?   A voltmeter?
3. Why must an ammeter shunt selector switch "make" before "break"?
4. Explain the operation of an ohmmeter.   A multimeter.
5. If an iron-vane instrument responds to i^2 and a rectifier instrument responds to I_{av}, how can they both read I_{rms}?
6. What are the advantages of a VTVM over a d-c voltmeter?
7. How can a CRO be used to measure voltage?   Frequency?   Phase?
8. Explain the operation of CRO sweep, trigger, and blanking circuits.
9. Explain the operation of an electronic counter.
10. Distinguish between active and passive transducers; list 3 of each.
11. Why are bridge and potentiometer measurements so accurate?
12. Explain the operation of an unbalanced bridge as a transducer.
13. Explain the operation of a self-balancing potentiometer.
14. How could a strain gauge be used to measure pressure?
15. How could a differential transformer be used to measure level?

EXERCISES

1. Design a multirange ammeter with ranges of 10, 50, and 250 mA and 1, 2, and 5 A, using a 10-mA movement with 60 Ω internal resistance.

2. Design a multirange milliammeter with ranges of 1, 10, 50 and 150 mA using a 50-μA movement with 5000 Ω internal resistance.

3. Design a multirange voltmeter with ranges of 3, 10, 50, and 150 V using the movement of Exercise 1.

4. Repeat Exercise 3 with the movement of Exercise 2.

5. Design an ohmmeter, using the movement of Exercise 2 with a half-scale reading of: (a) 10,000 Ω (b) 500 Ω.

6. In the circuit of Fig. 21.29, an ammeter with an internal resistance of 100 Ω is:
(a) inserted at point *a* and reads 6 mA, and then
(b) inserted at point *b* and reads 6 mA.
Estimate the original current in each case.

7. In the circuit of Fig. 21.29, a voltmeter with an internal resistance of 20 kΩ is:
(a) connected from point *a* to *c* and reads 2 V, and then
(b) connected from point *a* to *d* and reads 2 V.
Estimate the original voltage in each case.

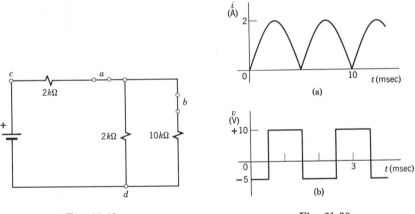

Fig. 21.29   **Fig. 21.30**

8. Electrodynamometer, rectifier, and peak-reading instruments, all calibrated in rms values, are used to measure the current in Fig. 21.30a. Predict the reading on each instrument.

9. Repeat Exercise 8 for the voltage in Fig. 21.30b.

10. On a CRO the vertical amplifier is set at 0.5 V/cm and the horizontal sweep is set at 5 msec/cm. Sketch the pattern observed when a voltage $v = 3 \sin 200\pi t$ V is applied to the vertical input. (Assume sweep starts at $t = 0$.)

11. Repeat Exercise 10 for a voltage $v = 2 \cos (100\pi t - \pi/3)$ V.

12. On a CRO vertical and horizontal amplifiers are set at 1 V/cm. Sketch the pattern observed when the voltages applied to the vertical and horizontal inputs are:

(a) $v_v = 5 \cos 100t$ and $v_h = 5 \cos 300t$ V.

(b) $v_v = 5 \cos 200t$ and $v_h = 5 \cos (500t + \pi/2)$ V.

13. The speed of a rotating shaft is to be measured using a phototube and an electronic counter. Sketch a suitable arrangement.

14. Devise an electrical circuit to measure the level of fuel in a tank using a parallel-plate capacitor.

15. In the Wheatstone bridge of Fig. 21.17, determine R_x when:

(a) $R_A = 1000\ \Omega$, $R_B = 200\ \Omega$, and $R = 122\ \Omega$.

(b) $R_A = 1000\ \Omega$, $R_B = 2500\ \Omega$, and $R = 256\ \Omega$.

16. Derive Eq. 21-13.

17. In the Maxwell bridge of Fig. 21.19, $R_A = 1000\ \Omega$, and $C_B = 0.05\ \mu$F. $R_B = 1250\ \Omega$ and $R = 240\ \Omega$ for a balance at 1000 cps. Determine the parameters of the unknown.

18. A strain gauge with a gauge factor of 2 is used in the circuit of Fig. 21.20 with $R = 120\ \Omega$ and the d-c voltage source replaced by a voltage $v_s = 10 \cos 10^5\ t$ V. Predict the output voltage if the gauge is subjected to a periodic strain with a maximum value of 200 μ inch/inch and a frequency of 20 cps.

19. Design a circuit for displaying the v-i characteristic of a diode on a CRO. Assume that the horizontal and vertical amplifiers have a common internal ground.

20. Two diodes with Zener voltages of 6.2 V and 8.2 V are available. Design a circuit to provide a stable potentiometer reference voltage of 2.0 V.

21. A differential transformer has the characteristics of Fig. 21.24b where the voltage scale is 1 volt/cm and the displacement scale is 0.02 inch/cm. (The excitation of the primary is 10 V rms at 5 kc.) If the displacement of the core is $0.01 + 0.002 \cos 20\pi t$ inches, predict the output voltage and the percentage of modulation.

◆ CONTROL SYSTEM CHARACTERISTICS

◆ TRANSFER FUNCTIONS

◆ DYNAMIC RESPONSE OF SYSTEMS

◆ FEEDBACK CONTROL SYSTEMS

CHAPTER **22**

Automatic Control Systems

One characteristic which distinguishes modern man from his predecessors is his use of great amounts of power. A second distinguishing characteristic is his ability to control that power precisely. At one extreme of the power spectrum is the multimegawatt electric power system so precisely controlled that a simple reluctance motor driven by the system becomes an accurate timing device. At the other extreme is the picture provided by a few millimicrowatts of controlled energy received from a satellite exploring remote regions of space. Between these extremes are innumerable applications of control to heating systems, assembly plants, metallurgical processes, and oil refineries and to traffic flow, water supply, turbine operation, aircraft landing, and missile guidance.

Despite their great variety, automatic control systems can be analyzed into a few basically similar components. In Watt's *flyball governor*, perhaps the first automatic control device, a rotating spindle carrying flyweights (Fig. 22.1) is driven by the governed engine. The engine speeds up until the centrifugal force of the flyweights overcomes the force of the speed adjusting spring and partially closes the throttle valve. An increase in load on the engine momentarily reduces its speed, reduces the centrifugal force of the flyweights, allows the throttle valve to open, and accelerates the engine until the set speed is reached. The components of the governor are shown in the block diagram of Fig. 22.2. General

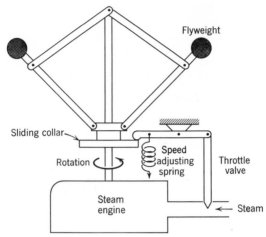

Fig. 22.1 Flyball governor.

terms for the functions performed and the variables existing at various points in the system are shown in italics.

Most of the elements employed in control systems are familiar to us from our previous study. Sensors and transducers are used to measure variables and convert them to electrical form. Computers or error detectors are used in determining the difference between reference and feedback variables. Controllers and amplifiers are used to develop signals to actuate the controlled system. Motors are used to provide the "muscle" for system control. Feedback elements are used to facilitate the comparison of output and reference variables. Note that only signals appear in the block diagram of a control system. Power inputs (steam to the engine of Fig. 22.2 or heat from the furnace in Fig. 22.3) are essential to the operation, but ordinarily they do not enter into control calculations.

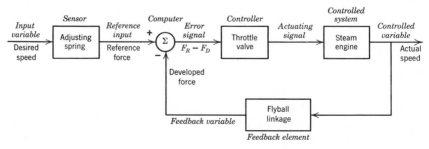

Fig. 22.2 Block diagram of flyball governor.

The study of automatic control represents a continuation of our analysis of linear systems, the central topic of this book, and also it provides an opportunity to apply our knowledge of circuit principles, device characteristics, and system techniques. First, we look at the operation of some illustrative examples to discover the essential characteristics of control systems, the benefits obtained by using feedback, and the problems which arise in system design. Then we extend our methods of circuit analysis to permit handling systems incorporating a variety of different elements, each described by a transfer function. Using the new method, we next determine the dynamic behavior of some electromechanical devices. Finally, we consider how to obtain control systems with the necessary accuracy and stability.

CONTROL SYSTEM CHARACTERISTICS

The flyball governor is an example of a *regulator* which maintains a speed, frequency, or voltage constant within specified limits. In a regulator the reference is constant, although it may be adjustable. In a *follower* such as the self-balancing potentiometer shown in Fig. 21.22, the variation of the output duplicates the variation of the input. If the output variable is a motion or position such as the aircraft heading in an autopilot, the system is called a *servomechanism*. Regulating and following can be performed accurately and rapidly using systems employing feedback.

Open-Loop and Closed-Loop Systems

An ammeter is an example of a useful *open-loop* device. To obtain the desired accuracy, the magnet is carefully formed and patiently aged, the moving coil is exactly designed, and the mechanism is precisely fabricated. After the instrument is calibrated it is assumed that the output deflection is an accurate indication of the input current.

A similar device could be used to control the heating of a home by providing a fuel valve opening directly related to the outside temperature. For comfort, however, the valve controller should also take into account such factors as wind velocity, sun radiation, and the number of people in the room. If sufficient data were available, some of these factors could be taken into account by a computer (Fig. 22.3a), but we suspect that there must be a better method of control. In the *closed-loop* system of Fig. 22.3b, a thermostat is used to compare the actual temperature with the desired temperature. Whenever the actual is less than

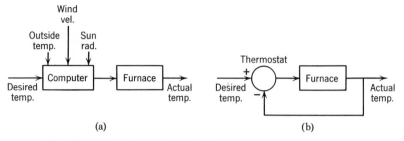

Fig. 22.3   Open-loop and closed-loop temperature controls.

the desired temperature, the furnace is on; otherwise it is off.† This simple on-off control system illustrates two general benefits of closed-loop systems.   It automatically takes into account factors whose effects are known imprecisely or not at all, and it provides accurate overall performance using inexpensive elements of low individual accuracy.

The Control Problem

A characteristic of closed-loop systems which may be disadvantageous is revealed if we assume that the home is heated by means of hot water circulating in pipes buried in a concrete slab.   The energy storage capacity of the slab introduces a time lag in the response of the heating system. If the time lag is several hours, as it might well be, the slab would not begin to radiate heat until long after the thermostat turned on, and it would continue to radiate long after the thermostat turned off.   The combination of the amplification needed for accurate control and the energy storage inherent in any physical system may result in erratic behavior.   (In what form does amplification appear in a heating system?)

Providing a feedback path in a system containing amplification may create instability.   In a *stable* system the response to an impulse disturbance dies away as time increases (Fig. 22.4a).   In an *unstable* system a sudden disturbance may give rise to sustained oscillations or to an uncontrolled increase in a critical variable.   By definition, an unstable system is incapable of control.   Unfortunately, the requirements of accuracy and stability are incompatible and this creates a difficult design problem for the control engineer.

For high accuracy, only a small error signal (see Fig. 22.2) can be tolerated (in the steady state) and therefore the controller must possess

---

† In practice there is some *dead zone* in which the temperature difference is not sufficient to activate the thermostat.

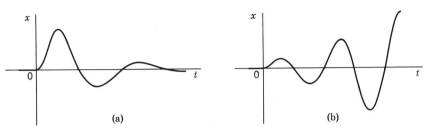

Fig. 22.4 Impulse response of stable and unstable systems.

high amplification. With high amplification, however, the correction is great and this may lead to instability. Stability can be provided by auxiliary elements which increase the cost and weight and reduce the reliability. The control engineer's problem is to provide the necessary accuracy and speed with adequate stability and reliability at a minimum cost and weight.

System Response

One approach to design is to synthesize a possible system, analyze its performance, and compare its performance with the specifications. The performance in terms of accuracy and stability may be deduced from the response of the system to various inputs. In predicting the response, it is convenient to assume that the system is linear and that the input is an impulse, a step, or a sinusoid.

A great deal can be learned about a system from its frequency response, i.e., the amplitude and phase of the output signal in response to an input signal of constant amplitude and variable frequency. From our study of oscillators we know that if at any frequency the open-loop response (the quantity $-\mathbf{GH}$ in Eq. 19-4) has a magnitude of unity and a phase angle of $\pm 180°$, oscillation buildup is possible. The *Nyquist stability criterion* is based on this principle and establishes the necessary conditions for stability.

The Nyquist criterion is applied to steady-state forced response data. An alternative approach is to consider the natural response of the system as revealed by a pole-zero plot in the complex plane. We know from our study of circuits that the poles of the admittance function of a one-port correspond to natural response current components. We need to extend this concept to include the treatment of the two-port elements employed in control systems. By plotting the possible locations of the poles of the appropriate function as system parameters are varied, the so-called *root locus*, we can determine whether a system is stable, and if it is not, what changes can provide stability.

TRANSFER FUNCTIONS

For exponential signals of the form Ve^{st} the response of a one-port is determined by its admittance $Y(s)$. For the circuit of Fig. 22.5, the admittance is

$$\frac{Ie^{st}}{V_1e^{st}} = Y(s) = \frac{1}{R + 1/sC} = \frac{sC}{sCR + 1} = \frac{1}{R} \cdot \frac{s}{s + 1/RC} \qquad (22\text{-}1)$$

To determine the complete response current, we combine the forced and natural current components. For a step-voltage input, the forcing function is V_1e^{0t} where $s = 0$; at $s = 0$ the admittance is zero, therefore the forced current is zero. The admittance function has a pole at $s = -1/RC$ so the natural response is of the form $i = A_1e^{-t/RC}$. Assuming the capacitance C is initially uncharged, at $t = 0^+$, $v_C = 0$ and

$$i = \frac{V_1}{R} = A_1e^0 = A_1$$

Therefore,

$$i(t) = \frac{V_1}{R} e^{-t/RC} \qquad (22\text{-}2)$$

as shown in Fig. 22.5c.

The Transfer Function Concept

Exponential currents and voltages at the terminals of a one-port are related by the admittance function. Is there a similar relation between the output and input voltages when the circuit of Fig. 22.5 is considered as a two-port? If so, by using the voltage-divider principle (Eq. 8-4)

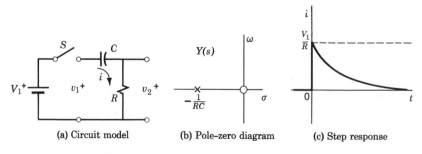

(a) Circuit model   (b) Pole–zero diagram   (c) Step response

Fig. 22.5 Step response of an *RC* circuit.

we could express the ratio of the output voltage to the input voltage as

$$T(s) = \frac{R}{R + 1/sC} = \frac{s}{s + 1/RC} \tag{22-3}$$

where $T(s)$ is the voltage *transfer function*. To determine the output voltage for a step input voltage using our established procedure, we would first note that $T(s)$ has a zero at $s = 0$ and a pole at $s = -1/RC$ as before. We would conclude that the forced component of v_2 is zero, since $T(0) = 0$, and the natural response is of the form $A_1'e^{-t/RC}$. At $t = 0^+$, $v_C = 0$ and

$$V_2 = V_1 = A_1'e^0 = A_1'$$

Therefore,

$$v_2(t) = V_1 e^{-t/RC} \tag{22-4}$$

which is identical with the expression obtained from $v_2 = iR$ where i is given by Eq. 22-2.

We define the transfer function as the ratio of two exponential functions of time, and we conclude from this simple illustration that *the transfer function is derived and interpreted just as an admittance or impedance function.* Note that an immittance is the ratio of two quantities measured at the same port, whereas a transfer function is the ratio of two quantities measured at different ports. The two quantities may be entirely different in physical nature.

For the special case of sinusoidal excitation, the transfer function (Eq. 22-3) becomes

$$\frac{\mathbf{V}_2}{\mathbf{V}_1} = \mathbf{T}(j\omega) = \frac{R}{R + 1/j\omega C} = \frac{R}{\sqrt{R^2 + (1/\omega C)^2}} \bigg/ \tan^{-1} \frac{-1/\omega C}{R} \tag{22-5}$$

where $\mathbf{V}_2$ and $\mathbf{V}_1$ are the output and input phasors. It was pointed out in Chapter 3 that the phasor $\mathbf{V}_1 = V_1 e^{j\theta_1}$ is a *transform* of the sinusoidal function of time $v_1 = V_{1m} \cos(\omega t + \theta_1)$. This transform, always shown in boldface type, represents the sinusoidal function. In this chapter let us employ transforms† of exponential functions as well so that $V_1(s)$ might represent a function $v_1 = A_1 e^{s_1 t} + A_2 e^{s_2 t} + \cdots$ defined for

---

† The Laplace transformation is a mathematical operation which can be used to transform functions of time into functions of the complex variable s. Here the transfer function $T(s)$ is the ratio of the Laplace transforms of voltages $v_1(t)$ and $v_2(t)$ where v_1 and v_2 are defined for $t > 0$ and are equal to zero for $t \le 0$. Powerful methods are available for determining the complete response of a system directly from the transfer function using Laplace transformation. See Gardner and Barnes, *Transients in Linear Systems*, John Wiley and Sons, New York 1942.

$t > 0$. Using this notation, we rewrite Eq. 22-3 as

$$\frac{V_2(s)}{V_1(s)} = T(s) = \frac{s}{s + 1/RC} \qquad (22\text{-}6)$$

The value of the transfer function concept and the transform notation in control system analysis is illustrated in the following example.

EXAMPLE 1

The circuit model of a d'Arsonval movement is shown in Fig. 22.6.
(a) Draw a block diagram for this device.
(b) Derive the transfer function for the relation between deflection and applied voltage.
(c) Write the transfer function for sinusoidal excitation.

SOLUTION. The governing equations and the corresponding transfer functions are:

$$v = Ri \qquad\qquad \frac{I(s)}{V(s)} = \frac{1}{R}$$

$$T_d = k_T i \qquad\qquad \frac{T_d(s)}{I(s)} = k_T$$

$$T_d = J\frac{d\omega}{dt} + D\omega + \frac{1}{K}\int \omega\, dt \qquad \frac{\Omega(s)}{T_d(s)} = \frac{1}{sJ + D + 1/sK}$$

$$\theta = \int \omega\, dt \qquad\qquad \frac{\Theta(s)}{\Omega(s)} = \frac{1}{s}$$

(a) If the third transfer function is rearranged,

$$\frac{1}{sJ + D + 1/sK} = \frac{sK}{s^2JK + sDK + 1}$$

and the block diagram is as shown in Fig. 22.6b.

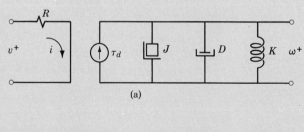

(a)

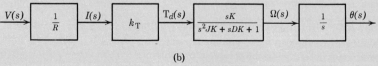

(b)

Fig. 22.6 D'Arsonval movement circuit model and block diagram.

(b) The transfer functions here correspond to the block "gains" employed in Chapter 19. Following the reasoning displayed in Fig. 19.6, we conclude that the overall transfer function of blocks in cascade is the product of the individual transfer functions or

$$T(s) = \frac{\Theta(s)}{V(s)} = \frac{1}{R} \times k_T \times \frac{sK}{s^2JK + sDK + 1} \times \frac{1}{s} = \frac{k_T(K/R)}{s^2JK + sDK + 1}$$

(c) For sinusoidal excitation,

$$\mathbf{T} = \mathbf{T}(j\omega) = \frac{\Theta}{\mathbf{V}} = \frac{k_T(K/R)}{1 - \omega^2JK + j\omega\,DK}$$

Advantages in Using Transfer Functions

Automatic control systems tend to be complicated and any simplification is welcome. In analysis, one possible approach is to write a set of differential equations and solve them simultaneously. A more convenient approach is based on the transfer function concept. The following observations are based on Figs. 22.2 and 22.6 and the accompanying discussion:

Control systems usually consist of combinations of cascaded elements, and block diagram representation is convenient.

If each element is characterized by its transfer function, an overall transfer function can be determined by using the rules of block diagram algebra.

The individual transfer functions consist of relatively simple algebraic factors and the overall function is just a combination of these.

Analogous transfer functions are used in characterizing electrical, mechanical, hydraulic, and pneumatic elements and the interpretation of one is applicable to all.

The transfer function approach permits the determination of the transient response or the steady-state sinusoidal response.

Looking at this list, we can understand why the transfer function approach is used universally.

DYNAMIC RESPONSE OF SYSTEMS

Control systems are useful only insofar as they are able to cope with changing conditions. In evaluating a regulator, we are interested in its *dynamic* behavior, its response to a sudden change in load, for example. In a follower there may be a change in the input variable or there may be a *disturbance* at some point in the system. In general, such changes are random and therefore unpredictable except on a statistical basis. For our purposes a good approach is to determine the dynamic behavior described by the complete response to a step function. An alternative approach is to consider the frequency response for steady-state sinusoidal inputs. In either approach we rely on the transfer function.

Dynamic Analysis

Transfer functions are derived from linear ordinary differential equations, so devices characterized by transfer functions must be represented by models made up of lumped, linear elements. The circuit models we have used to represent electrical, electronic, and electromagnetic devices satisfy this requirement, so transfer functions can be determined directly as in Example 1. In some cases further simplification is possible by ignoring factors which have negligible effect on the behavior being investigated. In Example 1, the inductance of the meter coil was ignored for this reason.

Once the transfer function is obtained, the complete step response can be determined following the procedure outlined in Chapter 6. The forced response is calculated using the transfer function evaluated at $s = 0$. (How is $s = 0$ related to the step function?) The natural response consists of terms identified with poles of the transfer function. (Why not use the zeros?) The undetermined coefficients are evaluated from initial conditions. In a control system the initial conditions are usually zero, corresponding to a state of equilibrium prior to the initiation of the change.

First-Order Systems

The order of a system is defined by the highest power of s in the denominator of the transfer function. For the RC circuit of Fig. 22.7, the transfer function is (using the voltage-divider principle)

$$T(s) = \frac{1/sC}{R + 1/sC} = \frac{1/RC}{s + 1/RC} \qquad (22\text{-}7)$$

Since s appears in the denominator to the first power only, this is a first-order system. For $s = 0$, $T(s) = T(0) = 1$ and the forced response is just $v_{2f} = A_0 = V_1$. A pole of the denominator appears at $s = -1/RC$, so the natural response contains a term $e^{-t/RC}$. The complete response is

$$v_2 = v_{2f} + v_{2n} = V_1 + A_1 e^{-t/RC} \qquad (22\text{-}8)$$

Assuming the capacitor is initially uncharged, at $t = 0^+$, $v_C = 0$,

$$v_2 = 0 = V_1 + A_1 e^0 \qquad \text{and} \qquad A_1 = -V_1$$

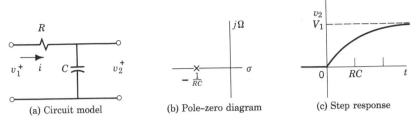

(a) Circuit model   (b) Pole–zero diagram   (c) Step response

Fig. 22.7   A first-order electrical circuit.

The step response is

$$v_2 = V_1 - V_1 e^{-t/RC} \tag{22-9}$$

as shown in Fig. 22.7c.

First-order transfer functions of the form of Eq. 22-3 and Eq. 22-7 occur frequently in control systems, and it is worthwhile to generalize from the results obtained in these two specific cases.   For a first-order system having a transfer function of the form

$$T(s) = \frac{ks}{s + \alpha} \tag{22-10a}$$

the step response $y(t)$ is always of the form

$$y(t) = Ye^{-\alpha t} \tag{22-10b}$$

For a system having a transfer function of the form

$$T(s) = \frac{k}{s + \alpha} \tag{22-11a}$$

the step response $y(t)$ is always of the form

$$y(t) = Y(1 - e^{-\alpha t}) \tag{22-11b}$$

The presence of a zero at $s = 0$ in the first transfer function (Eq. 22-10a) completely changes the step response.

EXAMPLE 2

A d-c shunt motor with constant field excitation is used to position an indicator in a servomechanism.   Derive the transfer function and predict the dynamic speed response.

SOLUTION.   For use in dynamic analysis the circuit model of Fig. 18.8 may be modified.   Let us make the following simplifying assumptions:

The inductance of the armature circuit is negligibly small.

The magnetic flux is constant and $K\phi$ is replaced by k_1.

The total friction of motor and load is represented by D.

The total inertia of motor and load is represented by J.

The load torque is negligible compared to inertia and friction torques.

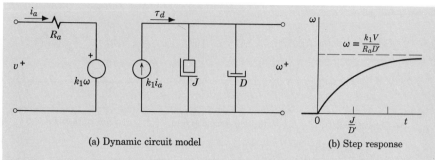

(a) Dynamic circuit model   (b) Step response

Fig. 22.8   Example 2.   Dynamic response of a shunt motor.

On the basis of these assumptions, the circuit model is as shown in Fig. 22.8a. The governing differential equations are

$$J\frac{d\omega}{dt} + D\omega = \tau_d = k_1 i_a \tag{22-12}$$

and

$$i_a = \frac{v - k_1\omega}{R_a}$$

Solving for v and collecting terms, we obtain

$$v = \frac{R_a}{k_1}\left(J\frac{d\omega}{dt} + D\omega + \frac{k_1^2}{R_a}\omega\right) \tag{22-13}$$

Noting that k_1^2/R_a has the same dimensions as the friction coefficient D, let us define an *equivalent friction coefficient* D' where

$$D' = D + \frac{k_1^2}{R_a} \tag{22-14}$$

Making this substitution and assuming exponential variation of v and ω, we can write the transfer function as

$$T(s) = \frac{\Omega(s)}{V(s)} = \frac{k_1/R_a}{sJ + D'} \tag{22-15}$$

This equation is of the same form as Eq. 22-11a.   The forced response to a step of magnitude V is (for $s = 0$)

$$\omega_f = \frac{k_1 V}{R_a D'}$$

The denominator has a pole at $s = -D'/J$.   Therefore, the total step response is

$$\omega = \frac{k_1 V}{R_a D'}(1 - e^{-D't/J}) \tag{22-16}$$

as shown in Fig. 22.8b.   The speed ω increases until it is limited by equivalent friction torque alone.

Second-Order Systems

Example 2 indicates that a shunt motor with constant field current behaves as a first-order system in responding to a step armature voltage input. Suppose now the armature current is held constant and the input signal is a step field voltage. How would the same motor respond in this case? The answer to this question lies in the form of the transfer function. The derivation of this transfer function illustrates the convenience of our approach and indicates the direction of our next step toward an understanding of dynamic response.

Again we need to reduce the analytical labor by making simplifying assumptions. As before we assume that D and J represent total friction and inertia of the motor and load. The inductance of the field circuit is large and cannot be neglected. In this case, let us assume that operation is on the linear portion of the magnetization curve and flux is directly proportional to field current. Since i_a is constant, $\tau_d = K\phi i_a = k_2 i_f$. On the basis of these assumptions, the circuit model is as shown in Fig. 22.9a.

Let us use our knowledge of device behavior and system analysis to derive the overall transfer function in terms of the elements. For the field circuit alone, the transfer function relating field current and voltage (actually an admittance) is

$$T_1(s) = \frac{I_f(s)}{V_f(s)} = \frac{1}{sL_f + R_f} \tag{22-17}$$

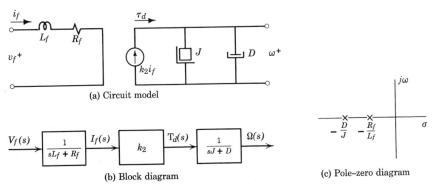

(a) Circuit model

(b) Block diagram

(c) Pole–zero diagram

Fig. 22.9 A field-excited shunt motor.

For the motor as a transducer, the transfer function relating developed torque and field current is

$$T_2(s) = \frac{T_d(s)}{I_f(s)} = k_2 \qquad (22\text{-}18)$$

For the mechanical side of the motor (see Eq. 22-12) the transfer function relating shaft velocity and developed torque is

$$T_3(s) = \frac{\Omega(s)}{T_d(s)} = \frac{1}{sJ + D} \qquad (22\text{-}19)$$

These three transfer functions are shown in Fig. 22.9b.

Applying the rules of block diagram algebra, we obtain the overall transfer function

$$T(s) = \frac{I_f(s)}{V_f(s)} \times \frac{T_d(s)}{I_f(s)} \times \frac{\Omega(s)}{T_d(s)} = \frac{\Omega(s)}{V_f(s)} = \frac{k_2}{(sL_f + R_f)(sJ + D)} \qquad (22\text{-}20)$$

What is the character of the step response of this system? There are two poles of the transfer function corresponding to two roots of the denominator (Fig. 20.9c). In other words, since s appears in the denominator to the second power, this is a second-order system. Combining the forced response with the natural response, we anticipate that the total step response is of the form

$$\omega(t) = \frac{k_2}{R_f D} V_f + A_1 e^{-R_f t/L_f} + A_2 e^{-Dt/J} \qquad (22\text{-}21)$$

Even without evaluating A_1 and A_2, we can see that in this case there are two time constants influencing the response. The fact that field current builds up slowly tends to make the response sluggish. Also, the inertia of the motor and load limits the rate of change of shaft velocity. Since a rapid response is usually desired in a control system, this mode of operation is less desirable than armature voltage control.

In this case, the two poles are real and negative. From our experience with electric circuits, we expect that in another case there might be complex roots and an entirely different form of response.

EXAMPLE 3

Predict the step response of the d'Arsonval movement in Example 1 (Fig. 22.6). SOLUTION. We assume that the movement is at rest and then at $t = 0$ a step voltage is applied. The transfer function is

$$T(s) = \frac{\Theta(s)}{V(s)} = \frac{k_T K/R}{s^2 JK + sDK + 1}$$

so the forced response is

$$\theta_f = T(0) \times V = \frac{k_T K}{R} V$$

To find the poles of the transfer function, we find the roots of the denominator. Where

$$s^2 JK + sDK + 1 = 0 \qquad (22\text{-}22)$$

the roots are

$$s_1, s_2 = -\frac{D}{2J} \pm \sqrt{\left(\frac{D}{2J}\right)^2 - \frac{1}{JK}} \qquad (22\text{-}23)$$

In general, the complete response is

$$\theta = \frac{k_T K}{R} V + A_1 e^{s_1 t} + A_2 e^{s_2 t} \qquad (22\text{-}24)$$

Reasoning by analogy from the mathematically similar electrical circuit (Fig. 4.10), we predict that the form of the response is dependent upon the nature of the roots s_1 and s_2. If the roots are real and unequal, the response is over-damped. If the roots are imaginary, the response is underdamped or oscillatory. If the roots are equal, the response is critically damped.

Normalized Response of a Second-Order System

The response anticipated in Example 3 is encountered so frequently in control system analysis that it deserves detailed attention. As before (Eq. 4-18b), we define the *undamped natural frequency* as

$$\omega_n = \sqrt{1/JK} \qquad (22\text{-}25)$$

Another useful quantity is the ratio of the actual damping parameter D to D_c, the value for critical damping. Since for critical damping the discriminant is zero, the corresponding value of D_c is $2\sqrt{J/K}$. The *damping ratio* ζ (zeta) is defined as

$$\zeta = \frac{D}{D_c} = \frac{D}{2\sqrt{J/K}} \qquad (22\text{-}26)$$

The *natural frequency* ω of an underdamped system can be expressed in terms of ω_n and ζ. In this oscillatory case (see Eq. 4-18c) the discriminant is negative and

$$\omega = \sqrt{\frac{1}{JK} - \frac{D^2}{4J^2}} = \frac{1}{\sqrt{JK}} \sqrt{1 - \frac{D^2}{4J/K}} = \omega_n \sqrt{1 - \zeta^2} \quad (22\text{-}27)$$

In terms of these definitions, the transfer function of a second-order system (see first equation in Example 3) becomes

$$T(s) = \frac{Y(s)}{X(s)} = \frac{k}{s^2 + 2\omega_n \zeta s + \omega_n^2} \qquad (22\text{-}28)$$

Let us now determine the response $y(t)$ to a step of magnitude X for a system characterized by the transfer function of Eq. 22-28. By inspection, the forced response is

$$y_f = \frac{k}{\omega_n{}^2} X = Y \qquad (22\text{-}29)$$

The roots of the denominator are determined from

$$s^2 + 2\omega_n \zeta s + \omega_n{}^2 = 0 \qquad (22\text{-}30)$$

whence

$$s_1, s_2 = -\omega_n(\zeta \pm \sqrt{\zeta^2 - 1}) \qquad (22\text{-}31)$$

The complete response is of the form

$$y(t) = \frac{k}{\omega_n{}^2} X + A_1 e^{s_1 t} + A_2 e^{s_2 t} \qquad (22\text{-}32)$$

The coefficients A_1 and A_2 can be determined from the initial conditions assuming that at $t = 0^+$, $y = 0$ and $dy/dt = 0$. After several algebraic steps, the normalized response is found to be†

$$\frac{y}{Y} = 1 - \frac{\zeta + \sqrt{\zeta^2 - 1}}{2\sqrt{\zeta^2 - 1}} e^{-(\zeta - \sqrt{\zeta^2 - 1})\omega_n t} + \frac{\zeta - \sqrt{\zeta^2 - 1}}{2\sqrt{\zeta^2 - 1}} e^{-(\zeta + \sqrt{\zeta^2 - 1})\omega_n t}$$
$$(22\text{-}33)$$

Choosing y/Y and $\omega_n t$ as the normalized variables, the response is as plotted in Fig. 22.10.

These curves, developed by Gordon Brown, are useful in predicting the response of a system whose parameters are known or in estimating the parameters of a system whose response is known. If the damping ratio is small, say, $\zeta = 0.2$, the output variable rises rapidly to the steady-state value, *overshoots* by 50%, and oscillates several times before the natural response component becomes negligible. If the damping ratio is large, say, $\zeta = 1.5$, the output variable approaches the steady-state value very slowly. If $\zeta = 1.0$, the damping is at the critical value and the output variable approaches the steady-state value at the maximum rate possible without overshoot. If rapid response is desired and a small amount of overshoot is tolerable, a design value of $\zeta = 0.8$ might be specified.

---

† For $\zeta = 1$ this form of the equation is indeterminate; the response with critical damping is $y/Y = 1 - (1 + \omega_n t)e^{-\omega_n t}$. For $\zeta < 1$, it is more convenient to express the response as a damped sinusoid.

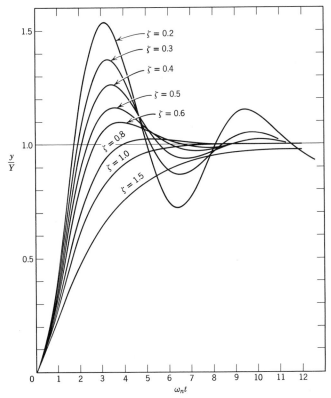

Fig. 22.10 Normalized response curves for second-order system.

EXAMPLE 4

A d'Arsonval movement to be used in a pen recorder has a rotational inertia $J = 2.5 \times 10^{-8}$ kg-m^2. It is to have a damping ratio $\zeta = 0.8$ and an undamped natural frequency $\omega_n = 200$ rad/sec. Specify the spring compliance, determine the developed torque required for a full-scale deflection of 0.8 radian, and estimate the time required for the deflection to reach 0.98 of the steady-state value.

SOLUTION. Assuming that the movement is represented by the circuit model of Fig. 22.6a (Example 1), this second-order system is characterized by the transfer function of Eq. 22-28. From Eq. 22-25 the necessary spring compliance is

$$ K = \frac{1}{\omega_n{}^2 J} = \frac{1}{4 \times 10^4 \times 2.5 \times 10^{-8}} = 10^3 \text{ rad/N-m} $$

For a full-scale deflection of 0.8 rad, the torque required is

$$ \tau_d = \frac{\Theta}{K} = \frac{0.8 \text{ rad}}{10^3 \text{ rad/N-m}} = 8 \times 10^{-4} \text{ N-m} $$

For $\zeta = 0.8$, Fig. 22.10 indicates that $y/Y = 0.98$ when $\omega_n t \cong 3.6$. Therefore,

$$t \cong \frac{3.6}{\omega_n} = \frac{3.6}{200} = 0.018 \text{ sec}$$

System Time Constants

One of the virtues of the transfer function is the variety of useful ways in which it can be interpreted. In several examples we have seen that the form of the step response of a system is determined by the poles of $T(s)$. The *pole* and *zero* locations are explicit when the transfer function is written in the form

$$T(s) = \frac{k(s + \beta)}{(s + \alpha_1)(s + \alpha_2)} \tag{22-34}$$

For the special case of real negative poles and a zero at the origin ($\beta = 0$), the pole-zero diagram is as shown in Fig. 22.11a.

Rewriting Eq. 22-34 (for $\beta = 0$) as

$$T(s) = \frac{ks/\alpha_1\alpha_2}{(s/\alpha_1 + 1)(s/\alpha_2 + 1)} = \frac{k's}{(s\tau_1 + 1)(s\tau_2 + 1)} \tag{22-35}$$

focuses attention on a different set of system characteristics. Here τ_1 and τ_2 are the *time constants* of the natural response terms. The relation of the time constants to the step response is shown in Fig. 22.11b.

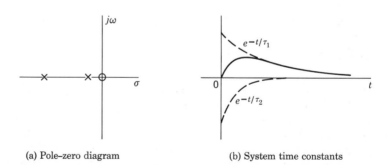

(a) Pole–zero diagram   (b) System time constants

Fig. 22.11   Interpretations of the transfer function.

EXAMPLE 5

Determine the transfer function of a first-order servomechanism to meet the following specifications:

Maximum displacement: 25°
Error: no greater than 0.5° after 2 sec
Static gain: 10

SOLUTION. For behavior similar to that in Fig. 22.7c, we conclude that the form of the necessary transfer function is (Eq. 22-11a)

$$T(s) = \frac{Y(s)}{X(s)} = \frac{k}{s + \alpha} = \frac{k\tau}{s\tau + 1}$$

to provide a step response

$$\frac{y}{Y} = 1 - e^{-t/\tau}$$

An error of 0.5° corresponds to 2% of the maximum displacement, therefore,

$$1 - 0.98 = e^{-t/\tau} = \tfrac{1}{50}$$

and

$$\tau = \frac{t}{\ln 50} = \frac{2}{3.9} \cong 5.1$$

For a gain of $Y/X = 10$ at $s = 0$, $k\tau = 10$; therefore the desired system transfer function is

$$T(s) = \frac{10}{5.1s + 1}$$

System Frequency Response

Another useful interpretation of the transfer function is in terms of the steady-state response, i.e. amplitude and phase angle, as a function of frequency. In some cases, a laboratory measurement of frequency response is the best method of determining the system characteristics. Given a transfer function, the frequency response is obtained directly by substituting $s = j\omega$. For the system described by $T(s) = 1/(s\tau + 1)$, the frequency response is

$$\frac{V_2}{V_1} = T = \frac{1}{1 + j\omega\tau} = \frac{1}{\sqrt{1 + (\omega\tau)^2}} \ \underline{/\tan^{-1} - \omega\tau} \qquad (22\text{-}36)$$

It is convenient to follow the procedure of H. W. Bode and plot gain in decibels where (Eq. 11-46)

$$\text{Gain in db} = 20 \log \frac{V_2}{V_1} \qquad (22\text{-}37)$$

Using the gain at zero frequency as a base, the Bode chart of Eq. 22-36 is as shown in Fig. 22.12c. For $\omega\tau \gg 1$, the gain is inversely proportional to $\omega\tau$ and the gain curve is a straight line with a slope of -20 db/decade. The gain curve can be approximated by asymptotes which intersect at the *breakpoint* or *corner frequency*. At the breakpoints the phase angle is $-45°$ and the gain is actually down 3 db. One important virtue of the Bode chart is that the response curve for the *product* of two transfer

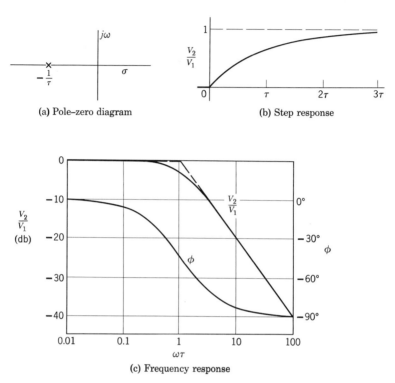

(a) Pole–zero diagram   (b) Step response

(c) Frequency response

Fig. 22.12 Interpretations of $T(s) = 1/(s\tau + 1)$.

functions is just the *sum* of the two response curves when gains are plotted in db.

EXAMPLE 6

Laboratory data for the response curve of an amplifier are plotted as small circles in Fig. 22.13a. Determine the transfer function of the amplifier.

SOLUTION. It appears that at high and low frequencies the response drops off at about 20 db per decade. On the basis of this evidence (and some experience!), the dashed straight-line approximation is drawn. The high-frequency response with a breakpoint ($\omega\tau_2 = 1$) at 10^4 rad/sec corresponds to a transfer function of the form

$$\mathbf{T}_2 = \frac{1}{1 + j\omega\tau_2} = \frac{1}{1 + j\dfrac{\omega}{\omega_2}} = \frac{1}{1 + j10^{-4}\omega}$$

The low-frequency response indicates that, for $\omega\tau_1 \ll 1$, the gain is directly proportional to frequency. With a breakpoint ($\omega\tau_1 = 1$) at 30 rad/sec this corresponds to a transfer function of the form

$$T_1 = \frac{j\omega\tau_1}{1 + j\omega\tau_1} = \frac{j\omega/30}{1 + j\omega/30}$$

For the middle frequencies around $\omega = 10^3$, $T_2 \cong 1$ and $T_1 \cong 1$. By Eq. 22-37 the midfrequency gain of the amplifier is

$$A = \frac{V_2}{V_1} = \text{antilog } \tfrac{40}{20} = 10^2 = 100$$

The amplifier can be represented by the three ideal elements shown in Fig. 22.13b or by the single transfer function

$$T = \frac{j\omega\frac{100}{30}}{(1 + j\omega/30)(1 + j10^{-4}\omega)} \tag{22-38}$$

(How does phase angle vary with frequency for this amplifier?)

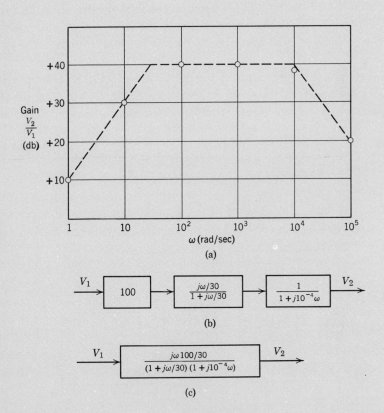

(a)

(b)

(c)

Fig. 22.13 Example 6. Frequency response curve and transfer functions.

FEEDBACK CONTROL SYSTEMS

With an understanding of transfer functions and the associated dynamic responses we are ready to consider control systems with feedback. Our aim is to learn how they operate, how they can be used to improve system performance, and how system stability can be insured. Because of our experience with circuits and electromechanical devices we choose an electrical system as an illustration.

A Voltage Regulator

The purpose of a voltage regulating system is to hold the controlled voltage within specified limits in spite of changes in load or other operating conditions. The output voltage of the unregulated, separately excited, constant-speed, d-c generator in Fig. 22.14a varies with changes in load current because of the armature-resistance voltage drop. The variation can be reduced by "closing the loop" through an operator with his eye on the voltmeter and his hand on the field rheostat (Fig. 22.14b). The "controller" notes the "error" between the voltmeter pointer position and the "reference" and takes the necessary "action" to reduce the error to zero.

In the compound generator of Fig. 22.15 the effect of a load change is fed back by means of the series winding (see Example 3 in Chapter 18). If operation is on the linear portion of the magnetization curve and

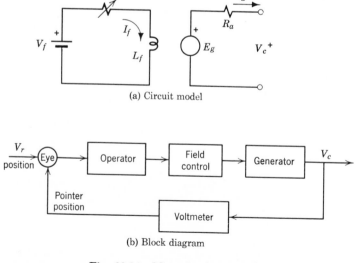

(a) Circuit model

(b) Block diagram

Fig. 22.14 Manual voltage regulator.

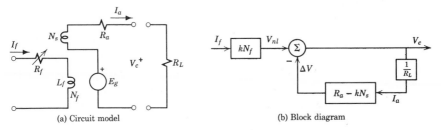

(a) Circuit model   (b) Block diagram

Fig. 22.15 Steady-state operation of a compound generator.

changes are slow, the governing equation is

$$V_c = E_g - I_a R_a = k(N_f I_f + N_s I_a) - I_a R_a$$

$$= V_{nl} - \Delta V = k N_f I_f - I_a(R_a - k N_s) \qquad (22\text{-}39)$$

where N is the number of turns.

The corresponding block diagram is shown in Fig. 22.15b. For flat compounding, the term $R_a - k N_s$ is made equal to zero, $\Delta V = 0$, and $V_c = V_{nl}$. But there are two inadequacies in this system. First, the feedback loop contains an element R_a which changes with temperature (and therefore with I_a) and factor k which changes with magnetic flux (and therefore with I_a). Second, there is no amplification in the loop and the total error is incorporated in the output.

The voltage regulator in Fig. 22.16 represents an improvement. Here the output voltage is compared to a reference, and the difference is ampli-

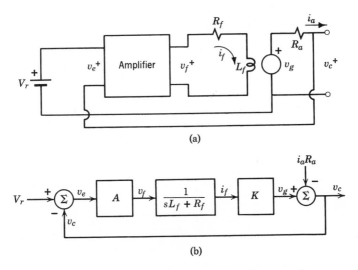

(a)

(b)

Fig. 22.16 Wiring and block diagrams for voltage regulator.

fied and used to decrease the discrepancy. In anticipation of a rapid
response, we show the variables as instantaneous values. The operation
is: A sudden change in load current reduces output voltage v_c and greatly
increases the error voltage $v_e = V_r - v_c$; the error voltage is then amplified and applied to the field circuit, tending to increase i_f and restore the
output voltage. For linear operation, the governing equations are:

$$v_e = V_r - v_c \qquad\qquad v_g = Ki_f$$

$$v_f = Av_e \qquad\qquad v_c = v_g - i_aR_a \qquad\qquad (22\text{-}40)$$

$$v_f = L_f \frac{di_f}{dt} + R_f i_f$$

When each of these relations is represented by an element, the block
diagram is as shown.

In this representation the voltage drop $V_a = i_aR_a$ is introduced as a
disturbance to the system. One approach to evaluating the performance
of the regulator is to determine its response to a step in load current I_a.
In this situation the reference voltage V_r is constant and the important
relation is between I_a and V_c. To focus attention on this relation, the
block diagram is redrawn as shown in Fig. 22.17. Here the forward
transfer function $G(s) = +1$. With V_r constant, $v_e = -v_c$ and the feedback transfer function relating v_g to v_c is

$$H(s) = -\frac{KA}{sL_f + R_f} = -\frac{KA/L_f}{s + R_f/L_f} = -\frac{K'}{s + \alpha} \qquad (22\text{-}41)$$

where K' is a new constant and $\alpha = R_f/L_f$. For this configuration, the
overall gain with feedback (Eq. 19-4) is

$$\frac{V_c(s)}{I_a(s)} = -R_aG_f(s) = R_a\frac{-1}{1 - H(s)} = \frac{-R_a}{1 + [K'/(s + \alpha)]} = \frac{-R_a(s + \alpha)}{s + \alpha + K'}$$
$$(22\text{-}42)$$

With the transfer function known, the step response of the system is
determined from forced and natural components and initial conditions.

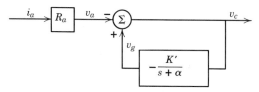

Fig. 22.17 Voltage regulator with disturbance
input.

The forced component (for $s = 0$) is

$$v_f = -\frac{R_a \alpha}{\alpha + K'} I_a = -\frac{R_a R_f / L_f}{R_f / L_f + KA / L_f} I_a = -\frac{R_a R_f I_a}{R_f + KA} \quad (22\text{-}43)$$

The natural response is defined by the pole of $G_f(s)$ and

$$v_n = A_1 e^{-(\alpha + K')t} \quad (22\text{-}44)$$

The performance of the regulator is revealed by the variation of the total controlled voltage v_c as a function of time after the introduction of the disturbance I_a. In general,

$$v_c = A_0 + A_1 e^{-(\alpha + K')t} \quad (22\text{-}45)$$

If speed is constant as assumed, the generated voltage v_g cannot suddenly change because i_f cannot suddenly change. (Why not?) Therefore, if the no-load output voltage is V_c and a current I_a is suddenly drawn at $t = 0$, at $t = 0^+$

$$v_c = V_c - I_a R_a = A_0 + A_1 e^0 = A_0 + A_1 \quad (22\text{-}46)$$

After a long time the natural response dies away and the output voltage is the initial voltage plus the forced response to the step function. At $t = \infty$, therefore,

$$v_c = V_c + v_f = V_c - \frac{R_a R_f I_a}{R_f + KA} = A_0 + A_1 e^{-\infty} = A_0 \quad (22\text{-}47)$$

Solving Eqs. 22-47 and 22-46 for A_0 and A_1, we obtain

$$v_c = V_c - \frac{R_f}{R_f + KA} I_a R_a - I_a R_a \left(1 - \frac{R_f}{R_f + KA}\right) e^{-(R_f + KA)t/L_f} \quad (22\text{-}48)$$

The effect of the various parameters is illustrated in the following numerical example.

EXAMPLE 7

The shunt generator in Fig. 22.16 ($R_a = 1\ \Omega$, $R_f = 100\ \Omega$, $L_f = 20$ H) is rated at 100 V and 10 A. The magnetization curve can be approximated by the relation $v_g = 100 I_f$ V where I_f is in amperes.

(a) Predict the effect of a load current of 10 A on the output voltage of the generator operating without feedback.

(b) Repeat part (a) with the feedback circuit shown incorporating an amplifier with voltage gain $A = 100$.

SOLUTION. (a) With the field current adjusted for rated voltage at no load but without feedback, the output voltage under load is

$$V = v_g - I_a R_a = 100 - 10 \times 1 = 90 \text{ V}$$

The application of this load results in a 10% voltage drop.

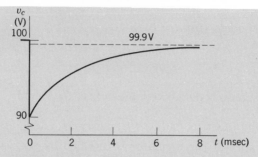

Fig. 22.18 Step response of a voltage regulator.

(b) With feedback, Eq. 22-48 applies. Now

$$\frac{R_f}{R_f + KA} = \frac{100}{100 + 100 \times 100} \cong 0.01$$

and

$$\frac{R_f + KA}{L_f} = \frac{100 + 100 \times 100}{20} \cong 500$$

hence

$$v_c = V_c - 0.01 I_a R_a - I_a R_a (1 - 0.01) e^{-500t} \qquad (22\text{-}49)$$

For $v_c = V_c = 100$ V initially and $I_a R_a = 10 \times 1 = 10$ V introduced at $t = 0$,

$$v_c = 100 - 0.01 \times 10 - 10(0.99) e^{-500t}$$

or

$$v_c = 99.9 - 9.9 e^{-500t} \qquad (22\text{-}50)$$

As shown in Fig. 22.18, the voltage drops abruptly to 90 V, but within a few milliseconds it has been increased to 99.9 V. The application of a 10-A load results in a 0.1 % voltage drop compared to the 10 % voltage drop expected in the same generator without feedback.

Improving Response

An open-loop system is "ignorant of its own output." In contrast, a closed-loop system is continually reminded of what is occurring at the output terminals. The principal virtue of feedback in amplifiers (Chapter 19) is the ability to provide satisfactory operation under widely ranging conditions. In control applications, feedback can greatly improve system performance by reducing errors or by extending the frequency response or by reducing the time constant of a system component.

In the voltage regulator of Example 7, the difference between the controlled voltage and the reference voltage, the *error*, is the input to the amplifier. The purpose of the system is to drive this error to zero. On the other hand, some error must exist to provide the necessary input. As an illustration, consider an aircraft rudder control. The difference between the actual rudder position and that called for by the pilot is sensed and amplified. The output of the amplifier is the input to a motor which provides the torque to actuate the rudder. In a turn, considerable torque is required and therefore there must be some steady-state error. This error is kept small by using high amplification.

It is characteristic of control systems that the input consists of random variations. These may be slow or fast corresponding to low and high frequencies. The ability of the system to respond satisfactorily to random variations can be evaluated in terms of its steady-state frequency response as shown by a Bode plot (Fig. 22.12c). The frequency response of a mechanical system (such as the d'Arsonval movement in Example 4) can be extended by using feedback. The technique is similar to that employed to extend the frequency response of an amplifier (see Example 4 in Chapter 19). In an amplifier, increased bandwidth is obtained at the expense of gain. In a servomechanism, extended frequency response is obtained at the sacrifice of simplicity. Some form of amplification is always required.

The speed of response is another limiting factor in the performance of control systems. It is desirable that the system have a low dynamic error as well as a low steady-state error. How can the time constant of a physical element be reduced using feedback? The method is illustrated in the following example.

EXAMPLE 8

In a chemical plant, water flows into an open mixing tank (Fig. 22.19a) and then out the pipe at the bottom. The rate of flow is governed by an ON-OFF inlet valve V_o; the head h in the tank increases until the rate of flow out Q_o (directly proportional to h in this case of laminar flow) is equal to the flow rate in Q_i. In normal operation, the tank is frequently drained and refilled. Devise a system to reduce the delay in reaching steady-state conditions after draining.

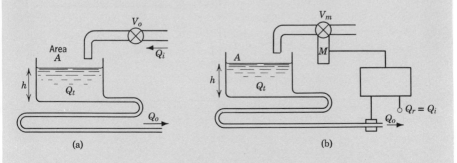

Fig. 22.19 Example 8.

SOLUTION. With the aid of feedback and some auxiliary equipment, the time
constant of this unit can be reduced.   For the original arrangement, the governing equation is

$$Q_i = Q_o + \frac{dQ_t}{dt}$$

or

$$Q_i = kh + A\frac{dh}{dt} \tag{22-51}$$

where $Q_t = Ah$ is the total quantity in the tank.
The transfer function is

$$T_o(s) = \frac{H(s)}{Q_i(s)} = \frac{1}{sA + k} \tag{22-52}$$

with a time constant $\tau_o = A/k$.

In Fig. 22.19b, Q_o is sensed and converted to an electrical signal which is compared to a reference signal Q_r corresponding to the original rate Q_i.   The error
$Q_o - Q_r$ is amplified and the amplified signal controls the motorized valve M.
As shown in the block diagram (Fig. 22.20a), the overall gain of the amplifier
and valve is G_v.   The system response with feedback (Eq. 19-4) is

$$Q_o = kh = Q_i\frac{G_v/(sA + k)}{1 + G_v/(sA + k)} = Q_i\frac{G_v}{sA + k + G_v} \tag{22-53}$$

The new transfer function is

$$T_1(s) = \frac{H(s)}{Q_i(s)} = \frac{G_v/k}{sA + (k + G_v)} \tag{22-54}$$

with a time constant $\tau_1 = A/(k + G_v)$.

If, by proper design of the amplifier and valve, a gain $G_v = 9k$ is obtained, the
new time constant $\tau_1 = \tau_o/10$.   The corresponding variations of water level with
time are shown in Fig. 22.20b.

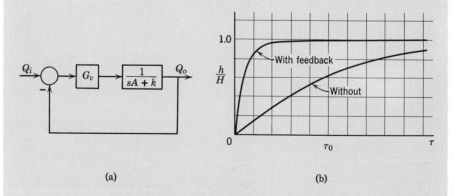

(a)   (b)

Fig. 22.20   Reduction of time constant.

Stability

We see that feedback can improve the performance of a system by making it faster, more accurate, or responsive over a wider range of frequencies. In each case amplification is necessary, and the degree of improvement is related to the amount of amplification. The combination of amplification and feedback may also make the system unstable and therefore ineffective.

The physical basis for instability is revealed in Fig. 22.21. If the blocks are linear and the signals are sinusoidal, a signal **B** is fed back to the summing point and compared to the reference input **R**. The return signal **B** is the open-loop transfer function **GH** times the error signal **E**. If a 180° phase shift has been introduced, the input signal is reinforced. This results in greater output and still greater return signal **B**. The resulting oscillation builds up until the amplitude is limited by saturation due to nonlinear effects, or until the system fails because of excessive amplitude of some variable such as force or current. As mentioned previously (see p. 645), it is not necessary to apply a sinusoidal signal of the particular frequency. Any impulsive input, such as closing a switch, is sufficient to initiate oscillation.

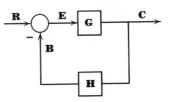

Fig. 22.21 Basic feedback system.

The mathematical basis for instability is revealed in the gain equation. For this form of the basic feedback circuit

$$\mathbf{G}_f = \frac{\mathbf{G}}{1 + \mathbf{GH}} \qquad (22\text{-}55)$$

If for any frequency the denominator is zero, the gain increases without limit and the system is unstable. The denominator is zero if the open-loop transfer function **GH** is just equal to $-1 + j0$. An alternative statement is that the system is unstable if any poles of the overall transfer function

$$T(s) = \frac{G(s)}{1 + G(s)H(s)} \qquad (22\text{-}56)$$

are on the $j\omega$ axis or in the right half of the complex frequency plane. (Where are the poles for the functions whose responses are given in Fig. 22.4?)

In designing automatic feedback control systems, much of the engineer's work is concerned with stability analysis and there are many books devoted to the subject.† After the system has been designed to perform the desired function, precautions must be taken to insure stability. Amplifier gains, time constants, gear ratios, and damping ratios must be selected so that the poles of the transfer function are kept out of the right half of the s plane. Sometimes compensating networks are placed in series with system components to cancel out undesirable poles. Auxiliary feedback loops may also be used to provide stability.

The basic question is whether the denominator of $T(s)$ has any roots in the right half of the s plane. If the denominator is known in factored form (see Eq. 4-34) this question is readily answered. In general, however, $G(s)$ and $H(s)$ are polynomials in s and finding the roots is a tedious operation. Another possible approach is to plot the amplitude and phase of **GH** as functions of frequency as in Fig. 22.12. If the gain is 1 at a phase shift of $\pm 180°$, the system is unstable.

From the design engineer's viewpoint, the practical problem is to determine the effect on stability of variations in system parameters. To optimize system design, he must provide adequate stability with the specified performance at the least cost (in complexity, reliability, weight, or dollars). Various methods have been developed to provide convenient solutions to this problem in the practical case where the system transfer functions are quite complicated.

One of the most widely used techniques in system analysis is the *root-locus method* developed by W. R. Evans in 1948. By this technique, the poles of the transfer function are located graphically as the system parameters are varied. The value of such a graphical method can be illustrated by a specific numerical example. For the system defined by

$$G(s) = \frac{K(s+2)}{s(s+1)(s+4)(s+10)} \qquad H(s) = 1 \qquad (22\text{-}57)$$

the overall transfer function is

$$T(s) = \frac{G(s)}{1 + G(s)} = \frac{K(s+2)}{K(s+2) + s(s+1)(s+4)(s+10)} \qquad (22\text{-}58)$$

---

† See, for example, R. N. Clark, *Introduction to Automatic Control Systems*, John Wiley and Sons, New York, 1962; or J. J. D'Azzo and C. H. Houpis, *Feedback Control System Analysis and Synthesis*, McGraw-Hill Book Co., New York, 1960.

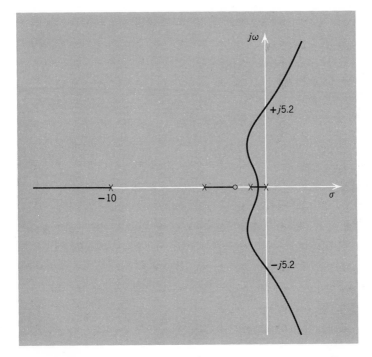

Fig. 22.22 All points satisfying $\underline{/G(s)}$ = ±180°, ±540°, (From R. N. Clark, *Introduction to Automatic Control Systems*, by permission.)

The transfer function has a zero at $s = -2$, and for $K = 0$, poles at $s = 0$, -1, -4, and -10. Using the root-locus technique,† the loci of all points satisfying the relation

$$\underline{/G(s)} = \pm 180° + n(360°) \qquad (22\text{-}59)$$

are as shown in Fig. 22.22. The roots move along the loci as K is varied. As K increases from zero, the poles which start at $s = 0$ and $s = -1$ come together and then diverge along the curved locus. For values of K which result in poles close to the $j\omega$ axis, the step response of the system is highly oscillatory. The critical value of K for stability occurs where the poles are on the $j\omega$ axis. On the basis of the root-locus plot, an experienced systems engineer can decide on an appropriate value of K.

---

† See R. N. Clark, *op. cit.*, p. 192.

SUMMARY

◆ Automatic feedback control systems employ sensors, error detectors, amplifiers, actuators, and feedback elements to provide rapid and accurate control.

Control system analysis is based on circuit principles, device characteristics, and system techniques.

◆ In comparison to an open-loop system, a closed-loop system is capable of greater accuracy over a wider range of conditions using less precise control elements.

The control engineer's problem is to provide the necessary performance with adequate stability at minimum cost.

System performance can be predicted on the basis of step response.

◆ The transfer function is the ratio of two exponential functions of time; it is derived and interpreted just as an immittance function.

The transform $X(s)$ represents the exponential function $x(t)$ for $t > 0$.

Transfer functions can be determined directly from circuit models.

Transfer functions follow the rules of block diagram algebra.

Frequency response is obtained directly from the transfer function.

Step response is the sum of forced response (for $s = 0$) and natural response determined by the poles of the denominator of $T(s)$.

◆ The order of a system is defined by the highest power of s in the denominator of the transfer function. The step response is:

$y(t) = A_0 + Ae^{st}$ for a first-order system, and

$y(t) = A_0 + A_1 e^{s_1 t} + A_2 e^{s_2 t}$ for a second-order system.

Normalized curves display the effect on response of damping ratio ζ.

◆ The system transfer function may be written in terms of pole and zero locations, in terms of time constants, or in terms of steady-state characteristics ($s = j\omega$).

On a Bode chart (gain in db versus log frequency), the response curve for the product of two transfer functions is the sum of the individual response curves.

◆ Feedback can improve control system performance by reducing errors, by extending the frequency response, or by reducing time constants.

◆ The combination of amplification and feedback may result in instability. Much of the systems engineer's work is concerned with stability analysis.

REVIEW QUESTIONS

1. Why don't power inputs appear in a control system block diagram?
2. Explain in system terminology how highway traffic speed is regulated.
3. Explain in system terminology how body temperature is regulated.
4. What information on system performance is provided by step response?
5. Define "transform," "transfer function," and "step response."
6. Outline the procedure for determining step response from the transfer function.
7. What information is obtained from the poles of $T(s)$? The zeros?
8. What form of step response is indicated by complex poles of $T(s)$?
9. Define ζ. What are its dimensions? Why is it useful?
10. What value of damping ratio results in a 20% overshoot?

EXERCISES

1. Draw and label a block diagram of a voltage regulator incorporating a reference voltage V_r, a generator G, an amplifier A, an adder, and feedback to control an output voltage V_c.
2. Sketch the step response of a stable and an unstable first-order system.
3. Given the circuit in Fig. 22.23,
   (a) Define and derive the transfer function.
   (b) Sketch the pole-zero diagram and the step response.
4. Repeat Exercise 3 for the flywheel in Fig. 22.24.

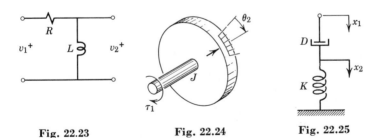

| Fig. 22.23 | Fig. 22.24 | Fig. 22.25 |

5. Repeat Exercise 3 for the dashpot and spring in Fig. 22.25.
6. Given $T(s) = A(s + \beta)/(s + \alpha)$, determine the step response.
7. Repeat Exercise 3 for the circuit of Fig. 22.26, where $R = 0.5$ MΩ and $C = 1\ \mu$F.
8. In Fig. 22.27, a shunt motor with constant field excitation drives a spring-loaded shaft ($K = 1.2 \times 10^4$ rad/N-m). The equivalent friction torque of the motor is $D' = 3 \times 10^{-5}$ N-m-sec/rad and the motor inertia is $J = 6 \times 10^{-6}$ kg-m^2. Derive the transfer function relating angle θ and input voltage v and sketch the expected step response.

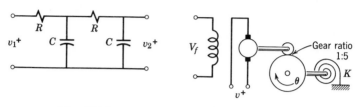

Fig. 22.26   Fig. 22.27

9. Repeat Exercise 8 where K is reduced to 10^{+3} rad/N-m.

10. A shunt motor ($J = 2 \times 10^{-6}$ kg-m² and $D = 8 \times 10^{-5}$ N-m-sec/rad) is operated with constant armature current. The inductance of the field circuit is 200 mH and the resistance is 20 Ω. Derive the transfer function relating shaft velocity to field voltage and predict (and sketch) the step response.

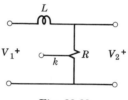

Fig. 22.28

11. In order to reduce the time constant of the circuit in Fig. 22.28, a fraction k of the voltage across R is to be fed back. The feedback voltage is combined with a new input voltage V_0 and introduced into an amplifier of gain A which supplies V_1.

(a) Draw a labeled wiring diagram and a block diagram showing the system with feedback.

(b) Determine the step response of the system and compare the time constants with and without feedback.

(c) Design the system (specify V_0, k, and A) so that the step response with feedback has the same amplitude but is 10 times as fast.

◆ ◆ ◆ IN RETROSPECT

THE CONCEPT FLOW CHART on the front end-paper is like a road map which shows us where we have been. Repeatedly we have started with a physical phenomenon, seen where it is useful in an engineering application, and then devised a model of a device incorporating the phenomenon. Using these models, we have learned to predict the behavior of circuit elements, electronic devices, transformers, electromechanical devices, and simple systems. In some situations we have chosen, or been forced, to take into account nonlinearity. Where linear models are appropriate, we have used the powerful methods of linear system analysis, not only to predict performance, but also to draw general conclusions.

IN PROSPECT ◆ ◆ ◆

BUT THIS IS JUST a first course in electrical engineering. Where do we go from here? So far our emphasis has been on linear, lumped circuits. We have only hinted at the implications of nonlinearity, and we have said nothing about distributed systems. We have only introduced the concept of fields, and we have not even mentioned the important topic of waves. These subjects all lie ahead of you.

In predicting the behavior of devices, we have been limited to conventional applications of existing devices. If you are to design new systems incorporating novel applications of electronic or electromechanical devices you must learn much more about these devices and about systems. And if you are to create new and original devices you must gain a much deeper understanding of physical phenomena.

The road ahead looks inviting; it is sure to be challenging, and it should be interesting. Have a pleasant journey.

APPENDIX

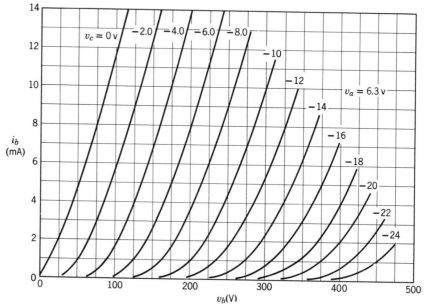

Fig. A1 Average plate characteristics of the 6J5 triode.   (Courtesy General Electric Co.)

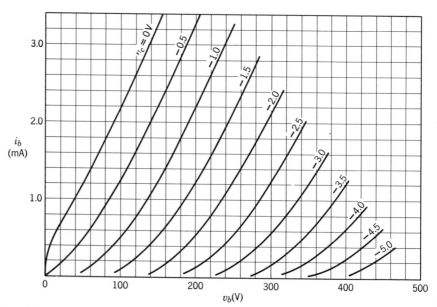

Fig. A2 Average plate characteristics of the 12AX7 twin triode.   (Courtesy General Electric Co.)

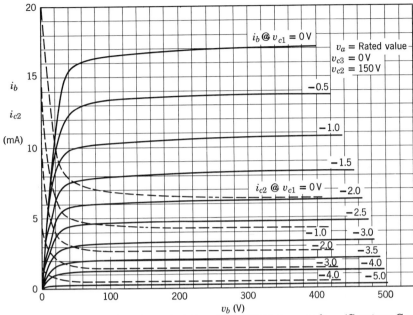

Fig. A3 Average plate characteristics of the 6AU6-A pentode. (Courtesy General Electric Co.)

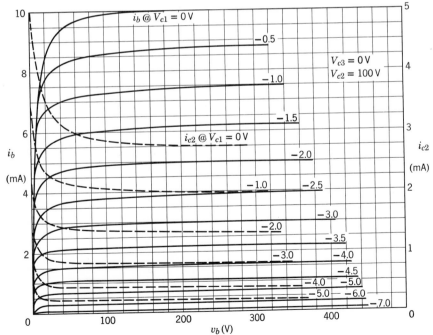

Fig. A4 Average plate characteristics of the 6SJ7 pentode. (Courtesy General Electric Co.)

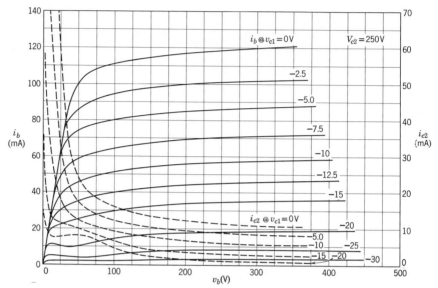

Fig. A5 Average plate characteristics of 6AQ5-A beam-power pentode. (Courtesy General Electric Co.)

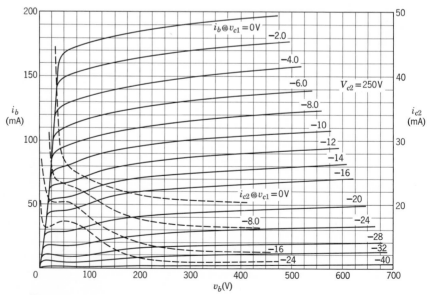

Fig. A6 Average plate characteristics of 6L6-GC beam-power pentode. (Courtesy General Electric Co.)

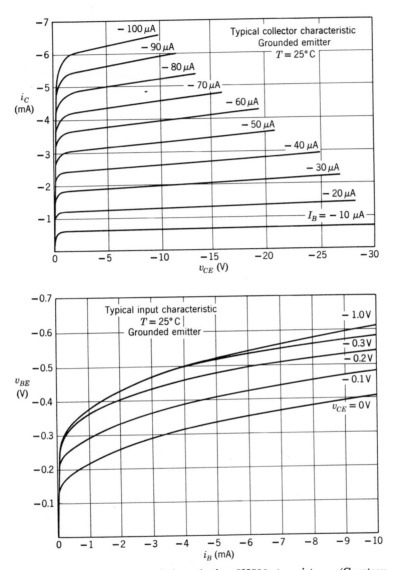

Fig. A7 Typical characteristics of the 2N502 transistor. (Courtesy Philco Corp.)

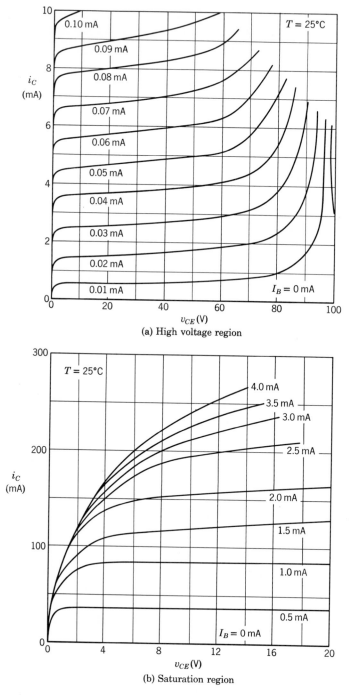

(a) High voltage region

(b) Saturation region

Fig. A8   Collector characteristics for 2N699B transistor.   (Courtesy Fairchild Semiconductor)

Answers to Selected Exercises

Chapter 2

1. 1800 C
4. (a) 0.0735 mm/sec; (b) 1.36×10^9 A
7. (a) 2400 V/m, 3.84×10^{-16} N; (b) 1.92×10^{-16} J
10. (a) 40 W; (b) 12 W; (c) 52 W; (d) 66.7 J
16. (a) $i = 2$ mA at $t = 20$ msec; (b) $v_L = 5$ mV at $t = 10$ msec;
    (c) $v_C = 4$ V at $t = 20$ msec
17. (a) 4 mW; (b) -5 mW; (c) 15 μJ
19. (a) $I^2 T^4 M^{-1} L^{-2}$; (b) $MLI^{-1} T^{-3}$
22. (a) 0.44 J; (b) into magnetic field; (c) 800 V
25. $I_m = V_m \sqrt{C/L}$
28. (a) $V_s = 120$ V, $R_s = 0.6\ \Omega$; (b) $I \cong 22$ A
30. (a) $-10 \sin t$ V; (b) $-20 - 15 \cos t$ V, $20t - 10 \sin t$ V;
    (c) $25 \cos^2 t$ J, $100t^2$ J
33. (a) $v_{cb} = -i_1 R$, $v_{cd} = L d(i_1 + i_2)/dt$;

    (b) $0 = -V - i_1 R - L d(i_1 + i_2)/dt + V_0 - (1/C) \int_0^t i_1\, dt$

36. 5 A

Chapter 3

3. $i(t) = 8.5 e^{-t/3}$ 6. 0.53 sec
8. (a) $40 + 60 e^{-50t}$ kV; (b) 40 kV
10. (c) $i = 6 \cos (250\pi t + \pi/4)$ A
12. (a) $8 + j12.66$; (b) $50\ \underline{/113.1°}$; (d) $0.5\ \underline{/-6.9°}$; (e) $2\ \underline{/90°}$;
    (g) $25\ \underline{/-83.1°}$
15. (a) $2\ \underline{/45°} = 1.4 + j1.4$; (b) $50\ \underline{/-60°} = 25 - j43.3$;
    (c) $100\ \underline{/-30°} = 86.6 - j50$
17. (a) $5 \cos (\omega t + 53.1°)$, $10 \cos (\omega t + 60°)$, $5 \cos (\omega t - 30°)$
21. $v_t = 58.5 \cos (\omega t - 26°)$ V

Chapter 4

2. $0 = V - (1/C)\int i_C\, dt - V_0 + L\, di_L/dt$
5. (a) $0, 0, V/R_1$; (c) $v_L = -(R/R_1)Ve^{-(R/L)t}$
8. (b) $M = 2e^{-0.69t/1600}$ mg
10. (a) 49.4 J; (b) $p = \tau_f\omega$
11. 1250 ft
15. (a) $i(t) = Ie^{-Rt/L}$, $di/dt = -(R/L)I$
18. (e) $0.233\,M\Omega$
21. (a) $0, 60$ V, $0, -60$ V; (b) -12 A/sec, 48 A/sec^2;
    (e) $-3e^{-2t}\sin 4t$ A
25. 0.0078%
27. $i = I_0e^{-Rt/2L} - (I_0Rt/2L)e^{-Rt/2L}$
30. $v_C = -5e^{-2t}$ V
32. (b) $Z(0) = 2\,\Omega$; (d) $v(t) = 20e^{-4t}$ V
34. poles at 0 and $-2/RC$, zero at $-1/RC$
37. poles at $-0.5 \pm j0.5$, zero at -1
40. poles at $-2 \pm j1$, zero at -4
43. $v(t) = 32.3e^{-500t}\sin(200t + 158°)$ V
46. $v(t) = 16e^{-800t} - 4e^{-200t}$ V

Chapter 5

3. $-5e^{-2t}$ V   6. 4.5 V
10. (c) $v(t) = 22.4\cos(2000t - 56.5°)$ V
12. $i(t) = 10\cos(1000t + 90°)$ A
15. $45 \pm j60\Omega$ 18. $34.6\,\Omega$
21. (b) 0.9875 or 1.0125 Mc
24. (a) $i(t) = 0.106\cos(2000t + 45°)$ A;
    (b) $v_R(t) = 25\sqrt{2}\cos(2000t - 45°)$ V
27. (a) $D + 1/sK$; (b) $X = FK$;
    (d) $f(t) = V_m\sqrt{D^2 + (1/\omega K)^2}\cos(\omega t - \text{arccotan } D\omega K)$

Chapter 6

3. (a) 0; (b) V; (c) V/R; (d) $C_1V/(C_1 + C_2)$
6. (a) $v_C = 12(1 - e^{-t/4\times10^{-3}})$ V, $i = 6e^{-t/4\times10^{-3}}$ mA
10. $V = 110.5$ V, $R = 90.5\,\Omega$
12. For $t > 20$ msec, $i(t) = 1.5 - 0.24e^{-50(t-0.02)}$ A
15. (a) $i(t) = 10.1\cos(1745t - 71.8°) - 3.09e^{-561t}$ A;
    (c) $t = 1.61$ msec
18. $T = CR_1R/(R_1 + R)$
21. $i(t) = 69.4(e^{-2680t} - e^{-37,300t})$ mA
24. $i(t) = 0.04\cos 2000t$ A
25. $i(t) = 20,000\, e^{-100t}$ A

Chapter 7

3. (a) 2 A, 2.12 A; (b) 6 V, 7.28 V
6. 1.5 A, 2 A   **9.** $0.259VI$
12. (a) 69.5 A, 6.67 kVAR; (b) $R = 1.035\ \Omega$, $C = 1.92$ mF
15. (a) 0.6, $30 - j40\ \Omega$
18. 10 kW $+ j30$ kVAR
20. 397 to 3350 pF   **24.** Poles at $-1 \pm j4.9$
27. (b) 0.08 A; (c) 25 Ω, 40 nF; (d) 80 V
30. 12.7 mH, 9.1 Ω
32. (a) 200 pF; (b) 1200 V; (c) 40 V
35. 50π **39.** 5 mH, 2 Ω
41. (a) 100 kc; (b) 480 Ω
45. 12.7 A   **48.** 6.35 A, 53.1°
51. (b) 22 A, 38.1 A; (d) 8.7 kW

Chapter 8

3. (a) $0.2 - j0.25$ ℧; (b) $1.95 + j2.44\ \Omega$
6. 220 $\underline{/-22.4°}$ V, 432 $\underline{/56.2°}$ Ω
9. 1/60 A, 600 Ω **12.** $(V - IR)/(R_1 + R)$
14. $2 + 4\cos 1000t$ A   **17.** 0, 5, 25 Ω
21. (a) 0; (b) 60 V; (c) 60 V
25. 0.16 A   **27.** 7.07 $\underline{/-45°}$ V
30. 0.21 $\underline{/-86°}$ A, 470 $\underline{/+86°}$ Ω
33. (b) 4 mA (inadequate representation for $v = -1$ V)
35. 25 mA   **39.** 3.1 mA   **42.** 2.1 mA

Chapter 9

2. 5.93×10^6 m/sec, 3.4×10^{-8} sec, 100 eV
5. (a) 6.01×10^6 m/sec; (b) same
8. 1.6×10^{-16} N at S 37° W
11. (a) 9.37×10^{-3} cm/V; (b) 889 V
14. Tungsten by 10^{13}
18. (a) 6×10^6 m/sec; (b) 102 eV; (c) 5.1 W
20. $\times 0.707$, $\times 2$
22. (a) $I_b = 20V_b^{3/2}$ μA; (b) $\cong 3$ mA
25. $\cong 2 \times 10^{-4}$ m/sec
28. (a) 1.7×10^9;
      (c) $p = 4.26 \times 10^{21}$ m^{-3}, $n = 1.47 \times 10^{17}$ m^{-3};
      (d) 1.72 mV
31. (a) 6.6×10^{24} m^{-3}
36. $J_p \cong 200$ A/m^2 **39.** 56 mA
44. $n \cong 1.2$ **46.** $A_v \cong 90$ **50.** $A_i \cong 50$

53. (b) $V_{cc} = -2$ V; (e) $A_v \cong 65$
55. (c) $A_i \cong 60$; (d) 4.5 V peak or 3.18 V rms

Chapter 10

6. 0.7 V in series with 0.07 Ω
8. 4.1 mA
12. (a) $v_L = 2.5 \sin 2000t$ V
15. (b) $\mu = 100$, $g_m = 1$ m℧, $r_p = 100$ kΩ
19. $r_p = 6700$ Ω, $g_m = 3$ m℧
24. 14.7 kΩ   **26.** $1.1 \underline{/158°}$ V
30. (a) 1.2 mV; (b) 42 mV
34. (b) 1.0 mA, 4.0 V
35. (b) $i_s = 3.02$ μA, $A_i = 66.2$

Chapter 11

3. 26.5 μF
6. (a) 10.6 to 31.8 mA; (b) 3.6 mA
9. (a) 0.87 to 1.1 mA; (b) 0.025 mA
12. (a) 3 mA, 133 Ω; (b) 36%
16. (a) 18.75 W; (b) 38.6%
17. (c) −19.6, 1.6 cps, 230 kc
21. $f_1 = 3.14$ cps, $f_2 = 127.5$ kc
24. (a) 0.48 cps; (b) 0.314 μF; (c) 41.9 pF
27. (a) 63.98 db; (b) 67.96 db, 60 db
29. (a) 100 W; (b) 62.5 kW
33. $h_{fe} \cong 80$, $f_T \cong 160$ Mc

Chapter 12

3. (a) 25%; (b) 50%; (c) 33%
6. 143 V, 0.06, 12°, 0.6 A
9. (a) 333 V; (b) 3.4 H; (c) 15.6; (d) $\cong 0.6$ V
12. (a) 5%; (b) 4.3%; (c) 0.8%
15. (b) 15.2%   **18.** 143,000

Chapter 13

1. $v_2 = iR = (R/L) \int v_1 \, dt$
4. (b) 0.094 V
8. (b) 10 V; (d) clamping
11. (a) 000011, 000101, 001100, 010100; (b) 3, 6, 10, 19
16. 10 Ω, 20 MΩ (for $I_{CO} = 1$ μA)
19. (a) −9.75 V, −0.196 V

Chapter 15

5. $\mu I/2R$, $\mu NI/2R$ 8. 0.016 IT
9. (a) 370; (b) 960; (c) 5600
11. 7.8 mWb, 12.5 mWb
13. (a) 16.5 A; (b) 4%
15. 11.6 A   18. (c) $B \cong 0$

Chapter 16

3. $L \cong 32$ H for low current operation
5. 188 turns, 18.3 A   8. 75 W, 125 W
8. 75 W, 125 W
11. (a) $1000t$, $10t$; (b) 0.6 A
15. (b) 0.125 A; (d) 5 A
17. (a) 94%; (b) 90%   19. $\cong 8:1$, $\cong 12$ db

Chapter 17

3. (b) $u = (f_a R/B^2 l^2)(1 - e^{-B^2 l^2 t/RM}$
4. (a) $u = 200t$ m/sec; (d) 64.8 N
8. (a) 105 mA; (b) 635 A-t
11. 0.0167 Ω, 30 kΩ   14. (c) $2 \Omega l^2 \cos \Omega t$
17. 50π V   18. Emf $\cong 240$ V   21. 0.004 N-m
26. 5 A   27. 24 mA

Chapter 18

2. 212 V   4. 250 V
7. (a) 0.3 Ω; (b) $V = 62.2 I_f - 0.3 I_a$; (c) 1 t
10. (b) 875 rpm, 95 N-m; (c) 1250 rpm
13. 13.7 hp   16. 74%, 65%
18. (a) 78%; (b) 7%   21. (a) 2 poles, 5900 A
24. (b) Speed same, power angle $\cong$ doubled, pf decreased slightly.
27. (a) 50 A; (b) 722 V, 20°; (c) 1430 N-m
28. 2 A   30. 8 poles, 5% slip   38. 10 hp
40. (a) 4.8 kW; (b) 894 rpm   46. 40 N-m

Chapter 19

1. (a) R/R_L; (b) $-\mu R_L/(R_L + r_p + \mu R)$
3. $Y = (G_2 X_2 - G_1 X_1)/(1 + G_2)$
7. $G = G_a G_b G_c$, $H = G_d/G_c - 1/G_a$
12. $-\mu R_L/[R_L + r_p + \mu R_L R_1/(R_1 + R_2)]$
15. $\mathbf{G} = 100 \underline{/180°}$

18. (a) $0.055 \ \mu\text{F}$; (b) $10.15 \ \mu\text{F}$, No
21. (a) 20%; (b) 4% **24.** $H \cong 0.05$
29. $0.942, \ 47.6 \ \Omega$ **33.** $v_{oc} \cong 0.98 v_s$

Chapter 20

4. $\cong 0.003\%$ **5.** $\cong 0.1\%$
7. $-(R/R_1)(1 + sR_1C_1)$
13. $d^2x/dt^2 + 10dx/dt + 2x = -f(t)$

Chapter 21

3. $240 \ \Omega$, $700 \ \Omega$, $4000 \ \Omega$, $10{,}000 \ \Omega$
6. (a) $6.163 \ \text{mA}$ **7.** (a) $2.09 \ \text{V}$
9. $7.92 \ \text{V}$, $8.33 \ \text{V}$, $7.07 \ \text{V}$
15. (a) $610 \ \Omega$
18. $v_o = 2.5 \sin 40\pi t \cos 10^5 t \ \text{mV}$
21. $v_o = 0.6 + 0.12 \cos 20\pi t$

Chapter 22

3. (a) $T(s) = s/(s + R/L)$; (b) pole at $-R/L$, zero at 0
5. $X_2(s)/X_1(s) = s/(s + 1/KD)$
6. $v_2(t) = AV_1e^{-\alpha t} + (AV_1\beta/\alpha)(1 - e^{-\alpha t})$

Index

LIST OF SYMBOLS

a acceleration,
turn ratio

A amplifier gain,
area

A   amperes

B magnetic flux density,
susceptance

C capacitance

C   coulombs

C_p thermal capacity

d distance

D   diffusion coefficient,
electric flux density,
frictional resistance

e charge of an electron,
natural logarithm base
2.718 . . .

e, E electromotive force

$\mathcal{E}$ electric field strength

f frequency

f, F force

F   farads

$\mathcal{F}$ magnetomotive force

g thermal generation rate

g_m transconductance

G conductance

G   transfer function

h hybrid parameter

h   hour

H magnetic field intensity

H   henrys

H   feedback function

i, I current

j complex operator $\sqrt{-1}$

J current density,
rotational inertia

J   joules

k Boltzmann's constant

k, K constant of proportionality

K compliance

K' stiffness

l length

L inductance

m mass of an electron

m   meters

M mass,
mutual inductance

n electron concentration,
rotational speed

n, N number of elements

N   newtons

p hole concentration,
number of poles

p, P power

q, Q electric charge

q_r rate of heat flow

Q quality factor

r radius,
ripple factor

r_p dynamic plate resistance

R recombination rate,
resistance